OCCUPATIONAL
Health and Safety

**FOR TECHNOLOGISTS,
ENGINEERS, AND MANAGERS**

OCCUPATIONAL
Health and Safety

FOR TECHNOLOGISTS, ENGINEERS, AND MANAGERS

Canadian Edition

DAVID L. GOETSCH
CEO, Institute for Continual Improvement

GENE OZON
Algonquin College

PEARSON

Prentice
Hall

Toronto

Library and Archives Canada Cataloguing in Publication

Goetsch, David L
    Occupational health and safety for technologists, engineers, and
managers / David L. Goetsch, Gene Ozon. — Canadian ed.

Includes index.
ISBN 0-13-127580-1

1. Industrial safety—Canada.   2. Industrial hygiene—Canada.
I. Ozon, Gene II. Title.

T55.G63 2005   658.4'08   C2005-905740-8

ISBN 0-13-127580-1

Vice-President, Editorial Director: Michael J. Young
Executive Acquisitions Editor: Dave Ward
Signing Representative: Helene Goulet
Marketing Manager: Leigh-Anne Graham
Senior Developmental Editor: Joel Gladstone
Production Editor: Charlotte Morrison-Reed
Copy Editor: Trish O'Reilly
Proofreader: Ann McInnis
Production Manager: Wendy Moran
Permissions Research: Amanda McCormick
Composition: Carolyn E. Sebestyen
Art Director: Mary Opper
Cover and Interior Design: Michelle Bellemare
Cover Images: Getty Images (background); Alamy (sign)

1 2 3 4 5   10 09 08 07 06

Printed and bound in the United States of America.

I would like to dedicate this book to
those who could have used my company
and to those whose company I could have used
during the many late evenings of its making.

Gene Ozon

Brief Contents

Contents

Preface

BACKGROUND

The field of occupational health and safety has undergone significant change over the past two decades. There are many reasons for this. Some of the more prominent include the following: technological changes that have introduced new hazards in the workplace; proliferation of health and safety legislation and corresponding regulations; increased pressure from regulatory agencies; growing understanding by managers that workers in a safe and healthy workplace are typically more productive; health care and workers' compensation cost increases; increased pressure from environmental groups and the public; a growing interest in ethics and corporate responsibility; professionalization of health and safety occupations; increased pressure from labour organizations and employees in general; rapidly mounting costs associated with product safety and other types of litigation; and increasing incidents of workplace violence.

All of these factors, when taken together, have made the job of the modern health and safety professional more challenging and more important than it has ever been. These factors have also created a need for an up-to-date book on workplace health and safety that contains the latest information for Canadians who have a stake in this profession in the age of global competition and rapid technological change.

WHY WAS THIS BOOK WRITTEN AND FOR WHOM?

This book was written to fill the need for an up-to-date, Canadian, practical teaching and learning resource that focuses on the needs of modern health and safety professionals practising in the workplace. It is intended for use in universities, colleges, and corporate training settings that offer programs, courses, workshops, and seminars in occupational health and safety. Educators and students in such disciplines as industrial technology, manufacturing technology, industrial engineering, engineering technology, occupational safety, management, and supervision will find this book both valuable and easy to use. The direct, straightforward presentation of material focuses on making the theories and principles of occupational health and safety practical and useful in a real-world setting. Up-to-date research has been integrated throughout in a down-to-earth manner.

ORGANIZATION OF THE BOOK

The text contains 26 chapters, each focusing on a major area of concern for modern health and safety professionals. The chapters are grouped into five sections, dealing with specific areas of health and safety.

- General Principles of Health and Safety
- Chemical and Biological Hazards
- Physical Hazards
- Management of Occupational Health and Safety
- Issues in Health and Safety Today

A standard chapter format is used throughout the book. Each chapter begins with a list of learning objectives and ends with a comprehensive summary. Following the summary, each chapter offers review questions, key terms and concepts, useful Weblinks, and endnotes. Within each chapter are case studies to promote classroom discussion, as well as at least one safety fact or myth. These materials are provided to encourage review, stimulate additional thought, and provide opportunities for applying what has been learned. In addition, key terms appear in bold within the text, with their definitions provided in the page margin to reinforce comprehension.

HOW THIS BOOK DIFFERS FROM OTHERS

This book was written to address health and safety issues in the Canadian workplace. In the age of global competition, health and safety in the Canadian workplace has changed dramatically. Many issues, concerns, and factors relating specifically to modern workplace environments have been given more attention, greater depth of coverage, and more illumination here than in other textbooks. Some of the areas receiving more attention and specific occupational examples include

- WHMIS
- Stress-related problems
- Life safety
- Evolving roles of health and safety professionals
- Health and safety training
- Human factors in safety
- Environmental issues and ISO 14000 standards
- Computers, robots, and automation
- Ethics and safety
- Bloodborne pathogens in the workplace
- Ergonomics and safety
- Relationship between safety and quality
- Workplace violence
- Repetitive strain injuries (RSIs)
- Terrorism threats in the workplace

NEW TO THE CANADIAN EDITION

This Canadian edition of *Occupational Health and Safety* contains much new and updated material, including the following:

- Chapters 1-5 provide a Canadian perspective on the evolution of health and safety. Canadian people and events that shaped the course of health and safety in this country are highlighted in this section. Among the people and events discussed are: Sir William Meredith, Dr. James Ham, the Elliot Lake miners strike, the sinking of the *Ocean Ranger,* and the Westray Mine disaster.

- Chapter 7, covering WHMIS, is entirely new to Section 2.
- Section 3, Physical Hazards, makes specific references to Canadian legislation and compares the differences amongst different Canadian jurisdictions; for example, it compares noise regulations for each province and territory. Specific problems posed by our diverse country, such as temperature extremes, are also discussed.
- Section 4 explores safety management from a Canadian perspective in the global marketplace.
- Section 5 looks at issues facing Canada today. Floods, power blackouts, ice storms, and border security are just some of the challenges facing workplaces and government agencies. Whistle-blower protection, violence, and ethics are other workplace issues that Canadian health and safety professionals must deal with.

Canadian content has also been added in the following features:

- Useful Weblinks, related to topics discussed, provide an additional learning resource for teachers and students.
- Fact boxes, myth boxes, case studies, and discussion boxes use Canadian examples, where appropriate.
- Metric measurements along with references to Canadian legislation, associations, and organizations are used throughout.

INSTRUCTOR RESOURCES

Instructor's Manual: This manual includes answers to the Review Questions at the end of each chapter (ISBN 0-13-197933-7).

Test Item File: The Test Bank contains 10 true/false and 5 multiple choice questions for every chapter (ISBN 0-13-204523-0).

Both the Instructor's Manual and Test Item File are available for downloading from a password-protected section of Pearson Education Canada's online catalogue (vig.pearsoned.ca). Navigate to your book's catalogue page to view a list of those supplements that are available. See your local sales representative for details and access.

Acknowledgments

The author acknowledges the invaluable assistance of the editors and staff at Pearson Education Canada in developing the Canadian edition of this book: Dave Ward, Executive Acquisitions Editor; Joel Gladstone, Senior Developmental Editor; Charlotte Morrison-Reed, Production Editor; Trish O'Reilly, Copy Editor; and Ann McInnis, Proofreader.

Finally, the author would like to thank the following people who took time and effort to provide thoughtful and meaningful reviews during the development of this textbook:

Warren J. Fox, British Columbia Institute of Technology

Paul G. Halleran, College of the North Atlantic

Helen Mersereau, University College of Cape Breton

Don Sayers, University of New Brunswick

Gary Stroich, Northern Alberta Institute of Technology

Caroline Wakim, Algonquin College

Moreen Jones Weekes, Centennial College

Kathryn Woodcock, Ryerson University

OCCUPATIONAL
Health and Safety

FOR TECHNOLOGISTS, ENGINEERS, AND MANAGERS

Health and Safety Movement, Then and Now

1

CHAPTER

LEARNING OBJECTIVES

- Describe the developments in safety before the industrial revolution.
- Create a timeline of the milestones in the safety movement.
- Explain how workplace tragedies have changed the safety movement.
- Summarize the role of organized labour.
- Describe the role of specific health problems.
- List the key components of accident prevention programs.
- Describe the health and safety movement today.

The **safety movement** in Canada has developed steadily since the first half of the 20th century. About 75 years ago, at the beginning of the Great Depression, industrial **accident**s were commonplace in this country; for example, in 1930, the number of fatalities due to industrial accidents recorded was 1607.[1] During this period, legislation, precedent, and public opinion all favoured management. There were few protections for workers' safety. Seventy years later in 2000 the population and the workforce had more than tripled, however, the number of occupational fatalities in Canada had dropped to 882.[2]

Working conditions for today's industrial employees have improved significantly. The chance of a worker being killed in an industrial accident is less than half of what it was 60 years ago.[3] In 1997 the fatality rate in Canada was about 6.5 per 100 000 workers. Although our numbers are improving, we lag far behind other countries, such as Sweden, with a fatality incidence rate of 2.1 per 100 000 workers and the United Stated with 4.46 per 100 000 workers. In some industries, such as construction, the death rate is as high as 31 per 100 000. Statistics paint only part of the picture, but every day three Canadian families face the reality that a loved one will not be returning from work, and of those that do, one out of 31 will miss at least one day to recover from a workplace injury.[4]

SAFETY MOVEMENT
Began during World War II when all of the various practitioners of occupational health and safety began to see the need for cooperative efforts. This movement is very strong today.

ACCIDENT
An unplanned or unexpected event that results in injuries to people or loss of product or process.

1

Improvements in safety, until now, have been the result of pressure for legislation to promote health and safety, the steadily increasing costs associated with accidents and injuries, and the professionalization of safety as an occupation. Improvements in the future are likely to come as a result of greater awareness of the cost effectiveness and resultant competitiveness gained from a safe and healthy workforce.

This chapter examines the history of the safety movement in Canada and how it has developed over the years. Such a perspective will help practising and prospective safety professionals form a better understanding of both their roots and their future.

DEVELOPMENTS BEFORE THE INDUSTRIAL REVOLUTION

It is important for students of industrial health and safety to first study the past. Understanding the past can help health and safety professionals examine the present and future with a sense of perspective and continuity. Modern developments in health and safety are neither isolated nor independent. Rather, they are part of the long continuum of developments in the health and safety movement.

CODE OF HAMMURABI
Developed around 2000 B.C. during the time of the Babylonians by the ruler Hammurabi, this code encompassed all of the laws of the land at that time. The significant aspect for our purposes is that it contained clauses dealing with injuries, allowable fees for physicians, and monetary damages assessed against those who injured others.

The continuum begins with the days of the ancient Babylonians. During that time, circa 2000 B.C., their ruler Hammurabi developed his **Code of Hammurabi**. The code encompassed all of the laws of the land at that time, showed Hammurabi to be a just ruler, and set a precedent followed by other Mesopotamian kings. The significance of the code from the perspective of health and safety is that it contained clauses dealing with injuries, allowable fees for physicians, and monetary damages assessed against those who injured others.[5] This clause from the code illustrates Hammurabi's concern for the proper handling of injuries: "If a man has caused the loss of a gentleman's eye, his own eye shall be caused to be lost."[6]

This movement continued and emerged in later Egyptian civilization. As evidenced by the temples and pyramids that still remain, the Egyptians were an industrious people. Much of their labour was provided by slaves, and there is ample evidence that slaves were not treated well; that is, unless it suited the needs of the Egyptian taskmasters.

One such case occurred during the reign of Ramses II (circa 1500 B.C.), who undertook a major construction project, the Ramesseum. To ensure the maintenance of a workforce sufficient to build this huge temple bearing his name, Ramses created an industrial medical service to care for the workers. They were required to bathe daily in the Nile and were given regular medical examinations. Sick workers were isolated.[7]

The Romans were vitally concerned with health and safety, as can be seen from the remains of their construction projects. The Romans built aqueducts, sewerage systems, public baths, latrines, and well-ventilated houses.[8]

As civilization progressed, so did health and safety developments. In 1567, Philippus Aureolus produced a treatise on the pulmonary diseases of miners. Titled *On the Miners' Sickness and Other Miners' Diseases,* the treatise covered diseases of smelter workers and metallurgists and diseases associated with the handling of and exposure to mercury. Around the same time, Georgius Agricola published his treatise *De Re Metallica,* emphasizing the need for ventilation in mines and illustrating various devices that could be used to introduce fresh air into mines.[9]

The 18th century saw the contributions of Bernardino Ramazzini, who wrote *Discourse on the Diseases of Workers.* Ramazzini drew conclusive parallels between diseases suffered by workers and their occupations. He related occupational diseases to the handling of harmful materials and to irregular or unnatural movements of the body. Much of what Ramazzini wrote is still relevant today.[10]

The Industrial Revolution changed forever the methods of producing goods. According to Joseph LaDou, the changes in production brought about by the Industrial Revolution can be summarized as follows:

- The introduction of **inanimate power** (i.e., steam power) to replace people and animal power,
- The substitution of machines for people,
- The introduction of new methods for converting raw materials, and
- The organization and specialization of work, resulting in a division of labour.[11]

INANIMATE POWER
Power that is lacking life or spirit. During the Industrial Revolution, humans and animals were replaced with inanimate power (e.g., steam power).

These changes necessitated a greater focusing of attention on the health and safety of workers. Steam power increased markedly the potential for life-threatening injuries, as did machines. The new methods used for converting raw materials also introduced new risks of injuries and diseases. Specialization, by increasing the likelihood of boredom and inattentiveness, also made the workplace a more dangerous environment.

LEGISLATIVE MILESTONES IN THE CANADIAN SAFETY MOVEMENT

The safety movement in this country traces its roots to England. During the Industrial Revolution, child labour in factories was common. The hours were long, the work hard, and the conditions often unhealthy and unsafe. Following an outbreak of fever among the children working in their cotton mills, the people of Manchester, England, began demanding better working conditions in the factories. Public pressure eventually forced a government response, and in 1802 the Health and Morals of Apprentices Act was passed. This was a milestone piece of legislation: It marked the beginning of governmental involvement in workplace safety.

In the 1880s when the industrial sector was booming and the Industrial Revolution in full swing, hazardous working conditions were commonplace, especially in the factories of the larger urban centres such as Montreal and Toronto, where children were exploited. The public outcry against these conditions led to the birth of occupational health and safety legislation in Canada. In 1884 the Ontario Factories Act was passed. Its main purpose was to stop child labour and establish some basic rules of conduct for factory owners. The Act limited working days to 10 hours and set a minimum age limit of 12 years for boys and 14 for girls.[12] However, the rules were vague and difficult to enforce and ultimately did very little to limit injuries or accidents in the factories.

**EMPLOYER-BIASED
LAWS**
A collection of laws that
favoured employers over
employees in establishing
a responsibility for workplace safety.

**CONTRIBUTORY
NEGLIGENCE**
An injured worker's own
negligence contributed to
the accident. If the ac-
tions of employees con-
tributed to their own
injuries, the employer is
absolved of any liability.

**FELLOW SERVANT
RULE**
Employers are not liable
for workplace injuries that
result from negligence of
other employees.

ASSUMPTION OF RISK
Based on the theory that
people who accept a job
assume the risks that go
with it. It says employees
who work voluntarily
should accept the conse-
quences of their actions
on the job rather than
blaming the employer.

**WORKERS'
COMPENSATION**
Developed to allow injured
employees to be compen-
sated appropriately with-
out having to take their
employer to court.

Common law precedents established in England in the early 1800s were adopted by Canadian courts in the later part of the century when dealing with employer/worker disputes regarding injuries. Workers who were injured on the job had the right to sue their employer, but the cost of such a suit was in itself an adequate deterrent for most low-paid workers. Those who did make it to court had the cards stacked against them, because the **employer-biased laws** that existed at the time provided three lines of defence to employers:

Contributory Negligence If a worker's action, in any way contributed to the injury or accident, then the worker would be deemed fully responsible, no damages would be paid, and the full blame would be placed upon the employee.

Fellow Servant Rule An employer could not be held liable for any injury to a worker if any other worker was negligent in his duties. This essentially meant that in order for employers to be held liable, they would have to have been personally involved in the accident.

Assumption of Risk Another defence used by employers at the time was that the worker accepted the risks and inherent dangers when employment was accepted. (Today's thrill-seekers may be familiar with the phrase, because signature of an "assumption of risk release waiver" is often required before embarking on many dangerous activities.)

One of the most important developments in the history of the safety movement in Canada occurred in 1914 when **workers' compensation** was introduced. Workers' compensation actually had its beginnings in Germany in 1884, but the practice soon spread throughout the rest of Europe. The Ontario government began studying the German program in 1900 but didn't develop much momentum for change until 1910, under pressure from both labour and industry.[13] Ontario Premier James Whitney then appointed Sir William Meredith to investigate the options for a workers' compensation program for Ontario. Through intense research and travel throughout Europe, Meredith was able to draft his own set of rules, which became The Ontario Workmen's Compensation Act of 1914.

The delay in including the provision for compensating injured workers into Canadian law (30 years after the passage of similar legislation in Germany) was largely due to a difference in workplace safety priorities: The focus in Germany had been on the provision of compensation for injured workers, whereas the main objective in Canada was to improve working conditions through labour laws, with the aim of reducing the number of workplace injuries.

Each provincial and territorial jurisdiction subsequently enacted its own legislation, all based on the basic principles that Sir William Meredith put forth in Ontario in 1914. Workers' compensation is examined in more depth in Chapter 5.

The next significant development in the history of Canada's health and safety movement came with the passage of Industrial Standards Acts in Ontario, Alberta, and Quebec in 1935. These acts were intended to parallel the Wagner Act (more correctly known as the National Labor Relations Act) in the United States. Although the Wagner Act dealt with the workers' right to form and participate in labour unions and to engage in collective bargaining with employers, the Canadian acts confined themselves mainly to setting out rules for employers regarding pay and hours of work — particularly in the construction, clothing, and furniture industries. In Ontario, the Act gave the provincial government the power to set wages and hours of work in some sectors. Unlike the American Wagner Act, although they legalized collective bargaining, the Canadian acts did not encourage the formation of unions.

World War II affected every aspect of life for most Canadians, whether at home or fighting overseas. Of those who did remain, most were called upon to support the war effort. Factories mobilized around the clock to produce the supplies and hardware required for the war. Since most of the reasonably fit men were off fighting, the factories were staffed by a large number of women as well as by older men. This precious (because scarce) labour resource was trained well and the best equipment and resources were provided. Productivity and safety were a very high priority and accident rates fell. Ergonomic studies by the military were applied to civilian factory workers to enhance productivity and reduce accidents and injuries.

The next significant advance in occupational health and safety was made in Saskatchewan with the passing of the **Occupational Health and Safety Act** in 1972. The first such legislation of its kind in North America, this act provided for the establishment of occupational health and safety committees in the workplace. Often referred to as joint occupational health and safety committees, these groups consisted of both management and workers. The birth of these joint committees provided the foundation for two of the three fundamental rights that all Canadians now exercise: the **right to participate** and the **right to know**. The following year the Act was amended to include the third basic right we have as workers in Canada: the **right to refuse**.

The Royal Commission on Health and Safety in Mines in Ontario represents another major milestone in the safety movement in Canada. Prompted by the Elliott Lake miners' strike in 1974 (see more below) and chaired by Dr. James Ham, what became known as the **Ham Commission** first presented the philosophy of an **internal responsibility system**. This system gives responsibility to both employers and workers to cooperate to control occupational health and safety hazards. By its nature, this system is self-regulating, with minimal interference or enforcement from outside agencies. The system assigns specific duties to both workers and management, and it is in the best interest of both parties to fulfill their assigned roles. The taxpayer also saves because fewer safety officers are required to monitor each workplace. The recommendations of the Ham Commission form the basis of Ontario's Occupational Health and Safety Act, passed in 1978.

Another significant development, specifically in the protection of workers who handle or are exposed to hazardous materials, **WHMIS** (Workplace Hazardous Materials Information System) legislation became law when the federal government passed Bill C-70 in 1987. This bill established the criteria for identifying hazardous materials and defined the format and content of labels for containers of hazardous materials and related material safety data sheets. WHMIS provides the information to back up the workers' right to know about hazards in the workplace, which was enshrined in earlier legislation. Each province and territory has incorporated WHMIS into its own Health and Safety Act.

Figure 1–1 summarizes some significant milestones in the development of the safety movement in Canada.

OCCUPATIONAL HEALTH AND SAFETY ACT
Legislation that sets out the rights and duties of all parties in the workplace for the protection of workers against hazards on the job.

RIGHT TO PARTICIPATE
Workers' basic right to participate in their own safety (i.e., committees).

RIGHT TO KNOW
Workers' basic right to be informed of any hazards that exist in the workplace.

RIGHT TO REFUSE
Workers' basic right to refuse work that they feel is unsafe.

HAM COMMISSION
Royal commission headed by Dr. James Ham in 1975, dealing with miners illnesses, laid the foundation for Ontario's first Occupational Health and Safety Act.

INTERNAL RESPONSIBILITY SYSTEM
A mechanism to allow employers, supervisors, and workers to monitor each other's actions and ensure compliance with the act.

Figure 1–1
Milestones in the safety movement.

B.C.	
2000	Code of Hammurabi
1500	Ramses, maintenance of the workforce
400	Hippocrates observes colic in lead mine workers
25	Pliny identifies lead, mercury, sulphur, and zinc as occupational hazards
A.D.	
1500	Philippus Aureolus, miners' sickness and disease from metal vapour
1500	Agricola, *De Re Metallica*, mine ventilation requirements
1600	French hat makers suffer dementia from mercury exposure
1700	Ramazzini, father of occupational medicine
1750	The Industrial Revolution
1788	Chimney Sweeps Act passed in England
1800s	Common law, anti-labour laws
1884	First workers' compensation program (Germany)
1900	Comprehensive legislation developed
1926	Heinrich, development of several accident theories and models
1929	The Great Depression
1935	Industrial Standards Act
1939	World War II
1972	Canada's first Occupational Health and Safety Act (Saskatchewan)
1974	Elliot Lake miners' strike
1975	Ham Commission
1987	WHMIS introduced
2003	Bill C-45, the Westray Bill

WHMIS
Workplace Hazardous Material Information System. A national communication system, implemented on October 31, 1988, that provides the worker with information on the production, use, storage, and safe handling of hazardous materials in the workplace.

TRAGEDIES THAT HAVE CHANGED THE SAFETY MOVEMENT IN CANADA

Health and safety tragedies in the workplace have greatly accelerated the pace of the safety movement in Canada. On a global scale, stories in the news about devastating workplace disasters are frequent, but in Canada they are fewer. However, occasionally some region is faced with the consequences of a major workplace accident. Three significant disasters to occur in Canadian workplaces were the Elliot Lake miners' strike in Ontario, the sinking of the Ocean Ranger drilling rig off the Newfoundland coast, and the Westray Mine explosion in Nova Scotia. This section briefly explains these three milestone events and their lasting effects on the health and safety movement in Canada.

Elliot Lake Miners' Strike

In 1974, Elliot Lake uranium miners went on strike to protest deplorable health and safety conditions in their industry, which had led to very high rates of lung cancer. Although no single event at the mine may be considered a tragedy, the collective effects of the mining conditions at the time were indeed tragic. In 1969, five years before the strike, the Ontario Workman's Compensation Board stated that 16 out of 20 deaths of Elliot Lake miners were the result of lung cancer.[14]

As we have seen above, the strike at Elliot Lake in 1974 would turn out to be the catalyst for the creation of Ontario's Occupational Health and Safety Act. The Ham Commission's 1976 report made over 100 recommendations for the mining industry and for workplaces in general. These recommendations not only provided the basis for the Ontario Occupational Health and Safety Act, passed in 1978, but also enhanced safety regulations in most other industries throughout Canada.

Sinking of the Ocean Ranger

On Valentine's Day in 1982, as the Ocean Ranger sat 175 nautical miles off the Newfoundland coast, anchored to the ocean floor, a violent storm raged. The storm caused a window to smash in the ballast control room and from that point on, a tragic chain of events caused the world's largest offshore drilling rig to capsize. Given the brutal weather conditions and the distance from land, any attempts to rescue survivors from the icy waters were fruitless: 84 people, including 56 Newfoundlanders, perished that stormy night in the cold Atlantic.

Because the rig was registered in the United States but had a Canadian crew and was in Canadian waters, both the Canadian and American governments ran their own inquiries. The Canadian inquiry was called the Royal Commission on the Ocean Ranger Marine Disaster, while the American investigation was a joint inquiry of the US Coast Guard and the National Transportation Safety Board. As a result of the Royal Commission on the Ocean Ranger Disaster, several safety systems were developed and installed on offshore oil rigs. Other changes resulting from the inquiry were engineering changes to the ballast control system to improve rig stability, improved training for rig personnel, better survival suit access, and regular engineering inspections. The recommendations resulting from both inquiries have made offshore oil exploration much safer. However, the power of the ocean can exceed any safety system. The Ocean Ranger, like the Titanic, was said to be "unsinkable."

Westray Mine Disaster

Like most workplace disasters, the Westray mine explosion was the result of "actions, omissions, mistakes, incompetence, apathy, cynicism, stupidity and neglect," said Mr. Justice Peter Richard in his report on the tragedy.[15] On May 9, 1992, at 5:18 a.m., a little less than two months after the mine's official opening, methane gas in the mine ignited, causing an explosion so large that it was felt in two nearby communities. The blast trapped and killed 26 miners. The community was devastated, even though they were all too familiar with loss of life in the mines.

An inquiry into the accident took five years and cost nearly $5 million. The report's title, *The Westray Story: A Predictable Path to Disaster*, foreshadows the tone of the document. It points out a lengthy list of shortcomings and makes several recommendations for improving coal mine safety. Charges laid against two managers were eventually dropped because there were no laws at the time that held company senior officers liable in such cases. Although laws ensuring **employer liability** have existed throughout the world for over 100 years, gaps in Canadian law provided employers with immunity from responsibility for their workers' safety. Finally in November 2003, after years of lobbying by the United Steel Workers Union, Bill C-45 — or the Westray Bill — became law. These amendments to the Criminal Code now hold corporations and their senior officers accountable for criminal negligence in the workplace.

EMPLOYER LIABILITY
In 1877, the Employer's Liability Law was passed and established the potential for employers to be liable for accidents that occurred in the workplace.

ROLE OF ORGANIZED LABOUR

Organized labour has played a crucial role in the development of the safety movement in Canada. From the outset of the Industrial Revolution in this country, organized labour has fought for safer working conditions and appropriate compensation for workers injured on the job. Many of the earliest developments in the safety movement were the result of long and hard-fought battles by organized labour.

ORGANIZED LABOUR
A group of employees who joined together to fight for the rights of all employees (i.e., unions).

The Trade Union Act of 1872, which legalized unions in Canada, was the first big step in Canadian industrial labour relations. Later, in 1919, the general strike in Winnipeg, which was Western Canada's largest city at the time, established unions as a significant force for workers' interests. During the strike, 30 000 workers joined forces, bringing the city to a standstill for 42 days. The strike ended on "Bloody Saturday" when two civilian demonstrators were killed and several labour leaders were arrested.

In the 1920s, reflecting the advances in automation, many of the old craft unions were replaced by industrial unions. And in 1956, in the course of uniting several Canadian unions, the Canadian Labour Congress was formed. In 1961, with support from the CLC, the NDP political party was formed.

Although the role of unions in promoting safety is generally acknowledged, one school of thought takes the opposite view, holding that union involvement actually slowed the development of the safety movement. Proponents of this view maintain that unions allowed their demands for safer working conditions to become entangled with their demands for better wages and, as a result, they met with resistance from management. Regardless of the point of view, however, there is no question that working conditions in the earliest years of the safety movement often reflected management's insensitivity to safety concerns.

Among the most important contributions of organized labour to the safety movement in Canada was their work to overturn **anti-labour laws** relating to safety in the workplace. These laws, as mentioned above, were the fellow servant rule, the statutes defining contributory negligence, and the concept of assumption of risk.[16]

ANTI-LABOUR LAWS
Nineteenth century laws that strongly favoured employers.

Because the overwhelming majority of industrial accidents involve negligence on the part of one or more workers, historically employers had little to worry about. Therefore, they had little incentive to promote a safe work environment. Organized labour has clearly played a significant role in bringing unsafe working conditions to the attention of the general public. Public awareness

— and, in some cases, outrage — eventually led to these employer-biased laws being overturned.

The Ontario Workplace Health and Safety Agency, in a report published in 2004, "found that 78–79 percent of unionized workplaces reported high compliance with health and safety legislation, while only 54–61 percent of non-unionized workplaces reported such compliance."[17] This would indicate that pressure from unions still plays an important part in workplace health and safety.

DISCUSSION CASE

What Is Your Opinion?

Two health and safety students are debating the issue of corporate responsibility. Tom thinks that industry has clearly demonstrated its unwillingness over the years to provide a safe and healthy work environment for employees. He offers such examples as the Westray and Elliot Lake mines as evidence. Janet agrees that industry does, indeed, have a checkered past on health and safety, but she thinks employers have learned that their workforce is a valuable asset that should be protected. Tom's response is, "Take away federal and provincial regulations, and industry would return to their old ways in less than a year." Join this debate. What is your opinion?

ROLE OF SPECIFIC HEALTH PROBLEMS

Specific health problems linked to workplace hazards have played a significant role in the development of the modern health and safety movement. These health problems contributed to public awareness of dangerous and unhealthy working conditions, which, in turn, led to legislation, regulations, better work procedures, and better working conditions.

Lung disease in coal miners was a major problem in the 1800s, particularly in Great Britain, where much of the Western world's coal was mined at the time. Frequent contact with coal dust led to a widespread outbreak of anthrocosis among Great Britain's coal miners. Also known as the *black spit,* this disease persisted from the early 1800s, when it was first identified, until around 1875 when it was finally eliminated by such health and safety measures as ventilation and decreased work hours.

In the 1930s, Great Britain saw a resurgence of lung problems among coal miners. By the early 1940s, British scientists were using the term *coal-miner's pneumoconiosis,* or CMP (now more usually known as coal workers' pneumoconiosis or CWP), to describe a disease from which many miners suffered. Great Britain designated CMP a separate and compensable disease in 1943. Health problems, however, were not limited to coal miners. Other types of miners developed a variety of diseases, the most common of which was silicosis. Again, it took a huge outcry from those affected — like the Elliot Lake miners discussed earlier, for example — to focus attention on a serious workplace problem.

Mercury poisoning is another health problem that has contributed to the evolution of the health and safety movement by focusing public attention on unsafe conditions in the workplace. The disease was first noticed among the citizens of a Japanese fishing village in the early 1930s. This disease, with symptoms such as convulsions, loss of vision and hearing, and in extreme cases paralysis or death, was common in Minamata, but extremely rare throughout the rest of Japan. After investigation of the situation, it was discovered that a nearby chemical plant periodically dumped methyl mercury into the bay that was the village's primary source of food. Consequently, the citizens of this small village ingested hazardous doses of mercury every time they ate fish from the bay.

Mercury poisoning also became an issue in Canada after the Ojibwa families on the English-Wabigoon River discovered that their main source of food was severely contaminated in 1970. From 1962 up to that point, Dryden Chemicals had dumped 10 tonnes of mercury (used in the pulp bleaching process for the paper industry) into the river. In 1985, the people of Grassy Narrows and White Dog reserves received close to $17 million in compensation. Great Lakes Forest Products Ltd., which bought Dryden Chemicals Ltd. in 1979, contributed $6 million, the previous owner, Reed Inc., paid $5.75 million, and the federal and provincial governments paid the rest.

The legacy of such disregard for public health and safety is still evident today, however. A study of the people of Grassy Narrows and White Dog in 2004 found many of the classic long term symptoms of mercury poisoning — numbness in the hands, upper body, and legs; pain in the joints; loss of skin sensation; impaired balance; and poor muscle coordination — in a number of people ranging in age from teens to 70s. As well, "[m]ercury poisoning can lead to a weakening of the immune system and therefore high levels of other illnesses in these communities may be related to mercury."[18]

Today, mercury is considered a "designated" substance and its use and handling is strictly regulated in each province and territory. Canada wide standards are also enforced by Environment Canada to ensure unified environmental protection goals are met. (A distinguishing factor between occupational health and safety issues and environmental issues is often whether exposure to harmful substances spreads beyond the workplace. When harmful products are used in the workplace the problem is with occupational health and safety. When the public is exposed to these products, the concern is environmental.)

As with other substances that cause various forms of lung cancer, asbestos was also an important substance in the evolution of the modern health and safety movement. By the time it was determined that asbestos was a hazardous material, the fibres of which can cause asbestosis or lung cancer (mesothelioma), thousands of buildings contained the substance. As these buildings began to age, the asbestos, particularly that used to insulate pipes, began to break down. And as asbestos breaks down, it releases dangerous microscopic fibres into the air. These fibres are so hazardous that removing asbestos from old buildings has become a highly specialized task requiring special equipment and training.

With so many health issues developing in various workplaces through out the world, the focus for many occupational health and safety professionals has gradually shifted from **occupational accidents** to **occupational diseases**. Illnesses caused by many workplace products may not begin to show up in the worker for several years — or even decades — after exposure. Because of this **latency period**, the correlation between the diseases and the workplace can easily go unnoticed, which is why historically occupational health and safety prac-

**OCCUPATIONAL
ACCIDENT**
Unplanned event that causes injury to a worker.

**OCCUPATIONAL
DISEASES**
Pathological conditions brought about by workplace conditions or factors.

LATENCY PERIOD
Time after exposure to a hazardous product before symptoms appear.

titioners have been more concerned with injuries and other immediate effects of accidents.

DEVELOPMENT OF ACCIDENT PREVENTION PROGRAMS

In the modern workplace there are many different types of **accident prevention** programs ranging from the simple to the complex. Widely used accident prevention techniques include failure minimization, fail-safe designs, isolation, lockouts, screening, personal protective equipment, redundancy, timed replacements, and many others. These techniques are individual components of broader safety programs. Such programs have evolved since the late 1800s.

In the early 1800s, employers had little concern for the safety of workers and little incentive to be concerned. Consequently, organized safety programs were nonexistent, a situation that continued for many years. However, between World War I and World War II, industry discovered the connection between quality and safety. Then, during World War II, troop call-ups and deployments created severe labour shortages. Faced with these shortages, employers could not afford to lose workers to accidents or for any other reason. This realization created a greater openness toward giving safety the serious consideration it deserved. For example, according to the Society of Manufacturing Engineers, around this time industry began to realize the following:

- Improved engineering could prevent accidents.
- Employees were willing to learn and accept safety rules.
- Safety rules could be established and enforced.
- Financial savings from safety improvement could be reaped by savings in compensation and medical bills.[19]

With these realizations came the long-needed incentive for employers to begin playing an active role in creating and maintaining a safe workplace. This, in turn, led to the development of organized safety programs sponsored by management. Early safety programs were based on the "**three E's of safety**": engineering, education, and enforcement (see Figure 1–2). The engineering aspects of a safety program involve making design improvements to both product

ACCIDENT PREVENTION
The act of preventing a happening that may cause loss or injury to a person.

THREE E's OF SAFETY
Engineering, education, and enforcement.

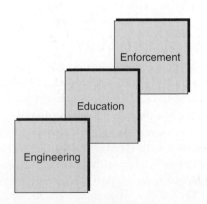

▶ **Figure 1–2**
Three E's of safety.

and process. By altering the design of a product, the processes used to manufacture it can be simplified and, as a result, made less dangerous. In addition, the manufacturing processes for products can be engineered in ways that decrease potential hazards associated with the processes.

The education aspect of a safety program ensures that employees know how to work safely, why it is important to do so, and that safety is expected by management. Safety education typically covers the what, when, where, why, and how of safety.

The enforcement aspect of a safety program involves making sure that employees abide by safety policies, rules, regulations, practices, and procedures. Supervisors and fellow employees play a key role in the enforcement aspects of modern safety programs.

THE HEALTH AND SAFETY MOVEMENT TODAY

The health and safety movement has come a long way since the Industrial Revolution. Today there is widespread understanding of the importance of providing a safe and healthy workplace. The tone was set during and after World War II when all of the various practitioners of occupational health and safety began to see the need for cooperative efforts. These practitioners included safety engineers, safety managers, industrial hygienists, occupational health nurses, and physicians.

One of the earliest and most vocal proponents of the cooperative or integrated approach was H. G. Dyktor. He proposed the following objectives of integration:

- Learn more through sharing knowledge about health problems in the workplace, particularly those caused by toxic substances.
- Provide a greater level of expertise in evaluating health and safety problems.
- Provide a broad database that can be used to compare health and safety problems experienced by different companies in the same industry.
- Encourage accident prevention.
- Make employee health and safety a high priority.[20]

SAFETY FACT

Safety Movement and War

World War II actually had a positive effect on the modern health and safety movement. During the war, there was a shortage of able-bodied, skilled workers in factories supporting the war effort because most of these workers were in the armed services. Consequently, preserving the health and safety of the relatively few skilled workers still available was paramount. The law of supply and demand suddenly made workplace safety a significant issue, which it still is today. The military war is over, but the economic war still rages. To be competitive in this international conflict, employers today must follow the lead of their predecessors during World War II and protect their employees.

NEW MATERIALS, NEW PROCESSES, AND NEW PROBLEMS

The job of the health and safety professional is more complex than it has ever been. The materials out of which products are made have become increasingly complex and exotic. Engineering metals now include carbon steels, alloy steels, high-strength low-alloy steels, stainless steels, managing steels, cast steels, cast irons, tungsten, molybdenum, titanium, aluminum, copper, magnesium, lead, tin, zinc, and powdered metals. Each of these metals requires its own specialized processes.

Nonmetals are more numerous and have also become more complex. Plastics, plastic alloys and blends, advanced composites, fibrous materials, elastomers, and ceramics also bring their own potential hazards to the workplace.

In addition to the more complex materials being used in modern industry and the new health and safety concerns associated with them, modern industrial processes are also becoming more complex. As these processes become automated, the potential hazards associated with them often increase. Computers; lasers; industrial robots; nontraditional processes such as explosive welding, photochemical machining, laser beam machining, ultrasonic machining, and chemical milling; automated material handling; water-jet cutting expert systems; flexible manufacturing cells; and computer-integrated manufacturing have all introduced new health and safety problems in the workplace and new challenges for the health and safety professional.

Chapter 24 is devoted to coverage of the special health and safety problems associated with computers, robots, and automation. In addition, coverage of specific aspects of these problems is provided in different chapters throughout this book.

RAPID GROWTH IN THE PROFESSION

The complexities of the modern workplace have made health and safety a growing profession. Diploma and degree programs in industrial technology typically include industrial safety courses. Some engineering degree programs have health and safety tracks. Several colleges and universities offer full degrees in occupational health and safety.

The inevitable result of the increased attention given to industrial health and safety is that more large companies are employing health and safety professionals and more small companies are assigning these duties to existing employees. This trend is likely to continue as employers see their responsibilities for health and safety spread beyond the workplace to the environment, the community, the users of their products, and the recipients of their by-products and waste. Support for employing health and safety professionals in the workplace also comes from the corporate financial departments, who see the increasing value of such employees.

SUMMARY

1. Health and safety awareness has a long history. There is evidence of occupational health and safety efforts as far back as the time of the Egyptian

pharaohs. The Code of Hammurabi, circa 2000 B.C., contained clauses that could be interpreted as early attempts at workers' compensation. There is also evidence of concern for health and safety during the time of the Romans.

2. Milestones in the development of the safety movement in Canada include the following: first workers' compensation programs in 1914, first health and safety act in 1972, Elliott Lake miners' strike in 1974, right to refuse unsafe work in 1976, WHMIS in 1987, and the Westray Bill in 2003.

3. Organized labour has played a crucial role in the development of the safety movement in Canada. Particularly important was the work of unions to overturn anti-labour laws inhibiting safety in the workplace.

4. Specific health problems associated with the workplace have contributed to the development of the modern health and safety movement. These problems include lung diseases in miners, mercury poisoning, and lung cancer tied to asbestos, silica, and coal.

5. Tragedies such as the Elliot Lake miners' strike in Ontario, the sinking of the Ocean Ranger drilling rig off the Newfoundland coast and the Westray Mine explosion in Nova Scotia have changed the face of the safety movement in Canada.

6. The health and safety movement today is characterized by professionalization and integration. The health and safety team of a large company may include an industrial chemist or engineer, radiation control specialist, industrial safety engineer or manager, occupational nurse, counsellor, psychologist, and dietitian. New materials and processes are introducing new health and safety problems, making the integrated approach a practical necessity and promoting growth in the profession.

KEY TERMS AND CONCEPTS

Accident	Latency period
Accident prevention	Occupational accidents
Anti-labour laws	Occupational diseases
Assumption of risk	Occupational Health and Safety Act
Code of Hammurabi	Organized labour
Contributory negligence	Right to know
Employer-biased laws	Right to participate
Employer liability	Right to refuse
Fellow servant rule	Safety movement
Ham Commission	Three E's of safety
Inanimate power	WHMIS
Internal responsibility system	Workers' compensation

REVIEW QUESTIONS

1. To what cause(s) can the improvements in workplace safety made to date be attributed?

2. Explain the significance of the Code of Hammurabi in terms of the safety movement.

3. What significance has the mining industry had on the development of occupational health and safety throughout history?

4. Explain how major events in at least three provinces contributed to the development of occupational health and safety in Canada.

5. What are the three fundamental rights enjoyed by all Canadian workers?

6. What impact did labour shortages in World War II have on the safety movement?

7. Explain how workplace tragedies have affected the safety movement. Give examples.

8. Summarize briefly the role that organized labour has played in the advancement of the safety movement.

9. Define the following terms: fellow servant rule, contributory negligence, assumption of risk.

WEBLINKS

Canadian Auto Workers
www.caw.ca/index.asp

The CAW is the largest private sector union in Canada, with a long and rich history that has had a major impact on Canadian labour, reaching well beyond the automotive industry. Throughout the website, there is evidence of their significant role in advancing health and safety awareness.

Canadian Occupational Safety Magazine
www.industrialsourcebook.com

Your gateway to a world of online industrial and safety information. This online magazine has hundreds of interesting articles and safety resources, such as product reviews and links to other resources.

Human Resources and Skills Development Canada (HRSDC)
www.hrsdc.gc.ca/en/cs/comm/hrsd/about_us.shtml

The Department of Human Resources and Skills Development (HRSD) is responsible for providing all Canadians with the tools they need to thrive and prosper in the workplace and community. This site contains links to workplace health and safety statistics and legislation.

International Labour Organization
www.ilo.org

The International Labour Organization is the UN specialized agency that seeks the promotion of social justice and internationally recognized human and labour rights. It was founded in 1919 and is the only surviving major creation of the Treaty of Versailles, which brought the League of Nations into being; it became the first specialized agency of the UN in 1946.

ENDNOTES

1. (March 1931). "Fatal Industrial Accidents in Canada in 1930." *The Labour Gazette*, 365–373. [Online]. Available: http://socserv.socsci.mcmaster.ca/maclabour/resources/labour_gazette/ accidents_and_illness/31-365. (Retrieved June 20, 2004).

2. Canadian Centre for Occupational Health and Safety. (no date). *Performance Report for Period ending March 31, 2003*. [Online]. Available: http://www.ccohs.ca/ccohs/reports/ perform_03.html. (Retrieved June 20, 2004).

3. S. Minter. "The Birth of OSHA." *Occupational Hazards* (July 1998): 59.

4. Ottawa and District Labour Council. (no date). "Injury and Death Due to Work." [Online]. Available: http://www.ottawalabour.org/april28_facts.htm. (Retrieved June 20, 2004).

5. J. LaDou, ed., *Introduction to Occupational Health and Safety* (Chicago: National Safety Council, 1986), 28.

6. Ibid., 28.

7. A. Soubiran, "Medical Services under the Pharaohs," *Abbottempo* 1 (1963): 19–23.

8. J. LaDou, *Occupational Health and Safety*, 31.

9. Ibid., 34.

10. Ibid., 35.

11. Ibid., 37.

12. D. W. Martyn Bone. (November 2003). "Historical Summary: Ontario in the 1880s." [Online]. Available: http://xenon.xe.com/~mbone/webtree/1880. (Retrieved June 20, 2004).

13. Wally Fox-Decent. (April 2003). "A Look Way, Way Back at Our Compensation History." *Canadian Occupational Safety*. [Online]. Available: http://www.industrialsourcebook.com/ cgi-bin/archivef.pl?id=477. (Retrieved June 20, 2004).

14. Roger Moody. (1992). "The Gulliver File — Mines People and Land: A Global Battleground." *The Gulliver Rio Algom Dossier*. [Online]. Available: http://www.sea-us.org.au/gulliver/ rioalgom.html. (Retrieved June 20, 2004).

15. Martyn O'Malley. (May 9, 2002). The Horror of Westray. *CBC News Online*. Available: http://www.cbc.ca/news/features/westray.html. (Retrieved June 20, 2004).

16. S. Minter and V. Sutcliff, "Fighting Two Wars," *Occupational Hazards* (July 1998): 41.

17. Rory O'Neill. (2002). "When It Comes to Health and Safety, Your Life Should Be in Union Hands." *Labour Education* 1, no. 126. [Online]. Available: http://www.ilo.org/public/ english/dialogue/actrav/publ/126/neill.pdf. (Retrieved June 20, 2004).

18. Minter and Sutcliff, "Fighting Two Wars," 41.

19. Julie Fine. (November/December 2004). "Communities Still Affected Decades Later: Mercury Poisoning at White Dog." Manitoba Eco-Network. *Eco-Journal* 14, no. 5 (Nov./Dec. 2004). [Online]. Available: http://www.mbeconetwork.org/archives/eco-j-14(5).asp#WhiteDog. (Retrieved April 20, 2005).

20. H. G. Dyktor, "Integration of Industrial Hygiene with Industrial Medicine," *Industrial Medicine* 9, no. 4 (1940): 193.

Accidents and Their Effects

LEARNING OBJECTIVES

- Compare the number of accidents and fatalities in the workplace to those from other sources.
- Describe the severity of workplace accidents in Canada using statistical data.
- Identify the different types of workplace injuries.
- Describe the various characteristics of lost time workplace accidents.
- Compare lost time injury rates for various industries.
- Identify the direct costs of accidents.
- Identify the hidden costs of accidents.
- Compare different accident cost estimation models.

There is a long history of debate in this country concerning the effect of accidents on industry and the cost of preventing accidents. Historically, the prevailing view was that **accident prevention** programs were too costly. The more contemporary view is that accidents are too costly and that accident prevention makes sense economically. As a result, accident prevention, which had previously been advocated on a moral and legal basis, is now justified in purely economic terms.

Accidents are the fifth leading cause of death in this country after cancer, heart disease, stroke, and lung disease. This ranking is based on all types of accidents, including motor vehicle accidents, drowning, fires, falls, and natural disasters as well as work-related accidents.

Although deaths from murder tend to be more newsworthy than workplace deaths, their actual impact is far less. For example, there were 550 murders in Canada in 2001. **Workplace accidents**, on the other hand, cause about 900 deaths every year in Canada. Labour unrest also seems to attract more media attention than workplace accidents. In 1998, the number of lost work days due to occupational injuries was six times higher than the number of days lost due to strikes and lockouts. The following compelling statistics should help place

ACCIDENT PREVENTION
The act of preventing a happening that may cause loss or injury to a person.

WORKPLACE ACCIDENTS
Accidents that occur at an employee's place of work.

workplace accidents and deaths in the proper perspective, notwithstanding their apparent lack of newsworthiness:

- In 1998, there were 793 666 workplace accidents in Canada; almost half resulted in lost work time.
- That year, 798 people lost their lives as a result of accidents.
- One in 18 workers was injured at work, representing one injury every nine seconds.
- A total of 15 539 606 work days were lost — or the equivalent of 62 000 full time jobs.
- Between 1994 and 1998, workers' compensation boards paid an average of $6000 per active case.
- In 1998, a lost time injury occurred in Canada every 19 seconds.
- On average, more than three people die from workplace injuries each day.
- In 1998, workers' compensation payments to injured workers cost the Canadian economy $77 500 every minute.[1]

HEALTH AND SAFETY PROFESSIONAL
An individual whose profession (job) is to be concerned with health and safety measures in the workforce.

This chapter provides the student and the practising **health and safety professional** with the information needed to have a full understanding of workplace accidents and their effect on workers and industry in Canada. This understanding will help both workers and management to ensure that health and safety in the workplace remain a top priority.

LOST TIME BECAUSE OF WORKPLACE INJURIES

LOST TIME
The amount of time that an employee was unable to work due to an injury.

WORKPLACE INJURIES
Injuries that occur while an employee is at work.

An important consideration when assessing the effect of accidents on industry and on workers is the amount of **lost time** due to **workplace injuries**. Human Resources and Skills Development Canada (HRSDC), has collected massive amounts of data related to the Canadian workforce. Much of the information in this chapter is from HRSDC, provided to them by workers' compensation boards from across the country. The reader should consider that, as compelling as the numbers may be, these statistics and figures do not include the thousands of injuries that are not reported or that are compensated directly by the employer.

Lost Time Injuries by Industry

LOST TIME INJURY
An injury or illness due to a work-related accident or exposure to a noxious substance that results in an employee missing work and for which the employee receives compensation for lost income.

By monitoring the number of **lost time injuries** in each industry, comparisons can be made to other occupations and to other businesses within the same industrial category. One primary use of this data is to establish workers' compensation premium rates. As for any type of insurance, the premiums will be higher if the inherent risk of injury or loss is greater. When lost time accidents are disproportionately high in a particular industry, this serves as a warning to a variety of agencies and organizations that these sectors need greater attention.

Figure 2–1, comparing lost time injuries by industry, shows manufacturing as the greatest source of lost time injuries. This sector has the greatest number of workers and the greatest number of lost time injuries — and represents 29.06% of total injuries in all sectors combined, even though only 16.44% of workers are employed in the manufacturing industry. The next largest group is the retail industry, which represents 12.49% of the workforce, but only contributes to 10.63% of the injuries. Although the overall number of workers in the retail trade rivals that in manufacturing, the likelihood of a lost time injury occurring in retail work is much lower. (Although the data in Figure 2–1 — and in Figure 2–2 later — are from 1998, trends have not changed significantly since then.)

A relatively small number of people were employed in the logging and forestry sector but the risk of lost time injuries is higher for this sector than for any of the other sectors listed. Other high-risk industries include construction and transportation; while education, communication and other utilities, and real estate were among the safest. Workers at the lowest risk of injury are those in the finance and insurance industry. Of this group, only one in 483 workers sustained a lost time injury.

Industry	Number of Lost Time Injuries	Percentage of Injuries by Industry	Number of Workers	Percentage of Workers by Industry
Manufacturing	109 076	29.06%	1 872 600	16.44%
Retail trade	39 913	10.63%	1 422 600	12.49%
Health and social services	36 664	9.77%	1 124 500	9.87%
Construction	29 647	7.90%	499 000	4.38%
Transportation and storage	25 622	6.83%	488 400	4.29%
Accommodation, food and beverage services	22 219	5.92%	846 900	7.43%
Wholesale trade	21 682	5.78%	731 000	6.42%
Government services	17 958	4.78%	669 600	5.88%
Industry unspecified or undefined	16 198	4.32%	S/O	S/O
Other services	13 358	3.56%	243 100	2.13%
Business services	9 736	2.59%	798 600	7.01%
Educational services	7 445	1.98%	930 900	8.17%
Communication and other utilities	7 066	1.88%	384 400	3.37%
Logging and forestry	5 210	1.39%	66 700	0.59%
Agriculture and related services	4 237	1.13%	418 700	3.68%
Mining, quarrying, and oil wells	4 015	1.07%	142 700	1.25%
Real estate operator and insurance agent	1 999	0.53%	200 600	1.76%
Not coded	1 486	0.40%	S/O	S/O
Finance and insurance	1 073	0.29%	518 000	4.55%
Fishing and trapping	756	0.20%	34 000	0.30%
Total	375 360	100.00%	11 392 300	100.00%

Figure 2–1

Percentage of lost time injuries and percentage of workers by industry, 1998.

Source: Human Resources and Skills Development Canada. (April 28, 2003). "General Statistics on Occupational Injuries and Fatalities, 1994–1998." [Online]. Available: http://www.hrsdc.gc.ca/asp/gateway.asp?hr=/en/lp/lo/ohs/statistics/naosh/2.shtml&hs=oxs#2.1. (Retrieved February 27, 2005).

INCIDENT RATE
The number of accidents per given number of workers.

The relative risk involved in a particular industry is reflected in its lost time **incident rate**. The incident rate is refers to the number of accidents per given number of workers. Between 1995 and 1998, the logging industry had a 20% decline in lost time injuries, resulting in its incident rate dropping from 9.96 to 7.81 per 100 workers. Between 1997 and 1998, several other sectors experienced an increase in lost time incident rates.

Lost Time Injuries by Type of Injury

SPRAIN
The result of torn ligaments.

STRAIN
The result of overstretched or torn muscles.

CONTUSION
A bruise resulting from a blow.

To effectively direct their efforts towards reducing lost time from work due to accidents, managers and health and safety practitioners must know which injuries result in the greatest amount of lost time. **Sprains** and **strains** are by far the most common type of injury. In 1998, the 151 581 strains and sprains reported accounted for 40% of all lost time occupational injuries. From 1994 to 1998, the number of lost time injuries involving strains and sprains decreased by 20%.[2]

Figure 2–2 shows that strains and sprains were three times as frequent as the second most common types of injuries: **contusions**, crushing, and bruises. Cuts, lacerations, and punctures were also included in the top three most common types of injuries. Together these top three types of injuries accounted for two thirds of all lost time injuries.

Further down the list, the frequency with which injuries occur drops dramatically. However, some industries and occupations have a very high incident rate for some types of injury. Comprehensive record keeping by employers is vital to identifying which types of injuries are of most concern.

Lost Time Injuries by Body Part

PERSONAL PROTECTIVE EQUIPMENT (PPE)
Any type of clothing or device that puts a barrier between the worker and the hazard (e.g., safety goggles, gloves, hard hats, and so on).

In 1998, back problems were the most common type of lost time injury in Canada.[3] More than one quarter of all occupational injuries were to the back. The frequency of back injuries is a concern, but so also is the potential severity and the far reaching effects of these injuries on the workers and their families. Various means of protecting the worker from injury are available, such as using **personal protective equipment**, changing the products or materials used, providing machine guarding, and using ergonomic design. Reducing the number and severity of back injuries often involves ergonomic factors such as changing the manner in which a certain task is performed or altering workstation design.

Finger and leg injuries ranked second and third, respectively, with about 11% and 8% of lost time occupational injuries. The back, fingers, legs and shoulders are the parts of the body where workers were most often injured in 1998, accounting for more than half of all lost time occupational injuries.

The effects of injuries to some parts of the body are often more serious than statistics reveal. Disabilities and impairments resulting from injuries to eyes, ears, and brain, for example, can dramatically influence not only working ability but the quality of life outside work for those people affected.

Lost Time Injuries by Source

What action, product, material, tool, or item caused injury to the worker? Dangerous machinery, chemicals, or tools cause many injuries, but by far the most common cause is bodily motion. In 1998, bodily motion caused 10 times

Nature of Injury	Number of Lost Time Injuries
Sprains and strains	151 581
Contusions, crushing, bruise	50 303
Cut, laceration, puncture	34 325
Occupational injury not classified	22 696
Fracture	22 123
Inflammation or irritation	18 878
Nature of injury not coded	14 950
Multiple injuries	9 947
Scratches, abrasions	9 838
Other occupational injury or illness	9 265
Burn or scald	7 183
Occupational illness not classified	4 429
Hernia, rupture	4 263
Dislocation	2 809
Concussion — brain, cerebral	1 878
Amputation or enucleation	1 868
Poisoning, systemic	1 606
Chemical burn	1 559
Radiation effects	1 403
Hearing loss or impairment	1 101
Contagious or infectious disease	972
Dermatitis	953
Electric shock, electrocution	640
Lower respiratory condition	279
Allergic condition, allergic reaction	182
Asphyxia, strangulation, drowning	73
Freezing, frostbite	70
Heat stroke, sunstroke, heat cramps, heat exhaustion	54
Pneumoconiosis	53
Non personal damage	44
Upper respiratory conditions	35
Total	375 360

Figure 2–2
Number of lost time injuries by nature of injury.
Source: Association of Workers' Compensation Boards of Canada. (1999). "Work Injuries and Diseases, 1994–1998, Canada," 12–19.

more lost time injuries than did powered hand tools.[4] Protecting the worker not only involves providing the proper tools, equipment, and workstation design, but must also incorporate training the worker in safe procedures. As we have seen in the previous section, incorrect procedures frequently result in injury to the back.

While injuries from most sources decreased from 1996 to 1998, the number of lost time injuries caused by drugs and medicines more than quadrupled — from 38 to 170 — and the number caused by infectious and parasitic agents increased by more than 70% — from 368 to 639.[5]

Other Factors Affecting Lost Time Injuries

OVEREXERTION
The result of employees working beyond their physical limits.

Overexertion, the result of employees working beyond their physical limits, accounted for nearly 25% of all reported injuries in 1998.

Lost time injury statistics also reveal that gender, age, and even the time of year can be a factor in workplace injuries: For every 100 men in the workforce, 3.43 lost time accidents were reported, while only 1.55 women out of 100 suffered similar injuries. (Although, from 1997 to 1998, both genders showed a decrease in the incident rate for lost time injuries, with men making a greater improvement.) The statistics show us that younger workers also have more accidents: With the working population divided into three age groups, 15 to 29, 30 to 55, and 55 and older, the greatest number of lost time accidents occurred in the 15 to 29 group. Among other notable facts regarding young workers is that the body part injured most frequently on young workers (15 to 29 years old) is the hands — as opposed to the back for all workers. Even the season may have an effect: From 1996 to 1998, the greatest numbers of injuries occurred in August and the fewest in December.[6] (In the section in Chapter 3 on the domino effect, we will see one of the reasons that more workplace accidents are likely to occur in the summer.)

DISCUSSION CASE

What Is Your Opinion?

Jeremy Anderson has been a safety engineer at Takacs Manufacturing Inc. for over 20 years. Roger Davey, his protegé, started at Takacs Inc. only one week ago, after graduating from a three year safety engineering diploma program. Over lunch, they had a discussion about lost time workplace injuries. During the discussion, Jeremy said he thought back injuries were still the problem that safety professionals should worry about the most. Roger disagreed. He said strains and sprains were the most common type of injury in the workplace. What is your opinion?

IAPA
Industrial Accident Prevention Association, the largest health and safety consulting association in Canada.

DIRECT COST
Identifiable uninsured cost incurred as a result of an accident.

COSTS OF ACCIDENTS

To gain a proper perspective on the economics of workplace accidents, we must view them in the overall context of all accidents. In 1996, Maureen Shaw, President and Chief Executive Officer of the **IAPA**, the largest health and safety consulting association in Canada, suggested a conservative estimate of the overall cost of accidents in Canada of approximately $31 billion.[7]

The **direct costs** of workplace accidents are those that are easily identified and quantified. The expenses incurred by the employer, such as wages paid to an injured worker and damaged goods and equipment, are obvious, but the costs borne by the state and outside institutions should also be considered.

There is a tendency for most companies to disregard the significance of the cost of accidents. Major accident damage costs are usually covered by some form of insurance. Minor damage is often considered as a cost of doing business and is written off as maintenance. And injured workers are covered by workers' compensation. The uninsured costs of accidents, however, can add up to quite a significant amount. These less obvious expenses, which can be described as hidden or **indirect costs**, could include:

INDIRECT COSTS
Costs that are not directly identifiable with work-place accidents.

- Time lost by uninjured workers. Many workers lose time because they watched or assisted the injured party.
- Production slowdowns. Productivity may suffer if equipment or facilities are damaged.
- Non-compensated time lost by injured workers. Wages may be paid while waiting for workers' compensation. In most jurisdictions, the employer is required to pay the wages for the injured worker for the remainder of the day in which the injury occurred.
- Cost of overtime. Overtime at a premium rate is often required by other workers to cover the lost output of the injured worker.
- Reduced output of replacement workers. It is very likely that the replacement worker will not be as productive as the regular employee.
- Reduced output of the injured worker after return to work. Most workers will take some time to resume normal productivity after an injury.
- Supervisors' activities. Supervisors may spend time addressing issues related to the accident instead of performing their normal duties, which would include enhancing productivity.
- Accident investigation, record keeping, and claims processing. Personnel from upper management to clerical staff will spend time away from their normal duties, filing reports, filling out forms, etc.
- Damage to equipment or machinery. Costs such as repairs, rentals, or replacement of equipment are often incurred because of an accident.

Another cost associated with workplace accidents is a tarnished corporate image resulting from repeated reports of accidents and injuries taking place at a particular business. Companies that are viewed by the public or their customers as having little regard for their employee's' health and safety will lose business to those that actively promote workplace safety.

Clearly, accidents on and off the job cost Canadian industry dearly. Every dollar that is spent responding to accidents is a dollar that could have been reinvested in modernization, research and development, facility upgrades, and other competitiveness-enhancing activities.

ESTIMATING THE COST OF ACCIDENTS

Even decision makers who support accident prevention must consider the relative costs of such efforts. Clearly, accidents are expensive. However, to be successful, health and safety professionals must be able to show that accidents are more expensive than prevention. To do this, they must be able to estimate the cost of accidents. This section will explore various cost estimating methods, from pioneers in the field such as Heinrich and Simonds to more contemporary models used by Hansen and the Manitoba Heavy Construction Association.

Estimating Hidden Costs

Safety professionals often use the *iceberg analogy* when talking about the real costs of accidents. Accident costs are like an iceberg in that their greatest portion is hidden from view.[8] In the case of icebergs, the larger part is hidden beneath the surface of the water. In the case of an accident, the larger part of the actual cost is also hidden beneath the surface. Figure 2–3 illustrates how the hidden cost can far exceed the direct cost of an accident. The same analogy may also be used to compare insured vs. uninsured accident costs.

According to Daniel Corcoran,

> When a serious accident occurs, there is usually a great deal of activity associated with the accident. There may be a slowdown in production near the site of the accident, for instance. There also will be a need to replace the injured worker, at least temporarily, and there will be costs associated with the learning curve of the replacement worker.
>
> The supervisor and the accident investigation team probably will need to spend time conducting an investigation, and there will be a lot of time spent on the administration of paper work related to the accident.[9]

There are many different models that can be used for estimating both the direct and indirect costs of accidents. Some of these models are so complex that their usefulness is questionable. The ratio of direct to indirect cost can vary greatly depending on the model used. For instance, the federal government is

Figure 2–3
The direct costs represent only the tip of the iceberg.

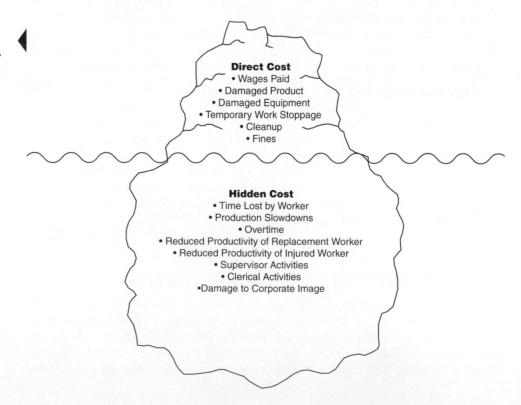

Direct Cost
• Wages Paid
• Damaged Product
• Damaged Equipment
• Temporary Work Stoppage
• Cleanup
• Fines

Hidden Cost
• Time Lost by Worker
• Production Slowdowns
• Overtime
• Reduced Productivity of Replacement Worker
• Reduced Productivity of Injured Worker
• Supervisor Activities
• Clerical Activities
• Damage to Corporate Image

Checklist for
Estimating the Hidden Costs of Accidents

✓ Paid time to the injured employee on the day of the accident.

✓ Paid time of any emergency-responder personnel involved (including ambulance driver).

✓ Paid time of all employees who were interviewed as part of the accident investigation.

✓ Paid time of the safety personnel who conducted the accident investigation.

✓ Paid time of the Human Resources personnel who handled the workers' compensation and medical aspects of the accident.

✓ Paid time of the supervisor involved in the accident investigation and accident response.

✓ Paid time to employees near the accident who stopped working (or slowed down) temporarily as a result of the accident.

✓ Paid time to employees who spent time talking about the accident as news of it spread through the company's grapevine.

▶ **Figure 2–4**
Some accident costs that might be overlooked.

much more conservative in its estimates than the $31 billion given above by Maureen Shaw of the IAPA. HRSDC has conducted studies that conclude that the ratio of direct to indirect cost is approximately 1:1.[10] Using very similar definitions for direct and indirect, Health Canada is a little more liberal in their estimate, concluding that indirect costs are 50 to 300% greater than direct costs.[11] The checklist in Figure 2–4 is a simple and straightforward tool that can be used to estimate the hidden costs of accidents.

The ratio of direct cost to hidden cost not only varies from model to model, it also changes from workplace to workplace. Over fifty years ago, W. H. Heinrich introduced a 4:1 ratio to compare insured cost to uninsured cost. Although others performing similar studies showed ratios ranging from 2.3:1 to 101:1, they all reach the same conclusion: that the hidden costs far exceed the direct or insured cost.[12]

Another early health and safety practitioner to develop a procedure for estimating accident costs was an American professor, Rollin H. Simonds. Professor Simonds states that in order to have value, a cost estimate must relate directly to the specific company in question. Applying broad industry cost factors will not suffice. To arrive at company-specific figures, Simonds recommends that costs associated with an accident be divided into *insured* and *uninsured* costs.[13]

Determining the insured costs of accidents is a simple matter of examining accounting records. The next step involves calculating the uninsured costs. Simonds recommends that accidents be divided into the following four classes:

- **Class 1 accidents.** Lost workdays, permanent partial disabilities, and temporary total disabilities.
- **Class 2 accidents.** Treatment by a physician outside the company's facility.
- **Class 3 accidents.** Locally provided first aid, property damage of less than $100, or the loss of fewer than eight hours of work time.
- **Class 4 accidents.** Injuries that are so minor they do not require the attention of a physician, result in property damage of $100 or more, or cause eight or more work hours to be lost.[14]

Average uninsured costs for each class of accident can be determined by pulling the records of all accidents that occurred during a specified period and sorting the records according to class. For each accident in each class, record every cost that was not covered by insurance. Compute the total of these costs by class of accident and divide by the total number of accidents in that class to determine an average uninsured cost for each class, specific to the particular company.

Figure 2–5 is an example of how the average cost of a selected sample of Class 1 accidents can be determined. In this example, there were four Class 1 accidents in the pilot test. These four accidents cost the company a total of $554.23 in uninsured costs, or an average of $138.56 per accident. Using this information, accurate cost estimates of an accident can be figured, as can accurate predictions.

In estimating the cost of accidents, the Manitoba Heavy Construction Association follows the lead of James Hansen. Hansen is a research strategist with the IAPA. He suggests that the costs involved in industrial accidents be divided into two categories, "subjective" and "objective." Subjective costs, like hidden or uninsured costs, may be very difficult to quantify.

Objective costs are those that can be measured and for which a specific dollar value can be assigned. Although different employers may have about 50 subcategories, all measurable accident costs may be divided into five categories.[15]

**Figure 2–5
Uninsured costs worksheet.**

Class of Accident	Accident Number							
Class 1	1	2	3	4	5	6	7	8
Cost A	16.00	6.95	15.17	3.26				
Cost B	72.00	103.15	97.06	51.52				
Cost C	26.73	12.62	—	36.94				
Cost D	—	51.36	—	38.76				
Cost E	—	11.17	—	24.95				
Cost F	—	—	—	13.41				
Cost G	—	—	—	—				
Total	114.73	185.25	112.23	142.02				

Grand Total: $554.23

Average Cost per Accident: $138.56 (grand total ÷ number of accidents)

Signature: _____   Date: _____

1. **Compensation and Benefits.** The first category is compensation and benefit costs. These include charges for medical rehabilitation, pension and lump sum payments, and survivor benefits.

2. **Damage to Capital Assets.** The second category focuses on the cost of damage to materials, equipment, and property.

3. **Lost Productivity.** A third category is that of lost productivity and production. When an accident occurs, all construction activity in the area of the incident is usually shut down. Workers rush to assist the victim or escape from a hazardous situation. If the injured employee is able to return to work, he or she may be placed on lighter duties. The employer ultimately bears the financial cost in terms of lower productivity.

4. **Legal Expenses.** Legal costs may be one of the highest costs of a workplace accident. In many situations, government fines alone can reach into the hundreds of thousands of dollars.

5. **The final catch-all category is "miscellaneous costs."** These can include everything from consultants' fees to quick fix safety solutions put into place after the accident. These are usually poorly thought out policies and procedures designed to show that the employer is really concerned about safety, despite the recent accident. Unfortunately, because they lack the real commitment of management, the effects of these programs may be short term and ineffective.

SAFETY FACT

Small Profit Margin, Big Losses

To compete in today's global market, many companies are operating at a very narrow profit margin. When an accident takes place, the money lost can be very difficult to recover. Figure 2–6, below, shows, for example, that a $1000 loss incurred from an accident would require $12 500 in additional sales to recoup if the company was operating at an 8% profit margin. As the profit margin goes down, the additional sales required to get the money back will increase.

Accident Cost:	Additional Sales Required to Recover the Cost: Profit Margin				
	2%	4%	6%	8%	10%
$50	$2500	$1250	$833	$625	$500
$500	$25 000	$12 500	$8333	$6250	$5000
$1000	$50 000	$25 000	$16 667	$12 500	$10 000
$10 000	$500 000	$250 000	$166 667	$125 000	$100 000
$25 000	$1 250 000	$625 000	$416 667	$312 000	$500 000
$500 000	$25 000 000	$12 000 000	$8 333 333	$6 250 000	$5 000 000

Figure 2–6
Additional sales required to recover the cost of an accident.

SUMMARY

1. Accidents are the fifth leading cause of death in this country after cancer, heart disease, stroke and lung disease.
2. In 1998, workers' compensation payments to injured workers cost the Canadian economy $77 500 every minute.
3. In 1998, a lost time injury occurred in Canada every 19 seconds.
4. On average, over three people die from workplace injuries each day.
5. The manufacturing industry has the greatest number of lost time injuries, while the logging industry has the highest incident rate.
6. Sprains and strains are by far the most common type of injury.
7. In 1998, back problems were the most common type of lost time injury in Canada.
8. HRSDC estimates the direct cost of accidents in Canada in 1998 to be $4.65 billion and the indirect cost to be $9.3 billion. Some estimates put the indirect cost as high as $31 billion.
9. As the profit margin goes down, the additional sales required to recover money lost due to accidents increases.

KEY TERMS AND CONCEPTS

Accident prevention

Accidents

Contusion

Direct accident costs

Health and safety professional

IAPA

Incident rate

Indirect accident costs

Lost time

Lost time injury

Overexertion

Personal protective equipment

Sprains and strains

Workplace injuries

Workplace accidents

REVIEW QUESTIONS

1. What are the leading causes of death in Canada?
2. When the overall cost of an accident is calculated, what elements make up the cost?
3. Which industry has the greatest number of lost time injuries?
4. Lost time injuries to which body part are most common among all workers?
5. Explain the difference between the rate of accidents and the number of accidents. Which term best describes the relative risk involved with a particular occupation or industry?

6. List five direct costs associated with an accident. List five indirect costs associated with an accident.

7. Using a workplace with which you are familiar, provide an example of accidents that would fall under each class of accident as outlined by Simonds.

WEBLINKS

Association of Workers' Compensation Boards of Canada
www.awcbc.org

The Association of Workers' Compensation Boards of Canada provides data compiled from the provincial and territorial workers' compensation boards.

Human Resources and Skills Development Canada (HRSDC)
**www.hrsdc.gc.ca/asp/gateway.asp?hr=/en/lp/lo/ohs/statistics/naosh/1.shtml&h
    s=oxs**

HRSDC has statistics on workplace injuries and fatalities.

The Workers' Compensation Board of British Columbia
www.healthandsafetycentre.org/sc/calculator/default.htm

The Workers' Compensation Board of British Columbia's website provides an easy to use tool for calculating the costs of accidents.

ENDNOTES

1. Human Resources and Skills Development Canada. (April 28, 2003). "General Statistics on Occupational Injuries and Fatalities, 1994–1998." [Online]. Available: http://www.hrsdc.gc.ca/asp/gateway.asp?hr=/en/lp/lo/ohs/statistics/naosh/1.shtml&hs=oxs. (Retrieved February 27, 2005).

2. Human Resources and Skills Development Canada. (April 28, 2003). "General Statistics on Occupational Injuries and Fatalities, 1994–1998." [Online]. Available: http://www.hrsdc.gc.ca/asp/gateway.asp?hr=/en/lp/lo/ohs/statistics/naosh/2.shtml&hs=oxs# 2.3. (Retrieved February 27, 2005).

3. Ibid.

4. Ibid.

5. Ibid.

6. Ibid.

7. *Environmental Science and Engineering Magazine.* (May 1996). "Canadians Underestimate 31 Billion Dollar Workplace Accident Costs." [Online]. Available: http://www.esemag.com/0596/canadian.html. (Retrieved February 27, 2005).

8. Daniel Corcoran, "The Hidden Value of Safety," *Occupational Health and Safety* 71, no. 6 (June 2002): 20–22.

9. Corcoran, "The Hidden Value of Safety," 22.

10. Human Resources and Skills Development Canada, "General Statistics on Occupational Injuries and Fatalities."

11. Public Health Agency of Canada. (January 8, 2004). "Glossary of Frequently Used Terms." [Online]. Available: http://www.hc-sc.gc.ca/hppb/fitness/work/glossary_e.html. (Retrieved February 27, 2005).

12. John A. Fletcher and Hugh M. Douglas, *Total Environmental Control* (National Profile Limited, 1986), 35.

13. National Safety Council, *Accident Prevention Manual for Industrial Operations: Administration and Programs,* 9th ed. (Chicago: National Safety Council, 1988), 158.

14. Ibid., 158.

15. Debbie Culbertson, "The Real Cost," *Occupational Health and Safety* 24, no. 3 (September 2001): 12.

Theories of Accident Causation

LEARNING OBJECTIVES

Apply the following theories of accident causation to the workplace:

- domino
- human factors
- accident/incident
- epidemiological
- systems
- combination
- behavioural

Each year, work-related accidents take an enormous toll on Canadian workers and the economy. The very compelling statistics put forth in Chapter 2 demonstrate the magnitude of the problem. These workplace accidents degrade both the economic stability of many businesses and the quality of life for those injured and their families. The first step in preventing accidents is to identify their cause.

Why do accidents happen? This question has concerned health and safety decision makers for decades, because in order to prevent accidents we must know why they happen. Over the years, several theories of accident causation have evolved that attempt to explain why accidents occur. Models based on these theories are used to predict and prevent accidents.

The most widely known theories of accident causation are the domino theory, the human factors theory, the accident/incident theory, the epidemiological theory, the systems theory, the combination theory, and the behavioural theory. This chapter provides practising and prospective safety professionals with the information they need to understand fully and apply these theories.

DOMINO THEORY OF ACCIDENT CAUSATION

An early pioneer of accident prevention and industrial safety was Herbert W. Heinrich, an official with the Travelers Insurance Company. In the late 1920s, after studying the reports of 75 000 industrial accidents, Heinrich concluded that

- 88% of industrial accidents are caused by unsafe acts committed by fellow workers.
- 10% of industrial accidents are caused by unsafe conditions.
- 2% of industrial accidents are unavoidable.[1]

DOMINO THEORY
Injuries are caused by the action of preceding factors. Removal of the central factor negates the action of the preceding factors and, in so doing, prevents accidents and injuries.

Heinrich's study laid the foundation for his *Axioms of Industrial Safety* and his theory of accident causation, which came to be known as the **domino theory**. So much of Heinrich's theory has been discounted by more contemporary research that it is now considered outdated. However, because some of today's more widely accepted theories can be traced back to Heinrich's theory, students of industrial safety should be familiar with his work.

Heinrich's Axioms of Industrial Safety

Heinrich summarized what he thought health and safety decision makers should know about industrial accidents in 10 statements he called "Axioms of Industrial Safety." These axioms can be paraphrased as follows:

1. Injuries result from a completed series of factors, one of which is the accident itself.
2. An accident can occur only as the result of an unsafe act by a person and/or a physical or mechanical hazard.
3. Most accidents are the result of unsafe behaviour by people.
4. An unsafe act by a person or an unsafe condition does not always immediately result in an accident/injury.
5. The reasons that people commit unsafe acts can serve as helpful guides in selecting corrective actions.
6. The severity of an accident is largely fortuitous, and its cause is largely preventable.
7. The best accident prevention techniques are analogous with the best quality and productivity techniques.
8. Management should assume responsibility for safety because it is in the best position to get results.
9. The supervisor is the key person in the prevention of industrial accidents.
10. In addition to the direct costs of an accident (e.g., compensation, liability claims, medical costs, and hospital expenses), there are also hidden or indirect costs.[2]

According to Heinrich, these axioms encompass the fundamental body of knowledge that must be understood by decision makers interested in preventing accidents. Any accident prevention program that takes all 10 axioms into account is more likely to be effective than a program that leaves out one or more axioms.

Heinrich's Domino Theory

Perhaps you have stood up a row of dominoes, tipped the first one over, and watched as each successive domino topples the one next to it. This is how Heinrich's theory of accident causation works. According to Heinrich, there are five factors in the sequence of events leading up to an accident. These factors can be summarized as follows:

1. **Ancestry and social environment.** Negative character traits that may lead people to behave in an unsafe manner can be inherited (**ancestry**) or acquired as a result of the **social environment**.
2. **Fault of person.** Negative character traits, whether inherited or acquired, are why people behave in an unsafe manner and why hazardous conditions exist.
3. **Unsafe act/mechanical or physical hazard. Unsafe acts** committed by people and **mechanical** or **physical hazards** are the direct causes of accidents.
4. **Accident.** Typically, accidents that result in injury are caused by falling or being hit by moving objects.
5. **Injury.** Typical injuries resulting from accidents include lacerations and fractures.[3]

Heinrich's theory has two central points: (1) Injuries are caused by the action of **preceding factors**; and (2) removal of the **central factor** (unsafe act/**hazardous condition**) negates the action of the preceding factors and, in so doing, prevents accidents and injuries.

Domino Theory in Practice

Construction Products Company (CPC) is a distributor of lumber, pipe, and concrete products. Its customers are typically small building contractors. CPC's facility consists of an office in which orders are placed and several large warehouses. Contractors place their orders in the office. They then drive their trucks through the appropriate warehouses to be loaded by CPC personnel.

Because the contractors are small operations, most of their orders are also relatively small and can be loaded by hand. Warehouse personnel go to the appropriate bins, pull out the material needed to fill their orders, and load the materials on customers' trucks. Even though most orders are small enough to be loaded by hand, many of the materials purchased are bulky and cumbersome to handle. Because of this, CPC's loaders are required to wear such personal protection gear as hard hats, padded gloves, steel-toed boots, and lower-back-support belts.

For years CPC's management team had noticed an increase in minor injuries to warehouse personnel during the summer months. Typically, these injuries consisted of nothing worse than minor cuts, scrapes, and bruises. However, this past summer had been different. Two warehouse workers had sustained serious back injuries. These injuries have been costly to CPC both financially and in terms of employee morale.

An investigation of these accidents quickly identified a series of events and a central causal behaviour that set up a *domino effect* that, in turn, resulted in the injuries. The investigation revealed that CPC's warehouses became so hot during the summer months that personal protection gear was uncomfortable. As

ANCESTRY
A person's line of descent.

SOCIAL ENVIRONMENT
The general value system of the society in which an individual lives, works, grows up, and so on.

UNSAFE ACT
An act that is not safe for an employee.

MECHANICAL HAZARDS
Those associated with power-driven machines, whether automated or manually operated.

PHYSICAL HAZARDS
Include noise, vibration, extremes of temperature, and excessive radiation.

PRECEDING FACTORS
Factors that led up to an accident.

CENTRAL FACTOR
The main issue or factor in a problem or act.

HAZARDOUS CONDITION
A condition that exposes a person to risks.

a result, warehouse personnel simply discarded it. Failure to use appropriate personal protection gear in the summer months had always led to an increase in injuries. However, because the injuries were minor in nature, management had never paid much attention to the situation. It was probably inevitable that more serious injuries would occur eventually.

To prevent a recurrence of the summer-injury epidemic, CPC's management team decided to remove the causal factor — failure of warehouse personnel to use their personal protection gear during the summer months. To facilitate the removal of this factor, CPC's management team formed a committee consisting of one executive manager, one warehouse supervisor, and three warehouse employees.

The committee made the following recommendations: (1) provide all warehouse personnel with training on the importance and proper use of personal protection gear; (2) require warehouse supervisors to monitor the use of personal protection gear more closely; (3) establish a company policy that contains specific and progressive disciplinary measures for failure to use required personal protection gear; and (4) implement several heat reduction measures to make warehouses cooler during the summer months.

CPC's management team adopted all of the committee's recommendations. In doing so, it removed the central causal factor that had historically led to an increase in injuries during the summer months.

HUMAN FACTORS THEORY OF ACCIDENT CAUSATION

The **human factors theory** of accident causation attributes accidents to a chain of events ultimately caused by **human error**. It consists of the following three broad factors that lead to human error: overload, inappropriate response, and inappropriate activities (see Figure 3–1).

Overload
Overload amounts to an imbalance between a person's capacity at any given time and the load that person is carrying in a given state. A person's capacity is the product of such factors as his or her natural ability, training, state of mind, fatigue, stress, and physical condition. The load that a person is carrying consists of tasks for which he or she is responsible and added burdens resulting from **environmental factors** (noise, distractions, and so on), **internal factors** (personal problems, emotional stress, and worry), and **situational factors** (level of risk, unclear instructions, and so on). The state in which a person is acting is the product of his or her motivational and arousal levels.

Inappropriate Response and Incompatibility
How a person responds in a given situation can cause or prevent an accident. If a person detects a hazardous condition but does nothing to correct it, he or she has responded inappropriately. If a person removes a safeguard from a machine in an effort to increase output, he or she has responded inappropriately. If a person disregards an established safety procedure, he or she has responded in-

HUMAN FACTORS THEORY
Attributes accidents to a chain of events ultimately caused by human error.

HUMAN ERROR
A mistake that is made by a human, not a machine.

OVERLOAD
Amounts to an imbalance between a person's capacity at any given time and the load that person is carrying in a given state.

ENVIRONMENTAL FACTORS
Characteristics of the environment in which an employee works that can affect his or her state of mind or physical conditions, such as noise or distractions.

INTERNAL FACTORS
Factors that can add a burden on a person and interfere with his or her work, such as personal problems.

SITUATIONAL FACTORS
Environmental factors that can affect an employee's safety and that can differ from situation to situation.

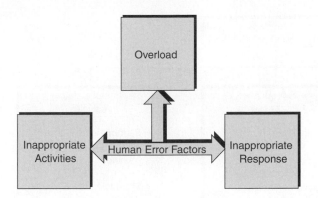

Figure 3–1
Factors that cause human errors.

appropriately. Such responses can lead to accidents. In addition to **inappropriate responses**, this component includes workstation incompatibility. The incompatibility of a person's workstation with regard to size, force, reach, feel, and similar factors can lead to accidents and injuries.

Inappropriate Activities

Human error can be the result of **inappropriate activities**. An example of an inappropriate activity is a person who undertakes a task that he or she doesn't know how to do. Another example is a person who misjudges the degree of risk involved in a given task and proceeds based on that misjudgment. Such inappropriate activities can lead to accidents and injuries. Figure 3–2 summarizes the various components of the human factors theory.[4]

INAPPROPRIATE RESPONSE
A response in which a person disregards an established safety procedure.

INAPPROPRIATE ACTIVITIES
Activities undertaken with disregard for established safety procedures.

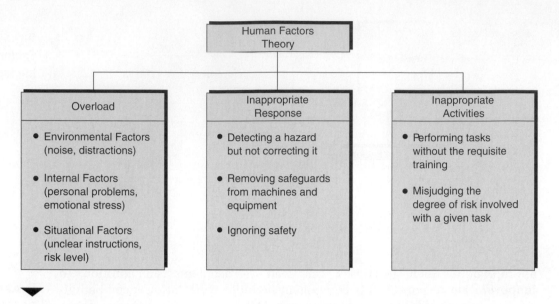

Figure 3–2
Human factors theory.

Human Factors Theory in Practice

Kitchenware Manufacturing Incorporated (KMI) produces aluminum kitchenware for commercial settings. After 10 years of steady, respectable growth, KMI suddenly saw its sales triple in less than 6 months. This rapid growth was the result of KMI's successful entry into European and Asian markets.

The growth in sales, although welcomed by both management and employees, quickly overloaded and, before long, overwhelmed the company's production facility. KMI responded by adding a second shift of production personnel and approving unlimited overtime for highly skilled personnel. Shortly after the upturn in production, KMI began to experience a disturbing increase in accidents and injuries. During his accident investigations, KMI's safety manager noticed that human error figured prominently in the accidents. He grouped all of the human errors identified into three categories: (1) overload, (2) inappropriate response, and (3) inappropriate activities.

In the category of *overload,* he found that the rush to fill orders was pushing production personnel beyond their personal limits in some cases, and beyond their capabilities in others. Stress, insufficient training of new employees, and fatigue all contributed to the overload. In the category of *inappropriate response,* the safety manager determined that many of KMI's production personnel had removed safeguards from their machines in an attempt to speed up production. All of the machines involved in accidents had had safeguards removed.

In the category of *inappropriate activities,* the safety manager found that new employees were being assigned duties for which they weren't yet fully trained. As a result, they often misjudged the amount of risk associated with their work tasks.

With enough accident investigations completed to identify a pattern of human error, the safety manager prepared a presentation containing a set of recommendations for corrective measures for KMI's executive management team. His recommendations were designed to prevent human-error-oriented accidents without slowing production.

ACCIDENT/INCIDENT THEORY OF ACCIDENT CAUSATION

The **accident/incident theory** is an extension of the human factors theory. It was developed by Dan Petersen and is sometimes referred to as the Petersen accident/incident theory.[5] Petersen introduced such new elements as **ergonomic traps**, the decision to err, and systems failures, while retaining much of the human factors theory. A model based on his theory is shown in Figure 3–3.

ACCIDENT/INCIDENT THEORY
Theory of accident causation in which overload, ergonomic traps, or a decision to err lead to human error.

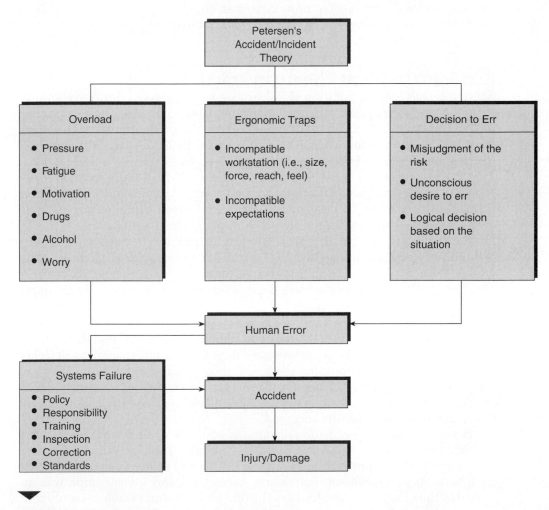

Figure 3–3
Accident/incident theory.

ERGONOMIC TRAP
An unsafe condition unintentionally designed into a workstation.

UNSAFE BEHAVIOUR
The manner in which people conduct themselves that is unsafe to them or to another.

CAUSAL RELATIONSHIP
A situation in which an action leads to a certain result.

In this model, overload, ergonomic traps, or a decision to err lead to human error. The decision to err may be conscious and based on logic or it may be unconscious. A variety of pressures such as deadlines, peer pressure, and budget factors can lead to **unsafe behaviour**. Another factor that can influence such a decision is the "It won't happen to me" syndrome.

The systems failure component is an important contribution of Petersen's theory. First, it shows the potential for a **causal relationship** between management decisions or management behaviour and safety. Second, it establishes management's role in accident prevention as well as the broader concepts of health and safety in the workplace.

Following are just some of the different ways that systems can fail, according to Petersen's theory:

- Management does not establish a comprehensive safety policy.
- Responsibility and authority with regard to safety are not clearly defined.
- Safety procedures such as measurement, inspection, correction, and investigation are ignored or given insufficient attention.
- Employees do not receive proper orientation.
- Employees are not given sufficient safety training.

Accident/Incident Theory in Practice

Poultry Processing Corporation (PPC) processes chickens and turkeys for grocery chains. Poultry processing is a labour-intensive enterprise involving a great deal of handwork. A variety of different knives, shears, and cleavers are used. Much of the work is monotonous and repetitive. Selected parts of the overall process must be done in cold conditions.

PPC has gone to great lengths to ensure that workstations are ergonomically sound, that personal protection gear is used as appropriate, and that adequate precautions are taken to prevent illness and injuries. As a result, PPC is an award-winning company in the area of workplace health and safety.

Consequently, the poultry-processing industry was shocked when a class action lawsuit was filed against PPC on behalf of over 50 employees, all of whom claimed to be suffering from carpal tunnel syndrome. Because of PPC's excellent health and safety record, most observers felt sure that the company would be vindicated in the end.

The company's policies and procedures relating to health and safety were investigated thoroughly by consultants brought in by both PPC and the attorney for the plaintiffs. Over 100 witnesses gave depositions, and several preliminary hearings were held. By the time the trial finally rolled around, both sides had accumulated mountains of paper and filing cabinets full of evidence. Then, suddenly and without advance notice, PPC offered a substantial financial settlement, which the plaintiffs accepted.

It was one of PPC's outside consultants who discovered what had caused the increased incidence of carpal tunnel syndrome. The company had always used a centralized approach to managing health and safety. Responsibility for such tasks as measurement, inspection, correction, and investigation was assigned to the safety manager, Joe Don Huttle. Huttle had an excellent record during his 20 years in the poultry-processing industry, with the last five spent at PPC. In fact, he was so well respected in the industry that his peers had elected him president of a statewide safety organization. This, as it turned out, is where PPC's troubles began.

When Huttle took it over, the safety organization had experienced a three-year decline in membership and was struggling to stay afloat financially. He had been elected as "the man who could save the organization." Intending to do just that, Huttle went right to work. For months at a time he worked seven days a week, often spending as much as two weeks at a time on the road. When he was in his office at PPC, Huttle was either on the telephone or doing paperwork for the safety organization.

Within six months, he had reversed the organization's downhill slide, but not without paying a price at home. During the same six-month period, his duties at PPC were badly neglected. Measurement of individual and group safety performance had come to a standstill. The same was true of inspection, correction, investigation, and reporting.

It was during this time of neglect that the increased incidence of carpal tunnel syndrome occurred. Safety precautions that Huttle had instituted to guard against this particular problem were no longer observed properly once the workers realized that he had stopped observing and correcting them. Measurement and inspection might also have prevented the injuries had Huttle maintained his normal schedule of these activities.

PPC's consultant, in a confidential report to executive managers, cited the *accident/incident theory* in explaining his view of why the injuries occurred. In this report, the consultant said that Huttle was guilty of applying "It won't happen here" logic when he made a conscious decision to neglect his duties at PPC in favour of his duties with the professional organization. Of course, the employees themselves were guilty of not following clearly established procedures. However, because Huttle's neglect was also a major contributing factor, PPC decided to settle out of court.

EPIDEMIOLOGICAL THEORY OF ACCIDENT CAUSATION

Traditionally, safety theories and programs have focused on accidents and the resulting injuries. However, the current trend is toward a broader perspective that also encompasses the issue of industrial hygiene. **Industrial hygiene** concerns environmental factors that can lead to sickness, disease, or other forms of impaired health.

This trend has, in turn, led to the development of an epidemiological theory of accident causation. Epidemiology is the study of causal relationships between environmental factors and disease. The **epidemiological theory** holds that the models used for studying and determining these relationships can also be used to study causal relationships between environmental factors and accidents or diseases.[6]

Figure 3–4 illustrates the epidemiological theory of accident causation. The key components are **predispositional characteristics** and **situational characteristics**. These characteristics, taken together, can either result in or prevent conditions that may result in an accident. For example, if an employee who is particularly susceptible to peer pressure (predisposition characteristic) is pres-

INDUSTRIAL HYGIENE
An area of specialization in the field of industrial health and safety that is concerned with predicting, recognizing, assessing, controlling, and preventing environmental stressors in the workplace that can cause sickness or serious discomfort.

EPIDEMIOLOGICAL THEORY
Holds that the models used for studying and determining epidemiological relationships can also be used to study causal relationships between environmental factors and accidents or diseases.

PREDISPOSITIONAL CHARACTERISTICS
Human personality characteristics that can have a catalytic effect in causing an accident.

SITUATIONAL CHARACTERISTICS
Factors that can change from setting to setting and can have a catalytic effect in causing an accident.

sured by his co-workers (situational characteristic) to speed up his operation, the result will be an increased probability of an accident.

Epidemiological Theory in Practice

Jane Andrews was the newest member of the loading unit for Parcel Delivery Service (PDS). She and the other members of her unit were responsible for loading 50 trucks every morning. It was physically demanding work, and she was the first woman ever selected by PDS to work in the loading unit. She had gotten the job as part of the company's upward mobility program. She was excited about her new position because within PDS, the loading unit was considered a springboard to advancement. Consequently, she was eager to do well. The responsibility she felt toward other female employees at PDS only intensified her anxiety. Andrews felt that if she failed, other women might not get a chance to try in the future.

Before beginning work in the loading unit, employees must complete two days of training on proper lifting techniques. The use of back-support belts is mandatory for all loading dock personnel. Consequently, Andrews became concerned when the supervisor called her aside on her first day in the unit and told her to forget what she had learned in training. He said, "Jane, nobody wants a back injury, so be careful. But the key to success in this unit is speed. The lift-

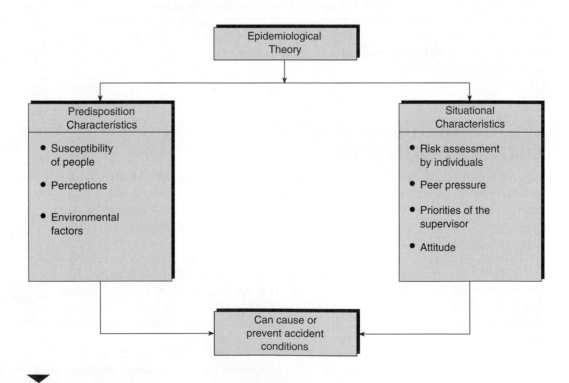

Figure 3–4
Epidemiological theory.

ing techniques they teach in that workshop will just slow you down. You've got the job, and I'm glad you're here. But you won't last long if you can't keep up."

Andrews was torn between following safety procedures and making a good impression on her new supervisor. At first, she made an effort to use proper lifting techniques. However, when several of her co-workers complained that she wasn't keeping up, the supervisor told Andrews to "keep up or get out of the way." Feeling the pressure, she started taking the same shortcuts she had seen her co-workers use. Positive results were immediate, and Andrews received several nods of approval from fellow workers and a "good job" from the supervisor. Before long, Andrews had won the approval and respect of her colleagues.

However, after two months of working in the loading unit, she began to experience persistent lower-back pain. Andrews felt sure that her hurried lifting techniques were to blame, but she valued the approval of her supervisor and fellow workers too much to do anything that might slow her down. Finally, one day while loading a truck, Andrews fell to the pavement in pain and could not get up. Her back throbbed with intense pain, and her legs were numb. She had to be rushed to the emergency room of the local hospital. By the time Andrews checked out of the hospital a week later, she had undergone major surgery to repair two ruptured discs.

Jane Andrews's situation can be explained by the *epidemiological theory* of accident causation. The predisposition factor was her susceptibility to peer pressure from her co-workers and supervisor. The applicable situational factors were peer pressure and the priorities of the supervisor. These factors, taken together, caused the accident.

SYSTEMS THEORY OF CAUSATION

A system is a group of regularly interacting and interrelated components that together form a unified whole. This definition is the basis for the **systems theory** of accident causation. This theory views a situation in which an accident may occur as a system comprising the following components: person (host), machine (agency), and **environment**.[7] The likelihood of an accident occurring is determined by how these components interact. Changes in the patterns of interaction can increase or reduce the probability of an accident.

For example, an experienced employee who operates a numerically controlled five-axis machining centre in a shop environment may take a two-week vacation. Her temporary replacement may be less experienced. This change in one component of the system (person/host) increases the probability of an accident. Such a simple example is easily understood. However, not all changes in patterns of interaction are this simple. Some are so subtle that their analysis may require a team of people, each with a different type of expertise.

The primary components of the systems model are the person-machine-environment, information, decisions, risks, and the task to be performed.[8] Each of the components has a bearing on the probability that an accident will occur. The systems model is illustrated in Figure 3–5.

As this model shows, even as a person interacts with a machine within an environment, three activities take place between the system and the task to be performed. Every time a task must be performed, there is the risk that an acci-

SYSTEMS THEORY
Views a situation in which an accident may occur as a system comprising the following components: person (host), machine (agency), and environment.

ENVIRONMENT
The aggregate of social and cultural conditions that influence the life of an individual.

dent may occur. Sometimes the risks are great; at other times, they are small. This is where information collection and decision making come in.

DISCUSSION CASE

What Is Your Opinion?

"All accidents, one way or another, are the result of human error."

"No, accidents are the result of a combination of things. I like the combination theory."

"You're both wrong. Accidents are best explained by the domino theory."

So the debate went in Dr. Jameson's class at Burton University. What is your opinion concerning the various theories of accident causation?

Based on the information that has been collected by observing and mentally noting the current circumstances, the person weighs the risks and decides whether to perform the task under existing circumstances. For example, say a machine operator is working on a rush order that is behind schedule. An important safety device has malfunctioned on his machine. Simply taking it off will interrupt work for only five minutes, but it will also increase the probability of an accident. However, replacing it could take up to an hour. Should the operator remove the safety guard and proceed with the task or take the time to replace it? The operator and his supervisor may assess the situation (collect information), weigh the risks, and make a decision to proceed. If their information was right and their assessment of the risks accurate, the task will probably be accomplished without an accident.

Figure 3–5
Systems theory model.

However, the environment in which the machine operator is working is unusually hectic, and the pressure to complete an order that is already behind schedule is intense. These factors are **stressors** that can cloud the judgment of those collecting information, weighing risks, and making the decision. When stressors are introduced between points 1 and 3 in Figure 3–5, the likelihood of an accident increases.

STRESSORS
Stimuli that cause stress.

For this reason, Firenzie recommends that five factors be considered before beginning the process of collecting information, weighing risks, and making a decision:

- The job requirements.
- The workers' abilities and limitations.
- The gain if the task is successfully accomplished.
- The loss if the task is attempted but fails.
- The loss if the task is not attempted.[9]

These factors can help a person achieve the proper perspective before collecting information, weighing risks, and making a decision. It is particularly important to consider these factors when stressors such as noise, time constraints, or pressure from a supervisor may tend to cloud one's judgment.

Systems Theory in Practice

Precision Tooling Company (PTC) specializes in difficult orders that are produced in small lots, and in making corrections to parts that otherwise would wind up as expensive rejects in the scrap bin. In short, PTC specializes in doing the types of work that other companies cannot, or will not, do. Most of PTC's work comes in the form of subcontracts from larger manufacturing companies. Consequently, living up to its reputation as a high-performance, on-time company is important to PTC.

Because much of its work consists of small batches of parts to be reworked, PTC still uses several manually operated machines. The least experienced machinists operate these machines. This causes two problems. The first problem is that it is difficult for even a master machinist to hold to modern tolerance levels on these old machines. Consequently, apprentice machinists find holding to precise tolerances quite a challenge. The second problem is that the machines are so old that they frequently break down.

Complaints from apprentice machinists about the old machines are frequent. However, their supervisors consider time on the old "ulcer makers" to be one of the rites of passage that upstart machinists must endure. Their attitude is, "We had to do it, so why shouldn't you?" This was where things stood at PTC when the company won the Johnson contract.

PTC had been trying for years to become a preferred supplier for H. R. Johnson Company. PTC's big chance finally came when Johnson's manufacturing division incorrectly produced 10 000 copies of a critical part before noticing the problem. Simply scrapping the part and starting over was an expensive solution. Johnson's vice president for manufacturing decided to give PTC a chance.

PTC's management team was ecstatic! Finally, they had an opportunity to partner with H. R. Johnson Company. If PTC could perform well on this one, even more lucrative contracts were sure to follow. The top managers called a companywide meeting of all employees. Attendance was mandatory. The CEO explained the situation as follows:

Ladies and gentlemen, we are faced with a great opportunity. I've just signed a contract with H. R. Johnson Company to rework 10 000 parts that their manufacturing folks produced improperly. The rework tasks are not that complicated, but every part has got to go through several manual operations at the front end of the rework process. This means our manual machining unit is going to have to supply the heroes on this job. I've promised the manufacturing VP at Johnson that we would have his parts ready in 90 days. I know that's a lot to do in so short a period of time, but Johnson is in a real bind here. If we can produce on this one, they won't forget us in the future.

This put PTC's apprentice machinists on the spot. If PTC didn't perform on this contract, it would be their fault. They cursed their old machines and got to work. The CEO had said the rework tasks would not be "that complicated," but, as it turned out, the processes weren't that simple either. The problem was tolerances. Holding to the tolerances specified in the Johnson contract took extra time and a special effort on every single part. Before long, the manual machining unit was behind schedule, and management was getting nervous. The situation was made even worse by the continual breakdowns and equipment failures experienced. The harder the unit supervisor pushed, the more stressed the employees and machines became.

Predictably, it wasn't long before safety procedures were forgotten, and unreasonable risks were being taken. The pressure from management, the inexperience of the apprentice machinists, and the constant equipment failures finally took their toll. In a hurry to get back on schedule, and fearing that his machine would break down again, one machinist got careless and ran his hand into the cutter on his milling machine. By the time the machine had been shut down, his hand was badly mutilated. In the aftershock of this accident, PTC was unable to meet the agreed-upon completion schedule. Unfortunately, PTC did not make the kind of impression on H. R. Johnson's management team that it had hoped.

This accident can be explained by the systems theory. The *person-machine-environment* chain has a direct application in this case. The person involved was relatively inexperienced. The machine involved was old and prone to breakdowns. The environment was especially stressful and pressure packed. These three factors, taken together, resulted in this serious and tragic accident.

COMBINATION THEORY OF ACCIDENT CAUSATION

COMBINATION THEORY
The actual cause of an accident may be explained by combining many models.

There is often a degree of difference between any theory of accident causation and reality. The various models presented with their corresponding theories in this chapter attempt to explain why accidents occur. For some accidents, a given model may be very accurate. For others, it may be less so. Often the cause of an accident cannot be adequately explained by just one model or theory. Thus, according to the **combination theory**, the actual cause may combine parts of several different models. Safety personnel should use these theories as appropriate both for accident prevention and accident investigation. However, they should avoid the tendency to try to apply one model to all accidents.

Combination Theory in Practice

Crestview Grain Corporation (CGC) maintains 10 large silos for storing corn, rice, wheat, barley, and various other grains. Because stored grain generates fine dust and gases, ventilation of the silos is important. Consequently, all of CGC's silos have several large vents. Each of these vents uses a filter similar to the type used in home air conditioners that must be changed periodically.

There is an element of risk involved in changing the vent filters because of two potential hazards. The first hazard comes from unvented dust and gases that can make breathing difficult, or even dangerous. The second hazard is the grain itself. Each silo has a catwalk that runs around its inside circumference near the top. These catwalks give employees access to the vents that are also near the top of each silo. The catwalks are almost 30 metres (100 feet) above ground level, they are narrow, and the guardrails on them are only knee high. A fall from a catwalk into the grain below would probably be fatal.

Consequently, CGC has well-defined rules that employees are to follow when changing filters. Because these rules are strictly enforced, there had never been an accident in one of CGC's silos — that is, not until the Juan Perez tragedy occurred. Perez was not new to the company. At the time of his accident, he had worked at CGC for over five years. However, he was new to the job of silo maintenance. His inexperience, as it turned out, would prove fatal.

It was time to change the vent filters in silo number 4. Perez had never changed vent filters himself. He hadn't been in the job long enough. However, he had served as the required "second man" when his supervisor, Bao Chu Lai, had changed the filters in silos 1, 2, and 3. Because Chu Lai was at home recuperating from heart surgery and would be out for another four weeks, Perez decided to change the filters himself. Changing the filters was a simple enough task, and Perez had always thought the second-man concept was overdoing it a little. He believed in taking reasonable precautions as much as the next person, but in his opinion, CGC was paranoid about safety.

Perez collected his safety harness, respirator, and four new vent filters. Then he climbed the external ladder to the entrance-exit platform near the top of silo number 4. Before going in, Perez donned his respirator and strapped on his safety harness. Opening the hatch cover, he stepped inside the silo onto the catwalk. Following procedure, Perez attached a lifeline to his safety harness, picked up the new vent filters, and headed for the first vent. He changed the first two filters without incident. It was while he was changing the third filter that tragedy struck.

The filter in the third vent was wedged in tightly. After several attempts to pull it out, Perez became frustrated and gave the filter a good jerk. When the filter suddenly broke loose, the momentum propelled Perez backwards and he toppled off the catwalk. At first it appeared that his lifeline would hold, but without a second person to pull him up or call for help, Perez was suspended by only the lifeline for over 20 minutes. He finally panicked, and in his struggle to pull himself up, knocked open the buckle of his safety harness. The buckle gave way, and Perez fell over 15 metres (50 feet) into the grain below. The impact knocked off his respirator, the grain quickly enveloped him, and Perez was asphyxiated.

The accident investigation that followed revealed that several factors combined to cause the fatal accident — the combination theory. The most critical of these factors were as follows:

- Absence of the supervisor.
- Inexperience of Perez.
- A conscious decision by Perez to disregard CGC's safety procedures.
- A faulty buckling mechanism on the safety harness.
- An unsafe design (only a knee-high guardrail on the catwalk).

BEHAVIOURAL THEORY OF ACCIDENT CAUSATION

The behavioural theory of accident causation and prevention is often referred to as *behaviour-based safety* (BBS). BBS has both proponents and critics. One of the most prominent proponents of BBS is E. Scott Geller, a senior partner of Safety Performance Solutions, Inc. and a professor of psychology. It is appropriate that Geller is a professional psychologist because BBS is the application of behavioural theories from the field of psychology to the field of occupational safety.

According to Geller, there are seven basic principles of BBS: (1) intervention that is focused on employee behaviour; (2) identification of external factors that will help understand and improve employee behaviour (from the perspective of safety in the workplace); (3) direction of behaviour with activators or events antecedent to the desired behaviour, and motivation of the employee to behave as desired with incentives and rewards that will follow the desired behaviour; (4) focus on the positive consequences that will result from the desired behaviour as a way to motivate employees; (5) application of the scientific method to improve attempts at behavioural interventions; (6) use of theory to integrate information rather than to limit possibilities; and (7) planned interventions designed with the feelings and attitudes of the individual employee in mind.[10]

Those who have studied psychology will recognize BBS as an innovative and practical application of standard behavioural theory to the field of occupational safety. These theories are relevant in any situation in which certain types of human behaviours are desired while others are to be avoided. Positive reinforcement in the form of incentives and rewards is used to promote the desired (safe) behaviours.

Proponents of BBS use the "ABC" model to summarize the concept of understanding human behaviour and developing appropriate interventions when the behaviour is undesirable (unsafe). Geller explains the model as follows:

> Behavior-based safety trainers and consultants teach the ABC model (or three-term contingency) as a framework to understand and analyze behavior or to develop interventions for improving behavior. As given in BBS principle 3 . . . the "A" stands for activators or antecedent events that precede behavior ("B") and "C" refers to the consequences following behavior or produced by it. Activators direct behavior, whereas consequences motivate behavior.[11]

Two other advocates of BBS, Bruce Fern and Lori Alzamora, propose the expansion of the ABC model to ABCO.[12] The "O" stands for outcomes. They explain the addition as follows:

> "*Outcome*" refers to the longer-term results of engaging in safe or unsafe behavior. For example, an antecedent of a sign requiring employees to wear safety goggles could produce the behavior of putting on the goggles, the consequence of avoiding

an eye injury, and the outcome of being able to continue working and enjoying time with the family. On the other hand, the consequence of not wearing goggles could be an eye injury with a potential outcome of blindness, time off the job, and a reduced quality of life. Failure to address the issue of outcomes represents a lost opportunity to give employees a good reason for engaging in safe behaviors.[13]

Behavioural Theory in Action

Mark Potter is the safety manager for Excello Corporation. Several months ago, he became concerned because employees seemed to have developed a lax attitude toward wearing hard hats. What troubled Potter was that there is more than the usual potential for head injuries because of the type of work done in Excello's plant and he had personally witnessed two near misses in less than a week. An advocate of behaviour-based safety (BBS), he decided to apply the ABC model in turning this unsafe behaviour pattern around.

His first step was to remove all of the old "Hard Hat Area" signs from the plant and replace them with newer, more noticeable signs. Then he scheduled a brief seminar on head injuries and cycled all employees through it over a two-week period. The seminar took an unusual approach. It told a story of two employees. One was in a hospital bed surrounded by family members he did not even recognize. The other was shown enjoying a family outing with happy family members. The clear message of the video was "the difference between these two employees is a hard hat." These two activities were the antecedents to the behaviour he hoped to produce (all employees wearing hard hats when in a hard hat area).

The video contained a powerful message and it had the desired effect. Within days, employees were once again disciplining themselves to wear their hard hats (the desired behaviour). The consequence was that near misses stopped and no head injuries have occurred at Excello in months. The outcome of this is that Excello's employees have been able to continue enjoying the fruits of their labour and the company of loved ones.

DRUGS AND ACCIDENT CAUSATION

One of the most pernicious causes of accidents on the job is chemicals — but not the kind industrial hygienists generally concern themselves with.[14] The chemicals alluded to here are the illicit drugs and alcohol used by employees. Drugs and alcohol are the root cause or contributing cause of many accidents on the job every year. Consequently, safety professionals need to be on guard for employees who are drug and alcohol abusers.

According to Stephen Minter,

> The workplace cannot be separated from the society around it, and substance abuse continues to be a serious and costly health and safety issue for employers. According to surveys by the Department of Health and Human Services, some 77 percent of drug users are employed — more than 9 million workers. An estimated 6.5 percent of full-time and 8.6 of part-time workers use illicit drugs. More than a third of all workers between the ages of 18 and 25 are binge drinkers . . . . Alcoholism alone causes 500 million lost days annually (125 million days are lost each year due to work-related injuries) . . . . Some 20 percent of workers report that they have been

put in danger or injured, or had to work harder, redo work or cover for a co-worker, as a result of a co-worker's drinking.[15]

These discouraging statistics are why so many companies implement drug-free workplace programs. In fact, since 1989 federal contractors have been required to do so. Such programs typically include the following components: drug-free workplace policy, supervisory training, employee education, employee assistance programs, and alcohol and drug testing.

Establishing drug-free workplace programs is typically the responsibility of the human resources department. However, health and safety professionals should be aware of the workplace problems that can be caused by alcohol and drug abuse. Further, if a cross-functional team of representatives from various departments is convened by the human resources department for the purpose of developing a drug-free workplace program, the chief health and safety professional for the organization should be a member of that team.

MANAGEMENT FAILURES AND ACCIDENT CAUSATION

One of the leading causes of accidents in the workplace is the failure of management to do its part to ensure a safe and healthy work environment. Different levels of management have different levels of responsibility. The level of management with the most direct, hands-on, day-to-day responsibility for workplace health and safety is the supervisory level. Supervisors play a critical role in making sure that employees work in a safe and healthy environment.

Role of the Supervisor in Workplace Health and Safety

Health and safety professionals cannot do their jobs effectively without the full cooperation and day-to-day assistance of first-line supervisors. Supervisors and safety professionals must be partners when it comes to providing a safe and healthy workplace for employees. Supervisors should be assigned responsibility for the work environment and for the safety of employees in their units. Health and safety professionals should be readily available to help supervisors fulfill this responsibility.

Key responsibilities of supervisors relating to workplace health and safety include the following:

- Orienting new employees to the safe way to do their jobs.
- Ensuring that new and experienced employees receive the health and safety training they need on a continual basis.
- Monitoring employee performance and enforcing safety rules and regulations.
- Assisting health and safety professionals in conducting accident investigations.
- Assisting health and safety professionals in developing accident reports.
- Keeping up to date on safety issues.
- Setting a positive example for employees that says "the safe way is the right way."

Typical Management Failures That Cause Accidents

Management failures represent a major cause of accidents on the job. If management is serious about providing a safe and healthy work environment for employees, it must (1) show employees that safe and healthy work practices are expected by including such practices in job descriptions, monitoring employee work practices, and setting an example of safe and healthy work practices; (2) provide training in how to work safely, including orientation training for new employees as well as ongoing updated training for experienced employees; (3) include safe and healthy work practices as criteria in the periodic performance appraisals of employees; and (4) reinforce safe and healthy work practices by rewarding and recognizing employees who use them. Common examples of management failures include the following:

Poor housekeeping or improper use of tools, equipment, or facilities. Management either has not developed the necessary requirements or has but does not enforce them. The management failure in this case could be lack of safety procedures (failure to let employees know the expectations), lack of training (failure to give employees the knowledge and skills they need to work safely), or failure to properly supervise (failure to monitor employee actions).

Pressure to meet deadlines. Sometimes management has developed a good health and safety policy, established good health and safety procedures, built health and safety expectations into job descriptions and performance appraisals, and provided the necessary training only to put all of this aside when a rush order comes in. This may be the most problematic of the many different types of management failures that can occur because it can undermine all of the organization's health and safety efforts. When management allows health and safety procedures to be ignored or, worse yet, encourages them to be ignored to speed up production in the short run, employees soon get the message that health and safety are important only when there is no rush. This is an example of management failing to set the proper example.

SUMMARY

1. The domino theory of accident causation was one of the earliest developed. The theory posits that injuries result from a series of factors, one of which is an accident. The theory is operationalized in 10 statements called the Axioms of Industrial Safety. According to this theory, there are five factors in the sequence of events leading to an accident: ancestry and social environment, fault of person, unsafe act/mechanical or physical hazard, accident, and injury.

2. The human factors theory of accident causation attributes accidents to a chain of events ultimately caused by human error. It consists of three broad factors that lead to human error: overload, inappropriate response, and inappropriate activities.

3. The accident/incident theory of accident causation is an extension of the human factors theory. It introduces such new elements as ergonomic traps, the decision to err, and systems failures.

4. The epidemiological theory of accident causation holds that the models used for studying and determining the relationships between environmental factors and disease can be used to study the causal relationships between environmental factors and accidents.

5. The systems theory of accident causation views any situation in which an accident may occur as a system with three components: person (host), machine (agency), and environment.

6. The combination theory of accident causation posits that no one model or theory can explain all accidents. Factors from two or more models may be part of the cause.

7. There are seven principles of behaviour-based safety: intervention; identification of internal factors; motivation to behave in the desired manner; focus on the positive consequences of appropriate behaviour; application of the scientific method integration of information; and planned interventions.

KEY TERMS AND CONCEPTS

Accident/incident theory

Ancestry

Causal relationship

Central factor

Combination theory

Domino theory

Environment

Environmental factors

Epidemiological theory

Ergonomic traps

Hazardous condition

Human error

Human factors theory

Inappropriate activities

Inappropriate responses

Industrial hygiene

Internal factors

Mechanical or physical hazards

Overload

Preceding factors

Predispositional characteristics

Situational characteristics

Situational factors

Social environment

Stressors

Systems theory

Unsafe acts

Unsafe behaviour

REVIEW QUESTIONS

1. Explain the domino theory of accident causation, including its origin and its impact on more modern theories.

2. What were the findings of Herbert W. Heinrich's 1920s study of the causes of industrial accidents?

3. List five of Heinrich's Axioms of Industrial Safety.

4. Explain the following concepts in the domino theory: preceding factor, central factor.

5. What are the three broad factors that lead to human error in the human factors theory? Briefly explain each.

6. Explain the systems failure component of the accident/incident theory.

7. What are the key components of the epidemiological theory? How does their interaction affect accident causation?

8. Explain the systems theory of accident causation.

9. What impact do stressors have in the systems theory?

10. List five factors to consider before making workplace decisions that involve risk.

11. Explain the principles of behaviour-based safety.

WEBLINKS

Article by Abdul Raouf
http://turva.me.tut.fi/iloagri/natu/tac.htm
Informative short article on accident causation.

IAPA
www.iapa.ca/home/home.asp
The Industrial Accident Prevention Association (IAPA) is a not-for-profit, member-driven organization operating in the Province of Ontario since 1917. Their site contains numerous safety resources and links for members and the public.

Institute for Work & Health
www.iwh.on.ca/about/who.php
The Institute for Work & Health is an independent, not-for-profit organization whose mission is to conduct and share research with workers, labour organizations, employers, clinicians, and policy makers to promote, protect, and improve the health of working people.

NASA
www.hq.nasa.gov/office/codeq/accident/accident.pdf
This NASA website gives the viewer a lighthearted look at accidents and their cause.

ENDNOTES

1. H. W. Heinrich, D. Petersen, and N. Roos, *Industrial Accident Prevention,* 5th ed. (New York: McGraw-Hill, 1980).
2. Ibid.
3. Ibid.
4. Ibid.
5. Ibid.

6. M. A. Topf, "Chicken/Egg/Chegg!" *Occupational Health and Safety* 68, no. 6 (June 1999): 60–66.

7. D. L. Goetsch, *Implementing Total Safety Management* (Upper Saddle River, NJ: Prentice Hall, 1998), 227.

8. Ibid.

9. Ibid.

10. E. S. Geller, "Behavior-Based Safety: Confusion, Controversy, and Clarification," *Occupational Health and Safety* 68, no. 1 (January 1999): 40–49.

11. Ibid., 44.

12. B. Fern and L. P. Alzamora, "How and Why Behavioral Safety Needs to Change," *Occupational Health and Safety* 68, no. 9 (September 1999): 69.

13. Ibid.

14. Stephen G. Minter, "The Safety Threat from Within," *Occupational Hazards* 64, no. 4 (April 2002): 8.

15. Ibid.

Occupational Health and Safety Legislation in Canada

4
CHAPTER

LEARNING OBJECTIVES

- Describe the process of developing health and safety legislation in Canada.
- Describe the jurisdictions under which occupational health and safety laws fall.
- Compare provincial or territorial legislation to the federal jurisdiction.
- List the key players in occupational health and safety in Canada.
- Describe the role of the key players in occupational health and safety.

For society to function in a safe and productive manner, the activities of each member are governed by rules of conduct. These **laws** may restrict the activities of some while providing certain privileges for others. For laws to be effective, they must benefit society as a whole, be enforced, and have a component that deters deviation from those rules. This chapter describes how health and safety **legislation** is made and enforced in Canada, the role of the key players, and to which jurisdiction different legislation applies.

LAWS
Rules that limit behaviour.

LEGISLATION
Laws brought into force by a legislative body.

THE CANADIAN LEGAL SYSTEM

To fully appreciate the scope of our health and safety legislation, it is necessary to take a brief look at how our legal system has evolved to the point where it is today. The Canadian legal system is based largely on the English system. A major development in the British system was the signing of the **Magna Carta** (Great Charter) by King John of England in 1215. The significance of the Magna Carta was that for the first time the king's power could be limited and his subjects protected from arbitrary rule. Although King John was forced to agree to the terms of the Magna Carta in order to maintain power, the powerful barons renewed

MAGNA CARTA
Charter enacted in 1215 that limited the power of King John of England.

their allegiance to the king as a result and an important constitutional principle was established.

When Canada won its independence from Britain in 1876, the **British North America Act (BNA Act, 1876)** laid out the terms of reference for the new country, including the dividing up of power between the provinces and the federal government. Federal responsibility would include areas such as commerce, currency, the military, postal service, and criminal law. The provinces were given jurisdiction over the areas of marriage, shops, local taxation, maintenance of local resources, and hospitals. **The Constitution Act, 1982**, maintained the contents of the BNA Act, but also included a "charter of rights and freedoms," which guarantees all Canadian citizens the rights and freedoms that are often taken for granted by Canadians but are the envy of most other countries.

Acts and Regulations

Canada has a parliamentary system of government with each province being governed by a legislature. When a cabinet minister responsible for an area such as occupational health and safety decides that a new **statute** or **act** is needed or an existing one needs to be amended, she or he will have ministry staff draft a new law. After an internal review by the department or ministry, the minister will receive approval from the cabinet to introduce the new law in the legislature or parliament in the form of a **bill**. After the bill has been debated and amendments made, it will get three readings in the House. After the third reading the bill is given "royal assent" and then becomes an "act."[1]

Acts or statutes are the framework around which **regulations** are built. Many statutes consist largely of a list of powers to make regulations.[2] Regulations specify how the act is intended to be applied to each situation. For example, the act may require workers to use the correct procedures or equipment, but the details of those prescribed procedures or equipment are found in the related regulations. Several sets of regulations made under the occupational act cover various workplace sectors. For example, in Ontario, separate regulations are in place for construction projects, mines, industrial establishments, teachers, health care, and WHMIS and for designated substances, such as lead and mercury.

STANDARDS AND CODES

A **standard** is an operational principle, criterion, or requirement — or a combination of these. A **code** is a set of standards, rules, or regulations relating to a specific area. Standards and codes play an important role in modern health and safety management and engineering. These written procedures detail the safe and healthy way to perform job tasks and, consequently, to make the workplace safer and healthier.

Having written standards and codes that employees carefully follow can also decrease a company's exposure to costly litigation. Courts tend to hand down harsher rulings to companies that fail to develop or adapt, implement, and enforce appropriate standards and codes. Consequently, health and safety professionals should be familiar with the standards and codes relating to their company.

BRITISH NORTH AMERICA ACT (BNA ACT, 1876)
Established the constitutional layout of the new country, Canada, including the powers of the provincial and federal governments.

THE CONSTITUTION ACT, 1982
Provided Canada with a new constitution that included the charter of rights and freedoms.

STATUTE
Law made by provincial legislature or federal parliament.

ACT
Document containing laws made by provincial legislature or federal parliament.

BILL
Law in draft form.

REGULATIONS
Specific rules that often support other legislation.

STANDARD
An operational principle, criterion, or requirement pertaining to working conditions, methods, equipment, or materials in the workplace.

CODE
A set of standards, rules, or regulations relating to a specific area.

Numerous organizations develop standards for different industries. These organizations can be categorized broadly as follows: the government, professional organizations, and technical/trade associations.

Organizations that fall within these broad categories develop standards and codes in a wide variety of areas including, but not limited to, the following: fire protection, hazardous chemicals, instrumentation, insulation, lighting, lubrication, materials, noise/vibration, power, wiring, pressure relief, piping materials, piping systems, radiation exposure, safety equipment, shutdown systems, and ventilation.

To give some examples of the three types of organizations involved in developing standards, the widely accepted standards for many consumer products are those set by **Canadian Standards Association (CSA)**, which is a *government* agency. The American Conference of Governmental Industrial Hygienists (**ACGIH**), which develops and publishes recommended exposure limits for chemical and physical agents, is a *professional association*. (The ACGIH limits are the standard to which most jurisdictions refer when developing their own standards.) And the Heating, Refrigeration and Air Conditioning Institute of Canada (HRAI), which sets standards and provides certification to members of the heating and refrigeration field, is a *trade association*.

CANADIAN STANDARDS ASSOCIATION (CSA) Independent agency that develops national standards for the performance of many products inside and outside of the workplace.

ACGIH American Conference of Governmental Industrial Hygienists. A professional association that develops and publishes recommended exposure limits for chemical and physical agents.

OCCUPATIONAL HEALTH AND SAFETY JURISDICTIONS

Workers in Canada are covered by occupational health and safety legislation under one of two jurisdictions. Most workers are covered by health and safety laws of their province or territory, while about 10% of workers are covered by federal legislation. Each province or territory has its own version of an occupational health and safety act and corresponding regulations for various sectors. Figure 4–1 lists the legislation and who administers it in each jurisdiction. The format and content of the acts are very similar for each province and territory.

Workers employed directly by the federal government or by the following employers are covered by the **Canada Labour Code**, Part II:

- Federal crown corporations
- Interprovincial trucking, shipping, and bridges
- Airlines and airports
- Railways
- Telephone, television, and radio broadcasters
- Banks
- Grain elevators
- Other specific employers

CANADA LABOUR CODE Legislation that sets out the rights and duties of federal employees who work under federal jurisdiction. About 10% of the Canadian workforce is covered by the Canada Labour Code.

HOW WORKERS ARE PROTECTED

The federal legislation is very similar in format and content to that of the provinces or territories. The occupational health and safety acts for the provinces and territories are divided into "sections" that are, in turn, often divided into subsections to expand on a particular area of concern. For example,

Jurisdiction	Legislation	Administration
Newfoundland and Labrador www.whscc.nf.ca	Occupational Health and Safety Act	Workplace Health, Safety and Compensation Commission of Newfoundland and Labrador
Prince Edward Island www.wcb.pe.ca/	Occupational Health and Safety Act	Workers Compensation Board of Prince Edward Island
Nova Scotia www.gov.ns.ca/enla/ohs/	Occupational Health and Safety Act	Department of Environment and Labour
New Brunswick www.whscc.nb.ca	Occupational Health and Safety Act	Workplace Health, Safety and Compensation Commission
Quebec www.csst.qc.ca/portail/fr/	Occupational Health and Safety Act	Commission de la santé et de la sécurité du travail
Ontario www.gov.on.ca/LAB/	Occupational Health and Safety Act	Ministry of Labour
Manitoba www.gov.mb.ca/labour/safety/index.html	Workplace Safety and Health Act	Department of Labour and Immigration
Saskatchewan www.labour.gov.sk.ca/safety/	Occupational Health and Safety Act	Saskatchewan Labour
Alberta www3.gov.ab.ca/hre/whs/	Occupational Health and Safety Act and OHS Code	Department of Human Resources and Employment
British Columbia www.worksafebc.com	Workers Compensation Act	Ministry of Skills Development and Labour
Yukon Territory http://wcb.yk.ca/	Occupational Health and Safety Act	Yukon Workers' Compensation Health and Safety Board
Northwest Territories and Nunavut www.wcb.nt.ca	Safety Act	Workers' Compensation Board
Canada www.hrsdc.gc.ca	Canada Labour Code Part II	Human Resources and Skills Development Canada

Figure 4–1
Health and safety jurisdictions in Canada.

section five of the Safety Act for the Northwest Territories states the duty of workers in the following format:

5. Every worker employed on or in connection with an establishment shall, within the course of his or her employment,

    (a) take all reasonable precautions to ensure his or her own safety and the safety of other persons in the establishment; and

    (b) as the circumstances require, use devices or articles of clothing or equipment that are intended for his or her protection and provided to the worker by his or her employer, or required pursuant to the regulations to be used or worn by the worker.[3]

As shown below, in section 28 of Ontario's Occupational Health and Safety Act, the duties of workers are presented in greater detail, but the basic principle and the format is very similar.

28. (1) A worker shall,

    (a) work in compliance with the provisions of this Act and the regulations;

    (b) use or wear the equipment, protective devices or clothing that the worker's employer requires to be used or worn;

    (c) report to his or her employer or supervisor the absence of or defect in any equipment or protective device of which the worker is aware and which may endanger himself, herself or another worker; and

    (d) report to his or her employer or supervisor any contravention of this Act or the regulations or the existence of any hazard of which he or she knows.

Idem

(2) No worker shall,

    (a) remove or make ineffective any protective device required by the regulations or by his or her employer, without providing an adequate temporary protective device and when the need for removing or making ineffective the protective device has ceased, the protective device shall be replaced immediately;

    (b) use or operate any equipment, machine, device or thing or work in a manner that may endanger himself, herself or any other worker; or

    (c) engage in any prank, contest, feat of strength, unnecessary running or rough and boisterous conduct.[4]

Section 126.(1) from the Canada Labour Code shown below also reveals the similarities in the presentation of the federal legislation to that of the provinces and territories:

Duties of Employees 126. (1) While at work, every employee shall

    (a) use any safety materials, equipment, devices and clothing that are intended for the employee's protection and furnished to the employee by the employer or that are prescribed;

    (b) follow prescribed procedures with respect to the health and safety of employees;

    (c) take all reasonable and necessary precautions to ensure the health and safety of the employee, the other employees and any person likely to be affected by the employee's acts or omissions;

    (d) comply with all instructions from the employer concerning the health and safety of employees;

    (e) cooperate with any person carrying out a duty imposed under this Part;

    (f) cooperate with the policy and work place committees or the health and safety representative;

(g)   report to the employer any thing or circumstance in a work place that is likely to be hazardous to the health or safety of the employee, or that of the other employees or other persons granted access to the work place by the employer;

(h)   report in the prescribed manner every accident or other occurrence arising in the course of or in connection with the employee's work that has caused injury to the employee or to any other person;

(i)   comply with every oral or written direction of a health and safety officer and appeals officer concerning the health and safety of employees.

(j)   report to the employer any situation that the employee believes to be a contravention of this Part by the employer, another employee or any other person.[5]

Regardless of the jurisdiction, all workers are granted three basic rights, either directly or indirectly. They are the right to know, the right to participate, and the right to refuse.

The right for a worker to "know," refers to the workers' right to be informed of both any potential hazard they may face and of the means to protect themselves from it. The **Workplace Hazardous Materials Information System (WHMIS)** is an important component in the workers' right to know. WHMIS, which will be covered in more depth in Chapter 7, provides the worker with information on the hazards, use, storage, and safe handling of chemicals in the workplace.

The right to participate refers to the right each worker has to be involved in safety issues at work. This right can be granted directly, through representation on joint health and safety committees (JHSCs), or indirectly, through the workers' duty to inform others of hazards in the workplace. Later in the chapter we will take a closer look at joint occupational health and safety committees and their role in the workplace.

The right to refuse is granted to all Canadian workers and is dealt with at length in the statutes of most jurisdictions. Workers have the right to refuse to do work that they believe may harm them or another worker. The specific procedure for workers to follow and the steps taken in the event of a work refusal may be detailed in the act for that jurisdiction.

In most areas the basic procedure requires that a refusal will be investigated by a supervisor and a worker representative to decide the validity of the refusal. If the situation is deemed to be unsafe, the problem is rectified, but if no agreement can be reached between the two parties, a government inspector or officer will be called in to assess the matter. While waiting for a conclusion to the complaint, the worker who refused may be assigned alternate work but not dismissed. Workers are also protected from reprisal by the employer for refusing work in good faith or for abiding by any of the requirements of the act.

The right to refuse may be limited in some occupations that have obvious inherent danger or in which the public safety is concerned. For example, a police officer can not refuse to respond to a domestic dispute because of fear of getting hurt, but refusing to use a vehicle that has loose steering or faulty brakes for a regular street patrol would be very well justified. A similar case can be made for firefighters, workers in correctional institutes, and some health care workers. Although these occupations often involve high risk, these workers can expect to be provided with reasonable means of protection, whether performing routine tasks or responding to an emergency.

WHMIS

Workplace Hazardous Materials Information System. A national communication system, implemented on October 31, 1988, that provides the worker with information on the production, use, storage, and safe handling of hazardous materials in the workplace.

What Is Your Opinion?

Between 60 and 70 employees work at Contemporary Antiques in Edmonton, designing, manufacturing, and assembling antique replica furniture. Greg was asked by his supervisor Andre to use the new industrial table saw to cut 60 triangular blocks for a large furniture order that was overdue. Greg noticed that the factory-installed guard had been removed from the saw and felt it was now unsafe as a result. After inquiring about the guard of his co-workers, it was discovered that it had been thrown out, because one senior employee felt that it was not necessary and slowed production. Greg decided to refuse to perform the assigned task, believing that it was unsafe to operate the saw without the guard in place. Using the health and safety act for your jurisdiction, describe the proper steps required to take this matter to its proper conclusion. Would it be acceptable for another worker to cut the blocks on that saw while the parties involved dealt with the matter?

THE ROLE OF KEY PLAYERS

All workers have a moral and legal responsibility to protect themselves and their co-workers from hazards on the job; however, some workers play an even greater role in making the workplace safe. In some jurisdictions, added responsibilities, such as workplace inspections and accident investigation, are given to worker representatives or health and safety committee members. All workers are obligated to learn about the hazards in the workplace and take the steps necessary to protect themselves and their co-workers by employing whatever means are available, such as by using the proper **personal protective equipment (PPE)** provided by the employer.

The employer is required by law to provide a safe workplace for its employees, but as we have seen in Chapter 2, the cost of accidents, along with the legal and moral obligation, provides significant motivation to ensure workers' safety. Huge fines and even imprisonment also provide a substantial deterrent from neglecting workplace safety. An employer is also required to exercise "**due diligence**" with regard to employee safety. The duties of employers are listed in Sec. 25 of the Ontario Occupational Health and Safety Act. The definition of due diligence may be found in Sec. 25 (2)(h):

> **Sec. 25 (2)(h)** An employer shall take every precaution reasonable in the circumstances for the protection of a worker.[6]

The supervisor plays a crucial role in maintaining a safe workplace. The specific duties of the supervisor are spelled out in detail in the act for some provinces. When a worker is injured, one could ask the following questions: Was the worker informed of the hazards, was the worker trained to do the job properly, and was the worker provided with the equipment, tools, or facilities to protect themselves? Shortcomings in each case can be traced back to the supervisor. It should be noted that a job done "properly" is one that is done safely.

PERSONAL PROTECTIVE EQUIPMENT (PPE)
Any type of clothing or device that puts a barrier between the worker and the hazard (e.g., safety goggles, gloves, hard hats, and so on).

DUE DILIGENCE
Application of adequate effort under the circumstances.

Government at the provincial and federal level must support industry in reducing the number of accidents. The government has a responsibility to ensure that the best policies and programs are in place to protect the well being of its citizens. Unfortunately, government safety campaigns, advertisements, and changes to legislation are often most visible after some catastrophe or sensational workplace issue is publicized by the media. It is in the government's interest to promote occupational health and safety because the cost of accidents to the economy through increased health care costs and lost productivity can be enormous.

The government must use its resources to establish guidelines and standards. Information from outside agencies, such as the American Conference of Governmental Industrial Hygienists' (ACGIH's) exposure limits for chemicals, is sometimes used as a source for standards. Governments may also choose to establish their own agencies for research or enforcement. **The Canadian Centre for Occupational Health and Safety (CCOHS)**, for example, was created by the federal government to research and provide safety information resources to all Canadian workers.

Collection and sharing of data on occupational accidents and illness provides health and safety practitioners with the resources to see trends and locate areas of concern. When this data is collected by a central agency, such as CCOHS or the Association of Workers' Compensation Boards and other similar agencies, comparisons can be made among various occupations, employers, age groups, locations, etc. Long term trends help expose problems, such as industrial disease and illness in specific industries or locations. Historically, high rates of cancer or respiratory diseases would have been attributed to other causes, like lifestyle, geographic location, or demographics, but with this huge data base available, a correlation between certain diseases and occupations becomes more pronounced.

CANADIAN CENTRE FOR OCCUPATIONAL HEALTH AND SAFETY (CCOHS)
A federal government agency established to research and provide safety information resources to all Canadian workers.

JOINT OCCUPATIONAL HEALTH AND SAFETY COMMITTEES

The joint occupational health and safety committee is a partnership between workers and employer representatives, whose collective goal is to identify and solve health and safety problems in the workplace. The health and safety committee also ensures that the workers' right to know and right to participate are fulfilled. Workplace committees are mandatory in most workplaces in most jurisdictions in Canada, but the prescribed duties may vary for each area. In any workplace, the minister responsible may require that a health and safety committee be established if it is felt that the workers' safety would be improved. In smaller workplaces, where a committee is not warranted, a single safety representative is often required.

Depending on the jurisdiction, health and safety committees may be referred to as occupational health committees, workplace health and safety committees, or joint work site health and safety committees. This section describes the general makeup of and duties for health and safety committees in the workplace. For specific information in a particular jurisdiction, the relevant local legislation should be consulted. Figure 4–2 below summarizes the requirements for health and safety committees.

Legislation Requirements for Health and Safety Committees			
	When Do I Need One?	Size of Committee	Representation
Canada	Mandatory - 20 or more employees	At least 2	At least half to represent employees
British Columbia	Mandatory - when there are 20 or more employees or when "required by order"	Not less than 4	At least one half must be worker representatives
Alberta	As directed by the Minister	At least 3 and not more than 12	At least two employees and one employer or at least half employees
Saskatchewan	Mandatory - when 10 employees or more	At least 2 and not more than 12	At least half to represent employees
Manitoba	Mandatory - 20 or more employees as designated by Lt. Governor	At least 4 and not more than 12	At least half to represent employees
Ontario	Mandatory - 20 or more employees, when ordered by Minister, or where a designated substance is in use (no minimum number of employees)	At least 2 (fewer than 50 employees); at least 4 (50 or more employees)	At least half to represent employees
Quebec	Mandatory - 20 or more employees and where regulated	At least 4	At least half to represent employees
New Brunswick	Mandatory - 20 or more employees	As agreed upon by employees and employer	Equal representation
Nova Scotia	Mandatory - 20 or more employees	As agreed upon by employees and employer	At least half to represent employees
PEI	Agreed upon by employees and employers	Not specified	At least half to represent employees
Newfoundland	Discretionary - 10 or more employees	At least 2 and not more than 12	At least half to represent employees
Yukon	Mandatory - 20 or more employees	At least 4 and not more than 12	At least half to represent employees
Northwest Territories	As directed by Chief Safety Officer	Not specified	Equal representation

Figure 4–2
Health and safety committee requirements.

The employer is responsible for establishing a health and safety committee in the workplace. Although legislation outlines the conduct and duties of the health and safety committee in most areas, this represents only the minimum requirements and is often superseded by the committees' own **terms of reference**. The initial terms of reference for the committee are also established by the employer, but are usually tailored by the present committee to suit the particular workplace requirements. The terms of reference normally include items such as the number of committee members, the number of committee members required for a quorum, the term of office for members, the frequency of meetings and inspections, and other rules that are deemed to be necessary by the committee.

The health and safety committee members' activities should be performed with the support of management and the members are to be paid as if they are performing their normal jobs. Committee members who occasionally have access to confidential information on the company or its employees are required to honour the confidentiality of that information as required by the relevant federal, provincial, or territorial act. Activities of the JHSC include:

- Participating in developing and implementing programs to protect employees' health and safety,
- Dealing with employee complaints and suggestions concerning health and safety,
- Ensuring the maintenance and monitoring of injury and work hazard records,
- Monitoring and following up on hazard reports and recommending action,
- Setting up and promoting programs to improve employee training and education,
- Participating in all health and safety inquiries and investigations,
- Consulting with professional and technical experts,
- Participating in resolving workplace refusals and work stoppages,
- Making recommendations to management for accident prevention and safety program activities, and
- Monitoring the effectiveness of safety programs and procedures.[7]

Health and safety legislation in Canada is based on the **internal responsibility system** (IRS). The health and safety legislation for each jurisdiction lays out the rights and responsibilities for each of the parties within the workplace. The IRS provides a mechanism to allow employers, supervisors, and workers to monitor each other's actions and ensure compliance with the act. Rather than relying on an outside agency to enforce health and safety rules in a workplace, the IRS gives everyone a contributing role in workplace health and safety. It is in the best interest of all parties to strive for a safe and healthy workplace. When all parties work toward a common goal, the spirit of cooperation is fostered and the cost of administering and enforcing the act is reduced significantly.

It is also helpful to have those who are most familiar with their particular workplace play an active role in their own health and safety. Workers play a frontline role in identifying hazards in the workplace and have a sense of personal responsibility. The financial benefits, along with moral and legal obligations, usually ensure that the supervisor and employer diligently promote health and safety with the least amount of involvement by government enforcement agents.

TERMS OF REFERENCE
A set of rules under which the health and safety committee are to operate.

INTERNAL RESPONSIBILITY SYSTEM
A mechanism to allow employers, supervisors, and workers to monitor each other's actions and ensure compliance with the act.

SUMMARY

1. The Canadian legal system is based largely on the English system.

2. Health and safety legislation in most situations falls under provincial jurisdiction. Federal employees, which represent about 10% of Canadian workers, are covered by the Canada Labour Code.

3. Acts or statutes are the framework around which regulations are built.

4. Acts, regulations, standards, and codes are used to govern people's behaviour. These rules may be restrictive in some situations, but are meant to protect society as a whole.

5. The American Conference of Governmental Industrial Hygienists (ACGIH) and the Canadian Standards Association (CSA) are two agencies whose standards are widely accepted by most Canadian jurisdictions.

6. Health and safety legislation in Canada is based on the internal responsibility system. The internal responsibility system requires less government interference, thus reducing paperwork and cost.

7. The key players in health and safety are workers, supervisors, and employers. Government inspectors are also a key component in enforcement of the statutes for each jurisdiction.

KEY TERMS AND CONCEPTS

ACGIH

Act

British North America Act (BNA Act, 1876)

Canadian Centre for Occupational Health and Safety (CCOHS)

Canada Labour Code

Canadian Standards Association (CSA)

Constitution Act, 1982

Code

Due diligence

Internal responsibility system

Laws

Legislation

Magna Carta

Personal protective equipment (PPE)

Regulation

Standard

Statute

Terms of reference

WHMIS

REVIEW QUESTIONS

1. A provincial or federal politician sees that new legislation is required to address a serious occupational health and safety issue. Explain what steps are required for that elected member to take the issue from a concern expressed by a group of citizens or special interest group and transform it into an enforceable law.

2. Referring to local provincial or territorial legislation, what is the maximum penalty for an individual who is in breach of health and safety laws? What would be the maximum penalty for a corporation?

3. Define due diligence and describe how an employer's obligation to exercise due diligence ensures that health and safety concerns will not be overlooked.

4. With reference to local provincial or territorial legislation, in your own words, describe the main duties that employers, supervisors, and workers must undertake to promote a safe workplace.

5. What role does the media play in occupational health and safety?

6. List at least one moral, legal, and economic obligation that each of the following has to invest in workplace safety: worker, employer, supervisor, and government.

7. In which workplaces in your province or territory are joint occupational health and safety committees required?

8. Describe the composition of the health and safety committee and its key duties.

9. What are the benefits of the internal responsibility system? Can you think of any possible shortcomings of this system?

WEBLINKS

Figure 4–1 contains the website URLs for all the government agencies responsible for health and safety in each Canadian jurisdiction.

ENDNOTES

1. D. Estrin and J. Swaigen, *Environment on Trial: A Guide to Ontario Environmental Law and Policy*, 3rd ed. (Toronto: Emond Montgomery Publications Limited, 1993),10.
2. Ibid., 11.
3. Safety Act, Northwest Territories. Safety Act R.S.N.W.T. 1988, cS-1. Section 5.
4. Occupational Health and Safety Act. RSO 1990. Section 28 (1)(2). Queen's Printer for Ontario.
5. Canada Labour Code (R.S. 1985, c. L-2) Part II. Section 126.
6. Occupational Health and Safety Act. RSO 1990. Section 25 (2)(h). Queen's Printer for Ontario.
7. Canadian Centre for Occupational Health and Safety. (December 14, 1999). "OHS Answers." [Online]. Available: http://www.ccohs.ca/oshanswers/hsprograms/hscommittees/whatisa.html. (Retrieved August 4, 2004).

Workers' Compensation

5

CHAPTER

LEARNING OBJECTIVES

- List the fundamental objectives of workers' compensation.

- Describe the evolution of workers' compensation.

- Explain how workers compensation boards collect and distribute funds.

- Explain how experience rating can affect assessment rates.

- Describe the incentives for employers to reduce accident claims cost.

- Describe the benefits available to injured workers.

- Explain the problem of processing occupational diseases and stress claims.

OVERVIEW OF WORKERS' COMPENSATION

The concept of **workers' compensation** developed as a way to allow injured employees to be compensated appropriately without having to take their employer to court. The underlying rationale for workers' compensation had two aspects: (1) fairness to injured employees, especially those without the resources to undertake legal actions that are often long, drawn out, and expensive; and (2) reduction of the costs to employers associated with workplace injuries (e.g., legal, image, and morale costs). Workers' compensation is intended to be a no-fault approach to resolving workplace accidents by rehabilitating injured employees and minimizing their personal losses resulting from their reduced ability to perform and compete in the labour market.[1] Since its inception as a concept, workers' compensation has evolved into a system that pays out over $6 billion per year. In Ontario alone, the cost of benefits paid or provided directly to injured workers was over $2.5 billion in 2002.[2]

Workers' compensation represents a compromise between the needs of employees and the needs of employers. Employees give up their right to seek unlimited compensation for pain and suffering through legal action. Employers award the prescribed compensation (typically through insurance premiums) regardless of the employee's negligence. The theory is that in the long run both

WORKERS' COMPENSATION
Developed to allow injured employees to be compensated appropriately without having to take their employer to court.

employees and employers will benefit more than either would through legal action. As you will see later in this chapter, although workers' compensation has reduced the amount of legal action arising out of workplace accidents, it has not completely eliminated legal actions.

Objectives of Workers' Compensation

Workers' compensation laws vary from jurisdiction to jurisdiction. However, regardless of the language contained in the enabling legislation in a specific jurisdiction, workers' compensation as a concept has several widely accepted objectives:

- Replacement of income.
- Rehabilitation of the injured employee.
- Prevention of accidents.
- Cost allocation.[3]

INCOME REPLACEMENT
Replacement of current and future income, based on 90% of net pay for most jurisdictions.

REPLACEMENT OF INCOME Employees injured on the job lose income if they are unable to work. For this reason, workers' compensation is intended to replace the lost income adequately and promptly. Adequate **income replacement** is viewed as replacement of both current and future income. The amount of compensation awarded is based on a percentage of net income in all jurisdictions except Yukon. For Alberta, BC, Manitoba, NWT and Nunavut, Quebec, and Saskatchewan, compensation is based on 90% of net earnings, with the remaining provinces replacing income at rates from 75% to 85%. The rates for Yukon are derived from 75% of gross income. Workers' compensation benefits continue even if the employer goes out of business.

REHABILITATION OF THE INJURED EMPLOYEE A basic premise of workers' compensation is that the injured worker will return to work in every case possible, although not necessarily in the same job or career field. For this reason, a major objective of workers' compensation is to rehabilitate the injured employee. Occasionally an injured worker will need rehabilitation before he or she can return to work. There are two types of rehabilitation: medical and vocational. Both are available to workers whose ability to make a living is inhibited by physical and/or mental work-related problems.

MEDICAL REHABILITATION
Designed to provide the needed medical care at no cost to the injured employee until he or she is pronounced fit to return to work.

VOCATIONAL REHABILITATION
Involves providing the education and training needed to prepare the worker for a new occupation.

   Medical rehabilitation consists of providing whatever treatment is required to restore any lost ability to function to the extent that such restoration is possible. This may include such services as physical therapy or the provision of prosthetic devices. **Vocational rehabilitation** involves providing the education and training needed to prepare the worker for a new occupation if it is determined that she or he will not be able to return to the previous job. Whether the rehabilitation services are medical or vocational in nature, or both, the goal is to restore the injured worker's capabilities to the level that existed before the accident. The rehabilitation program is to provide the needed medical care at no cost to the injured employee until he or she is pronounced fit to return to work. The program also provides vocational training or retraining as needed. Both components seek to motivate the employee to return to the labour force as soon as possible.

   A major portion of our social interaction and our self image is provided by the workplace and by co-workers. Accordingly, workers are required in some and encouraged in other jurisdictions to maintain contact with their employer throughout their rehabilitation from a workplace illness or injury. Several programs are in place to assist the worker's return to work, sometimes in a new position or at a reduced capacity. The longer that a worker is away from the workplace, the less likely it is that rehabilitation will be successful.

ACCIDENT PREVENTION Preventing future accidents is a major objective of workers' compensation. The theory underlying this objective is that employers will invest in **accident prevention** programs in order to hold down compensation costs. All compensation boards offer incentives for employers to reduce accidents and their associated costs, through various programs, including premium discounts for those businesses that perform well and surcharges for those that perform poorly. Educational programs may be mandatory for businesses with high accident costs, while others may be rewarded with premium discounts for voluntarily participating in training.

COST ALLOCATION The potential risks associated with different occupations vary. For example, working as a miner is generally considered more hazardous than working as an architect. The underlying principle of **cost allocation** is to spread the cost of workers' compensation appropriately and proportionately among industries, ranging from the most to the least hazardous. The costs of accidents should be allocated in accordance with the accident history of the industry so that high-risk industries pay higher workers' compensation insurance premiums than do low-risk industries.[4]

HISTORICAL PERSPECTIVE

Before workers' compensation laws were enacted in Canada, injured employees had no way to obtain compensation for their injuries except to take their employer to court. Although common law did require employers to provide a safe and healthy work environment, injured employees bore the burden of proof that negligence in the form of unsafe conditions contributed to these injuries. According to the Society of Manufacturing Engineers, prior to passage of workers' compensation legislation, employees often had to sue their employer to receive compensation for injuries resulting from a workplace accident or **occupational disease**.[5]

Proving that an injury was the result of employer negligence was typically too costly, too difficult, and too time consuming to be a realistic avenue of redress for most injured employees. Typically, injured workers, having lost their ability to generate income, could barely afford to get by, much less pay medical expenses, legal fees, and court costs. Another inhibitor was the *fear factor*. Injured employees who hoped to return to work after recovering were often afraid to file suit because they feared retribution by their employer. Employers might not only refuse to give them their jobs back but might also **blackball** them with other employers. Add to this that fellow employees were often afraid to testify to the negligence of the employer and it is easy to see why few injured workers elected to take their employers to court.

Even with all of these inhibitors, some injured employees still chose to seek redress through the courts in the days before workers' compensation. Those who did faced a difficult challenge because the laws at that time made it easy

ACCIDENT PREVENTION
The act of preventing a happening that may cause loss or injury to a person.

COST ALLOCATION
Spreading the cost of workers' compensation appropriately and proportionately among industries, ranging from the most to the least hazardous.

OCCUPATIONAL DISEASES
Pathological conditions brought about by workplace conditions or factors.

BLACKBALL
To ostracize an employee.

for employers to defend themselves successfully. As explained in Chapter 1, all an employer had to do to win a decision denying the injured plaintiff compensation was show that at least one of the following conditions existed at the time of the accident:

1. *The injured **employee's negligence** was a factor that contributed to the accident.*
2. *There was negligence on the part of a fellow worker.*
3. *There was assumption of risk on the part of the injured employee.*

EMPLOYEE NEGLIGENCE
Condition that exists when an employee fails to take necessary and prudent precautions.

ASSUMPTION OF RISK
Based on the theory that people who accept a job assume the risks that go with it. It says employees who work voluntarily should accept the consequences of their actions on the job rather than blaming the employer.

Because the majority of workplace accidents involve at least some degree of negligence on the part of the injured worker or fellow employees, employers typically won these cases. Because it required little more than a verbal warning by the employer to establish grounds for **assumption of risk**, the odds were clearly against an injured employee being awarded compensation.

Workers' compensation had its beginning in Canada when it was introduced in Ontario in 1914 and became law on January 1, 1915. Sir William Meredith, who was appointed by Ontario Premier James Whitney, had been exploring the options for a workers' compensation program for Ontario. The five principles upon which Canada's first workers' compensation legislation were founded, still underpin the philosophy of today's workers' compensation programs.

1. **No fault.** Blame is not assigned to the worker or the employer and the injured worker is compensated without either party able to sue the other.
2. **Collective liability.** The cost of the program is shared by all employers. (This protected individual employers from financial ruin — in contrast to some other early systems where individual liability required the employer to provide compensation on their own.)
3. **Security of payment.** Injured workers are ensured payment regardless of the financial condition of the employer — or even if the employer has ceased to operate.
4. **Independent boards.** The workers' compensation boards operate independently of any political party's influence.
5. **Exclusive jurisdiction.** The board is the final authority for all claims and may judge any case independently, based on its individual merits.[6]

Within 15 years the rest of Canada was covered by some form of workers' compensation. These early plans provided for some wage replacement and were a vast improvement for injured workers over previous conditions. Through its evolution, workers' compensation now covers a far greater number of illnesses and injuries than it initially did, at an increased compensation level. These escalating expenses have given rise to the need for compensation boards and employers to curb workers' compensation costs through various incentive programs that reduce accident costs and encourage workers' quick return to normal employment.

MODERN WORKERS' COMPENSATION

The role of workers' compensation boards (WCBs) today goes far beyond simply doling out compensation payments to injured workers. WCBs have devel-

oped into a full service occupational health and safety resource in most jurisdictions. They provide training and certification for various workplace sectors,
along with developing and administering several programs that are designed to
reduce cost by reducing the number and severity of accidents and expediting
injured workers' return to the workplace.

Cost Allocation

Workers' compensation is an expensive concept. From the outset, one of the basic principles has been cost allocation. The costs associated with workers' compensation must be borne by employers as part of their overhead. Cost allocation
is the process of spreading the cost of workers' compensation across an industry so that no individual company is overly burdened. The cost of workers'
compensation includes the costs of premiums, benefits, and administration.
These costs have risen steadily over the years. Cost allocation is based on the
experience rating of the industry. In addition to being (theoretically) the fairest
method of allocating costs, this approach is also supposed to give employers an
incentive to initiate and participate safety programs.

    Workers' compensation is a form of insurance whose premiums reflect the
risk being covered, much like automobile insurance plans. Two key factors are
used to determine how much the employer will pay in premiums: One is the
relative risk to the worker in performing their normal duties and the other is
how well the worker does compared to his peers. A young male driver in a
sports car, for example, would represent a greater risk to the insurance company
than a middle aged female, so the premiums would be significantly higher for
the young male. So we would expect that, similarly, compensation premiums
would be much greater for a roofer than for a clerical office worker.

EXPERIENCE RATING
The recent safety performance of the company is reflected in the premiums
charged.

Accident Experience Rating

All covered occupations are assigned a rate code to determine the base premium
amount. Premiums are based on $100 of payroll. For example in Saskatchewan,
which has some of the lowest base rates in the country, the logging industry
pays $17.62 per $100 of payroll while banks and financial institutions pay only
18 cents per $100. If one logging company or financial institution had frequent
and/or costly accident experiences, they would have to pay a surcharge on their
assessment until their performance improved. Conversely, companies that exceed the safety performance of others in the same rate group will get a discount
on their premiums. These surcharges and discounts, which are usually based
on the previous three years, provide an incentive for employers to reduce the
number and severity of accidents in the workplace.

Injured Worker Benefits

Workers who miss work due to a work related injury may be eligible to receive
compensation to help replace lost income. The amount the injured worker receives is usually between 75 and 90% of their average net income before their
loss. As seen in Figure 5–1, a maximum amount of earnings is used in each
province or territory to determine the maximum possible compensation. For
2004, the greatest compensable income was $66 800 in Ontario, while the low-
est maximum was $41 200 in Prince Edward Island.

Figure 5–1
Maximum compensable earnings (2004).

Province or Territory	Maximum Compensable Earnings
British Columbia	$60 700
Alberta	$61 200
Saskatchewan	$53 000
Manitoba	$56 310
Ontario	$66 800
Quebec	$55 000
New Brunswick	$50 000
Nova Scotia	$43 200
Prince Edward Island	$41 200
Newfoundland and Labrador	$45 500
Yukon Territory	$65 800
Northwest Territories	$66 500
Nunavut	$66 500

Health care, prescription drugs, and therapy costs are covered by the compensation board. In most jurisdictions once the recovery from the injury is expected to proceed no further, benefits may be paid to compensate the worker for non-economic loss (the permanent physical, functional, or psychological loss the impairment causes that affects the worker's life outside of work as well as her or his ability to work). The amount of compensation is based on the level of impairment, the worker's age, and the number of his or her dependants. The spouse or dependant of a worker who dies because of a workplace accident or illness may be eligible for survivor benefits. Benefits may be paid by regular monthly installments or in a lump sum and include funeral expenses.

DISCUSSION CASE

What Is Your Opinion?

Mario and Vance are discussing compensation benefits awarded to injured workers. Mario states that he believes the generous benefits granted by most Canadian compensation boards encourage workers to stay off work longer than needed and that the workers would be more anxious to get back to work if the amount of compensation was reduced. Vance counters by saying that it is the liberal payments and a compassionate system that allow workers to recover completely from their injuries before returning to work. Do you agree with Mario or Vance? Should rates be increased or decreased?

HARMFUL ENVIRONMENTS

A **harmful environment** is often pictured as one in which being struck, overexertion, or falls result in a workers' compensation claim. Occupational diseases, however, have also become a huge part of workers' compensation boards' case loads. One problem with determining the validity of compensation claims for occupational diseases is that a link between the disease and the workplace has to be made. Cancer may be caused by many sources, so one may ask if the miner's lung cancer is due to exposure to silica dust or caused by decades of cigarette smoking? Another problem with assessing some industrial diseases is that the latency period of exposure to some workplace products may be decades.

A harmful environment does not have to be limited to its physical components either. Psychological factors (such as stress) can also be considered. In fact, the highest rate of growth in workers' compensation claims over the past two decades has been in the area of stress-related injuries. As we shall see in Chapter 22 the effects of workplace stress can be far reaching.

HARMFUL ENVIRONMENT A work environment in which physical or psychological factors exist that are potentially hazardous.

SUMMARY

1. Workers' compensation was developed to allow injured employees to be compensated without the need for litigation. It has four main objectives: replacement of income, rehabilitation, accident prevention, and cost allocation.

2. Prior to the enactment of workers' compensation laws, employees' only recourse when injured was through the courts, and the prevailing laws favoured employers.

3. Workers' compensation benefits accrue to the families and dependents of workers who are fatally injured.

4. All workers' compensation laws provide for payment of medical expenses.

5. Cost allocation is the process of attempting to spread the cost of workers' compensation across an industry so that no individual company is overly burdened. The cost of workers' compensation includes the cost of premiums, benefits, and administration.

6. The premiums charged to employers may be higher or lower than the base rate for a particular industry. This "experience rating" provides an incentive for employers to reduce the number and severity of workplace accidents.

KEY TERMS AND CONCEPTS

Accident prevention

Assumption of risk

Blackball

Cost allocation

Employee negligence

Experience rating

Harmful environment

Income replacement

Medical rehabilitation

Occupational diseases

Vocational rehabilitation

Workers' compensation

REVIEW QUESTIONS

1. Explain the underlying rationale of the concept of workers' compensation.

2. List four objectives of workers' compensation.

3. How does experience rating benefit companies with good safety records and punish those with a poor history?

4. Explain the reasons for the unprecedented increases in workers' compensation costs in Canada in recent decades.

5. Distinguish between medical and vocational rehabilitation.

6. Explain the most common workers' compensation cost-reduction strategies.

7. What benefits can injured workers or their families expect from the workers' compensation board?

WEBLINKS

Following are the websites for each of the Workers' Compensation Boards in each Canadian jurisdiction:

Workers' Compensation Board of British Columbia
www.worksafebc.com

Workers' Compensation Board of Alberta
www.wcb.ab.ca

Saskatchewan Workers' Compensation Board
www.wcbsask.com

Workers Compensation Board of Manitoba
www.wcb.mb.ca

Workplace Safety and Insurance Board of Ontario
www.wsib.on.ca

Commission de la santé et de la sécurité du travail
www.csst.qc.ca

Workplace Health, Safety and Compensation Commission of New Brunswick
www.whscc.nb.ca

Workers' Compensation Board of Nova Scotia
www.wcb.ns.ca

Workers Compensation Board of Prince Edward Island
www.wcb.pe.ca

Workplace Health, Safety and Compensation Commission of Newfoundland
and Labrador
www.whscc.nf.ca

Yukon Workers' Compensation Health and Safety Board
www.wcb.yk.ca

Workers' Compensation Board, Northwest Territories and Nunavut
www.wcb.nt.ca

ENDNOTES

1. "Workers' Comp Update," *Occupational Hazards* 61, no. 10 (October 1999): 51.
2. Workplace Safety and Insurance Board of Ontario. (2002). *Annual Report 2002*. [Online].
   Available: http://www.wsib.on.ca/ar2002_home_e.htm. (Retrieved February 27, 2005).
3. Ibid.
4. Ibid.
5. Ibid.
6. D. M. Boyle. "WCBs Failing Workers." (January 10, 2005). [Online]. Available:
   http://www.straightgoods.ca/ViewLetter.cfm?REF=1441. (Retrieved February 27, 2005).

Chemical Agents and Confined Spaces

LEARNING OBJECTIVES

- Define toxic substances.
- Describe the four routes of entry for toxic agents into the body.
- Compare the acute and chronic effects of toxic substances.
- Explain the difference between dose and concentration.
- Describe the possible effects of exposure to airborne contaminants.
- Describe the hazards associated with asbestos.
- Explain what ACGIH's threshold limit values are.
- List the questions to ask in the process of hazard recognition.
- Explain the different categories control measures may fall under.
- Describe the class system used for respirators.
- List the hazards commonly associated with confined space entry.
- Describe the steps to take before entering a confined space.

TOXIC SUBSTANCE
A substance that has a negative effect on the health of a person or animal or interferes with the normal biological function of the person.

CHEMICAL AGENTS
Single elements or compounds that may be toxic to humans.

BIOLOGICAL AGENTS
Living things or substances produced by living things that may cause harm to humans.

The most prominent hazards in the workplace are chemical, physical, biological, and ergonomic. Each of these types of hazard will be discussed in depth in a chapter (or, in the case of physical hazards, several chapters) of the book. We will begin here by focusing on chemical hazards.

Tens of thousands of **toxic substance**s can be found in workplaces and hundreds more are introduced each year. Many **chemical agents** to which workers are exposed are very toxic; these may be man-made or naturally occurring. Everyone is exposed to toxic substances every day, whether at work or home, but the concentrations we are exposed to are usually so small that our sophisticated bodies have the ability to excrete the poisons or render them non-toxic by altering their chemical makeup. This chapter will look at some of these chemical agents, their effect on the body, and how to limit exposure to them. Other toxic substances such as **biological agents** will be covered in Chapter 8.

TOXIC SUBSTANCES DEFINED

A toxic substance is one that has a negative effect on the health of a person or animal. Toxic effects are a function of several factors, including the following: (1) the properties of the substance, (2) the amount of the dose, (3) the level of exposure, (4) the route of entry, and (5) the resistance of the individual to the substance. Olishifski describes the issue of toxic substances as follows:

> When a toxic chemical acts on the human body, the nature and extent of the injurious response depends upon the dose received — that is, the amount of the chemical that actually enters the body or system and the time interval during which this dose was administered. Response can vary widely and might be as little as a cough or mild respiratory irritation or as serious as unconsciousness and death.[1]

ENTRY POINTS FOR TOXIC AGENTS

The development of preventive measures to protect against the hazards associated with industrial exposure requires first knowing how toxic agents enter the body. A toxic substance must first enter the bloodstream to cause health problems. The most common routes of entry for toxic agents are inhalation, absorption, injection, and ingestion (see Figure 6–1). These routes are explained in the following paragraphs.

Inhalation

The route of entry about which health and safety professionals should be most concerned is **inhalation**. Airborne toxic substances such as gases, vapours, dust, smoke, fumes, aerosols, and mists can be inhaled and pass through the nose, throat, bronchial tubes, and lungs to enter the bloodstream. The amount of a toxic substance that can be inhaled depends on the following factors: (1) the concentration of the substance, (2) the duration of exposure, and (3) breathing volume.

INHALATION
Taking gases, vapours, dust, smoke, fumes, aerosols, or mists into the body by breathing in.

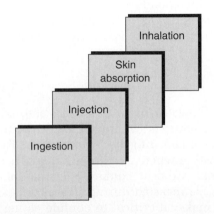

▶ **Figure 6–1**
Common routes of entry of toxic substances.

Inhalation Of Hazardous Substances

Most workers who work in dusty environments are concerned about breathing hazardous substances and take measures to limit their exposure by wearing respirators or dust masks, especially when the air looks contaminated. Most of these larger visible particles would have been filtered by our highly efficient, built-in air cleaning system. Between the hairs in our nose, the mucous lining our airway, and the design of our bronchia and alveoli, most particles don't get far enough into our lungs to cause damage. We excrete some of this material when we blow our nose and the rest is swallowed and processed by the digestive system. When the air looks clean we often let our guard down and do not wear respiratory protection. It is often these invisible particles that travel far into our lungs and cause the most damage.

According to Olishifski,

Inhalation, as a route of entry, is particularly important because of the rapidity with which a toxic material can be absorbed in the lungs, pass into the bloodstream, and reach the brain. Inhalation is the major route of entry for hazardous chemicals in the work environment.[2]

Absorption

ABSORPTION
Passage through the skin and into the bloodstream.

The second most common route of entry in an industrial setting is **absorption**, or passage through the skin and into the bloodstream.[3] The human skin is a protective barrier against many hazards. However, certain toxic agents can penetrate this barrier through absorption. Of course, unprotected cuts, sores, and abrasions facilitate the process, but even healthy skin will absorb certain chemicals. Humans are especially susceptible to absorbing such chemicals as organic lead compounds, nitro compounds, organic phosphate pesticides, TNT, cyanides, aromatic amines, amides, and phenols.

With many substances, the rate of absorption and, in turn, the hazard levels increase in a warm environment. The extent to which a substance can be absorbed through the skin depends on the factors shown in Figure 6–2. Another factor is body site. Different parts of the body have different absorption capabilities. For example, the forearms have a lower absorption potential than do the scalp and forehead.

Ingestion

INGESTION
Entry through the mouth.

Ingestion, not a major concern in an industrial setting, is entry through the mouth.[4] An ingested substance is swallowed. It moves through the stomach into the intestines and from there into the bloodstream. Toxic agents sometimes enter the body by ingestion when they are accidentally consumed by workers eating lunch or a snack. Airborne contaminants can also rest on food or the hands and, as a result, be ingested during a meal or snack. The possibility of ingesting toxic agents makes it critical to confine eating and drinking to sanitary areas away from the work site and to make sure that workers practise good

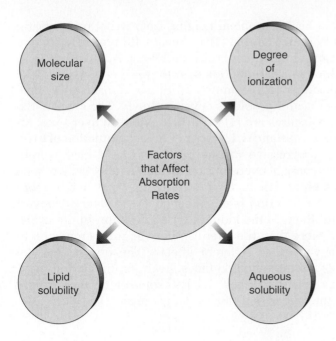

▶ Figure 6–2
**Substances can be
absorbed through the
skin.**

personal hygiene, such as by washing their hands thoroughly before eating or drinking.

As it moves through the gastrointestinal tract, the toxic substance's strength may be diluted. In addition, depending on the amount and toxicity of the substance, the liver may be able to convert it to a nontoxic substance. The liver can, at least, decrease the level of toxicity and pass along the substance to the kidneys, where some of the substance is eliminated in the urine.

Injection

Injection involves the introduction of a substance into the body by way of a needle and syringe, compressed air, high-pressure hydraulic lcaks, or any other capable medium. Consequently, this is not often a route of entry for a toxic substance in the workplace. Injection is sometimes used for introducing toxic substances in experiments involving animals. However, this approach can produce misleading research results because the needle bypasses some of the body's natural protective mechanisms.

INJECTION
A means of entry of toxic substances into the body through punctured skin.

EFFECTS OF TOXIC SUBSTANCES

The effects of toxic substances vary widely, as do the substances themselves. However, all of the various effects and exposure times can be categorized as being either acute or chronic.

Acute effects and exposures involve a sudden dose of a highly concentrated substance. They are usually the result of an accident (a spill or damage to a pipe)

ACUTE
Describes the effect of short term exposure.

that results in an immediate health problem ranging from irritation to death. Acute effects and exposures (1) are sudden, (2) are severe, (3) typically involve just one incident, and (4) cause immediate health problems. Acute effects and exposures are not the result of an accumulation over time.

CHRONIC
Effect of exposure over time.

Chronic effects and exposures involve limited continual exposure over time. Consequently, the associated health problems develop slowly. The characteristics of chronic effects and exposures are (1) continual exposure over time, (2) limited concentrations of toxic substances, (3) progressive accumulation of toxic substances in the body and progressive worsening of associated health problems, and (4) little or no awareness of exposures on the part of affected workers.

When a toxic substance enters the body, it eventually affects one or more body organs. Part of the liver's function is to collect such substances, convert them to nontoxics, and send them to the kidneys for elimination in the urine. However, when the dose is more than the liver can handle, toxics move on to other organs, producing a variety of different effects. The organs that are affected by toxic substances are the blood, kidneys, heart, brain, central nervous system, skin, liver, lungs, and eyes. Figure 6–3 lists some of the more widely used toxic substances and the organs that they endanger most.

RELATIONSHIP OF DOSES AND RESPONSES

Health and safety professionals are interested in predictability when it comes to toxic substances. How much of a given substance is too much? What effect will a given dose of a given substance produce? These types of questions concern dose–response relationships. A **dose** of a toxic substance can be expressed in a number of different ways depending on the characteristics of the substance; for example, amount per unit of body weight, amount per body surface area, or amount per unit of volume of air breathed. Olishifski expresses the dose–response relationship mathematically as follows:[5]

DOSE
The amount of ionizing radiation absorbed per unit of mass by part of the body or the whole body.

$$(C) \times (T) = k$$

Figure 6–3
Selected toxic substances and the organs that they endanger most.

Blood	Kidneys	Heart	Brain
Benzene	Mercury	Aniline	Lead
Carbon monoxide	Chloroform		Mercury
Arsenic			Benzene
Aniline			Manganese
Toluene			Acetaldehyde

Eyes	Skin	Lungs	Liver
Cresol	Nickel	Asbestos	Chloroform
Acrolein	Phenol	Chromium	Carbon tetrachloride
Benzyl chloride	Trichloroethylene	Hydrogen sulphide	Toluene
Butyl alcohol		Mica	
		Nitrogen dioxide	

where:

C = concentration

T = duration (time) of exposure

K = constant

Note that in this relationship, C times T is *approximately* equal to K. The relationship is not exact.

Three important concepts to understand relating to doses are dose threshold, lethal dose, and lethal concentration.

Dose Threshold

The **dose threshold** is the minimum dose required to produce a measurable effect. Of course, the threshold is different for different substances. In animal tests, thresholds are established using such methods as (1) observing pathological changes in body tissues, (2) observing growth rates (are they normal or retarded?), (3) measuring the level of food intake (has there been a loss of appetite?), and (4) weighing organs to establish body weight to organ weight ratios.

DOSE THRESHOLD
The minimum dose required to produce a measurable effect.

Lethal Dose

A **lethal dose** of a given substance is the dose that is highly likely to cause death. Such doses are established through experiments on animals. When lethal doses of a given substance are established, they are typically accompanied by information that is of value to medical professionals and industrial hygienists. Such information includes the type of animal used in establishing the lethal dose, how the dose was administered to the animal, and the duration of the administered dose. LD_{50} is commonly seen on material safety data sheets and indicates the dose at which 50% of the test subjects died. Lethal doses do not apply to inhaled substances. With these substances, the concept of lethal concentration is applied.

LETHAL DOSE
The dose that is lethal to the test subject by exposure through any means other than inhalation.

Lethal Concentration

A **lethal concentration** of an inhaled substance is the concentration that is highly likely to result in death. With inhaled substances, the duration of exposure is critical because the amount inhaled increases with every unprotected breath. This is commonly seen on material safety data sheets and indicates the concentration at which 50% of the test subjects died.

LETHAL CONCENTRATION
The concentration in air that is lethal to the test subject.

AIRBORNE CONTAMINANTS

It is important to understand the different types of airborne contaminants that may be present in the workplace.[6] Each type of contaminant has a specific definition that must be understood in order to develop effective health and safety measures to protect against it. The most common types of airborne contaminants are dusts, fumes, smoke, aerosols, mists, gases, and vapours (Figure 6–4).

- **Dusts.** Dusts are various types of solid particles that are produced when a given type of organic or inorganic material is scraped, sawed, ground, drilled, handled, heated, crushed, or otherwise deformed. The degree of hazard represented by dust depends on the toxicity of the parent material and the size and level of concentration of the particles.
- **Fumes.** The most common causes of fumes in the workplace are such manufacturing processes as welding, heat treating, and metallizing, all of which involve the interaction of intense heat with a parent material. The heat volatilizes portions of the parent material, which then condenses as it comes in contact with cool air. The result of this reaction is the formation of tiny particles that can be inhaled.
- **Smoke.** Smoke is the result of the incomplete combustion of carbonaceous materials. Because combustion is incomplete, tiny soot or carbon particles remain and can be inhaled.
- **Aerosols.** Aerosols are liquid or solid particles that are so small they can remain suspended in air long enough to be transported over a distance. They can be inhaled.
- **Mists.** Mists are tiny liquid droplets suspended in air. Mists are formed in two ways: (1) when vapours return to a liquid state through condensation; and (2) when the application of sudden force or pressure turns a liquid into particles.
- **Gases.** Unlike other airborne contaminants that take the form of either tiny particles or droplets, gases are formless. Gases are actually formless fluids. Gases become particularly hazardous when they fill a confined, unventilated space. The most common sources of gases in an industrial setting are from welding and the exhaust from internal combustion engines.
- **Vapours.** Certain materials that are solid or liquid at room temperature and at normal levels of pressure turn to vapours when heated or exposed to abnormal pressure. Evaporation is the most common process by which a liquid is transformed into a vapour.

In protecting workers from the hazards of airborne contaminants, it is important to know the permissible levels of exposure for a given contaminant

Figure 6–4
Common airborne contaminants.

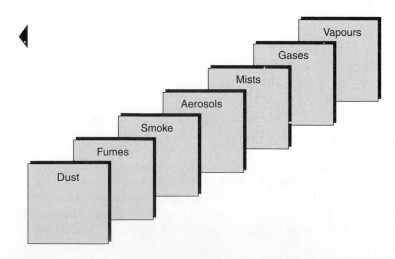

and to monitor continually the level of contaminants using accepted measurement practices and technologies. The topic of exposure thresholds is covered later in this chapter.

DISCUSSION CASE

What Is Your Opinion?

Remi and Noah are discussing the routes of entry of toxic chemicals into the body. Remi claims that, if given a choice, he would rather inhale than ingest a substance, because of the efficiency of the respiratory system in filtering the breathed air. Noah, on the other hand claims that the digestive system along with our kidneys and liver would be very effective in mitigating the effect of any toxins, so he would rather ingest the substance given the choice. What is your opinion?

EFFECTS OF AIRBORNE TOXINS

Airborne toxic substances are also classified according to the type of effect they have on the body. The primary classifications are shown in Figure 6–5 and explained in the following paragraphs. With all airborne contaminants, concentration and duration of exposure are critical concerns.

Irritants

Irritants are substances that cause irritation to the skin, eyes, and the inner lining of the nose, mouth, throat, and upper respiratory tract. However, they produce no irreversible damage. According to Olishifski,

> Irritants can be subdivided into primary and secondary irritants. A primary irritant is a material that exerts little systemic toxic action, either because the products formed on the tissues of the respiratory tract are nontoxic or because the irritant action is far in excess of any systemic toxic action. A secondary irritant produces irritant action on

IRRITANTS
Substances that cause irritation to the skin, eyes, and the inner lining of the nose, mouth, throat, and upper respiratory tract.

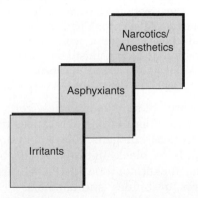

▶ Figure 6–5
Airborne toxic substances.

mucous membranes, but this effect is overshadowed by systemic effects resulting from absorption. Normally, irritation is a completely reversible phenomenon.[7]

Asphyxiants

Asphyxiants are substances that can disrupt breathing so severely that suffocation results. Asphyxiants may be simple or chemical in nature. A simple asphyxiant is an inert gas that dilutes oxygen in the air to the point that the body cannot take in enough air to satisfy its needs for oxygen. Common simple asphyxiants include carbon dioxide, ethane, helium, hydrogen, methane, and nitrogen. Chemical asphyxiants, by chemical action, interfere with the passage of oxygen into the blood or the movement of oxygen from the lungs to body tissues. Either way, the end result is suffocation due to insufficient or no oxygenation. Common chemical asphyxiants include carbon monoxide, hydrogen cyanide, and hydrogen sulphide.

Narcotics and Anesthetics

Narcotics and **anesthetics** are similar in that carefully controlled dosages can inhibit the normal operation of the central nervous system without causing serious or irreversible effects. This makes them particularly valuable in a medical setting. Dentists and physicians use narcotics and anesthetics to control pain before and after surgery. However, if the concentration of the dose is too high, narcotics and anesthetics can cause unconsciousness and even death. When this happens, death is the result of asphyxiation. Widely used narcotics and anesthetics include acetone, methyl-ethyl-ketone, acetylene hydrocarbons, ether, and chloroform.

EFFECTS OF CARCINOGENS

A **carcinogen** is any substance that can cause a malignant tumour or a **neoplastic growth**. A *neoplasm* is cancerous tissue or tissue that may become cancerous. Other terms used synonymously for carcinogen are *tumorigen, oncogen*, and *blastomogen*.

According to Olishifski,

It is well established that exposure to some chemicals can produce cancer in laboratory animals and man. There are a number of factors that have been related to the incidence of cancer — the genetic pattern of the host, viruses, radiation including sunshine, and hormone imbalance, along with exposure to certain chemicals. Other factors such as cocarcinogens and tumor accelerators are involved. It is also possible that some combination of factors must be present to induce cancers. There is pretty good clinical evidence that some cancers are virus-related. It may be that a given chemical in some way inactivates a virus, activates one, or acts as a cofactor.[8]

Medical researchers are not sure exactly how certain chemicals cause cancer. However, there are a number of toxic substances that are either known, or are strongly suspected, to be carcinogens. These include coal tar, pitch, creosote oil, anthracene oil, soot, lamp black, lignite, asphalt, bitumen waxes, paraffin oils, arsenic, chromium, nickel compounds, beryllium, cobalt, benzene, and various paints, dyes, tints, pesticides, and enamels.[9]

ASBESTOS HAZARDS

Asbestos was once thought to be a miracle material because of its many useful characteristics, including fire resistance, heat resistance, mechanical strength, and flexibility. As a result, asbestos was widely used in commercial and industrial construction between 1900 and the mid-1970s (see Figure 6–6).[10]

In the mid-1970s, medical research clearly tied asbestos to respiratory cancer, scarring of the lungs (now known as *asbestosis*), and cancer of the chest or abdominal lining (*mesothelioma*).[11] Although its use has been restricted in many countries since the 1970s and 1980s, the number of cases of asbestos related respiratory diseases continued to rise into the 1990s, because of its lengthy **latency period**. The International Labour Organization reports that 100 000 deaths per year are related to occupational asbestos exposure.[12]

The following passage on **friable asbestos** shows why asbestos is still a concern even though its further use has been banned:

> When asbestos becomes friable (crumbly), it can release fibers into the air that are dangerous when inhaled. As asbestos-containing material (ACM) ages, it becomes less viable and more friable. Asbestos can be released into the air if it is disturbed during renovation or as a result of vandalism.[13]

Removing and Containing Asbestos

When an industrial facility is found to contain asbestos, health and safety professionals are faced with the question of whether to remove it or contain it. Before making this decision, the following factors should be considered:

- Is there evidence that the ACM is deteriorating? What is the potential for future deterioration?
- Is there evidence of physical damage to the ACM? What is the potential for future damage?
- Is there evidence of water damage to the ACM or spoilage? What is the potential for future damage or spoilage?[14]

LATENCY PERIOD
Time after exposure to a hazardous product before symptoms appear.

FRIABLE ASBESTOS
Asbestos that is in a state of crumbling deterioration. When asbestos is in this state, it is most dangerous.

Figure 6–6
Asbestos use, 1900 to present.

SAFETY FACT

Respirable Silica Exposure and Lung Disease

Employees exposed to respirable silica are at risk of developing the lung disease silicosis. Particularly hazardous activities are hammering, drilling, chipping, crushing, loading, and dumping rock. Employees involved in abrasive blasting are also at risk. Symptoms of silicosis include coughing, difficulty in breathing, fever, and night sweats.

Most provinces have regulations that specify how certain hazardous products such as asbestos are to be handled. For example, asbestos is one of 11 *designated* substances for which Ontario has specific regulations that govern how workers deal with the substance at work. Several approaches can be used for dealing with asbestos in the workplace. The most widely used are removal, enclosure, and encapsulation.

REMOVAL Asbestos removal is also known as *asbestos abatement*. The following procedures are recommended for removal of asbestos: (1) the area in question must be completely enclosed in walls of tough plastic; (2) the enclosed area must be ventilated by high-efficiency particle absolute (HEPA) filtered negative air machines (these machines work somewhat like a vacuum cleaner in eliminating asbestos particles from the enclosed area); (3) the ACM must be covered with a special liquid solution to cut down on the release of asbestos fibres; and (4) the ACM must be placed in leakproof containers for disposal.[15]

ENCLOSURE Enclosure of an area containing ACMs involves completely encapsulating the area in airtight walls.[16] The following procedures are recommended for enclosing asbestos: (1) use HEPA-filtered negative air machines in conjunction with drills or any other tools that may penetrate or otherwise disturb ACMs; (2) construct the enclosing walls of impact-resistant and airtight materials; (3) post signs indicating the presence of ACMs within the enclosed area; and (4) note the enclosed area on the plans of the building.

ENCAPSULATION Encapsulation of asbestos involves spraying the ACMs with a special sealant that binds them together, thereby preventing the release of fibres.[17] The sealant should harden into a tough, impact-resistant skin. This approach is generally used only on acoustical plaster and similar materials.

Personal Protective Equipment for Asbestos Removal

It is important to use the proper types of personal protective clothing and respiratory devices. Clothing should be disposable and should cover all parts of the body.[18] According to Hughes, respirators used when handling asbestos should be "high-efficiency cartridge filter type (half-and-full-face types); any powered-air purifying respirator; any type C continuous-flow supplied-air, pressure-demand respirator, equipped with an auxiliary positive pressure self-contained breathing apparatus."[19]

INDOOR AIR QUALITY

Poor indoor air quality (IAQ) can cause a variety of health problems ranging from the temporary to the long term. Health problems commonly associated with poor indoor air quality include allergic reactions, respiratory problems, eye irritation, sinusitis, bronchitis, and pneumonia. Often, the cause of poor indoor air quality can be slipshod maintenance such as failure to keep fans, ductwork, and filters clean. Other contributors are the particles and gases that can be released by office equipment, carpets, paints, cleaning solvents, and office supplies.

One of the keys to maintaining a high level of air quality is to have adequate air exchange. A challenge faced by building tenants and owners is keeping heating and cooling costs down while maintaining a healthy environment. When less fresh air, or make-up air, is entered into the system, the cost of heating or cooling goes down, but the concentration of toxins goes up while the oxygen level drops.

Important factors in a building's ability to eliminate contaminated air and bring in fresh air are:

- Ventilation.
- Air infiltration rates.
- Airflow rates in ducts.
- Airflow patterns.
- Fume exhaust.

The most accurate methods available for measuring these factors fall under the broad heading of *tracer gas techniques*. A tracer gas is any gas or vapour not normally found in a building. The best have the following characteristics:

- Nontoxic.
- Nonallergic at the levels used.
- Chemically inert.
- Odourless and tasteless.
- Nonflammable and nonexplosive.
- Easily transported.
- Easily dispersed as an atmospheric gas.
- Easily and economically measured with a high degree of reliability.

The most widely used tracer gases are sulphur hexafluoride, halogenated refrigerants, and perfluorocarbons. To perform a tracer gas test, the following materials and equipment are needed:

- A suitable tracer gas.
- A device for measuring tracer gas concentrations.
- An air-sampling system.
- A tracer gas injection system.
- A data acquisition and control system.

There are several different types of tracer gas tests including tracer decay, constant concentration, buildup/decay, CO_2 measurement, and re-entrainment/recirculation. Regardless of the type of test used, the testing process involves the following steps:

1. Inject the tracer gas into the building.
2. Measure the concentration of the tracer gas in different parts of the building at different times over a certain period.

The data collected during a tracer gas test can give health and safety professionals the following types of information:

- Total air exchange rate for the building.
- Air change rate due to the operation of the building's HVAC system.
- Air change rate due to air infiltration and leakage.
- Percentage of outside air supplied by the building's HVAC system.
- Effectiveness of the ventilation system in removing contaminants.
- Distribution of the ventilation air throughout the building.

With this type of information available, health and safety personnel can determine whether there are pockets where contaminated air is trapped, whether the ventilation and air infiltration rates are sufficient, whether airflow rates through ducts are sufficient, whether airflow patterns are what they should be, and whether fume hoods are performing as they should. This type of information is needed to detect and prevent indoor air quality problems.

THRESHOLD LIMIT VALUES

How much exposure to a toxic substance is too much? How much is acceptable? Guidelines that answer these questions for health and safety professionals are developed and issued annually by the American Conference of Governmental Industrial Hygienists (ACGIH). The guidelines are known as **threshold limit values (TLVs)**. The ACGIH describes threshold limit values as follows:

> Threshold limit values refer to airborne concentrations of substances and represent conditions under which it is believed that nearly all workers may be repeatedly exposed day after day without adverse effect. Because of wide variation in individual susceptibility, however, a small percentage of workers may experience discomfort from some substances at concentrations at or below the threshold limit; a smaller percentage may be affected more seriously by aggravation of preexisting condition or by development of an occupational illness.
>
> Threshold limits are based on the best available information from industrial experience, from experimental human and animal studies, and, when possible, from a combination of the three. The basis on which the values are established may differ from substance to substance; protection against impairment of health may be a guiding factor for some, whereas reasonable freedom from irritation, narcosis, nuisance, or other forms of stress may form the basis for others.[20]

THRESHOLD LIMIT VALUES (TLVs)
The levels of exposure at which all employees may be repeatedly exposed to specified concentrations of airborne substances without fear of adverse effects. Exposure beyond TLVs is considered hazardous.

ACGIH's Classifications of TLVs and BEIs

The ACGIH develops threshold limit values (TLVs) and **biological exposure indices (BEIs)** to help health and safety professionals control certain chemical, biological, and physical health hazards in the workplace.[21] TLVs and BEIs are not legal standards and are not intended to be; rather, they are guidelines. However, their impact is increasingly felt, and in a positive way. As government organizations and agencies continue to find that political considerations make it difficult to promulgate legally authorized standards in a timely manner, the ability of the ACGIH to produce TLV guidelines that are updated annually makes its guidelines more and more valuable. Key concepts about TLVs and BEIs that should be understood by health and safety professionals are:

BIOLOGICAL EXPOSURE INDICES (BEIs)
Procedures used to determine the amount of material absorbed into the human body.

Asking ACGIH to Develop a TLV

What if you are a safety professional who believes that a given substance or agent should have a threshold limit value (TLV)? You may write to the Science Group of the American Conference of Governmental Industrial Hygienists, Inc. (ACGIH) and ask that a TLV be assigned. The request should contain documentation of why a TLV is needed, production volumes, uses, toxicity data, unique health hazards, and any other scientific data that may be relevant.

ACGIH
1330 Kemper Meadow Drive
Suite 600
Cincinnati, OH 45240
USA
513-742–2020
http://www.acgih.org

Threshold limit value–time-weighted average (TLV-TWA). The **time-weighted average** for a conventional eight-hour work day and a 40-hour work week for a given substance to which it is believed that nearly all workers may be repeatedly exposed on a daily basis without suffering ill effects. For example, the TLV-TWA for liquefied petroleum gas is 1000 parts per million (ppm).

Threshold limit value–short term exposure limit (TLV-STEL). The concentration of a given substance to which it is believed that workers may be exposed continuously for short periods without suffering ill effects. A STEL is defined as a 15-minute TWA exposure that should not be exceeded at any time during the work-day period. Also, exposures above the TLV-TWA up to the STEL should not exceed 15 minutes and should not occur more than four times in a day (with at least 60 minutes between exposures). For example, the TLV-STEL for isopropyl ether is 310 ppm.

Threshold limit value–ceiling (TLV-C). The concentration of a given substance that should not be exceeded at any point during an exposure period.

Biological exposure indices. The levels of determinants that are expected to be present in specimens taken from healthy workers who have been exposed to selected substances to the same extent as other workers with inhalation exposure to the substance at the TLV. For example, the BEI for acetone in the urine of a worker is 50 milligrams per litre (mg/L).

Physical agents. Substances or factors that can introduce added stress on the human body so that the effects of a given substance at the TLV might be magnified. Physical factors include acoustics (noise), ergonomic conditions, ionizing radiation, lasers, nonionizing radiation, subfrequency and static electric fields, and thermal stress (cold and heat). For example, the TLV for noise of 94 dB (average) is one hour per day.

TIME-WEIGHTED AVERAGE
The level of exposure to a toxic substance to which a worker can be repeatedly exposed on a daily basis without suffering harmful effects.

SHORT TERM EXPOSURE LIMIT
The maximum concentration of a given substance to which employees may be safely exposed for up to 15 minutes without suffering irritation, chronic or irreversible tissue change, or narcosis to a degree sufficient to increase the potential for accidental injury, impair the likelihood of self-rescue, or reduce work efficiency.

CEILING
The level of exposure that should not be exceeded at any time for any reason.

Calculating a TWA

Time-weighted averages (TWAs) can be calculated for exposures to given substances.[22] Olishifski gives the following formula for calculating the TWA for an eight-hour day:

$$TWA = \frac{CaTa + CbTb + \ldots CnTn}{8}$$

where

Ta = time of the first exposure period during the eight-hour shift

Ca = concentration of the substance in question in period a

Tb = another time period during the same shift

Cb = concentration of the substance in question in period b

Tn = nth or final time period in the eight-hour shift

Cn = concentration during period n

HAZARD RECOGNITION AND EVALUATION

The degree and nature of the hazard must be understood before effective hazard control procedures can be developed. This involves recognizing that a hazard exists and then making judgments about its magnitude with regard to chemical, physical, biological, and ergonomic stresses.

Questions that can be used for recognizing hazards in the workplace are as follows:

- What is produced?
- What raw materials are used in the process?
- What additional materials are used in the process?
- What equipment is used?
- What operational procedures are involved?
- What dust control procedures are involved?
- How are accidental spills cleaned up?
- How are waste by-products disposed?
- Is there adequate ventilation?
- Are processes equipped with exhaust devices?
- How does the facility layout contribute to employee exposure?
- Are properly working personal protective devices available?
- Are safe operating procedures recorded, made available, monitored, and enforced?[23]

Olishifski recommends that all processes be subjected to the following hazard recognition procedures:

- Determine the exposure threshold for each hazardous substance identified when applying the questions just listed, including airborne contaminants.
- Determine the level of exposure to each hazardous substance.
- Determine which employees are exposed to each hazardous material, how frequently, and for how long.
- Calculate the TWAs to the exposure thresholds identified earlier.[24]

For hazard evaluation, the following considerations are important: the nature of the material or substance involved, the intensity of the exposure, and the duration of the exposure. Key factors to consider are how much exposure is required to produce injury or illness; the likelihood that enough exposure to produce injury or illness will take place; the rate of generation of airborne contaminants; the total duration of exposure; and the prevention and control measures used.[25]

PREVENTION AND CONTROL

Most prevention and control strategies can be placed in one of the following four categories: (1) engineering controls, (2) ventilation, (3) personal protective equipment, and (4) administrative controls.[26] Examples of strategies in each category are given in the following paragraphs.

Engineering Controls

The category of **engineering controls** includes such strategies as replacing a toxic material with one that is less hazardous or redesigning a process to make it less stressful or to reduce exposure to hazardous materials or conditions. Other engineering controls are isolating a hazardous process to reduce the number of people exposed to it and introducing moisture to reduce dust.[27]

ENGINEERING CONTROLS
Strategies such as the design of tools and equipment or processes that eliminates the hazard at the source.

Ventilation

Exhaust ventilation involves trapping and removing contaminated air. This type of ventilation is typically used with such processes as abrasive blasting, grinding, polishing, buffing, and spray painting or finishing. It is also used in conjunction with open-surface tanks. Dilution ventilation involves simultaneously removing and adding air to dilute a contaminant to acceptable levels.[28]

Personal Protection from Hazards

When the work environment cannot be made safe by any other method, **personal protective equipment (PPE)** is used as a last resort. PPE imposes a barrier between the worker and the hazard but does nothing to reduce or eliminate the hazard. Typical equipment includes safety goggles, face shields, gloves, boots, earmuffs, earplugs, full-body clothing, barrier creams, and respirators.[29]

Occasionally, in spite of an employee's best efforts in wearing PPE, his or her eyes or skin will be accidentally exposed to a contaminant. When this happens, it is critical to wash away or dilute the contaminant as quickly as possible. Specially designed eyewash and emergency wash stations such as those shown in Figures 6–7, 6–8, and 6–9 should be readily available and accessible in any work setting where contaminants may be present.

PERSONAL PROTECTIVE EQUIPMENT (PPE)
Any type of clothing or device that puts a barrier between the worker and the hazard (e.g., safety goggles, gloves, hard hats, and so on).

Administrative Controls

Administrative controls involve limiting the exposure of employees to hazardous conditions using such strategies as rotating schedules, required breaks, work shifts, and other schedule-oriented strategies.[30]

Figure 6–7
Haws Model 700BT
Pedestal OMNI-FLO
eye-face station.
Source: Courtesy of Haws Drinking
Faucet Company.

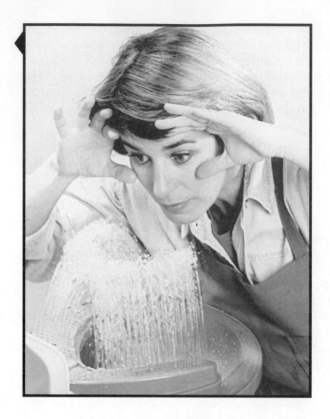

Figure 6–8
Haws Model 700BT
wall-mounted eye-
wash station.
Source: Courtesy of Haws Drinking
Faucet Company.

▶ **Figure 6–9**
Haws Model 8730
emergency polar
shower booth.
Source: Courtesy of Haws Drinking
Faucet Company.

Additional Strategies

The type of prevention and control strategies used will depend on the evaluation of the specific hazards present in the workplace. The Society of Manufacturing Engineers recommends the following list of generic strategies that apply regardless of the setting:

- Practising **good housekeeping**, including workplace cleanliness, waste disposal, adequate washing and eating facilities, healthful drinking water, and control of insects and rodents.
- Using special control methods for specific hazards, such as reduction of exposure time, film badges and similar monitoring devices, and continuous sampling with pre-set alarms.
- Setting up medical programs to detect intake of toxic materials.
- Providing training and education to supplement engineering controls.[31]

GOOD HOUSEKEEPING
Proper cleaning and maintenance of a work area.

Self-Protection Strategies

One of the best ways to protect employees from workplace hazards is to teach them to protect themselves. The Workplace Hazardous Materials Information System covered in the next chapter along with the following rules of self-protection are designed to protect workers and provide them with the means to protect themselves:

1. **Know the hazards in your workplace.** Take the time to identify all hazardous materials and conditions in your workplace and know the safe exposure levels for each.

2. **Know the possible effects of hazards in your workplace.** Typical effects of workplace hazards include respiratory damage, skin disease and irritation, injury to the reproductive system, and damage to the blood, lungs, central nervous system, eyesight, and hearing.

3. **Use personal protective equipment properly.** Proper use of personal protective equipment means choosing the right equipment, getting a proper fit, correctly cleaning and storing equipment, and inspecting equipment regularly for wear and damage.

4. **Understand and obey safety rules.** Read warning labels before using any contained substance, handle materials properly, read and obey signs, and do only authorized work.

5. **Practise good personal hygiene.** Wash thoroughly after exposure to a hazardous substance, shower after work, wash before eating, and separate potentially contaminated work clothes from others before washing them.[32]

GUIDELINES FOR RESPIRATORS

The respirator is one of the most important types of personal protective equipment available to individuals who work in hazardous environments (see Figures 6–10 and 6–11). Because the performance of a respirator can mean the difference between life and death, CSA publishes strict guidelines regulating the manufacture of respirators. The standard with which manufacturers must comply is CSA 294.4-02, Selection, Use and Care of Respirators.

SAFETY FACT

General Requirements for Eyewash Stations

Many provinces have adopted the ANSI Standard for eye wash stations. ANSI Standard Z358.1 states that emergency eyewash stations must deliver tepid water or solution for at least 15 minutes at a minimum flow rate of 0.4 gallons per minute. Other general requirements are as follows:

- The station must be able to flush both eyes simultaneously.

- The station must have freeze protection when the possibility of freezing exists.

- There must be no sharp projections in the operating area of the station.

- The station must have nozzles protected from contaminants.

- The station must not corrode in the presence of flushing fluid.

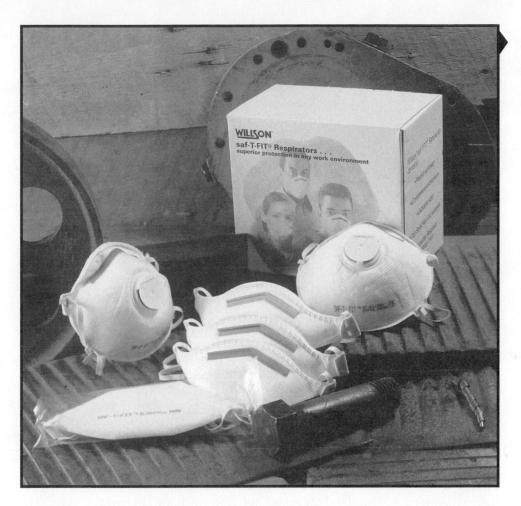

Figure 6–10
Breathing protection devices.
Source: Courtesy of Dalloz Safety (Willson Safety Equipment).

There are two types of respirators: air filtering and air supplying. Air-filtering respirators filter toxic particulates out of the air. The particulate filters used in air-filtering respirators are divided into three classes, each class having three levels of efficiency as follows:

Class N respirators may be used only in environments that contain no oil-based particulates. They may be used in atmospheres that contain solid or non-oil contaminants. Class R respirators may be used in atmospheres containing any contaminant. However, the filters in Class R respirators must be changed after each shift if oil-based contaminants are present. Class P respirators may be used in any atmosphere containing any particulate contaminant.

	Class N (Not Oil Resistant)	Class R (Oil Resistant)	Class P (Oil Proof)
Efficiency	95%	95%	95%
Efficiency	99%	99%	99%
Efficiency	99.97%	99.97%	99.97%

**Figure 6–11
Respirator.**
Source: Courtesy of Dalloz Safety
(Willson Safety Equipment).

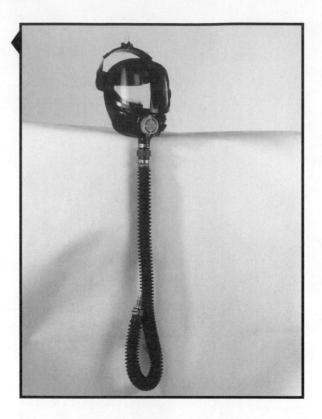

If there is any question about the viability of an air-filtering respirator in a given setting, employees should use air-supplying respirators. This type of respirator works in much the same way as an air tank for a scuba diver. Air from the atmosphere is completely blocked out, and fresh air is provided via a self-contained breathing apparatus.

SAFETY TIP

Contact Lenses on the Job

Arguments are often made against the use of contact lenses at work, because dust, particles or chemicals may become trapped behind them, compounding the effect of the foreign object. While wearing a full face respirator, a contact that pops out can't be replaced while wearing the equipment and it may also become trapped in the respirator valves, causing the respirator to malfunction. While others may argue that the contact lens can prevent harmful substances from reaching the eye, it is important that contacts not be perceived as a protective device. If contact lenses can be a factor in a worker's safety, the supervisor or employer should take any steps necessary to eliminate the hazard.

GENERAL SAFETY PRECAUTIONS

Following are a number of general safety precautions that apply in any settings, opened or confined spaces, where explosive and combustible materials are present.

1. **Prohibit smoking.** Smoking should be prohibited in any areas of a plant where explosive and combustible materials are present. Eliminating potential sources of ignition is a standard safety precaution in settings where explosions and fire are possible. In the past, such areas were marked off as restricted, and No Smoking signs were posted. It is becoming common practice to prohibit smoking on the premises altogether or to restrict smoking to designated areas that are well removed from hazard areas.

2. **Eliminate static electricity.** Static electricity occurs when dissimilar materials come into contact and then separate. If these materials are combustible or are near other materials that are combustible, an explosion can occur. Therefore, it is important to eliminate static electricity. The potential for the occurrence of static electricity can be reduced substantially by the processes of grounding and bonding. **Bonding** involves eliminating the difference in static charge potential between materials. *Grounding* involves eliminating the difference in static charge potential between a material and the ground. Figures 6–12, 6–13, and 6–14 illustrate these concepts.

BONDING
Used to connect two pieces of equipment by a conductor. Also, involves eliminating the difference in static charge potential between materials.

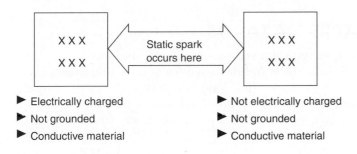

► Electrically charged
► Not grounded
► Conductive material

► Not electrically charged
► Not grounded
► Conductive material

► **Figure 6–12**
How static electricity occurs.

► A and B are connected by a bonding wire.

► Electrical charge is shared by A and B via the bonding wire eliminating charge differences between them.

► **Figure 6–13**
Bonding prevents static spark.

Figure 6–14
Grounding prevents static spark.

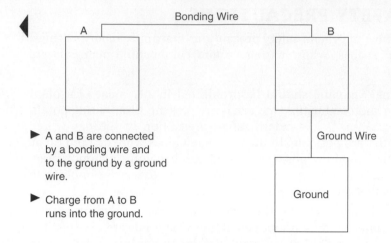

▶ A and B are connected by a bonding wire and to the ground by a ground wire.

▶ Charge from A to B runs into the ground.

3. **Use spark-resistant tools.** Sparks from tools used in settings where explosive and combustible materials are present represent a threat that must be addressed. In such settings, spark-resistant tools should be used to the maximum extent possible. Wooden, leather-faced, and rubber-covered tools can help prevent sparks that might ignite volatile materials.[33]

CONFINED SPACES HAZARDS

CONFINED SPACE
An area with limited means of egress that is large enough for a person to fit into, but is not designed for occupancy.

A **confined space** is any area with limited means of entry and exit that is large enough for a person to fit into but is not designed for occupancy. Examples of confined spaces include vaults, vats, silos, ship compartments, train compartments, sewers, and tunnels. What makes confined spaces hazardous, beyond those factors that define the concept, is their potential to trap toxic and explosive vapours and gases.

Certain substances have upper and lower flammable limits (sometimes referred to as "explosive limits," a less accurate label because some will flame without exploding). The LFL is the lowest concentration of a gas or a vapour that can generate a flame when in the presence of a sufficient ignition source. The upper flammable limit (UFL) is the highest concentration that can propagate a flame. The range between these two extremes is the flammable/explosive range (Figure 6–15).

In confined spaces, explosion hazards exist when the concentration of flammable gases is between the lower flammable limit (LFL) and the upper flammable limit (UFL). It is common practice to consider a 10% explosimeter reading, or 10% of the LFL, as a safe working environment.[34]

Health and safety professionals should be cautious, however, in assuming that 10% of a lower flammable limit (LFL) for a given substance constitutes an acceptable atmosphere. According to John Rekus, "Although 10 percent of the LFL may be acceptable for confined space entry *from a fire and explosion perspective*, this level may pose a concentration of gases or vapours that greatly exceeds the TLV. In addition combustible gas meters generally lack sufficient

▶ **Figure 6–15**
Flammable/explosive range for vapours and gases.

selectivity and sensitivity to detect air contaminants at levels that pose a potential health hazard. In fact, the meter may indicate a zero reading even when concentrations exceed the TLV. In these cases, more sensitive instruments will be needed to evaluate the atmosphere."[35]

Using a concentration of 10% of the LFL can be dangerous for two reasons: (1) the gas sensor used may be inaccurate; and (2) the threshold limit value (TLV) for some substances is exceeded at the LFL. For example, the TLV for acetone is 500 ppm, but the 10% LFL for acetone is 2500 ppm — or five times the TLV.

Health and safety professionals are well advised to take the following precautions when dealing with confined spaces that may have a toxic environment. First, use the most sensitive detection instrument available. Detector tubes, portable gas chromatographs, and infrared analyzers are all more accurate than combustible gas sensors. Second, compare the 10% LFL for any substance in question with its TLV, and let the TLV take precedence.

To ensure that a confined space is safe, the following questions should be asked and answered in the affirmative before allowing entry. A negative response to even one of these questions means that entry into the confined space in question is not yet safe.

- Are access and exit equipment such as ladders and steps in good working condition?
- Has the confined space been properly purged of toxic vapours and other toxic substances?
- Are all lines that transport potentially hazardous substances into or through the confined space turned off and properly capped?
- Are all moving equipment and moving parts of equipment in the confined space shut down and locked out?
- Has proper ventilation (natural or mechanical) been provided?
- Has the atmosphere inside the confined space been checked by appropriately sensitive detection devices?
- Have provisions been made to monitor continually the atmosphere inside the confined space during work?

In addition to the toxic and explosive hazards associated with confined spaces, there are often physical hazards. For example, tunnels often contain pipes that can trip an employee or that can leak, leaving liquid on the floor that can cause a fall. Empty liquid or gas storage vessels may contain mechanical equipment or pipes that must be carefully manoeuvred around, often in the dark.

WORKING IN CONFINED SPACES

Before entering a confined space, the worker should take the following measures:

1. **Shut down equipment/power.** Any equipment, steam, gas, power, or water in the confined space should be shut off and locked or tagged to prevent its accidental activation. Turning off valves for fuel, water, or product supply may not be adequate; blanking any lines will prevent these from entering the space if the valve is inadvertently opened.

2. **Test the atmosphere.** Test for the presence of airborne contaminants and to determine the oxygen level in the confined space. Fresh, normal air contains 20.8% oxygen. Ontario regulations for industrial establishments, R.R.O. 1990, Reg. 851, are typical of most Canadian jurisdictions in specifying the minimum and maximum safe levels of oxygen as 18% and 23%, respectively. Atmospheric tests indicate whether a respirator is required and, if so, what type, classification, and level. Figures 6–16, 6–17, 6–18, and 6–19 are examples of devices used for checking the atmosphere.

3. **Ventilate the space.** Spaces containing airborne contaminants should be purged to remove them. Such areas should also be ventilated to keep contaminants from building up again while an employee is working in the space.

4. **Have rescue personnel stand by.** Never allow an employee to enter a confined space without having rescue personnel standing by in the immediate vicinity. These personnel should be fully trained and properly equipped. It is not uncommon for an untrained, improperly equipped employee to be injured or killed trying to rescue a colleague who gets into trouble in a confined space.

Figure 6–16
SAFE T NET 2000
detection device.
Source: Courtesy of Gas Tech, Inc.

5. **Maintain communication.** An employee outside the confined space should stay in constant communication with the employee inside. Communication can be visual, verbal, or electronic (radio, telephone), depending on the distance between the employee inside and the entry point.

6. **Use a lifeline.** A lifeline attached to a full-body harness and a block and tackle will ensure that the employee who is inside can be pulled out should he or she lose consciousness. The apparatus should be rigged so that one employee working alone can pull an unconscious employee out of the confined space.

Ventilation of Confined Spaces

Before allowing employees to enter a confined space, it is important to make the space as safe as possible.[36] One of the most effective strategies for doing so is ventilation. Because confined spaces vary in size, shape, function, and hazard potential, there must be a number of different methods for ventilating them.

Before ventilating a confined space, it should be *purged*. Purging is the process of initially clearing the space of contaminants. Once the area has been purged, ventilation can begin. Ventilation is the process of continually moving

Figure 6–17
GT Land Surveyor detection device.
Source: Courtesy of Gas Tech, Inc.

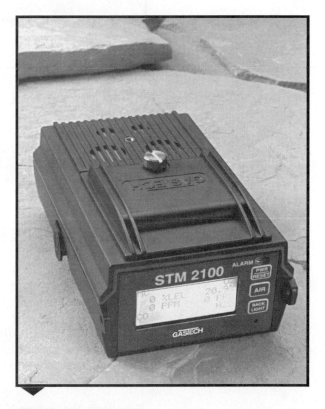

Figure 6–18
STM 2100 detection device.
Source: Courtesy of Gas Tech, Inc.

Figure 6–19
**SAFE T NET 150
detection device.**
Source: Courtesy of Gas Tech, Inc.

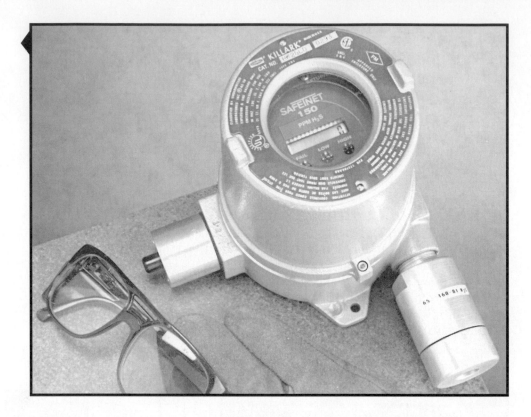

Figure 6–19
**SAFE T NET 150
detection device.**
Source: Courtesy of Gas Tech, Inc.

fresh air through a space. Ventilation, when properly done, will accomplish the following:

- Dilute and replace airborne contaminants that may still be present in the confined space.
- Ensure an adequate supply of oxygen (between 19.5 and 23.5%).
- Exhaust contaminants produced by work performed in the confined space (e.g., welding, painting, and so on).

Ventilation and Local Exhaust

Providing ventilation in a confined space can maintain a comfortable temperature, it can remove odours, and it can dilute contaminants. However, never depend solely on general ventilation to remove toxic contaminants from the air. To eliminate the hazards posed by toxic contaminants such as solvent vapours and welding fumes, it is necessary to exhaust the confined space aggressively. The combination of initial purging, local exhaust, and ventilation is the ideal approach. If contaminant concentrations remain too high even with this approach, employees should wear an appropriate respirator.

Rescue Preparation

The time to think about getting injured employees out of a confined space is well before they enter the space in the first place.[37] Every year, employees are killed trying to save an injured colleague inside a confined space. In an attempt to save injured colleagues, well-meaning employees, who are neither properly trained nor adequately equipped, often fall victim to the toxic atmosphere themselves and die. This is a tragic circumstance made even more so because it is unnecessary and avoidable.

With the right amount of planning and training, employees can be quickly and effectively rescued from confined spaces. Planning should answer the following questions:

- What types of injuries or incidents may occur in a given space?
- What types of hazards may be present in the space?
- What precautions should be taken by rescue personnel entering the space (e.g., lifelines, hoist, respirator, and so on)?
- How much manoeuvring room is there in the confined space?
- What if the victim needs first aid before he or she can be moved?

All of these questions should be answered in the organization's emergency action plan. In addition, all members of the rescue team should have received the training necessary to respond quickly, safely, and effectively. An effective response is one that is appropriate to the magnitude of the incident and is carried out safely.

DISCUSSION CASE

What Is Your Opinion?

"You'll be fine as long as you wear your respirator," said the supervisor to the employee as he entered the empty vessel. "There might be some residual toxic gas left over, but there won't be much. If you don't breathe it, the gas can't hurt you. Get in, do the inspection, and get out. It shouldn't take five minutes." Is this supervisor giving the employee accurate advice? What is your opinion?

SUMMARY

1. The most prominent hazards in the workplace are chemical, physical, biological, and ergonomic.
2. The main routes of entry for toxic agents are inhalation, absorption, and ingestion.
3. The most common types of airborne contaminants are dusts, fumes, smoke, aerosols, mists, gases, and vapours.
4. Asbestos, once thought to be a miracle material, is now known to be an extremely hazardous substance. It has been tied to respiratory cancer, scarring of the lungs, and cancer of the chest or abdominal lining. When identified in the workplace, asbestos should be handled by removal, enclosure, or encapsulation.

5. The three most important concepts to understand concerning exposure thresholds are time-weighted average (TWA), short term exposure limit, and exposure ceiling.

6. Hazard recognition procedures include determining the exposure threshold for each hazardous substance in the workplace, determining the level of exposure to each, determining which employees are exposed and for how long, and calculating the TWAs.

7. General prevention and control strategies include substitution, process changes, isolation, moisture to reduce dust, exhaust methods, ventilation, personal protective equipment, good housekeeping, special control methods, medical programs, and education and training.

8. A toxic substance is one that has a negative effect on the health of a person or animal. The effect produced by a toxic substance depends on its properties, the amount of the dose, the level of exposure, and the individual's resistance.

9. The route of entry of a toxic substance is an important consideration. Common routes of entry include ingestion, injection, absorption, and inhalation.

10. The dose threshold is the minimum dose of a toxic substance required to produce a measurable effect. A lethal dose is one that is highly likely to cause death. A lethal concentration of an inhaled substance is the concentration that is likely to cause death.

11. Exposures to toxic substances are either acute or chronic. Acute exposure involves sudden exposure to high concentrations of the substance in question. Chronic exposure involves limited but continual exposure to the substance in question.

12. Airborne contaminants are classified according to the type of effect that they have on the body. There are irritants, asphyxiants, and narcotics and anesthetics.

13. A carcinogen is any substance that can cause a malignant tumour or a neoplastic growth. Other terms used synonymously for carcinogen are *tumorigen, oncogen*, and *blastomogen*.

14. A confined space may be described as an area with limited means of entry and exit that is large enough for a person to fit into but is not designed for occupancy and that may expose a person to the risk of death, incapacitation, impairment of ability to self-rescue, injury, or acute illness.

15. Threshold limit value (TLV) refers to airborne concentrations of substances and represents conditions under which it is believed that nearly all workers may be repeatedly exposed day after day without adverse effect. TLVs are expressed as time-weighted average, short term exposure limit, and ceiling.

KEY TERMS AND CONCEPTS

Absorption	Biological exposure index (BEI)
Acute effects and exposures	Biological agents
Anesthetic	Bonding
Asphyxiants	Carcinogen

Ceiling	Irritants
Chemical agents	Latency period
Chronic effects and exposures	Lethal concentration
Confined space	Lethal dose
Dose	Narcotics
Dose threshold	Neoplastic growth
Engineering controls	Personal protective equipment (PPE)
Friable asbestos	Short term exposure limit
Housekeeping	Threshold limit value (TLV)
Ingestion	Time-weighted average (TWA)
Inhalation	Toxic substance
Injection	

REVIEW QUESTIONS

1. Define the term *toxic substance.*

2. Briefly explain the typical categories of hazards in the workplace.

3. What are the most common routes of entry for toxic agents?

4. Describe the following types of airborne contaminants: dusts, fumes, smoke, mists, and gases.

5. What factors should be considered in deciding whether to remove or contain asbestos?

6. Explain the following ways of dealing with asbestos in the workplace: removal, enclosure, and encapsulation.

7. Briefly explain the following concepts relating to exposure thresholds: time-weighted average, short term exposure limit, and exposure ceiling.

8. List the most important considerations when evaluating hazards in the workplace.

9. List five generic prevention and control strategies that can be used in any workplace.

10. Give an example of a prevention/control strategy in each of the following categories: engineering controls, ventilation, and personal protective equipment.

11. Explain five self-protection strategies that employees can use in the workplace.

12. List the factors that determine the effect that a toxic substance will have.

13. Explain the mathematical expression of the dose–response relationship.

14. Define the following terms: *dose threshold, lethal dose,* and *lethal concentration.*

15. Differentiate between acute and chronic effects and exposures.

16. List and describe the various classifications of airborne toxics.

17. What is a carcinogen?

18. What is a threshold limit value?

19. Define the following terms: *time-weighted average* and *ceiling*.

20. Explain the three classes of respirators.

WEBLINKS

American Conference of Governmental Industrial Hygienists (ACGIH)
www.acgih.org/home.htm

ACGIH establishes TLVs and BEIs that are accepted by most jurisdictions in Canada.

Canadian Centre for Occupational Health and Safety (CCOHS)
www.ccohs.ca

A federal government agency established to research and provide safety information resources to all Canadian workers. The site has a comprehensive chemical MSDS (material safety data sheet) database.

Centers for Disease Control and Prevention
www.cdc.gov/node.do/id/0900f3ec8000ebdc

This web page on the American Centres for Disease Control site provides the viewer with information on workplace chemical hazards.

ENDNOTES

1. J. B. Olishifski, "Overview of Industrial Hygiene," in *Fundamentals of Industrial Hygiene*, 3rd ed. (Chicago: National Safety Council, 1996), 152.
2. Ibid., 17.
3. Ibid.
4. Ibid., 14.
5. Ibid., 148.
6. Ibid., 18–19.
7. Ibid., 22–23.
8. Ibid., 368.
9. Ibid., 369.
10. Centers for Disease Control and Prevention, National Institute for Occupational Safety and Health (NIOSH). (no date). "NIOSH Safety and Health Topic: Asbestos." [Online]. Available: http://www.cdc.gov/niosh/topics/asbestos/. (Retrieved April 18, 2005).
11. Ibid.
12. J. Takala. International Labour Organization. (September 3, 2003). Asbestos Conference. [Online]. Available: http://www.ilo.org/public/english/protection/safework/accidis/asbestos-dresden1.pdf. (Retrieved, January 15, 2005).

13. Centers for Disease Control and Prevention (April 4, 2000). "NIOSH Safety and Health Topic: Asbestos." National Institute for Occupational Safety and Health. [Online]. Available: http://www.cdc.gov/niosh/asbestos.html, 4–7.
14. Ibid., 3–4.
15. Ibid., 48.
16. Ibid.
17. Ibid.
18. Ibid., 49.
19. Ibid.
20. American Conference of Governmental Industrial Hygienists, *Threshold Limit Values* (Cincinnati, OH: American Conference of Governmental Industrial Hygienists, 2003), 3.
21. Ibid., v–vi, 45, 44, 96, and 112.
22. Olishifski, "Overview of Industrial Hygiene," 21.
23. Ibid.
24. Ibid.
25. Ibid., 22.
26. Ibid., 25.
27. Ibid.
28. Ibid., 26.
29. Ibid.
30. Ibid., 27.
31. Ibid., 24.
32. Florida Department of Labor and Employment Security, Division of Safety, Toxic Substances Information Center, *What You Should Know About On-the-Job Health* (Tallahassee, FL: 1991), 3–15.
33. National Safety Council, *Accident Prevention Manual for Industrial Operations* (Chicago: National Safety Council, 1999), 425.
34. Eric LeBreton. Transport Canada. (December 11, 2002). "Confined Space." [Online]. Available: http://www.tc.gc.ca/canutec/en/articles/documents/confined.htm. (Retrieved, January 15, 2005).
35. John F. Rekus, "Confined Spaces: Is 10 Percent LFL Safe?" *Occupational Hazards* 62, no. 5 (May 2000): 72.
36. John F. Rekus, "Confined Space Ventilation," *Occupational Hazards* (March 1996): 35–38.
37. John F. Rekus, "Confined Space Rescue Planning," *Occupational Hazards* (March 1996): 45–48.

7 Workplace Hazardous Materials Information System (WHMIS) and Transportation of Dangerous Goods (TDG)

CHAPTER

LEARNING OBJECTIVES

- Explain the purpose of the WHMIS program.
- Compare the provincial/territorial and federal responsibilities for WHMIS.
- Describe the requirements for WHMIS labels.
- List the items required on a material safety data sheet (MSDS).
- Describe each WHMIS hazard symbol and its purpose.
- Describe the key elements of the transportation of dangerous goods (TDG) legislation.
- Compare WHMIS and TDG hazard classes.

One of the three basic rights Canadian workers enjoy is the *right to know* what hazards they may be exposed to on the job. Exposure to harmful chemicals is one such hazard — and one that is relevant to most workers. Although industrial environments most readily come to mind when we think about harmful chemicals in the workplace, even in service and clerical environments, products that can harm us in some manner are likely to be present. Workplace Hazardous Materials Information System (WHMIS) is a major component in a worker's right to know, because it provides employers and workers with the information needed to handle and use these potentially harmful products safely.

PURPOSE OF WHMIS

The WHMIS program is a Canada-wide system developed to provide Canadians with a consistent and effective means of dealing with hazardous materials in the workplace. The system was developed through the cooperation of industry, labour, and both federal and provincial and territorial governments and came into effect on October 31, 1988. The nature of this tripartite involvement is reflected in the design of the WHMIS logo seen in Figure 7–1.

The effects of exposure to **controlled products** covered by WHMIS can include mild irritation, mild and severe chemical burns, asphyxiation, damage to organs, cancer, and even death. WHMIS consists of three main components, which are designed to provide information to protect the worker using hazardous products: Firstly, supplier labels and workplace labels, which have specific requirements, are required on all controlled products used or stored in the workplace. Secondly, each product must also have a **material safety data sheet (MSDS)** that is easily accessible to the worker. The MSDS provides detailed information on the properties and safe handling requirements for each product. The third component is worker training. In order for a worker to adequately decipher the information provided on labels and MSDSs, the employer is obligated to provide the necessary education.

WHMIS LEGISLATION

WHMIS was developed through cooperation between the federal and the provincial/territorial levels of governments and both jurisdictions enforce the legislation. The main area of concern for the federal WHMIS legislation is ensuring that suppliers and manufacturers of controlled products provide information to users, through labelling and MSDSs. The provincial and territorial legislation is more concerned with employers obtaining adequate information on hazardous products and passing this on to the workers after the products have entered the workplace.[1]

There are five pieces of federal legislation that implement WHMIS:

1. The Hazardous Products Act, which requires suppliers who sell or import a hazardous material for use in a workplace in Canada to provide labels and MSDSs to their customers.

2. The Controlled Products Regulation, passed on January 20, 1988, under the authority of the Hazardous Products Act. This regulation defines what a controlled product is and also sets out in detail the information that the supplier is required to put on a label and an MSDS.

3. The Ingredient Disclosure List, issued on January 20, 1988, under the Hazardous Products Act. This list contains the names of chemicals that must be identified on an MSDS if they are ingredients of a controlled prod-

CONTROLLED PRODUCTS
Products identified under the federal Hazardous Products Act, whose use and handling are controlled under WHMIS legislation.

MATERIAL SAFETY DATA SHEETS (MSDSs)
These sheets contain all of the relevant information needed by safety personnel concerning specific hazardous materials.

▶ **Figure 7–1**
WHMIS logo.
Source: Health Canada. (June 2, 2003). "Workplace Hazardous Materials Information System (WHMIS)." [Online]. Available: http://www.hc-sc.gc.ca/hecs-sesc/whmis/whmis_symbols.htm (Retrieved February 28, 2005).

uct and present above a specified concentration. The Ingredient Disclosure List is not a finite list of chemicals to which WHMIS applies. Although most of the chemicals on the list are controlled products, WHMIS applies to many more chemicals than are on the list.

4. The Hazardous Materials Information Review Act, passed on June 30, 1987. This Act established the Hazardous Materials Information Review Commission, which is the federal agency that rules on claims for exemption from disclosing confidential business information. The Act also defines the type of information that a supplier or employer may withhold from a label or MSDS.

5. The Hazardous Materials Information Review Regulations, passed on January 20, 1988, under the Hazardous Materials Information Review Act. This regulation sets out the criteria that the Commission will use when assessing the validity of a claim for exemption and also sets out the fees to be paid when filing a claim for exemption or appealing a decision of the Commission.[2]

The provinces and territories have two pieces of legislation dealing with WHMIS. The Health and Safety Act for each jurisdiction outlines the general duties of employers and workers when dealing with hazardous materials; the more specific requirements are detailed in the Regulations. The Health and Safety Act or its equivalent will have sections dealing in depth with toxic substances. For example, Part IV of the Ontario Occupational Health and Safety Act, for Ontario, titled Toxic Substances, refers to material identification and MSDSs. The acts and regulations listed in Figure 7–2 cover workers in provincial and territorial jurisdictions.

WHMIS LABELS

WHMIS labels seen on controlled products in any workplace are a highly visible component of the program. Product labelling provides the user with information on the safe handling of the product along with a readily recognizable indicator that the worker is handling a potentially harmful product. Under WHMIS, two types of labels are seen on controlled products: supplier labels and workplace labels.

Supplier Labels

SUPPLIER LABEL
Identified by the WHMIS broken border, the supplier label is required as a condition of sale of controlled products.

Supplier Labels are recognized by their cross-hatched border. The manufacturer or importer of controlled products is responsible for labelling those products before they are delivered to the workplace. A typical supplier label is shown in Figure 7–3. Supplier labels have nine specific requirements:

1. Product identifier (name of product),
2. Supplier information (name of company),
3. A statement that an MSDS is available,
4. Hazard symbols (WHMIS class),
5. Risk phrases (the main hazards of the product),

6. Precautionary measures (safe use and handling),

7. First aid measures (emergency procedures),

8. English and French (may be two separate labels), and

9. The WHMIS hatched border (any colour that contrasts with the background).

British Columbia	• Workers' Compensation Act
	• Occupational Health and Safety Regulation, Part 5
Alberta	• Occupational Health and Safety Code
	• Part 29, Workplace Hazardous Materials Information System (WHMIS), Sections 395 to 414
Saskatchewan	• Occupational Health and Safety Act
	• Occupational Health and Safety Regulations, Part XXII
Manitoba	• The Workplace Safety and Health Act
	• Workplace Hazardous Materials Information System Regulation
Ontario	• Occupational Health and Safety Act
	• Workplace Hazardous Materials Information System (WHMIS) Regulation
Quebec	• Act Respecting Occupational Health and Safety
	• Regulation Respecting Information on Controlled Products
New Brunswick	• Occupational Health and Safety Act
	• Workplace Hazardous Materials Information System Regulation
Nova Scotia	• Occupational Health and Safety Act
	• Workplace Hazardous Materials Information System (WHMIS) Regulations
PEI	• Occupational Health and Safety Act
	• Workplace Hazardous Materials Information System Regulations
Newfoundland and Labrador	• Occupational Health and Safety Act
	• Workplace Hazardous Materials Information System (WHMIS) Regulations
Yukon Territory	• Occupational Health and Safety Act
	• Workplace Hazardous Materials Information System Regulations
Northwest Territories and Nunavut	• Safety Act
	• Work Site Hazardous Materials Information System Regulations

Figure 7–2
Provincial/territorial WHMIS legislation.
Source: CCOHS, http://www.ccohs.ca/oshanswers/legisl/intro_whmis.html.

Figure 7–3
Supplier label.

Source: Ontario Ministry of Labour. (February 2001). "Workplace Hazardous Materials Information System (WHMIS): A Guide to the Legislation." [Online]. Available: http://www.gov.on.ca/LAB/english/hs/whmis/whmis_appb.html (Retrieved January 12, 2005).

METHANOL

DANGER
POISON
FLAMMABLE
VAPOUR HARMFUL
MAY CAUSE BLINDNESS IF SWALLOWED

Keep away from heat, sparks and flame. No smoking. Container must be grounded when being emptied. Vapour may travel long distance. Avoid contact with eyes and skin. Do not inhale vapours or mist. Do not take internally. Harmful if absorbed through the skin.

FIRST AID: In case of contact, immediately flush eyes and skin with plenty of water for at least 15 minutes.

If swallowed, induce vomiting by sticking finger down throat, or by giving soapy water to drink. Repeat until vomit is clear.

If affected by vapour, move to fresh air.

If breathing has stopped, apply artificial respiration.

GET MEDICAL ATTENTION IMMEDIATELY.

PRECAUTIONS: Wear chemical goggles and resistant gloves. Wash thoroughly after handling. Use with enough ventilation to keep below TLV. Keep container closed. Never use pressure to empty container.

METHANOL

DANGER
POISON
INFLAMMABLE
VAPEURS NOCIVES
PEUT PROVOQUER LA CÉCITÉ, SI AVALÉ

Garder loin de la chaleur, des étincelles et de la flamme. Ne pas fumer. Brancher le contenant à une prise de terre avant de le vider de son contenu. Les vapeurs peuvent s'étendre sur de longues distances. Éviter tout contact avec les yeux et la peau. Ne pas respirer les vapeurs. Ne pas absorber. Nocif, si absorbé par la peau.

PREMIERS SOINS: En cas de contact avec les yeux ou la peau, laver à grande eau pendant au moins 15 minutes.

Si avalé, provoquer le vomissement en introduisant un doigt dans la gorge ou en faisant absorber de l'eau savonneuse à la victime. Répéter jusqu'à cessation du vomissement.

Sortir au grand air, si indisposé par les vapeurs.

Si la respiration est interrompue, recourir à la respiration artificielle.

OBTENIR DES SOINS MÉDICAUX IMMÉDIATS.

PRÉCAUTIONS: Porter des lunettes protectrices (pour produits chimiques) et des gants résistants. Se laver minutieusement après usage. Utiliser dans un endroit bien aéré, afin de maintenir le niveau de vapeurs tolérable. Garder le contenant fermé. Ne jamais user de pression en vidant le récipient.

SEE MATERIAL SAFETY DATA SHEET FOR PRODUCT
VOIR FICHE SIGNALETIQUE

ABC Company
Anytown, Ontario   Telephone 123-4567

Some controlled products brought into the workplace may be in containers smaller than 100 ml. In that case it would not be practical to attach a label containing the nine items listed above. On these smaller containers the WHMIS supplier label may omit the risk phrase, precautionary measures, and first aid measures, but all of the other items must remain.

On the other end of the spectrum, **bulk shipments** are sometimes received at the workplace from the supplier. "Bulk shipment" means a shipment of a controlled product that is contained without intermediate packaging, in

BULK SHIPMENT
A shipment of controlled product that is contained without intermediate packaging.

(a) A vessel with a water capacity of more than 454 litres,

(b) A freight container; a road vehicle; a railway vehicle; a portable tank; a freight container carried on a road vehicle, railway vehicle, ship, or aircraft; or a portable tank carried on a road vehicle, railway vehicle, ship, or aircraft,

(c) The hold of a ship, or

(d) A pipeline.[3]

Once the bulk shipments are at the workplace, the product will likely be stored in containers on sight, so applying a label to the bulk shipment would not accomplish the goal of WHMIS labelling, which is to provide a label at the workplace for the end user. The supplier may send labels with the product, include the specific labelling requirement in a separate letter, or add the required information to the MSDS.

Workplace Labels

Workplace Labels are used in certain situations where the controlled product is transferred from a container containing a supplier label into another for use in the workplace. A workplace label, as shown in Figure 7–4, has to contain the following information:

1. Product identifier (chemical name, brand name, or generic name),

2. Safe handling procedures, and

3. A reference to the MSDS.

A variation on the labelling requirements would include the use of **placards** in place of labels. Placards may be used when a label is not feasible, such as when the product is not in a container or is not completely packaged, or while awaiting the label from the manufacturer. Placards must contain the same information as a workplace label: product identifier, safe handling information, and an MSDS statement.

Another type of label found in some workplaces is a **laboratory label**. Two types of laboratory label are used: supply house labels and sample labels. Supply house labels are used on products for use in laboratories, and sample labels are used on samples sent to laboratories for analysis.

The table in Figure 7–5 shows a summary of WHMIS labelling requirements.

WORKPLACE LABEL
Required on controlled products in the workplace. Workplace labels require less content than supplier labels.

PLACARDS
Alternative to a temporary label or when workplace labels are not practical.

LABORATORY LABEL
Label required on controlled products that are intended solely to be used or tested in a lab. There are two types of laboratory labels: supply house labels and sample labels.

METHANOL

FLAMMABLE—DO NOT USE NEAR AN OPEN FLAME OR PROCESSES THAT GENERATE SPARKS

AVOID INHALING VAPOURS.

READ THE MATERIAL SAFETY DATA SHEET BEFORE USING THIS COMPOUND

Figure 7–4
Workplace label.

Requirements	Supplier Label		Workplace Label	Placard	Laboratory Label	
					Supply House	Sample
	< 100 ml	> 100 ml			< 10 kg.	< 10 kg.
Product Identifier	x	x	x	x	x	x
Supplier Identifier	x	x				x
MSDS Statement	x	x	x	x	x	
Hazard Symbol(s)	x	x				
Risk Phrase(s)		x			x	
Precautionary Measures		x			x	
First Aid Measures		x			x	
Safe Handling Info.			x	x		
Ingredients						x
Hazard Statement						x
Border	x	x				x
Bilingual	x	x			x	x

Figure 7–5
Summary of labelling requirements.

Source: Ontario Ministry of Labour. (February 2001). "Workplace Hazardous Materials Information System (WHMIS): A Guide to the Legislation." [Online]. Available: http://www.gov.on.ca/LAB/english/hs/whmis/whmis_4b.html (Retrieved January 12, 2005).

MATERIAL SAFETY DATA SHEETS

A material safety data sheet (MSDS) is a detailed technical document that is required from the supplier on the initial shipment of a controlled product. In Chapter 6, terminology found on typical MSDSs was discussed. WHMIS training provides the worker with an understanding of these terms and the ability to better decipher the information provided on the MSDS. The appearance of the MSDS may vary from manufacturer to manufacturer, but all MSDSs must contain the following information sections:

1. **Product Information:**
   - Product identifier.
   - Product use.
   - Manufacturer's name, street address, city, province, postal code, and emergency telephone number.
   - Supplier identifier and the supplier's street address, city, province, postal code, and emergency telephone number.
   - Product identification number (PIN).

2. **Hazardous Ingredients:**
   - Information required by subparagraphs 13(a)(i) to (iv) or paragraph 14(a) of the Hazardous Products Act.
   - CAS number.

- LD_{50} (species and route).
- LC_{50} (species and route).

3. **Physical Data:**

- Physical state (gas, liquid, or solid).
- Odour and appearance.
- Odour threshold.
- Vapour pressure.
- Vapour density.
- Evaporation rate.
- Boiling point.
- Freezing point.
- pH.
- Specific gravity.
- Coefficient of water/oil distribution.

4. **Fire or Explosion Hazard:**

- Conditions of flammability.
- Means of extinction.
- Flashpoint and method of determination.
- Upper flammable limit (% by volume).
- Lower flammable limit (% by volume).
- Auto-ignition temperature.
- Hazardous combustion products.
- Explosion data - sensitivity to mechanical impact.
- Explosion data - sensitivity to static discharge.

5. **Reactivity Data:**

- Conditions under which the product is chemically unstable.
- Name of any substance or class of substance with which the product is incompatible.
- Conditions of reactivity.
- Hazardous decomposition products.

6. **Toxicological Properties:**

- Route of entry, including skin contact, skin absorption, eye contact, inhalation, and ingestion.
- Effect of acute exposure to product.
- Effect of chronic exposure to product.
- Exposure limits.
- Irritancy of product.
- Sensitization to product.
- Carcinogenicity.
- Teratogenicity.
- Reproductive toxicity.
- Mutagenicity.
- Name of toxicologically synergistic products.

7. **Preventive Measures:**

- Personal protective equipment to be used.
- Specific engineering controls to be used.

- Procedures to be followed in case of leak or spill.
- Waste disposal.
- Handling procedures and equipment.
- Storage requirements.
- Special shipping information.

8. **First Aid Measures:**

   - Specific first aid measures.

9. **Preparation Information:**

   - Name and phone number of group, department, or party responsible for preparation of MSDS.
   - Date of preparation.[4]

WHMIS HAZARD CLASSES

HAZARD CLASS
One of six categories into which controlled products are placed.

Hazardous materials covered by WHMIS will fall into one of six **hazard classes**. Workers trained in WHMIS will quickly recognize the pictogram used to represent each class and division. The pictogram representing the hazard class of a controlled product must be present on supplier labels and may also be seen on workplace labels and MSDSs. The hazard classes and corresponding symbols are shown in Figure 7–6.

TRANSPORTATION OF DANGEROUS GOODS (TDG)

TDG ACT, 1992
Federal legislation governing the transportation of dangerous goods.

Each day dangerous goods are transported by land, air, and water to destinations around Canada. To minimize the potential harm to humans and the environment, the federal government has enacted legislation to regulate the transport of dangerous goods and the regulations thus created have been adopted by each provincial and territorial jurisdiction. The legislation is titled "Transportation of Dangerous Goods Act, 1992, an Act to promote public safety in the transportation of dangerous goods" or the **TDG Act, 1992.**

SAFETY FACT

Consumer Products

Did you ever wonder why the can of multi-purpose lubricant you purchased at the hardware store has different warning symbols on it than the same product you use at work? A different system of labelling is used for consumer products than is used for the workplace. The Consumer Chemicals and Containers Regulations, 2001 (CCCR, 2001) enforced by Health Canada has classified five hazard categories of products: toxic, corrosive, flammable, quick skin-bonding adhesives, and pressurized containers. The degree of the hazard is indicated by the border and the type of hazard by the inner symbol used as shown below in Figure 7–7.

While the Act includes components relating to education for those packaging and transporting the dangerous goods, enforcement and identification of the transported goods are key elements. For those contravening the TDG Act, penalties can range from $50 000 for a first offence to $100 000 for subsequent offences and up to two years in prison for an indictable offence. Labels and plac-

Class A - Compressed Gas

Class B - Flammable and Combustible Material

Divisin 1: Flammable Gas	Division 4: Flammable Solid
Division 2: Flammable Liquid	Division 5: Flammable Aerosol
Division 3: Combustible Liquid	Division 6: Reactive Flammable Material

Class C - Oxidizing Material

Class D - Poisonous and Infectious Material

Division 1: Materials Causing Immediate and Serious Toxic Effects

    Subdivision A: Very toxic material

    Subdivision B: Toxic material

Division 2: Materials Causing Other Toxic Effects

    Subdivision A: Very toxic material

    Subdivision B: Toxic material

Division 3: Biohazardous Infection Material

Class E - Corrosive Material

Class F - Dangerously Reactive Material

Figure 7–6

Classes and divisions of hazard symbols.

Source: Ontario Ministry of Labour. (February 2001). "Workplace Hazardous Materials Information System (WHMIS): A Guide to the Legislation." [Online]. Available: http://www.gov.on.ca/LAB/english/hs/whmis/whmis_appa.html (Retrieved January 12, 2005).

Symbol	The Danger	Product Examples
Explosive	This **container** can explode if it's heated or punctured. Flying pieces of metal or plastic can cause serious injuries, especially to the eyes.	• water repellant for shoes or boots in an aerosol container • spray paint in an aerosol container
Corrosive	This **product** will burn skin or eyes on contact, or throat and stomach if swallowed	• toilet bowl cleaner • oven cleaner
Flammable	This **product**, or its fumes, will catch fire easily if it's near heat, flames or sparks.	• contact adhesives • gasoline
Poison	Licking, eating, drinking, or sometimes smelling this **product** will cause illness or death	• windshield washer fluid • furniture polish

Figure 7–7
Consumer Chemicals and Containers Regulations warning labels.
Source: CCCR Regulations Services (Canada). (2004). "ICC The Compliance Center." [Online]. Available: http://www.thecompliancecenter.com/cccr.htm. (Retrieved May 6, 2005).

ards are used to identify which of the nine classes of goods are being transported or packaged. During an emergency, labels and placards allow the responder to identify the transported product and assist in protecting people and mitigating environmental damage. The nine classes are:

Class 1 - Explosives, including explosives within the meaning of the Explosives Act.

Class 2 – Gases: compressed, deeply refrigerated, liquefied or dissolved under pressure.

Class 3 - Flammable and combustible liquids.

Class 4 - Flammable solids, substances liable to spontaneous combustion, substances that on contact with water emit flammable gases.

Class 5 - Oxidizing substances, organic peroxides.

Class 6 - Poisonous (toxic) and infectious substances.

Class 7 - Radioactive materials and radioactive prescribed substances within the meaning of the Atomic Energy Control Act.

Class 8 - Corrosives.

Class 9 - Miscellaneous products, substances or organisms considered by the Governor-in-Council to be dangerous to life, health, property, or the environment when handled, offered for transport, or transported and prescribed to be included in this case.[5]

Figure 7–8 below compares WHMIS to TDG hazard classes.

An Overview of the Classes Used in the WHMIS and TDG Systems	
Workplace Hazardous Materials Information System (WHMIS)	**Transportation of Dangerous Goods (TDG)**

Class A Compressed Gases	Class 1 Explosives
	    Divisions 1–5 differentiated on the basis of hazard
	
	Class 2 Compressed Gases
	    Division 1: Flammable Gases
	    Division 2: Nonflammable, Nontoxic, Noncorrosive Gases
	    Division 3: Poisonous Gases
	    Division 4: Corrosive Gases

Class B Flammable and Combustible Material
    Division 1: Flammable Gases
    Division 2: Flammable Liquids
    Division 3: Combustible Liquids
    Division 4: Flammable Solids
    Division 5: Flammable Aerosols
    Division 6: Reactive Flammable Materials
	Class 3 Flammable Liquids
	    Divisions 1–3 differentiated on the basis
	    of flashpoint and form of transport
	
	Class 4 Flammable Solids, Spontaneously Combustible, Dangerous When Wet
	    Division 1: Flammable Solids
	    Division 2: Substances Liable to Spontaneous Combustion
	    Division 3: Substances That Emit Flammable Gases on Contact with Water

Class C Oxidizing Material	Class 5 Oxidizing Substances and Organic Peroxides
	    Division 1: Oxidizing Substances
	    Division 2: Organic Peroxides

Class D Poisonous and Infectious Material
    Division 1: Materials Causing Immediate and Serious Toxic Effect
    Division 2: Materials Causing Other Toxic Effects
    Division 3: Biohazardous Infectious Material
	Class 6 Poisonous and Infectious Substances
	    Division 1: Poisonous Substances
	    Division 2: Infectious Substances
	
	Class 7 Radioactive Materials

Class E Corrosive Material	Class 8 Corrosives

Class F Dangerously Reactive Material	Class 9 Miscellaneous Products or Substances
	    Division 1: Miscellaneous Dangerous Goods
	    Division 2: Environmentally Hazardous Substances
	    Division 3: Dangerous Wastes

Figure 7–8
Comparison of WHMIS and TDG hazard classes.
Source: Ontario Ministry of Labour. (February 2001). Workplace Hazardous Materials Information System (WHMIS): A Guide to the Legislation [Online]. Available: http://www.gov.on.ca/LAB/english/hs/whmis/whmis_8b.html (Retrieved January 12, 2005).

SUMMARY

1. Workplace Hazardous Materials Information System (WHMIS) supports the worker's right to know.

2. The WHMIS program is a Canada-wide system that was developed through the cooperation of industry, labour, and government.

3. The WHMIS program came into effect on October 31, 1988.

4. Controlled products covered by WHMIS can cause effects ranging from mild irritation to death.

5. Supplier labels are required on all controlled products shipped to the workplace.

6. Supplier labels require the following features: product identifier, supplier information, a statement that an MSDS is available, hazard symbols, risk phrases, precautionary measures, first aid measures, English and French, and the WHMIS hatched border.

7. Workplace labels need only the product name, safe handling instructions, and an MSDS statement.

8. Material safety data sheets (MSDSs) provide technical data on the product and information for safe use.

9. Controlled products will have at least one hazard class symbol associated with them and this must be visible on the supplier label.

10. The most prominent legislation covering the transportation of dangerous goods in Canada is the federal TDG Act, 1992.

11. The nine classes of goods under the TDG are explosives, gases, flammable and combustible liquids, flammable solids, oxidizing substances, poisonous (toxic) and infectious substances, radioactive materials, corrosives and miscellaneous products.

KEY TERMS AND CONCEPTS

Bulk shipments   Placards

Controlled products   Supplier label

Hazard class   TDG Act, 1992

Laboratory label   Workplace label

REVIEW QUESTIONS

1. How does the WHMIS program support Canadians' "right to know"?

2. Who is responsible for enforcing WHMIS legislation?

3. What items are required on a WHMIS supplier label?

4. What items are required on a WHMIS workplace label?

5. What information is contained on an MSDS?

6. What are the WHMIS hazard class symbols and where are they used?

7. What is the purpose of TDG legislation?

8. What are the nine TDG hazard classes?

WEBLINKS

Health Canada
www.hc-sc.gc.ca/hecs-sesc/whmis/

This is Health Canada's official WHMIS website. Answers to questions about the national program can be found here.

Canadian Centre for Occupational Health and Safety (CCOHS)
www.ccohs.ca/oshanswers/legisl/intro_whmis.html

On this site, CCOHS has summarized many of the key points about the WHMIS program and has provided some helpful links to more useful resources.

ENDNOTES

1. Ontario Ministry of Labour. (February 2001). "Workplace Hazardous Materials Information System (WHMIS): A Guide to the Legislation." [Online]. Available: http://www.gov.on.ca/LAB/english/hs/whmis/whmis_2.html. (Retrieved January 12, 2005).

2. Ibid.

3. Ibid., whmis_3.html.

4. Ibid., whmis_appc.html.

5. Transport Canada. (August 8, 2002). "Transportation of Dangerous Goods: A Primer." [Online]. Available: http://www.atl.ec.gc.ca/epb/factsheets/transportdg_e.html. (Retrieved January 15, 2005).

Biological Hazards

LEARNING OBJECTIVES

- Describe four types of biological agents.
- Explain how health care workers may be exposed to AIDS.
- Describe the preventative measures one should take to reduce the risk of exposure to AIDS.
- Compare the risks of exposure to hepatitis B, hepatitis C, and HIV.
- List the universal methods of protection one should employ for protection against contaminated blood.
- Explain the risk of SARS to health care workers.
- Explain the methods health care workers can use to protect themselves from needlestick injuries.

AIDS
Acquired immunodeficiency syndrome, describes the condition caused by the human immunodeficiency virus (HIV).

BLOODBORNE PATHOGEN
A disease-producing agent found in the blood.

HEPATITIS
An infection or inflammation of the liver.

SEVERE ACUTE RESPIRATORY SYNDROME (SARS)
A respiratory infection similar to pneumonia.

Acquired immunodeficiency syndrome **(AIDS)** has become one of the most difficult issues that health and safety professionals are likely to face today. It is critical that they know how to deal properly and appropriately with this controversial disease. In addition to AIDS, the modern health and safety manager must be concerned with other **bloodborne pathogens** including **hepatitis** B (HBV) and hepatitis C (HCV). In Canada the **severe acute respiratory syndrome (SARS)** outbreak in 2003 played havoc with the country's health care system and even affected the economy, especially that of the Toronto area. Globally, health care agencies have also had to control the spread of diseases such as **avian influenza**, also known as "bird flu." Avian flu is a public health concern because, although it occurs primarily in birds, it can be transmitted to humans. The first documented human infection was in Hong Kong in 1997; also of particular concern is a possible human-to-human transmission in Thailand in September 2004.

BIOLOGICAL HAZARDS

Harmful **biological agents** are living microorganisms or toxins produced by living plants or animals that have the ability to cause disease or illness in humans.

Health care workers and people who work with animals are at the greatest risk of exposure. Like chemical agents, previously discussed, exposure to biological agents may come from inhalation, ingestion, absorption, or through penetration of the skin. Different forms of biological agents may include:

- **Bacteria** – Microscopic single cell organisms found in food water and air. Three forms of bacteria are coccus, bacillus, and spirillium. Anthrax and food-borne bacteria such as salmonella and staphylococcus are some of the most commonly known.
- **Virus** – Microscopic organisms that invades a host to reproduce. Hepatitis A and B, human immunodeficiency virus (HIV), and rabies are types of viruses of which we often hear.
- **Parasites** – Organisms that live on or in a host and lay eggs to reproduce. Malaria, a disease to which 40% of the world's population is exposed, is caused by the plasmodium falciparum parasite. Ringworms and tapeworms are other common parasites.
- **Fungi** – Simple plants that feed on dead or living tissue of other organisms. Mould, yeast, athlete's foot, and mushrooms are types of fungi.

AIDS IN THE WORKPLACE

AIDS is feared, misunderstood, and, therefore, controversial. Modern health and safety professionals need to know the facts about AIDS and be prepared to use these facts to make the workplace safer. The **human immunodeficiency virus (HIV)** is the virus that causes AIDS. HIV attacks the immune system, resulting in a chronic, progressive illness that leaves infected people vulnerable to opportunistic infections and cancers. AIDS is fatal and there is no cure.[1]

While the prevalence of AIDS infections in the heath care and other industries is very low, many workers are at a high risk of exposure, especially from exposure to high risk groups like **intravenous drug user**s and those who have unprotected sex with multiple partners. The table in Figure 8–1 lists a number of high risk occupations and the protective measures that they should take.

The prevalence of AIDS among Canadians is demonstrated by the following facts:

- The total number of new AIDS cases reported in Canada in 2003 was 2499 and the numbers appear to be rising.
- The proportion of females testing positive in the first six months of 2004 was 26.6%, which is also an increasing trend, especially among young (15 to 29 years) women.
- While men who have sex with men continue to represent the largest group, the heterosexual group has taken over second place from intravenous drug users in the past seven years.[2]

SYMPTOMS OF AIDS

AIDS and various related conditions are caused when humans become infected with the human immunodeficiency virus (HIV). This virus attacks the human

AVIAN INFLUENZA
An infectious disease of birds caused by type A strains of the influenza virus.

BIOLOGICAL AGENTS
Living things or substances produced by living things that may cause harm to humans.

BACTERIA
Microscopic single cell organisms found in food, water, and air.

VIRUS
A microscopic organism that invades a host to reproduce.

PARASITE
An animal or plant that lives in or on a host.

FUNGI
Simple plants that feed on dead or living tissue of other organisms.

HUMAN IMMUNO-DEFICIENCY VIRUS (HIV)
The virus that causes acquired immunodeficiency syndrome (AIDS).

INTRAVENOUS DRUG USER
One who is administered drugs by means of injecting them directly into their veins.

Preventive Measures for Reducing Occupational Exposure to the AIDS Virus	
Occupation	**Preventive Measures**
Surgeons, nurses, and nursing aides	Wash hands. Use gloves. Wear goggles, gowns, and masks if splashing of body fluids is expected. Use disposable needles, syringes, and devices for mouth-to-mouth resuscitation. Bag and label contaminated linen.
Physicians and laboratory workers	Wash hands. Use coats and gloves. Wear goggles, gowns, and masks if splashing of body fluids is expected. Use disposable needles and syringes, mechanical pipetting devices, and biological safety cabinets. Disinfect work surfaces and equipment with sodium hypochlorite solution.
Ambulance workers	Wash hands. Use gloves. Use disposable needles, syringes, and devices for mouth-to-mouth resuscitation.
Dentists and other dental workers	Wash hands. Use gloves. Use disposable needles and syringes. Use goggles, gowns and masks if splashing of blood is expected.
Embalmers	Wash hands. Use gloves, gowns, boot-covers, goggles, and masks. Use disposable surgical instruments. Sterilize reusable equipment. Disinfect work surfaces with sodium hypochlorite solution.
Police and firefighters	Wash hands. Use gloves. Use disposable devices for mouth-to-mouth resuscitation.
Mental health institution workers and correctional service workers	Wash hands. Use gloves. Keep cleaning equipment in restricted areas. Use disposable devices for mouth-to-mouth resuscitation.

(continued)

Figure 8–1
Preventive measures for occupations with potential exposure to the AIDS virus.
Source: Canadian Centre for Occupational Health and Safety (CCOHS). (October 29, 1997). "OHS Answers, AIDS in the Workplace." [Online]. Available: http://www.ccohs.ca/oshanswers/diseases/aids/aids.html. (Retrieved March 2, 2005).

Cleaners	Wash hands.
	Use gloves.
	Keep cleaning equipment in restricted areas.
Laundry workers	Wash hands.
	Use gloves.
Incinerator attendants	Wash hands.
	Use gloves.
Post-mortem attendants	Wash hands.
	Use gloves.
	Wear goggles, masks, and boot-covers if splashing of blood and body fluids is expected.
	Bag, label, and incinerate wastes.

immune system, rendering the body incapable of repelling disease-causing microorganisms. Symptoms of the onset of AIDS are:

- Enlarged lymph nodes that persist.
- Persistent fevers.
- Involuntary weight loss.
- Fatigue.
- Diarrhea that does not respond to standard medications.
- Purplish spots or blotches on the skin or in the mouth.
- White, cheesy coating on the tongue.
- Night sweats.
- Forgetfulness.

How AIDS Is Transmitted

The HIV virus is transmitted in any of the following three ways: (1) sexual contact, (2) contact with blood or blood products, and (3) from mother to child during pregnancy or childbirth. Any act in which body fluids are exchanged can result in infection if either partner is infected. The following groups of people are at the highest level of risk with regard to AIDS: (1) homosexual men who do not take appropriate precautions during sex, (2) IV drug users who share needles, (3) people with a history of multiple blood transfusions or blood-product transfusions, such as hemophiliacs, and (4) sexually promiscuous people who do not take appropriate precautions during sex.

How AIDS Is Not Transmitted

There is a great deal of misunderstanding about how AIDS is transmitted. This can cause inordinate fear among fellow employees of HIV-positive workers. Health and safety professionals should know enough about AIDS transmission to enable them to reduce employees' fears about being infected through casual contact with an HIV-positive person.

Occupational Health & Safety magazine provides the following clarifications concerning the ways in which AIDS is *not* transmitted:

> AIDS is a blood-borne, primarily sexually transmitted disease. It is not spread by casual social contact in schools, workplaces, public washrooms, or restaurants. It is not spread via handshakes, social kissing, coughs, sneezes, drinking fountains, swimming pools, toilet facilities, eating utensils, office equipment, or by being next to an infected person.
>
> No cases of AIDS have been reported from food being either handled or served by an infected person in an eating establishment.
>
> AIDS is not spread by giving blood. New needles and transfusion equipment are used for every donor.
>
> AIDS is not spread by mosquitoes or other insects.
>
> AIDS is not spread by sexual contact between uninfected individuals — whether homosexual or heterosexual — if an exclusive sexual relation has been maintained.[3]

How AIDS Is Impacting the Workplace

The first step in dealing with AIDS at the company level is to develop a comprehensive AIDS policy. Health and safety professionals should be part of the team that drafts the initial policy and updates an existing policy. If a company has no AIDS policy, the health and safety professional should encourage the company to develop one. In all likelihood, most companies won't take much convincing.

According to Peter Minetos,

> Industry is doing its part to eliminate any unnecessary fear: Nearly half of companies surveyed offer their employees literature or other materials to keep them informed on the disease; more than half have an Employee Assistance Program (EAP) to deal with emotional problems concerning AIDS; two-thirds of those who have not yet addressed AIDS with employees plan to do so in the future.[4]

AIDS is having a widely felt impact in the workplace, particularly on employers. According to Minetos, employers are feeling the impact of AIDS in increased insurance premiums and health care costs, time-on-the-job losses,

DISCUSSION CASE

What Is Your Opinion?

J. B. Knotts isn't sure what to do. As health and safety director for Precision Machining and Manufacturing, he is concerned about protecting employees from workplace hazards. On the other hand, he is also concerned about protecting the privacy of his employees. Hence the dilemma that he now faces: He has just learned that Andrea Cobb, a lathe operator, is HIV positive. Cuts and abrasions from metal chips are common among lathe operators and other machinists. In fact, the machining supervisor had to administer minor first aid to a machine operator less than an hour ago. What if Andrea Cobb is cut or scraped? What about the blood? Knotts wonders if he should warn the other employees about Cobb's condition. What is your opinion?

decreased productivity, AIDS-related lawsuits, increased stress, and related problems that result from misconceptions about AIDS.[5]

The starting point for dealing with AIDS in the workplace is the development of a company policy that covers AIDS and other bloodborne pathogens. The policy should, at a minimum, cover the following areas: employee rights, testing, and education.

HEPATITIS B (HBV) AND HEPATITIS C (HCV) IN THE WORKPLACE

Hepatitis B (HBV)

Although the spread of HIV receives more attention, there is a far greater risk from the spread of hepatitis B (HBV). This bloodborne virus averages approximately 300 000 new cases per year compared with AIDS, which averages approximately 43 000 new cases. The hepatitis B virus is extremely strong compared with HIV. For example, it can live on surfaces for up to a week if it is exposed to air. Hepatitis B is also much more concentrated than HIV.

Hepatitis B is caused by a double-shelled virus. It can be transmitted in the following ways:

- Contact with blood.
- Contact with body fluids including tears, saliva, and semen.

The hepatitis B virus can live in body fluids for years. Carriers of the virus are at risk themselves, and they place others at risk. Persons infected with HBV may contract chronic hepatitis, cirrhosis of the liver, and primary heptocellular carcinoma. An HBV-infected individual is more than 300 times more likely to develop primary liver cancer than is a uninfected individual from the same environment. Unfortunately, it is possible to be infected and not know it because the symptoms can vary widely from person to person.

The symptoms of hepatitis B are varied but include:

- Jaundice.
- Joint pain.
- Rash.
- Internal bleeding.

SAFETY FACT

Employees at Greatest Risk from Viral Hepatitis

Employees who are at the greatest risk of necrosis of liver cells from viral hepatitis are those who are elderly and those who have diabetes mellitus, cancer, or any other illness severe enough to require surgery and transfusions.

HBV VACCINATION Universal immunization against HBV is now part of the publicly funded vaccine programs offered in all provinces and territories. Immunization with hepatitis B vaccine is recommended for those people who are at increased risk of occupational infection, namely, those exposed frequently to blood, blood products, and bodily fluids that may contain the virus.[6] The vaccination must be offered within 10 days of a person's initial assignment to a job where exposure to blood or other potentially infectious materials can be "reasonably anticipated."

The hepatitis B vaccination is a noninfectious, yeast-based vaccine given in three injections in the arm. It is prepared from recombinant yeast cultures, rather than human blood or plasma. Thus, there is no risk of contamination from other bloodborne pathogens, nor is there any chance of developing HBV from the vaccine.

The second injection should be given one month after the first, and the third injection six months after the initial dose. More than 90% of those vaccinated develop immunity to the hepatitis B virus. To ensure immunity, it is important for individuals to receive all three injections. At this point it is unclear how long the immunity lasts, so booster shots may be required at some point in the future.

The vaccine causes no harm to those who are already immune or to those who may be HBV carriers. Although employees may opt to have their blood tested for antibodies to determine the need for the vaccine, employers may not make such screening a condition of receiving the vaccination, nor are employers required to provide prescreening.

Each employee should receive counselling from a health care professional when the vaccination is offered. This discussion will help an employee determine whether inoculation is necessary.

Hepatitis C (HCV)

Hepatitis C virus (HCV) infection is a common chronic bloodborne infection. More than 5000 individuals in Canada — mostly young people — get this virus each year.[7] Most of these persons are chronically infected and may be unaware of their infection because they are not clinically ill. Infected persons serve as a source of transmission to others and are at risk for chronic liver disease or other HCV-related chronic diseases during the first two or more decades following the initial infection. Figure 8–2 summarizes tests that are used to detect HCV infection.

HCV is transmitted primarily through large or repeated direct percutaneous exposures to blood. Those most likely to get hepatitis C are:

- Drug users who share needles, spoons, straws, and other drug-related equipment that are contaminated with HCV.
- People who get tattoos or body parts pierced with dirty or unsterile needles and ink.
- People who received blood transfusions or blood products before 1992.
- People who share a razor or toothbrush with someone who has hepatitis C.[8]

Preventing and controlling HCV requires a comprehensive strategy comprised of at least the following activities:

Primary prevention activities:

- Screening and testing blood, plasma, organ, tissue, and semen donors.
- Virus inactivation of plasma-derived products.

Tests for Hepatitis C Virus (HCV) Infection	
Test	**Application**
Hepatitis C virus antibody (anti-HCV) • EIA (enzyme immunoassay) • Supplemental assay	• Indicates past or present infection, but does not differentiate between acute, chronic, or resolved infection. • All positive EIA results should be verified with a supplemental assay.
HCA RNA (hepatitis C virus ribonucleic acid) **Qualitative tests** • Reverse transcriptase polymerase chain reaction (RT-PCR) amplification of HCV RNA by in-house or commercial assays	• Detect presence of circulating HCV RNA. • Monitor patients on antiviral therapy.
Quantitative tests • RT-PCR amplification of HCV RNA by in-house or commercial assays • Branched chain DNA (bDNA) assays	• Determine concentration of HCV RNA. • Might be useful for assessing the likelihood of response to antiviral therapy.
Genotype • Several methodologies available (e.g., hybridization, sequencing)	• Group isolates of HCV based on generic differences into 6 genotypes and 90 subtypes. • With new therapies, length of treatment might vary based on genotype.
Serotype • EIA based on immunoreactivity to synthetic peptides	• No clinical utility

Figure 8–2
Various tests available for detecting the presence of HCV.
Source: US Centers for Disease Control and Prevention.

- Risk-reduction counselling and services.
- Implementation and maintenance of infection control practices.

  Secondary prevention activities:

- Identification, counselling, and testing of persons at risk.
- Medical management of infected persons.
- Education and training.
- Monitoring the effectiveness of prevention activities to develop improved prevention methods.

SEVERE ACUTE RESPIRATORY SYNDROME (SARS)

Severe acute respiratory syndrome (SARS) is a respiratory infection similar to pneumonia. SARS is a new disease caused by a corona virus, similar to the virus

Hepatitis C

Hepatitis C can be treated. It is important to find out if you have the virus and get treatment as soon as possible.

251 000 Canadians are infected with hepatitis C and, because there are no symptoms, 95 000 of them don't know it.

Most people newly infected with hepatitis C have no symptoms and are unaware of their infection, but they are still infectious.

Avoid the risk of hepatitis C: Don't share needles or injection drug equipment.

Hepatitis C is *not* spread by hugging, kissing, or shaking hands. It is *not* spread by means of food or water.

More than 5000 Canadians — many of whom are young people — are infected with the hepatitis C virus each year.

There is no vaccine for hepatitis C.[9]

that causes the common cold. After exposure and an incubation period of two to seven days, symptoms similar to that of the flu, such as a high fever, cough, and respiratory difficulty may develop.

While the effect on the health care system and the subsequent tourism losses suffered in Canada after the global SARS outbreak of 2003 were, indeed, wide ranging, the following facts show that the risks associated with the flu far outweigh the risk of SARS for most people:

- Flu causes an estimated 250 000 to 500 000 deaths worldwide each year.
- In Canada, as many as 500 to 1500 people, mostly seniors, die from pneumonia related to flu each year.
- During the SARS outbreak of 2003, 8098 probable cases and 774 deaths from SARS were reported worldwide.
- During that same period, 438 probable or suspected SARS cases caused 44 deaths in Canada.[10]

Who Is at Risk

The spread of SARS comes from close contact with the affected person. The virus is believed to be carried by saliva and other bodily secretions. Health care workers from various settings and occupations caring for affected patients are at risk and must protect themselves. Since SARS is a global problem, controlling the disease involves the cooperation of several jurisdictions.

The Canadian Centre for Occupational Health and Safety (CCOHS) provides the following information.

Health Canada, the Centers for Disease Control and Prevention (CDC) and the World Health Organization (WHO) have developed infection control guidance for workers at risk. The recommendations include:

Hand Washing

Hand washing is the most important hygiene measure in preventing the spread of infection. Hands must be washed before and after contact with a patient, after contact with body fluids, and after contact with items known to be contaminated with respiratory secretions. Plain soap may be used for routine hand washing.

Gloves

Gloves should be used as an additional measure, not as a substitute for hand washing. Gloves should be used before contact with the patient, and they should be removed and hands washed prior to leaving the patient's room.

Gowns

Long sleeved gowns should be worn by all health care workers if direct contact with the patient is anticipated.

Mask, Eye Protection, Face Shield

Health Canada and CDC in the US recommend N95 type respirators for use by health care workers during all patient contact. N95 filters belong to a group of air-purifying particulate filters certified by the National Institute for Occupational Health and Safety (NIOSH) and these certifications are used in Canada.

Particulate respirators are the same as what used to be called dust, fume, and mist respirators or masks. N-type filters are for airborne solid and water-based particulates. The "95" in N95 means that the filter can capture or stop 95% of the particulates 0.3 microns (micrometres) in diameter; but, to be effective the respirators must be well-fitted to the face to prevent leakage around the edges.

Surgical masks may offer some protection. However, the US FDA (Food and Drug Administration) has recommended that the labelling for surgical masks contain the following precaution statement: "Surgical masks, where worn properly may reduce potential exposure of the wearer to blood and body fluids but do not eliminate the risk of contracting any disease or infection."[11]

PREVENTING AND RESPONDING TO NEEDLESTICK INJURIES

Needlestick injuries are not a major concern in most workplaces outside of the health care industry, but they are enough of a concern that health and safety professionals should know how to prevent them and how to respond when they occur. An excellent source of help for health and safety professionals concerning needlestick injuries is the National Institute for Occupational Health and Safety (NIOSH). NIOSH maintains a website dedicated specifically to the prevention of needlestick injuries at: http://www.cdc.gov/niosh/topics/bbp/safer.

This website recommends a five-step model for developing, establishing, and maintaining a needlestick-prevention program:

NEEDLESTICK INJURIES
Injuries obtained through inadvertent puncture of the skin with hypodermic needles.

1. Form a sharps injury prevention team.
2. Identify priorities.
3. Identify and screen safer medical devices.
4. Evaluate safer medical devices.
5. Institute and monitor the use of the safer medical devices selected.[12]

Safety Needles

Employees who work with needles for taking blood, giving injections, or inserting intravenous systems should be considered at high risk for becoming infected with HIV. Whether inserting an IV, taking blood, or giving a vaccination, medical personnel live with the reality of potential bloodborne pathogen exposure every minute of the day. Studies have consistently shown that 50 to 85% of health care workers who have contracted a bloodborne disease cannot identify when or how they were exposed to bloodborne pathogens.

In addition, whereas more than one million accidental needlesticks are reported each year, it is estimated that 66% of accidental needlesticks go unreported. With the use of injury prevention devices, the Centers for Disease Control and Prevention estimate that the number of accidental needlesticks could be reduced by 76%. Not all devices that are called "safe" are safer. Injury prevention devices on syringes, IVs, catheters, blood-drawing equipment, vaccination instruments, lancets, and scalpels must be one-handed to be considered safer. Some sheathing devices require two-handed operation and often result in an increase in needlestick injuries. Figure 8–3 contains examples of syringes with safety features.

Responding to Needlestick Incidents

When, in spite of your best efforts at prevention, a needlestick injury does occur, the following steps are recommended:

1. Encourage bleeding where the skin is penetrated.
2. Wash the penetration area thoroughly with copious amounts of warm, soapy water (do not use a scrub brush).
3. If the eyes are somehow involved, wash them immediately with water.
4. If the mouth is somehow involved, rinse it immediately with water, but do not swallow.
5. Get the injured employee to the hospital as soon as possible.
6. Contact a clinical virologist.
7. Make sure that management personnel for the company in question are fully informed of the situation.[13]

Plastic shield slides over the
needle and locks to encase
the exposed point.

▶ **Figure 8–3**
**Examples of syringes
with safety features.**

Syringe with protective shield

With an extra push on
the plunger…

…the needle retracts into
the syringe.

Syringe with retractable needle

SUMMARY

1. Various forms of biological agents include bacteria, viruses, parasites, and fungi.

2. AIDS is known to be transmitted in three ways: sexual contact, contact with blood or blood products, and from mother to child during pregnancy or childbirth. AIDS is not spread through casual contact such as handshakes, eating utensils, sharing of toilet facilities, or coughing.

3. High-risk groups with regard to AIDS are homosexual men who do not take appropriate precautions during sex, IV drug users, people with a history of multiple blood transfusions (including hemophiliacs), and sexually promiscuous people who do not take appropriate precautions during sex.

4. The following precautions will help to reduce the chances of contracting AIDS: abstinence; mutually monogamous relationship or marriage with an infection-free partner; no multiple sexual partners; avoidance of sex with a high-risk person without taking proper precautions; no use of intravenous drugs or, if you use, no sharing of needles; use of a protective device while practising live or simulated CPR; and use of safety needles.

5. AIDS is having an impact on the workplace in the form of higher insurance premiums, time-on-the-job losses, decreased productivity, cost of AIDS-related lawsuits, and increased stress.

6. A corporate AIDS policy should have at least three components: employee rights, testing, and education.

7. Hepatitis B (HBV) poses an even greater threat than HIV. It is caused by a double-shelled virus. HBV is transmitted through blood, tears, saliva, and semen. It can stay alive for years in body fluids.

8. Hepatitis C (HCV) infection is a common chronic bloodborne infection. Approximately 5000 new cases are diagnosed in Canada every year. HCV is transmitted primarily through direct percutaneous exposure to blood.

9. During the SARS outbreak of 2003, 438 probable or suspected SARS cases caused 44 deaths in Canada.

10. The five-step model for preventing needlestick injuries is form a sharps injury team, identify priorities, identify and screen safer devices, evaluate the safer devices, institute and monitor the use of safer devices.

KEY TERMS AND CONCEPTS

Acquired immunodeficiency syndrome (AIDS)

Avian influenza

Bacteria

Biological agents

Bloodborne pathogen

Fungi

Hepatitis

Human immunodeficiency virus (HIV)

Intravenous drug user

Needlestick injuries

Parasite

Severe acute respiratory syndrome (SARS)

Virus

REVIEW QUESTIONS

1. What are four types of biological agents?

2. What do the acronyms *AIDS* and *HIV* mean?

3. List five symptoms of AIDS.

4. What are the three known ways that AIDS is transmitted?

5. List the groups of people who are considered high risk with regard to AIDS.

6. List five ways that AIDS is *not* transmitted.

7. Describe the ways in which AIDS is having an impact in the workplace.

8. What are the minimum components of a corporate AIDS policy?

9. List four ways to guard against contracting AIDS.

10. Explain why HBV poses more of a problem for safety personnel than HIV does.

11. Explain the primary prevention strategies for HCV.

12. What strategies can health care workers use to protect themselves during a SARS outbreak?

13. What are the recommended steps in a needlestick prevention program?

WEBLINKS

CCOHS
www.ccohs.ca/oshanswers/biol_hazards/

This Canadian Centre for Occupational Health and Safety web page has information on the biological hazards mentioned in the chapter plus several others.

Health Canada
www.hc-sc.gc.ca/english/protection/index.html

Health Canada collaborates internationally and with its provincial and territorial counterparts to protect the health of Canadians against current and emerging health threats.

Public Health Agency of Canada
www.phac-aspc.gc.ca/about_apropos/index.html

The government of Canada has created the new Public Health Agency of Canada and appointed a Chief Public Health Officer to look after health and health care issues.

World Health Organization
www.who.int/csr/en/

This World Health Organization web page, the Department of Communicable Disease Surveillance and Response informs the reader about what the WHO is doing on a global scale to protect against outbreaks of diseases, such as SARS and avian flu.

ENDNOTES

1. Health Canada. (January 15, 2005). "AIDS." [Online]. Available: http://www.hc-sc.gc.ca/english/diseases/aids.html. (Retrieved January 29, 2005).

2. Public Health Agency of Canada. (December 1, 2004). Volume 30–23. "At a Glance: HIV/AIDS Surveillance to 30 June 2004." [Online]. Available: http://www.phac-aspc.gc.ca/publicat/ccdr-rmtc/04vol30/dr3023ea.html. (Retrieved January 29, 2005).

3. "AIDS—The Basic Facts," *Occupational Health & Safety* 10, no. 3: 6.

4. P. Minetos, "Corporate America vs. AIDS," *Safety & Health* 138, no. 6: 34.

5. Ibid.

6. Public Health Agency of Canada. (October 23, 2002). "Vaccine Preventable Diseases, Hepatitis B." [Online]. Available: http://www.phac-aspc.gc.ca/dird-dimr/vpd-mev/hepatitis-b_e.html. (Retrieved January 29, 2005).

7. Public Health Agency of Canada. (September 22, 2003). "Hepatitis C, Frequently Asked Questions." [Online]. Available: http://www.phac-aspc.gc.ca/hepc/hepatitis_c/drhepc.html#mostlikely. (Retrieved January 29, 2005).

8. Ibid.

9. Public Health Agency of Canada. (March 24, 2004). "Hepatitis C, About Hepatitis C." [Online]. Available: http://www.phac-aspc.gc.ca/hepc/hepatitis_c/aboutfacts.html. (Retrieved January 29, 2005).

10. Health Canada. (December 20, 2004) "Flu? SARS?" [Online]. Available: http://www.hc-sc.gc.ca/english/diseases/flu_sars.html. (Retrieved January 29, 2005).

11. Canadian Centre for Occupational Health and Safety. (September 19, 2003). "OHS Answers, SARS." [Online]. Available: http://www.ccohs.ca/oshanswers/diseases/sars.html. (Retrieved January 29, 2005).

12. "Web-Based Information Could Help Prevent Needlestick Injuries," *Occupational Health & Safety* 17, no. 11 (November 2002): 3.

13. B. C. Yorker, "AIDS Testing," *AAOHN Journal* 36, no. 5: 231.

Ergonomic Hazards: Musculoskeletal Disorders (MSDs) and Cumulative Trauma Disorders (CTDs)

9

CHAPTER

LEARNING OBJECTIVES

- Define ergonomics and human factors.
- List the factors associated with physical stress.
- Explain the scope of ergonomic legislation in Canada.
- Describe common indicators of ergonomic problems.
- List common ergonomic problems found in the workplace.
- Describe the strategies used to solve common ergonomic problems.
- Explain how investments in ergonomics may be inhibited by economics.
- Describe cumulative trauma disorders (CTDs) and their causes.

The history of workplace development in the Western world is characterized by jobs and technologies designed to improve processes and productivity. All too often in the past, little or no concern was given to the impact of the job process or technology on workers. As a result, work processes and machines have sometimes been unnecessarily dangerous. Another result has been that new technologies have sometimes failed to live up to expectations. This is because, even in the age of high technology, human involvement in work processes is still the key to the most significant and enduring productivity improvements. If a machine or system is uncomfortable, difficult, overly complicated, or dangerous to use, human workers will not be able to derive its full benefit.

The proliferation of uncomfortable and dangerous workplace conditions, whether created by job design or unfriendly technologies, is now widely recognized as harmful to productivity, quality, and worker health and safety. The advent of the science of ergonomics is making the workplace more physically friendly. This, in turn, is making the workplace a safer and healthier place.

ERGONOMICS DEFINED

ERGONOMICS
The science of conforming the workplace and all of its elements to the worker.

Minimizing the amount of physical stress in the workplace requires continuous study of the ways in which people and technology interact. The insight gained from this study must then be used to improve the interaction. This is a description of the science of **ergonomics**. For the purpose of this book, ergonomics is defined as follows:

> Ergonomics is a multidisciplinary science that seeks to conform the workplace and all of its physiological aspects to the worker. Ergonomics involves the following:
> * Using special design and evaluation techniques to make tasks, objects, and environments more compatible with human abilities and limitations.
> * Seeking to improve productivity and quality by reducing workplace stressors, reducing the risk of injuries and illnesses, and increasing efficiency.

The word *ergonomics* is derived from the Greek language. *Ergon* is Greek for *work; nomos* means *laws.* Therefore, in a literal sense, ergonomics means work laws. In practice, it consists of the scientific principles (laws) applied in minimizing the physical stress associated with the workplace (work). Figure 9–1 summarizes some of the widely accepted benefits of ergonomics.

While there are benefits to be derived from ergonomics, there are also problems, both financial and health related, that can result from giving too little attention to ergonomics. The matter is complicated further because health problems tend to multiply a company's financial problems. Consequently, modern health and safety professionals need to be well versed in ergonomics.

HUMAN FACTORS AND ERGONOMIC HAZARDS

When the topic of ergonomics is discussed, the term *human factors* will usually find its way into the conversation.[1] But what is meant by the term? Tillman and Tillman define it as follows:

**Figure 9–1
Benefits of
ergonomics.**

* Improved health and safety for workers
* Higher morale throughout the workplace
* Improved quality
* Improved productivity
* Improved competitiveness
* Decreased absenteeism and turnover
* Fewer workplace injuries/health problems

Consumers are demanding safe and effective products. However, not all people have control over products they use. Therefore, all products must be carefully designed. For example, if a child car seat fails because it does not fit the child or is difficult to install, everyone will lose: the child, the parent, the designer, and the manufacturer . . . . Human factors is a profession to help ensure that equipment and systems are safe and easy to operate by human beings. A human factors researcher gathers and analyzes data on human beings (how they work, their size, their capabilities and limitations). A human factors engineer works with designers as a team to incorporate data into designs to make sure people can operate and maintain the product or system. Human factors professionals then determine the skills needed to operate or maintain a finished product. Human factors is difficult to define because it is a compilation of many sciences dealing with both humans and machines. Some of the disciplines human factors experts are trained in include the following: psychology, anthropology, engineering, biology, medicine, education, and physiology.[2]

Human Factors Defined

Tillman and Tillman further define human factors as a "science combining research and application of human data."[3] The concept can also be viewed as a science that bridges research about human beings and the application of that research to designing products and systems for human beings.

Human Factors in Action

Tillman and Tillman provide several examples of how the science of human factors fits into the systems design process. Perhaps the best way to get a feel for the concept of human factors is to consider several of these examples:

1. **Predesign analysis.** In this stage of the design process, human factors professionals conduct research to answer such questions as What is the best way for humans to interact with computers? What factors contribute to fatigue and stress in an office environment? How can designers overcome these factors?

2. **Preliminary design.** In this stage, human factors professionals study machine and human capabilities to determine which tasks should be undertaken manually and which should be automated.

3. **Detail design and development.** In design and development, human factors professionals define the environment required for operator safety, enhanced operator performance, and the reduction or prevention of operator stress and fatigue.

4. **Test and evaluation.** In this stage of the process, human factors professionals test actual humans using the prototype equipment or system.[4]

Human Factors and Safety

Human factors can play an important role in both product safety and workplace safety (where many products are used). What follows is how the science of human factors can help reduce both product and workplace hazards:

1. **Hazard elimination by design.** Human error is frequently the root cause or a contributing cause of accidents on the job. Intelligent design can reduce

human errors by providing controls that are simple to understand and operate and by proving human–machine interaction that is neither boring nor overly demanding physically.

2. **Provision and location of safety devices.** The design and location of safety devices such as emergency cutoff switches can reduce human error on the job, correspondingly reducing the chances of an accident.

3. **Provision of warning devices.** The colour, location, and wording of warning devices; the pitch and volume of warning signals; and the design of caution markings on gauges and video displays are all important factors in reducing the likelihood of human error that might lead to an accident. The science of human factors can help determine the appropriate way to apply all of these factors in a given setting.

4. **Establishment of procedures/provision of training.** When hazards cannot be realistically designed out of a system, administrative procedures for hazard reduction must be established and training relating to those procedures must be provided. Human factors professionals can help establish appropriate administrative procedures and help develop the necessary training.[5]

FACTORS ASSOCIATED WITH PHYSICAL STRESS

Eight variables that can influence the amount of physical stress experienced on the job are as follows:

Sitting versus standing.

Stationary versus moveable/mobile.

Large demand for strength/power versus small demand for strength/power.

Good horizontal work area versus bad horizontal work area.

Good vertical work area versus bad vertical work area.

Nonrepetitive motion versus repetitive motion.

Low surface versus high surface.

No negative environmental factors versus negative environmental factors.[6]

Sitting versus Standing

Generally speaking, sitting is less stressful than standing. Standing for extended periods, particularly in one place, can produce unsafe levels of stress on the back, legs, and feet. Although less so than standing, sitting can also be stressful unless the appropriate precautions are taken. These precautions include proper posture, a supportive back rest, and frequent standing/stretching movement.

Stationary versus Mobile

Stationary jobs are those done primarily at one workstation. Of course, even these jobs involve movement at the primary workstation and occasional movement to other areas. Mobile jobs, on the other hand, require continual movement from one station to another. The potential for physical stress increases with stationary jobs when workers fail to take such precautions as periodically standing/stretching/moving. The potential for physical stress increases with mobile jobs when workers carry materials as they move from station to station.

Large versus Small Demand for Strength/Power

In classifying jobs by these two criteria, it is important to understand that repeatedly moving small amounts of weight over a period of time can have a cumulative effect equal to the amount of stress generated by moving a few heavy weights. Regardless of whether the stress results from lifting a few heavy objects or repeated lifting of lighter objects, jobs that demand larger amounts of strength/power are generally more stressful than those requiring less.

Good versus Bad Horizontal Work Area

A good **horizontal work area** is one that is designed and positioned so that it does not require the worker to bend forward or to twist the body from side to side. Horizontal work areas that do require these movements are bad. Bad horizontal work surfaces increase the likelihood of physical stress.

Good versus Bad Vertical Work Area

Good **vertical work areas** are designed and positioned so that workers are not required to lift their hands above their shoulders or bend down in order to perform any task. Vertical work areas that do require these movements are bad. Bad vertical work areas increase the likelihood of physical stress.

Nonrepetitive versus Repetitive Motion

Repetitive motion jobs involve short-cycle motion that is repeated continually. Nonrepetitive jobs involve a variety of tasks that are not, or only infrequently, repeated. Repetition can lead to monotony and boredom. When this happens, the potential for physical stress increases.

HORIZONTAL WORK AREA
Refers to the limits of the horizontal plane in which the worker is required to perform a task. A good horizontal work area is designed and positioned so that it does not require the worker to bend forward or to twist the body from side to side.

VERTICAL WORK AREA
Refers to the limits of the vertical plane in which the worker is required to perform a task. A good vertical work area is designed and positioned so that workers are not required to lift their hands above their shoulders or bend down in order to perform any task.

REPETITIVE MOTION
Short-cycle motion that is repeated continually.

SAFETY FACT

Strains and Sprains Are Big Problems

Injuries associated with poor ergonomics have a significant impact within the Canadian economy. HRSDC reported that strain and sprain injuries were three times more often the cause of lost time injuries than the second place category of contusion, crushing, and bruising among Canadian workers in 1998.[7] A Statistics Canada study estimated that 2.3 million Canadians aged 20 or over reported repetitive strain injury (RSI) serious enough to limit their normal activities in the 12 months leading up to its 2000/2001 survey. The survey found that the majority of injuries were caused by work-related activity.[8]

Low versus High Surface Contact

Surface stress can result from contact with hard surfaces such as tools, machines, and equipment. High surface contact jobs tend to be more physically stressful than low surface contact jobs.

Presence versus Absence of Environmental Factors

ENVIRONMENTAL FACTORS
Characteristics of the environment in which an employee works that can affect his or her state of mind or physical conditions, such as noise or distractions.

Generally, the more **environmental factors** with which a worker has to contend on the job, the more stressful the job. For example, personal protective equipment, although conducive to reducing environmental hazards, can increase the amount of physical stress associated with the job.

ERGONOMIC REGULATIONS AND STANDARDS IN CANADA

Guidelines, standards, and codes of practice are produced and published by various agencies in Canada. Governments have available to them various resources from organizations such as the Canadian Standards Association (CSA), the National Institute of Occupational Health and Safety (NIOSH), and several others whose research is geared toward developing standards that protect most workers from injury and illness. The Canadian Centre for Occupational Health and Safety (CCOHS) also has a broad range of resources available to help develop safe workplaces, such as the features of a "good" office chair, as seen in Figure 9–2.

The Canadian Auto Workers, with the support of health care and safety associations, have been lobbying for ergonomic legislation that would provide enforceable standards that are consistent throughout the country. The most progressive and comprehensive ergonomic legislation in Canada is that in British Columbia. The health and safety regulations outline the specific requirements for a company's health and safety program to prevent musculoskeletal injuries (MSIs). A chart showing the seven steps in the MSI process from a booklet by the Workers' Compensation Board of BC, *Preventing Musculoskeletal Injuries, A Guide for Employers and Joint Committees*, is shown below in Figure 9–3.

SAFETY FACT

Keys to a Successful Ergonomics Program

Regardless of the type of organization, the keys to having a successful ergonomics program are:

* Commitment on the part of top management.
* A written program.
* Employee involvement.
* Continuous monitoring of the program.
* Adjusting as necessary based on the results of monitoring.

95–110

15–30 cm

20–30 cm

38–43 cm

35–51 cm

45 cm

**Allow clearance
for legs to cross**

2–5

**Figure 9–2
Ergonomic chair.**
Source: Canadian Centre for
Occupational Health and Safety
(CCOHS). (November 25, 1999).
"OHS Answers, Ergonomics."
[Online]. Available:
http://www.ccohs.ca/oshanswers/
ergonomics/office/chair.html.
(Retrieved March 2, 2005).

What do I need to know about selecting a good "ergonomic" chair?

The selection of a suitable chair is a critical step in preventing health problems in people who work in a sitting position. With the ergonomics approach, sitting is viewed as a specific, specialized activity, which is influenced by the way that a sitting person interacts with the working environment.

What are the features of a "good" chair?

Some features are mandatory for a good chair regardless of how you intend to use it:

- **Adjustability** - Check to see that seat height is adjustable.

- **Seat height range** - Check whether the seat height can be adjusted to the height recommended for the worker(s) who will use it. Other chairs may have to be selected for very short or tall workers.

- **Backrest** - Check to see that the backrest is adjustable both vertically and in the frontward and backward direction.

- **Seat depth** - Select the seats that suit the tallest and the shortest users.

- **Stability** - Check for the stability of the chair; a five-point base is recommended.

Figure 9–3
The seven steps in the MSI process.
Source: The Workers' Compensation Board of BC. (2004). *Preventing Musculoskeletal Injury (MSI): A Guide for Employers and Joint Committees.* [Online]. Available: http://www.worksafebc.com/publications/Health_and_Safety_Information/by_topic/assets/pdf/msi_employers.pdf. (Retrieved March 2, 2005).

Step 1
CONSULTATION
Consult with joint health and safety committee or worker health and safety representatives during each step in the MSI process below.

Step 2
EDUCATION
Educate workers about the risk factors, signs and symptoms of injury, and potential health effects.

Step 3
RISK IDENTIFICATION
Identify jobs with a risk of MSI.
Identify risk factors on these jobs.

Step 4
RISK ASSESSMENT
Assess identified risk factors to determine the degree of risk to the workers. Consult with affected workers and representative sample of other workers who perform the same tasks.

Step 5
RISK CONTROL
Implement control measures, where required, to eliminate or minimize the risk to workers.

Step 6
TRAINING
Train the worker in the use of control measures.

Step 7
EVALUATION
Evaluate control measures to determine their effectiveness to eliminate or minimize the risk of MSI. Where the risk has not been effectively controlled, re-examine the task.

COMMON INDICATORS OF PROBLEMS

Does my company have ergonomic problems? Are injuries and illnesses occurring because too little attention is paid to ergonomic factors? These are questions that modern health and safety professionals should ask themselves. But how does one answer such questions? According to NIOSH, the factors discussed in the following paragraphs can be examined to determine if ergonomic problems exist in a given company.[9]

Apparent Trends in Accidents and Injuries

By examining accident reports and documents such as workers' compensation accident forms, first-aid logs, insurance forms, and other available records of illnesses or injuries, health and safety professionals can identify trends if they exist. A pattern or a high incidence rate of a specific type of injury typically indicates that an ergonomic problem exists.

Monday Morning Syndrome Debunked

More workplace injury claims are filed on Monday than on any other day of the week. More than 23% of all workers' compensation claims are filed on Monday. This has led to a belief that employees are injuring themselves during non-work-related activities over the weekend and filing workers' compensation claims on Monday. The popular belief is that employees who don't carry personal medical insurance use this ploy to gain medical coverage under workers' compensation. However, a study conducted by Brian P. McCall and David Card under the auspices of the National Bureau of Economic Research raises questions about this belief. According to this study, the high incidence of workers' compensation claims filed on Monday can be attributed to such factors as the following:

- Lack of activity over the weekend, coupled with a sudden return to physical work on Monday.

- Effect of cold weather and age on muscles (Monday morning strains and sprains).

Source: Brian P. McCall and David Card, "Is Workers' Compensation Covering Uninsured Medical Costs?" Working Paper No. 5058, National Bureau of Economic Research, Cambridge, MA, 1996, 18.

Incidence of Cumulative Trauma Disorders

Factors associated with CTDs include a high level of repetitive work, greater than normal levels of hand force, awkward posture, high levels of vibration, high levels of mechanical stress, extreme temperatures, and repeated hand-grasping or pinch-gripping. By observing the workplace and people at work, health and safety professionals can determine the amount of exposure that employees have to these factors and the potential for ergonomics-related problems.

Absenteeism and High Turnover Rates

High absentee rates and high turnover rates can be indicators of ergonomic problems. People who are uncomfortable on the job to the point of physical stress are more likely to miss work or leave for less stressful conditions.

Employee Complaints

A high incidence of employee complaints about physical stress or poor workplace design can indicate the presence of ergonomic problems.

Employee-Generated Changes

Employees tend to adapt the workplace to their needs. The presence of many workplace adaptations, particularly those intended to decrease physical stress, can indicate the presence of ergonomic problems. Have employees added padding, modified personal protective equipment, brought in extra lighting, or made other modifications? Such employee-generated changes may be evidence of ergonomic problems.

Poor Quality

Poor quality of work, although not necessarily caused by ergonomic problems, can be the result of such problems. Poor quality of work is an indicator that there may be ergonomic problems and suggests a need for closer inspection.

Manual Material Handling

MANUAL MATERIAL HANDLING
Moving goods or equipment without the aid of machinery.

The incidence of musculoskeletal injuries is typically higher in situations that involve a lot of **manual material handling**. Musculoskeletal injuries increase significantly when the job involves one or more of the following: lifting large objects, lifting bulky objects, lifting objects from the floor, and lifting frequently. When such conditions exist, the company exposes itself to ergonomic problems and therefore needs to place more emphasis on preventing musculoskeletal injuries.

IDENTIFYING SPECIFIC ERGONOMIC PROBLEMS

A task analysis of the job in question can identify specific ergonomic problems. Figure 9–4 lists the types of problems that can be identified by a thorough task analysis.[10]

General Observation

General observation of a worker or workers performing the task(s) in question can be an effective task analysis technique. The effectiveness is usually enhanced if the workers are not aware that they are being observed. When observing employees at work, be especially attentive to tasks requiring manual material handling and repetitive movements.

Questionnaires and Interviews

Questionnaires and interviews can be used for identifying ergonomic problems. Questionnaires are easier to distribute, tabulate, and analyze, but interviews generally provide more in-depth information.

Figure 9–4
Problems that can be pinpointed by a task analysis.

- Tasks that involve potentially hazardous movements
- Tasks that involve frequent manual lifting
- Tasks that involve excessive wasted motion or energy
- Tasks that are part of a poor operations flow
- Tasks that require unnatural or uncomfortable posture
- Tasks with high potential for psychological stress
- Tasks with a high fatigue factor
- Tasks that could or should be automated
- Tasks that involve or lead to quality control problems

Videotaping and Photography

Videotaping technology has simplified the process of task analysis considerably. Videotaping records the work being observed as it is done, it is silent so it is not intrusive, and such capabilities as freeze and playback enhance the observer's analysis capabilities significantly. Photography can also enhance the observer's analysis capabilities by recording each motion or step involved in performing a task. If photography is used, be aware that flashes can be disruptive. High-speed film will allow you to take photographs without using a flash.

Drawing or Sketching

Making a neat sketch of a workstation or a drawing showing workflow can help identify problems. Before using a drawing or sketch as part of a task analysis, make sure that it is accurate. Ask an employee who is familiar with the area or process sketched to check the drawing.

Measuring the Work Environment

Measurements can help identify specific ergonomic problems. How far must a worker carry the material manually? How high does a worker have to lift an object? How much does an object weigh? How often is a given motion repeated? Answers to these and similar questions can enhance the effectiveness of the analysis process.

Understanding the Ergonomics of Aging

When identifying specific ergonomic problems in the workplace, don't overlook the special challenges presented by aging workers. A good ergonomics program adapts the job to the person. Because nearly 30% of the workforce is 45 years of age or older, organizations must be prepared to adapt workstations to employees whose physical needs are different from those of their younger counterparts.

In adapting workstations and processes for employees who are 45 or older, keep the following rules of thumb in mind:

- Nerve conduction velocity, hand-grip strength, muscle mass, range of motion, and flexibility all begin to diminish about age 45.
- Weight and mass tend to increase through about the early fifties.
- Height begins to diminish beginning around age 30.
- Lower back pain is more common in people 45 years of age and older.
- Visual acuity at close range diminishes with age.[11]

These rules of thumb mean that health and safety professionals cannot take a "one-size-fits-all" approach to ergonomics. Adaptations for older workers must be individualized and should take aging factors into account.

ERGONOMIC PROBLEM-SOLVING STRATEGIES

The factors that influence stress were explained earlier in this chapter. These factors can be combined in different ways, and the ways in which they are combined determine the type and amount of stress experienced. For the purpose of recommending ergonomic problem-solving strategies, the following combinations can be used:

- Seated repetitive work with light parts.
- Seated work with larger parts.
- Seated control work.
- Standing work.
- Standing for heavy lifting and/or carrying work in one place or in motion.
- Work with hands above chest height.
- Work with hand tools.
- Work with VDTs.[12]

Seated Repetitive Work with Light Parts

This type of work can produce more physical stress than one may suspect. Back, neck, shoulder, and lower leg pain are commonly associated with this type of work. Some of the problems associated with seated repetitive work are the result of the nature of the job: The fixed work position and repetitive motion can contribute to ergonomic problems. To solve these problems, it may be necessary to modify both the job and the workstation. Improvement strategies include the following:

- Include other work tasks to break the monotony of repetition.
- Use job rotation, with workers rotating through two or more different jobs.
- Adjust the height of the work surface and/or position.
- Use an adjustable chair equipped with hand, wrist, or arm supports as appropriate.
- Make sure that there is sufficient leg room (height, width, and depth).
- Use ergonomic devices to adjust the height and angle of work (see Figure 9–5).[13]

Figure 9–5
Adjust the angle of work to reduce stress.
Source: From a drawing by Robin J. Miller.

Seated Work with Larger Parts

This type of work, which involves interacting with objects that may be too large to manipulate manually, is associated with assembly and welding jobs. Problems associated with this type of work are typically related to posture, illumination, reach, and lifting. Ergonomic strategies for improving work conditions include the following:

- Use technology to lift and position the work for easy access that does not require bending, twisting, and reaching.
- Use supplemental lighting at the worksite.
- Use adjustable chairs and work surfaces as appropriate (see Figure 9–6).[14]

Seated Control Work

This type of work involves sitting in one location and using wheels, levers, knobs, handles, and buttons to control a process, system, or piece of equipment. The physical stress associated with this type of work is typically the result of excessive vibration or bending and twisting to achieve better visibility. Ergonomic strategies for improving work conditions include the following:

- Use an adjustable swivel chair with inflatable back and seat support.
- Provide comfortable and convenient locations for control devices.
- Use control devices that meet the following standards: finger control systems that do not require more than five newtons (1.1 pounds); hand levers that do not exceed 20 newtons (4.5 pounds).
- Position the control seat so that a clear line of sight exists between the work and the person controlling it.
- Provide a ladder if the workstation is more than 35 cm (14 inches) above ground.[15]

▶ **Figure 9–6**
Use adjustable work surfaces to reduce stress.
Source: From a drawing by Robin J. Miller.

Figure 9–7
**Adjust machines or
work surfaces to
reduce stress.**
Source: From a drawing by
Robin J. Miller.

Standing Work

This category includes most jobs that are performed while standing. Such jobs do not involve a great deal of repetitive motion but do involve handling medium to heavy materials. An example is a machine operator's job (lathe, mill, drill, punch, saw, and so on). Physical stress associated with this type of work includes leg, arm, and back strains. Occasionally, side strains occur when bending and twisting are necessary. Ergonomic strategies for improving work conditions include the following:

• Use adjustable machines and work surfaces to ensure the optimum height and position. When the machine height cannot be adjusted, portable platforms can serve the same purpose (Figure 9–7).
• When purchasing new machines, make sure there is a recess at the bottom for feet. This will allow the operator to stand close to the machine without having to bend over. Also, look for machines that have easily accessible controls that fall within a comfortable reach zone for operators.
• Provide ample free space around machines for moving material in and out and to allow for ease of movement in servicing machines.[16]

Standing for Heavy Lifting and Carrying

This type of work involves heavy lifting and moving material while standing. Lifting and moving may be a relatively small part of the job but are required somewhat regularly. The physical stress most commonly associated with this type of work is back and muscle strains resulting from improper lifting. Falls can also be a problem. Ergonomic strategies for improving work conditions include the following:

- Eliminate manual lifting to the extent possible using various lifting and hoisting technologies.
- Where manual lifting is necessary, train workers in proper lifting techniques.
- Provide sufficient room around all objects to allow lifting without twisting.
- Supply the appropriate personal protection equipment such as sure-grip shoes and gloves.
- Keep floors around materials to be lifted clean and dry to prevent slips.
- Do not allow manual carrying of heavy objects on stairs. Stairs increase the physical stress of carrying and, in turn, the potential for injury.[17]

Work with Hands above the Chest

This type of work can be done in either a standing or sitting position. It may or may not involve material handling. Physical stress associated with this type of work includes neck, upper body, and heart strain. Of these, the most potentially dangerous is heart strain. Prolonged work with the arms above the shoulder level requires the heart to work harder to pump blood to the elevated areas. Ergonomic strategies for improving work conditions include the following:

- Eliminate manual lifting to the extent possible by raising the work floor using lifts and various other technologies.
- Use extension arms or poles when the work floor cannot be raised.
- When purchasing new machines, look for machines with controls that are easily accessible below the horizontal plane of a worker's shoulders.[18]

Work with Hand Tools

All of the types of work presented in this section may involve the use of hand tools to some extent. However, because hand tools introduce a variety of potential hazards that are inherent in their use, they are best examined as a separate work type. Physical stresses most commonly associated with the use of hand tools include **carpal tunnel syndrome (CTS)** and muscle strains of the lower

CARPAL TUNNEL SYNDROME (CTS)
An injury to the median nerve inside the wrist.

SAFETY FACT

Back Belts

The controversy over the use of back belts continues as both hard and anecdotal evidence supporting each side of the argument is added to the issue. While the evidence of their benefits may be compelling, NIOSH has come to the following conclusions:

- Back belts should *not* be considered as personal protective equipment.
- Back belts should *not* be recommended for use in occupational situations.

    Their claim is that these belts can increase load on the cardiovascular system; reduce mobility, flexibility, and strength; and produce a false sense of security resulting in an increased risk of lifting heavier loads.

arm, hands, and wrist. Ergonomic strategies for improving the work conditions focus primarily on improving hand positions during the use of tools, enhancing the worker's grip on tools, and minimizing the amount of twisting involved. Following are some of these strategies:

- Select tools that are designed to keep hands in the rest position (palm down, gently curved, thumb outstretched, and knuckle of the index finger higher than that of the little finger).
- Reduce stress on the hand by selecting tools that have thick, rather than thin, handles (a good range for the diameter is 2 cm to 3 cm [0.8 to 1.2 inches]).
- Select tools that have enhanced gripping surfaces on handles such as knurling, filing, or other enhancements.
- To the extent possible, eliminate twisting by selecting tools designed so that the direction of movement or function is the same as the direction in which force is applied or by using technology (e.g., power screwdriver).
- For tools that do not involve twisting, select handles that have an oval-shaped cross section.
- Select tools with handles made of hard, nonpermeable materials that will not absorb toxic liquids that could be harmful to the skin.[19]

Work with VDTs

The video display terminal, primarily because of the all-pervasive integration of personal computers in the workplace, is now the most widely used piece of office equipment. This fact coupled with the ergonomic hazards associated with VDTs has created a whole new range of concerns for health and safety professionals. Using ergonomics to design a workstation will make it easier, safer, more comfortable, and more efficient to use. Following are some strategies that can be used to reduce the hazards associated with VDTs:

- **Arrange the keyboard properly.** It should be located in front of the user, not to the side. Body posture and the angle formed by the arms are critical factors (see Figure 9–8).
- **Adjust the height of the desk.** Taller employees often have trouble working at *average* height desks. Raising the desk with wooden blocks can solve this problem.
- **Adjust the tilt of the keyboard.** The rear portion of the keyboard should be lower than the front.
- **Encourage employees to use a soft touch on the keyboard and when clicking a mouse.** A hard touch increases the likelihood of injury.
- **Encourage employees to avoid wrist resting.** Resting the wrist on any type of edge can increase pressure on the wrist.
- **Place the mouse within easy reach.** Extending the arm to its full reach increases the likelihood of injury.
- **Remove dust from the mouse ball cavity.** Dust can collect, making it difficult to move the mouse. Blowing out accumulated dust once a week will keep the mouse easy to manipulate.
- **Locate the VDT at a proper height and distance.** The VDT's height should be such that the top line on the screen is slightly below eye level. The optimum distance between the VDT and user will vary from employee to employee, but it will usually be between 40 cm and 80 cm (16 and 32 inches).

- **Minimize glare.** Glare from a VDT can cause employees to adopt harmful postures. Changing the location of the VDT, using a screen hood, and closing or adjusting blinds and shades can minimize glare.
- **Reduce lighting levels.** Reducing the lighting level in the area immediately around the VDT can eliminate vision strain.
- **Dust the VDT screen.** VDT screens are magnets to dust. Built-up dust can make the screen difficult to read, contributing to eye strain.
- **Eliminate telephone cradling.** Cradling a telephone receiver between an uplifted shoulder and the neck while typing can cause a painful disorder called **cervical radiculopathy** (compression of the cervical vertebrae in the neck). Employees who need to talk on the telephone while typing should wear a headphone.
- **Require typing breaks.** Continuous typing for extended periods should be avoided. **Repetitive strain injuries** are cumulative. Breaking up the repetitive motion in question (typing and clicking) can help prevent the accumulation of strain.[20]

REPETITIVE STRAIN INJURY (RSI)
A broad and generic term that encompasses a variety of injuries resulting from cumulative trauma to the soft tissues of the body.

Head—Positioned directly over shoulders without straining, about an arm's length from the screen

Neck and Shoulders—Relaxed, without slouching

Back—Upright or inclined slightly forward from the hips; maintain the same spinal curve the back has when standing

Elbows—Relaxed at a 70°–135° angle

Wrist—Relaxed and straight, not angled up or down

Knees—Placed slightly lower than hips

Chair—Sloped slightly forward so knees are in the correct position

0°–60°

70°–135°

Screen—Positioned at eye level or slightly lower

Keyboard—Placed flat, close to elbow-level

Work Surface—Positioned at a height to allow the elbows to be relaxed at a 70°–135° angle; chair may need to be raised to accommodate this

Feet—Planted firmly on the floor. A footrest may be needed for shorter people or high work surfaces

Figure 9–8
Ergonomics of VDTs. The diagram highlights optimal postures and positions for the computer user.

DISCUSSION CASE

What Is Your Opinion?

"We need to bring in an ergonomics consultant. I'm concerned that all of a sudden we are going to begin seeing CTDs and back injuries resulting from some of our new processes and workstations. What do you think?" Mark Patron, Safety Director for Manufacturing Technologies Corporation, thought over the question before answering. "We don't need a consultant. The risk factors for CTDs and back problems are well known in the business. Let me check a couple of reference books and get back to you." Patron sees ergonomic issues as a normal part of his job. His boss thinks an ergonomics expert is needed. What is your opinion?

ECONOMICS OF ERGONOMICS

Perhaps the most under-researched subject relating to ergonomics is the cost effectiveness of health and safety. There are two main reasons for this: (1) such research is often more complex and extensive than the health and safety measures that have been undertaken; and (2) many decision makers think such studies are irrelevant because promoting health and safety is the right thing to do, regardless of costs. As with health and safety in general, there are no in-depth studies available that conclusively pin down the cost benefits of specific ergonomic measures.

According to Bedal,

> Does the application of ergonomic principles make good business sense? The good news is most industry experts believe ergonomics does make good business sense. But the bad news is that if you're looking for studies to prove ergonomics is worth the investment, you'll be hard pressed to find them. Very few true cost–benefit analyses on applying ergonomic principles in an industrial setting have been done.[21]

There is disagreement among well-informed professionals on whether ergonomic improvements should be expected to meet the test of cost–benefit analysis. However, there is growing support for research that will produce reliable data. This point of view is beginning to characterize the outlook of health and safety professionals in government and in academe.[22] Consequently, it is important to understand the problems in attempting to undertake or participate in cost–benefit studies.

Inhibitors of Cost–Benefit Studies

A number of factors inhibit hard research into the economics of ergonomics. Bedal summarizes the most problematic of these:

- Record-keeping systems in industry are not sufficient to support such studies. As a result, a base of comparison from which to work has not been established.
- Industry does not track injuries and illnesses in ways that provide the controls necessary for true hard research. There are no control groups against which to compare groups of injured workers.

High Cost of Pain

The Journal of the American Medical Association in November 2003 published a study that looked at one of those "hidden costs" — that of productivity losses caused by RSI [repetitive strain injury] and other injuries. It found that those who suffer from RSI averaged a loss of some 4.6 hours of productivity per week. The Toronto-based Industrial Accident Prevention Association (IAPA) pegs the cost to employers of workplace related injuries, including RSI, at close to $58 000 per employee.

Source: COS Editorial Team. (June 2004). "The Human Factor." *Canadian Occupational Safety.* [Online]. Available: http://www.industrialsourcebook.com/cgi-bin/archivef.pl?id=726. (Retrieved May 6, 2005).

- It is difficult and sometimes impossible to determine what improvements can be attributed directly to specific ergonomic strategies and what improvements should be attributed to other factors.
- Undertaking hard research studies requires a commitment of both time and money. A longitudinal study of the effects of a given ergonomic improvement may take three to five years to produce reliable data.
- Follow-up evaluations of injuries that summarize the direct and indirect costs do not exist to the extent necessary to contribute to hard research.[23]

These inhibitors cannot be overcome unless industrial firms are willing to invest enormous sums of money and time. Although the data produced by such investments would be valuable, it is generally not perceived as adding to a company's bottom line. Therefore, industry is likely to continue to rely on academe and governmental agencies for research. In today's intensely competitive international marketplace, industry is likely to invest all available funds in efforts that are perceived as improving productivity and quality. Consequently, hard research into the economics of ergonomics may remain a low priority for some time to come.

CUMULATIVE TRAUMA DISORDERS (CTDS)

The personal computer has become an all-pervasive and universal work tool. Jobs from the shop floor to the executive office now involve frequent, repetitive computer use. This means that people in the workplace are typing and clicking at an unprecedented pace. Frequent and, for some, constant computer use have led to an explosion of injuries heretofore seen mostly in the meat-packing industry. Collectively, these injuries are known as **cumulative trauma disorders (CTDs)**.

Definition

CTD is an umbrella term that covers a number of injuries caused by forceful or awkward movements repeated frequently over time. Other aggravating factors include poor posture, an improperly designed workstation, poor tool design,

CUMULATIVE TRAUMA DISORDERS (CTDs)
A term that covers a number of injuries caused by forceful or awkward movements repeated frequently over time.

Ergonomics in Office Automation

Increasing ergonomic problems resulting from office automation are leading to cumulative trauma disorders (CTDs). The types of CTDs occurring most frequently are:

Tendon-Related Disorders

- Tendinitis
- Tenosynovitis
- Stenosing tenosynovitis of the fingers (trigger finger)
- Stenosing tenosynovitis of the thumb (DeQuervain's disease)
- Peridentitis (strain)
- Ganglion cyst
- Lateral epicondylitis (tennis elbow)
- Bicipital tendinitis
- Rotator cuff tendinitis

Peripheral Nerve Entrapment

- Carpal tunnel syndrome
- Guyon tunnel syndrome
- Radial tunnel syndrome
- Pronator teres syndrome
- Cubital tunnel syndrome

Vascular

- Hand-arm vibration syndrome (Raynaud's phenomena)
- Ulnar artery thrombosis

Neurovascular

- Thoracic outlet syndrome

Muscular

- Focal dystonia
- Fibromyositis
- Tension neck syndrome
- Myositis

Joint/Joint Capsule

- Osteoarthritis
- Bursitis
- Synovitis

Source: Courtesy of Unimation, Inc.

and job stress. CTDs occur to the muscles, nerves, and tendons of the hands, arms, shoulders, and neck.

Classifications of CTDs

For years, CTDs have been incorrectly referred to as *carpal tunnel syndrome,* which is actually just one type of CTD. This is like referring to all trees as oaks. Figure 9–9 is a checklist of the most common CTDs organized into four broad classifications.[24]

MUSCLE AND TENDON DISORDERS Tendons connect muscles to bones. They can accommodate very little in the way of stretching and are prone to injury if overused. Overworking a tendon can cause small tears in it. These tears can become inflamed and cause intense pain. This condition is known as **tendinitis.**

TENDINITIS
Painful result of small tears in the tendon from overwork.

Muscle and Tendon Disorders
- ✓ Tendinitis
- ✓ Muscle damage (myofacial)
- ✓ Tenosynovitis
- ✓ Stenosing tenosynovitis
  - • DeQuervain's disease
  - • Trigger finger (flexor tenosynovitis)
- ✓ Shoulder tendinitis
- ✓ Bicipital tendinitis
- ✓ Rotator cuff tendinitis
- ✓ Forearm tendinitis
  - • Flexor carpi radialis tendinitis
  - • Extensor tendinitis
  - • Flexor tendinitis
- ✓ Epicondylitis
- ✓ Ganglion cysts

Cervical Radiculopathy

Tunnel Syndromes
- ✓ Carpal tunnel syndrome
- ✓ Radial tunnel syndrome
- ✓ Sulcus ulnaris syndrome
- ✓ Cubital tunnel syndrome
- ✓ Guyon's canal syndrome

Nerve and Circulation Disorders
- ✓ Thoracic outlet syndrome
- ✓ Raynaud's disease

Figure 9–9
CTD checklist — types of injury by classification.

Myofacial muscle damage can also be caused by overexertion. It manifests itself in soreness that persists even when resting. Muscles may burn and be sensitive to the touch. When sore muscles become inflamed and swell, the symptoms are aggravated even further by nerve compression. Tendons that curve around bones are encased in protective coverings called *sheaths.* Sheaths contain a lubricating substance known as synovial fluid. When tendons rub against the sheath too frequently, friction is produced. The body responds by producing additional synovial fluid. Excess build-up of this fluid can cause swelling which, in turn, causes pressure on the surrounding nerves, causing a condition known as **tenosynovitis**.

TENOSYNOVITIS
A condition resulting from an excess buildup of fluid that causes pressure on the surrounding nerve.

Chronic tenosynovitis is known as *stenosing tenosynovitis* of which there are two types: DeQuervain's disease and flexor tenosynovitis (trigger finger). DeQuervain's disease affects the tendon at the junction of the wrist and thumb. It causes pain when the thumb is moved or when the wrist is twisted. Flexor tenosynovitis involves the locking of a digit in a bent position, hence the term *trigger finger*. However, it can occur in any finger.

Shoulder tendinitis is of two types: bicipital and rotator cuff tendinitis. Bicipital tendinitis occurs at the shoulder joint where the bicep muscle attaches. The rotator cuff is a group of muscles and tendons in the shoulder that move the arm away from the body and turn it in and out. Pitchers in baseball and quarterbacks in football often experience rotator cuff tendinitis.

Forearm tendinitis is of three types: flexor carpi radialis tendinitis, extensor tendinitis, and flexor tendinitis. Flexor carpi radialis tendinitis causes pain in the wrist at the base of the thumb. Extensor tendinitis causes pain in the muscles in the top of the hand, making it difficult to straighten the hands. Flexor tendinitis causes pain in the fingers, making them difficult to bend.

Epicondylitis and *ganglion cysts* are two muscle and tendon disorders. Epicondylitis (lateral) affects the outside of the elbow, whereas epicondylitis (medial) affects the inside. The common term for this disorder is "tennis elbow." Ganglion cysts grow on the tendon, tendon sheath, or synovial lining, typically on top of the hand, on the nail bed, above the wrist, or on the inside of the wrist.

CERVICAL RADICULOPATHY
Compression of the cervical vertebrae in the neck.

CERVICAL RADICULOPATHY This disorder is most commonly associated with holding a telephone receiver on an upraised shoulder while typing. This widely practised act can cause compression of the cervical discs in the neck, making it painful to turn the head. Putting the body in an unnatural posture while using the hands is always dangerous.

TUNNEL SYNDROMES Tunnels are conduits for nerves that are formed by ligaments and other soft tissues. Damage to the soft tissues can cause swelling that compresses the nerves that pass through the tunnel. These nerves are the median, radial, and ulnar nerves that pass through a tunnel in the forearm and wrist. Pain experienced with tunnel injuries can be constant and intense. In addition to pain, people with a tunnel injury might experience numbness, tingling, and a loss of gripping power. The most common **tunnel syndromes** are carpal tunnel syndrome, radial tunnel syndrome, sulcus ulnaris syndrome, cubital tunnel syndrome, and Guyon's canal syndrome.

TUNNEL SYNDROMES
Injuries caused by compression of the nerves passing through a tunnel (a conduit formed by ligaments and other soft tissues)

NERVE AND CIRCULATION DISORDERS When friction or inflammation cause swelling, both nerves and arteries can be compressed, restricting the flow of blood to muscles. This can cause a disorder known as *thoracic outlet syndrome*.

SAFETY FACT

CTDs: Work-Related or Non-Work-Related?
CTDs present a difficult challenge to health and safety professionals on two levels. First, identifying the source of an employee's injury can be difficult because of the interplay of non-work-related activities such as hobbies, playing musical instruments, medications, previous surgeries, hypertension, and other disorders. Second, treatment and rehabilitation can be hindered by outside activities. Consequently, prevention programs should be broad enough to take outside activities into account.

The symptoms of this disorder are pain in the entire arm, numbness, coldness, and weakness in the arm, hand, and fingers.

If the blood vessels in the hands are constricted, *Raynaud's disease* can result. Symptoms include painful sensitivity, tingling, numbness, coldness, and paleness in the fingers. It can affect one or both hands. This disorder is also known as *vibration syndrome* because it is associated with vibrating tools.

CTD RISK FACTORS Some of the risk factors for CTDs of the upper extremities include:

- Repetitive and/or prolonged activities.
- Forceful exertions, usually with the hands (including pinch grips).
- Prolonged static postures.
- Awkward postures of the upper body, including reaching above the shoulders or behind the back, and twisting the wrists and other joints to perform tasks.
- Continued physical contact with work surfaces (soft tissue compression).
- Excessive vibration from power tools.
- Cold temperatures.
- Inappropriate or inadequate tool design.
- High wrist acceleration.
- Fatigue (inadequate recovery time).
- Use of gloves.

Preventing CTDs
The best way to prevent CTDs is proper work design. In addition, it helps to make employees aware of the hazards that can cause it. These hazards include poor posture at the workstation, inappropriate positioning of the hands and arms, a heavy hand on a keyboard or mouse, and any other act that repeatedly puts the body in an unnatural posture while using the hands. Ergonomically sound workstations can help prevent CTDs, especially when they can be modified to fit the individual employee. However, even the best ergonomic design cannot prevent a heavy hand on the keyboard or mouse. Consequently, ergonomics is only part of the answer. Following are some preventive strategies that can be applied in any organization:

1. **Teach employees the warning signs.** CTDs occur cumulatively over time. They sneak up on people. Employees should be aware of the following warning signs: weakness in the hands or forearms, tingling, numbness, heaviness in the hands, clumsiness, stiffness, lack of control over the fingers, cold hands, and tenderness to the touch.

2. **Teach employees how to stretch.** Employees whose jobs involve repetitive motion work such as typing may help prevent CTDs by using stretching exercises. Limbering up the hands and forearms each day before starting work and again after long breaks such as the lunch hour may help eliminate the stress on muscles and tendons that can lead to CTDs. The term "may"

**Figure 9–10
Checklist for safe selection and use of hand tools.**

Use Anthropometric Data

Anthropometric data has to do with human body dimensions. Such data can be used to determine the proper handle length, grip span, tool weight, and trigger length when selecting tools.

Reduce Repetition

Repetition is a hazard that can and should be reduced using such strategies as the following:

- Limit overtime.
- Change the process.
- Provide mechanical assists.
- Require breaks.
- Encourage stretching and strengthening exercises.
- Automate where possible.
- Rotate employees regularly.
- Distribute work among more employees.

Reduce the Force Required

The more force required, the more potential for damage to soft tissue. Required force can be reduced using the following strategies:

- Use power tools wherever possible.
- Use the power grip instead of the pinch grip.
- Spread the force over the widest possible area.
- Eliminate slippery, hard, and sharp gripping surfaces.
- Use jigs and fixtures to eliminate the pinch grip.

Minimize Awkward Postures

Awkward postures contribute to CTDs. The following strategies can reduce posture hazards:

- Keep the wrist in a neutral position.
- Keep elbows close to the body (90°–110° where bent).
- Avoid work that requires overhead reaching.
- Minimize forearm rotation.

is used because the jury is still out as to the efficacy of stretching. There is no consensus in the ergonomics community on this preventive measure.

3. **Teach employees to start slowly.** Long-distance runners typically start slowly, letting their bodies adjust and their breathing find its rhythm. They pick up the pace steadily, until eventually settling in at a competitive pace. This approach is an excellent example of how employees in CTD-prone jobs should work. Teach employees to limber up, then begin slowly and increase their pace gradually.

4. **Avoid the use of wrist splints.** Teach employees to position their hands properly without using wrist splints. Splints can cause the muscles that they support to atrophy, thereby actually increasing the likelihood of problems.

5. **Start an exercise group.** Exercises that strengthen the hands and forearms coupled with exercises that gently stretch hand and forearm muscles may be a preventive measure. Exercises that strengthen the back can help improve posture, and good posture helps prevent CTDs. As with stretching, the jury is still out on the efficacy of exercise as a preventive measure.

6. **Select tools wisely.** Cumulative trauma disorders (CTDs) are most frequently associated with the repetitive use of VDTs and hand tools. Selecting and using hand tools properly can help prevent CTDs. Figure 9–10 is a checklist for the proper selection and use of hand tools. Note that ergonomically designed hand tools will not overcome poor job design. Good job design and proper tool selection, together, are the best strategy.[25]

SUMMARY

1. Ergonomics is a multidisciplinary science that seeks to conform the workplace and all of its physiological aspects to the worker.

2. The word *ergonomics* is derived from the Greek language. *Ergon* means work and *nomos* means laws.

3. Human factors is a science that acts as a bridge between research about human beings and the application of that research to designing products and systems for human beings.

4. Common factors that can influence the amount of physical stress associated with a given job include sitting, standing, demand for strength/power, work area, type of motion, amount of surface contact, and environmental factors.

5. Most jurisdictions in Canada have no specific ergonomic regulations, but rather rely on general practices found in the act or regulations.

6. Common indicators of the existence of ergonomic problems include noticeable trends in accidents and injuries, a high incidence of cumulative trauma disorders (CTDs), absenteeism, high turnover rates, employee complaints, employee-generated changes, poor quality, and a high incidence of manual material handling.

7. Procedures for identifying specific ergonomic problems include general observation, questionnaires, interviews, videotaping, photography, drawing, sketching, and measuring.

8. In devising ergonomic problem-solving strategies, work might be divided into the following categories: seated repetitive work with light parts, seated work with larger parts, seated control work, standing work, standing work with heavy lifting or carrying work from place to place, work with hands above chest height, and work with hand tools.

9. There are two reasons why little hard research has been conducted concerning the economics of ergonomics: (1) the cost of such research is often more than the ergonomic improvements that were made; and (2) many people feel that ergonomic improvements should not have to be justified on the basis of cost effectiveness.

KEY TERMS AND CONCEPTS

Cervical radiculopathy	Repetitive motion
Cumulative trauma disorders (CTDs)	Tendinitis
Environmental factors	Tenosynovitis
Ergonomics	Tunnel syndromes
Horizontal work area	Vertical work area
Manual material handling	

REVIEW QUESTIONS

1. Define the term *ergonomics.* Explain its origins.

2. Explain how the following opposing factors can influence the amount of physical stress associated with a job: sitting versus standing, large versus small demand for strength/power, nonrepetitive versus repetitive motion.

3. Explain the concept of human factors and how it relates to ergonomics.

4. Define the term *CTD.* Describe the most common types.

5. List five risk factors associated with CTDs.

6. List and briefly explain three common indicators of the existence of ergonomic problems.

7. Describe three approaches that can be used to pinpoint specific ergonomic problems.

8. Describe an ergonomic problem-solving strategy for each of the following types of work: seated repetitive work with light parts, work with hands above chest height, and work with hand tools.

9. Explain why so little hard research has been done concerning the economics of ergonomics.

WEBLINKS

Canadian Centre for Occupational Health and Safety (CCOHS)
www.ccohs.ca/oshanswers/ergonomics/

Canada's national occupational health and safety resource has available information on numerous ergonomic issues facing Canadian workers.

Worksafe BC
http://ergonomics.healthandsafetycentre.org/s/Home.asp

On this site, one can see Canada's most comprehensive and progressive ergonomics legislation and programs that are administered by the Workers' Compensation Board of BC.

ENDNOTES

1. P. Tillman and B. Tillman, *Human Factors Essentials* (New York: McGraw-Hill, 1991), 3–22.
2. Ibid., 3–4.
3. Ibid., 9.
4. Ibid., 12–13.
5. Ibid., 21–22.
6. Swedish Work Environment Fund, *Making the Job Easier: An Ergonomics Idea Book* (Chicago: National Safety Council, 1998), 1–5.
7. Government of Canada, HRSDC. (April 28, 2003). "Occupational Injury Statistics by Selected Variables." [Online]. Available: http://www.hrsdc.gc.ca/asp/gateway.asp?hr=/en/lp/lo/ohs/statistics/naosh/2.shtml&hs=oxs#2.3. (Retrieved March 2, 2005).
8. Wilfred List. (June 2004). "Musculoskeletal Injuries in Need of Regulation." *Canadian Occupational Safety.* [Online]. Available: http://www.industrialsourcebook.com/cgi-bin/archivef.pl?id=723. (Retrieved August 20, 2004).
9. National Institute for Occupational Health and Safety (NIOSH), "Elements of Ergonomics Programs," [Online]. Available: http://www.cdc.gov/niosh.
10. Ibid., 12.
11. S. Minter, "Ergonomic Challenge: The Aging Workforce," *Occupational Hazards* 64, no. 9 (September 2002): 6.
12. NIOSH, "Elements of Ergonomics Programs," 13–14.
13. Ibid., 14.
14. Ibid., 15.
15. NIOSH, 16.
16. Ibid., 17.
17. Ibid., 18.
18. Ibid., 19.
19. Ibid., 20.
20. Roberta Carson, "Ergonomic Innovations: Free to a Good Company," *Occupational Hazards* (January 1996): 61–64.
21. T. Bedal, "The Economics of Ergonomics: What Are the Paybacks?", *Safety & Health,* 142, no. 4: 34.
22. Ibid., 38.
23. Ibid., 39.
24. Emil Pascarelli and Deborah Quilter, *Repetitive Strain Injury* (New York: Wiley, 1994), 49–62.
25. Roberta Carson, "Ergonomically Designed Tools," *Occupational Hazards* (September 1995): 50.

10 Mechanical Hazards and Machine Safeguarding

CHAPTER

LEARNING OBJECTIVES

- List five common mechanical injuries.
- Describe one method of risk assessment in machine operation.
- List the requirements for all safeguards.
- Describe three types of point-of-operation guards.
- Explain, using examples, how point-of-operation devices protect workers.
- Describe the key components of a machine guarding self-assessment.
- Describe the benefits of feeding and ejection systems.
- Describe the hazards created by robots and their effective safeguards.
- Outline the key components of a hazardous energy control system (lockout/tagout systems).
- Create a list of general precautions that apply to machines.
- List the minimum content of a company's machine safeguarding program.

Failure to provide proper machine guards and enforce their use can be costly for companies. Ford of Canada was fined $400 000 in 1999 for two violations of the Ontario Health and Safety Act that resulted in the death of Richard Nemeth. Ford plead guilty to failing to provide adequate machine guarding and failing to exercise due diligence.[1] Mechanical hazards that are not properly guarded are implicated in thousands of workplace injuries every year.

MECHANICAL HAZARDS
Those associated with power-driven machines, whether automated or manually operated.

Mechanical hazards are those associated with power-driven machines, whether automated or manually operated. Concerns about mechanical hazards date back to the Industrial Revolution and the earliest days of mechanization.

Machines driven by steam, hydraulic, or electric power introduced new hazards into the workplace. In spite of advances in safeguarding technologies and techniques, mechanical hazards are still a major concern today. In addition, automated machines have introduced new concerns.

COMMON MECHANICAL INJURIES

In an industrial setting, people interact with machines that are designed to drill, cut, shear, punch, chip, staple, stitch, abrade, shape, stamp, and slit such materials as metals, composites, plastics, and elastomers. If appropriate safeguards are not in place or if workers fail to follow safety precautions, these machines can apply the same procedures to humans. When this happens, the types of **mechanical injuries** that result are typically the result of cutting, tearing, shearing, crushing, breaking, straining, or puncturing (see Figure 10–1).

Cutting and Tearing

A cut occurs when a body part comes in contact with a sharp edge. The human body's outer layer consists of the following, starting from the outside: *epidermis*, the tough outer covering of the skin; *dermis*, the greatest part of the skin's thickness; *capillaries*, the tiny blood vessels that branch off the small arteries and veins in the dermis; *veins*, the blood vessels that collect blood from the capillaries and return it to the heart; and *arteries*, the larger vessels that carry blood from the heart to the capillaries in the skin. The seriousness of **cutting** or **tearing** the skin depends on how much damage is done to the skin, veins, arteries, muscles, and even bones.

Shearing

To understand what **shearing** is, think of a paper cutter. It shears the paper. Power-driven shears for severing paper, metal, plastic, elastomers, and com-

MECHANICAL INJURIES
Injuries that have occurred due to misuse of a power-driven machine.

CUTTING
Occurs when a body part comes in contact with a sharp edge.

SHEARING
Results from forces being applied to a body by two contacting parts moving parallel to the plane of contact.

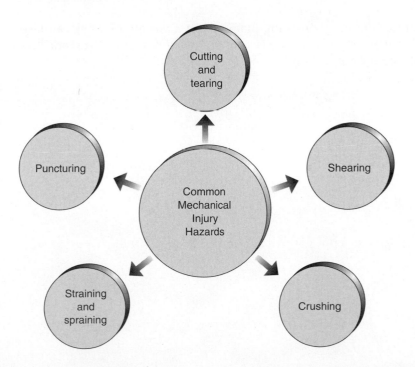

▶ **Figure 10–1**
Some common mechanical hazards.

posite materials are widely used in manufacturing. In times past, such machines often amputated fingers and hands. Such tragedies typically occurred when operators reached under the shearing blade to make an adjustment or placed materials there and activated the blade before fully removing their hand. Safeguards against shearing accidents are explained later in this chapter.

Crushing

CRUSHING

Occurs when a part of the body is caught between two hard surfaces that progressively move together, thereby crushing anything between them.

Injuries from **crushing** can be particularly debilitating, painful, and difficult to heal. They occur when a part of the body is caught between two hard surfaces that progressively move together, thereby crushing anything between them. Crushing hazards can be divided into two categories: *squeeze-point* types and *run-in points*.

Squeeze-point hazards exist where two hard surfaces, at least one of which must be in motion, push close enough together to crush any object that may be between them. The process can be slow, as in a manually operated vise, or fast, as with a metal-stamping machine.

Run-in point hazards exist where two objects, at least one of which is rotating, come progressively closer together. Any gap between them need not become completely closed. It need only be smaller than the object or body part lodged in it. Meshing gears and belt pulleys are examples of run-in point hazards (see Figures 10–2, 10–3, and 10–4).

Body parts can also be crushed in other ways, for example, a heavy object falling on a foot or a hammer hitting a finger. However, these are impact hazards, which are covered in Chapter 11.

Breaking

Machines used to deform engineering materials in a variety of ways can also cause broken bones. A break in a bone is known as a *fracture*. Fractures are classified as simple, compound, complete, and incomplete.

Figure 10–2
This nip point can pull hands, feet, or articles of clothing.

Nip point

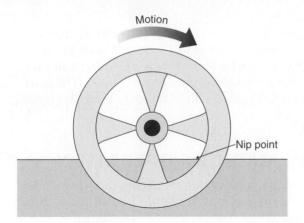

▶ **Figure 10–3**
Fingers might get caught between the bench top and the revolving wheel.

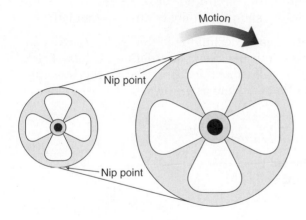

▶ **Figure 10–4**
Nip points can catch fingers, hands, hair, clothing, etc. with dangerous results.

A simple fracture is a break in a bone that does not pierce the skin. A compound fracture is a break that has broken through the surrounding tissue and skin. A complete fracture divides the affected bone into two or more separate pieces. An incomplete fracture leaves the affected bone in one piece but cracked.

Fractures are also classified as transverse, oblique, and comminuted. A transverse fracture is a break straight across the bone. An oblique fracture is diagonal. A comminuted fracture exists when the bone is broken into a number of small pieces at the point of fracture.

Straining and Spraining

There are numerous situations in an industrial setting when **straining** of muscles or **spraining** of ligaments is possible. A strain results when muscles are overstretched or torn. A sprain is the result of torn ligaments in a joint. Strains and sprains can cause swelling and intense pain.

STRAIN
The result of over-stretched or torn muscles.

SPRAIN
The result of torn ligaments.

PUNCTURING
Results when an object penetrates straight into the body and pulls straight out, creating a wound in the shape of the penetrating object.

Puncturing

Punching machines that have sharp tools can puncture a body part if safety precautions are not observed or if appropriate safeguards are not in place. **Puncturing** results when an object penetrates straight into the body and pulls straight out, creating a wound in the shape of the penetrating object. The greatest hazard with puncture wounds is the potential for damage to internal organs.

RISK ASSESSMENT IN MACHINE OPERATION

RISK ASSESSMENT
The process of quantifying the level of risk.

Risk assessment in this context is the process of quantifying the level of risk associated with the operation of a given machine. It should be a structured and systematic process that answers the following four specific questions:

- How *severe* are potential injuries?
- How *frequently* are employees exposed to the potential hazards?
- What is the *possibility* of avoiding the hazard if it does occur?
- What is the *likelihood* of an injury should a safety control system fail?[2]

The most widely used risk-assessment technique is the decision tree, coupled with codes representing these four questions and defined levels of risk. Figure 10–5 is an example of a risk-assessment decision tree. In this example, the codes and their associated levels of risk are as follows:

S = Severity

Question 1: Severity of potential injuries

S1   Slight injury (bruise, abrasion)
S2   Severe injury (amputation or death)

F = Frequency

Question 2: Frequency of exposure to potential hazards

F1   Infrequent exposure
F2   From frequent to continuous exposure

SAFETY FACT

Failure to Properly Guard Machines Can Be Expensive

Failure to properly guard machines can be costly to employers and tragic to employees. On April 10, 2000, Crossley Carpets received one of the largest fines ever for an occupational health and safety offence in Nova Scotia. On April 6, 1999, Sheila Gamble, married with two teenage children, was pulled into a carpet machine at the Crossley Carpet Mills plant in Truro, Nova Scotia, and was crushed to death. The judge in the case issued a fine of $75 000 to the company for failing to provide safeguarding that would have prevented the tragedy.[3]

P = Possibility

Question 3: Possibility of avoiding the hazard if it does occur

P1   Possible
P2   Less possible to not possible

L = Likelihood

Question 4: Likelihood that the hazard will occur

L1   Highly unlikely
L2   Unlikely
L3   Highly likely

Risk Levels

Associated risk factors ranging from lowest (B) to highest (4)

By applying the decision tree in Figure 10–5 or a similar device, the risk associated with the operation of a given machine can be quantified. This allows safety personnel to assign logical priorities for machine safeguarding and hazard prevention.

REQUIREMENTS FOR ALL SAFEGUARDS

The various machine motions present in modern industry involve mechanisms that rotate, reciprocate, or do both. This equipment includes tools, bits, chucks, blades, spokes, screws, gears, shafts, belts, and a variety of different types of stock. Safeguards can be devised to protect workers from harmful contact with such mechanisms while at the same time allowing work to progress at a productive rate. The National Safety Council has established the following requirements for safeguards.

1. **Prevent contact.** Safeguards should prevent human contact with any potentially harmful machine part. The prevention extends to machine operators and any other person who might come in contact with the hazard.

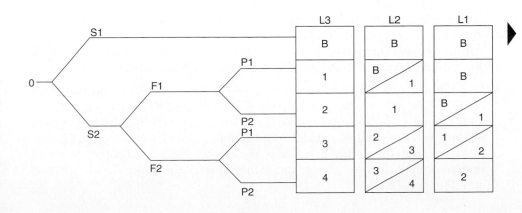

**Figure 10–5
Risk-assessment
decision tree.**

2. **Be secure and durable.** Safeguards should be attached so that they are secure. This means that workers cannot render them ineffective by tampering with or disabling them. This is critical because removing safeguards in an attempt to speed production is a common practice. Safeguards must also be durable enough to withstand the rigours of the workplace. Worn-out safeguards won't protect workers properly.

3. **Protect against falling objects.** Objects falling onto moving machine mechanisms increase the risk of accidents, property damage, and injury. Objects that fall on a moving part can be quickly hurled out, creating a dangerous projectile. Therefore, safeguards must do more than just prevent human contact. They must also shield the moving parts of machines from falling objects.

4. **Create no new hazard.** Safeguards should overcome the hazards in question without creating new ones. For example, a safeguard with a sharp edge, unfinished surface, or protruding bolts introduces new hazards while protecting against the old.

5. **Create no interference.** Safeguards can interfere with the progress of work if they are not properly designed. Such safeguards are likely to be disregarded or disabled by workers feeling the pressure of production deadlines.

6. **Allow safe maintenance.** Safeguards should be designed to allow the more frequently performed maintenance tasks (e.g., lubrication) to be accomplished without the removal of guards. For example, locating the oil reservoir outside the guard with a line running to the lubrication point will allow for daily maintenance without removing the guard.[4]

The design and construction of safeguards are highly specialized activities requiring a strong working knowledge of machines, production techniques, and safety. It is critical that all of the factors explained in this section be considered and accommodated during the design process.

POINT-OF-OPERATION GUARDS

POINT-OF-OPERATION GUARDS
Machine guards that provide protection right at the point where the user operates the machine.

FIXED GUARDS
Provide a permanent barrier between workers and the point of operation.

INTERLOCKED GUARDS
Shut down the machine when the guard is not securely in place or is disengaged.

Guards are most effective when used at the point of operation, which is where hazards to humans exist. Point-of-operation hazards are those caused by the shearing, cutting, or bending motions of a machine. Pinch-point hazards result from guiding material into a machine or transferring motion (e.g., from gears, pressure rollers, or chains and sprockets). Single-purpose safeguards, because they guard against only one hazard, typically are permanently fixed and non-adjustable. Multiple-purpose safeguards, which guard against more than one hazard, typically are adjustable.[5]

Point-of-operation guards are of three types, each with its own advantages and limitations: fixed, interlocked, and adjustable (Figure 10–6).

- **Fixed guards** provide a permanent barrier between workers and the point of operation. They offer the following advantages: They are suitable for many specific applications, can be constructed in-plant, require little maintenance and are suitable for high-production, repetitive operations. Limitations include the following: They sometimes limit visibility, are often limited to specific operations, and sometimes inhibit normal cleaning and maintenance.

- **Interlocked guards** shut down the machine when the guard is not securely in place or is disengaged. The main advantage of this type of guard is that it allows safe access to the machine for removing jams or conducting routine maintenance without the need for taking off the guard. There are also limitations. Interlocked guards require careful adjustment and maintenance and, in some cases, can be easily disengaged.
- **Adjustable guards** provide a barrier against a variety of different hazards associated with different production operations. They have the advantage of flexibility. However, they do not provide as dependable a barrier as other guards do, and they require frequent maintenance and careful adjustment.

Figures 10–7 through 10–12 show various guards used in modern manufacturing settings.

POINT-OF-OPERATION DEVICES

A number of different point-of-operation devices can be used to protect workers. The most widely used are explained in the following paragraphs.

- **Photoelectric devices** are optical devices that shut down the machine whenever the light field is broken. These devices allow operators relatively free movement. They do have limitations, including the following: They do not protect against mechanical failure, they require frequent calibration, and they can be used only with machines that can be stopped.
- **Radio-frequency devices** are capacitance devices that brake the machine if the capacitance field is interrupted by a worker's body or another object. These devices have the same limitations as photoelectric devices.
- **Electromechanical devices** are contact bars that allow only a specified amount of movement between the worker and the hazard. If the worker moves the contact bar beyond the specified point, the machine will not cycle. These devices have the limitation of requiring frequent maintenance and careful adjustment.
- **Pullback devices** pull the operator's hands out of the danger zone when the machine starts to cycle. These devices eliminate the need for auxiliary barriers. However, they also have limitations. They limit operator movement,

ADJUSTABLE GUARDS
Devices that provide a barrier against a variety of different hazards associated with different production operations.

PHOTOELECTRIC DEVICES
Optional devices that shut down the machine any time the light field is broken.

RADIO-FREQUENCY DEVICES
Capacitance devices that brake the machine if the capacitance field is interrupted by a worker's body or another object.

ELECTROMECHANICAL DEVICES
Contact bars that allow only a specified amount of movement between the worker and the hazard.

PULLBACK DEVICES
Pull the operator's hands out of the danger zone when the machine starts to cycle.

▶ Figure 10–6
Point-of-operation guards.

Figure 10–7
Series 12 PRO-TECH-TOR GATE GUARD used on an open-back power press.
Source: Courtesy of PROTECH SYSTEMS.

Figure 10–8
Series 17 CHECKMATE RIVET GUARD used on a foot-operated riveting machine.
Source: Courtesy of PROTECH SYSTEMS.

RESTRAINT DEVICES
Hold back the operator from the danger zone.

SAFETY TRIP DEVICES
Include trip wires, trip rods, and body bars that stop the machine when tripped.

TWO-HAND CONTROLS
Require the operator to use both hands concurrently to activate the machine.

must be adjusted for each individual operator, and require close supervision to ensure proper use.

• **Restraint devices** hold the operator back from the danger zone. They work well, with little risk of mechanical failure. However, they do limit the operator's movement, must be adjusted for each individual operator, and require close supervision to ensure proper use.

• **Safety trip devices** include trip wires, trip rods, and body bars. All of these devices stop the machine when tripped. They have the advantage of simplicity. However, they are limited in that all controls must be activated manually. They protect only the operator and may require the machine to be fitted with special fixtures for holding work.

• **Two-hand controls** require the operator to use both hands concurrently to activate the machine (e.g., a paper cutter or metal-shearing machine). This ensures that hands cannot stray into the danger zone. Although these controls do an excellent job of protecting the operator, they do not protect

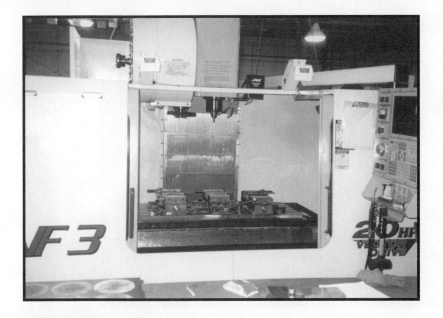

▶ **Figure 10–9**
**When the doors
are opened, the
milling tool stops
automatically.**

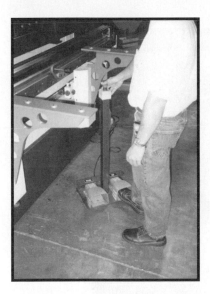

▶ **Figure 10–10**
**In order for this shear-
ing machine to cut,
both the foot pedal
and the hand button
must be engaged.**

onlookers or passers-by. In addition, some two-hand controls can be tampered with and made operable using only one hand.

• **Gates** provide a barrier between the danger zone and workers. Although
they are effective at protecting operators from machine hazards, they can
obscure the work, making it difficult for the operator to see.[6]

GATES

Provide a barrier between
the danger zone and
workers.

Figure 10–13 is a point-of-operation device that shuts down the machine
when an operator's hand breaks a light beam. How quickly will the machine
shut down? The stopping distance equation is as follows:

$$SD = \text{Stoptime [seconds} \times \text{hand speed constant 63"/second]}$$

Figure 10–11
This door protects the operator in the event of an exploding or shattering grinding wheel.

Figure 10–12
The safety door on this drilling machine must be closed or the drill will not operate.

MACHINE GUARDING SELF-ASSESSMENT

One of the most effective ways to ensure that machines are properly guarded is to conduct periodic self-assessments. These self-assessments can be conducted by safety personnel, supervisors, or employees. Developing self-assessment criteria and encouraging supervisors and employees to use them daily is an excellent strategy for health and safety professionals. The following questions can be used for conducting machine guarding self-assessments:

▶ **Figure 10–13**
Series 25 EAGLE EYE INFRA-RED LIGHT BARRIER.
A point-of-operation guarding system on a roller press machine.
Source: Courtesy of PROTECH SYSTEMS.

1. Are all machines that might expose people to rotating parts, nip points, flying chips, sparks, flying particles, or other similar hazards properly guarded?

2. Are all mechanical power transmission belts and the nip points they create properly guarded?

3. Are all exposed power shafts located less than seven feet above the working level properly guarded?

4. Are all hand tools and other hand-operated equipment inspected regularly for hazardous conditions?

5. Is compressed air used to clean tools, machines, equipment, and parts reduced to less than 200 kilopascals or 30 pounds per square inch (psi)?

6. Are power saws and similar types of equipment properly guarded?

7. Are the tool rests for grinding wheels set to within three millimetres or less of the grinding wheel?

8. Are hand tools regularly inspected on a systematic basis for burred ends, cracked handles, and other potentially hazardous conditions?

9. Are all compressed gas cylinders inspected regularly and systematically for obvious signs of defects, deep rusting, or leakage?

10. Do all employees who handle and store gas cylinders and valves know how to do so without causing damage?

11. Are all air receivers periodically and systematically inspected, including safety valves?

12. Are all safety valves tested regularly, systematically, and frequently?[7]

The Canadian Auto Workers (CAW), Health and Safety Department provides a thorough machine guarding checklist as reproduced in Figure 10–14.

FEEDING AND EJECTION SYSTEMS

Feeding and ejection systems can be effective safeguards if properly designed and used. The various types of feeding and ejection systems available for use with modern industrial machines are summarized as follows:

AUTOMATIC FEED
A system that feeds stock to the machine from rolls.

SEMIAUTOMATIC FEED
A system that uses a variety of approaches for feeding stock to the machine.

AUTOMATIC EJECTION
A system that ejects work pneumatically and mechanically.

SEMIAUTOMATIC EJECTION
A system that ejects the work using mechanisms that are activated by the operator.

- **Automatic feed** systems feed stock to the machine from rolls. Automatic feeds eliminate the need for operators to enter the danger zone. Such systems are limited in the types and variations of stock that they can feed. They also typically require an auxiliary barrier guard and frequent maintenance.
- **Semiautomatic feed** systems use a variety of approaches for feeding stock to the machine. Prominent among these are chutes, moveable dies, dial feeds, plungers, and sliding bolsters. They have the same advantages and limitations as automatic feed systems.
- **Automatic ejection** systems eject the work pneumatically or mechanically. The advantage of either approach is that operators don't have to reach into the danger zone to retrieve workpieces. However, these systems are restricted to use with relatively small stock. Potential hazards include blown chips or debris and noise. Pneumatic ejectors can be quite loud.[8]
- **Semiautomatic ejection** systems eject the work using mechanisms that are activated by the operator. Consequently, the operator does not have to reach into the danger zone to retrieve workpieces. These systems do require auxiliary barriers and can be used with a limited variety of stock.

ROBOT SAFEGUARDS

Robots have become commonplace in modern industry. The health and safety concerns relating to robots are covered in Chapter 24. Only the guarding aspects of robot safety are covered in this section. The main hazards associated with robots are (1) entrapment of a worker between a robot and a solid surface, (2) impact with a moving robot arm, and (3) impact with objects ejected or dropped by the robot.

WORK ENVELOPE
The total area within which the moving parts of a robot actually move.

The best guard against these hazards is to erect a physical barrier around the entire perimeter of a robot's **work envelope** (the three-dimensional area established by the robot's full range of motion). This physical barrier should be able to withstand the force of the heaviest object that a robot could eject.

Various types of shutdown guards can also be used. A guard containing a sensing device that automatically shuts down the robot if any person or object enters its work envelope can be effective. Another approach is to put sensitized doors or gates in the perimeter barrier that automatically shut down the robot as soon as they are opened.

CHAPTER 10   Mechanical Hazards and Machine Safeguarding   **175**

Machine Guarding Checklist

GUARDING REQUIREMENTS

1. Do the guards prevent workers' hands, arms, and other body parts from making contact with dangerous moving parts?

   Yes ☐   No ☐

2. Are the guards firmly secured and not easily removable?

   Yes ☐   No ☐

3. Do the guards ensure that no objects will fall into the moving parts or explode out?

   Yes ☐   No ☐

4. Do the guards permit safe, comfortable, and relatively easy operation of the machine?

   Yes ☐   No ☐

5. Can the machine be oiled or greased without removing the guard?

   Yes ☐   No ☐

6. Does the machine automatically shut down when the guard is removed?

   Yes ☐   No ☐

7. Can the existing guards be improved?

   Yes ☐   No ☐

MECHANICAL HAZARDS

The point-of-operation:

1. Is there a point-of operation guard provided for the machine?

   Yes ☐   No ☐

2. Does it keep the operator's hands, fingers, body out of the danger area?

   Yes ☐   No ☐

3. Is there evidence that the guards have been tampered with or removed?

   Yes ☐   No ☐

4. Could you suggest a more practical, effective guard?

   Yes ☐   No ☐

5. Could changes be made on the machine to eliminate the point-of-operation hazard entirely?

   Yes ☐   No ☐

Power transmission apparatus:

1. Are there any unguarded gears, sprockets, pulleys or flywheels on the apparatus?

   Yes ☐   No ☐

2. Are there any exposed belts or chain drives?

   Yes ☐   No ☐

3. Are there any exposed set screws, key ways, collars, etc.?

   Yes ☐   No ☐

4. Are starting and stopping controls within easy reach of the operator?

   Yes ☐   No ☐

5. If there is more than one operator, are separate controls provided?

   Yes ☐   No ☐

Other moving parts:

1. Are guards provided for all hazardous moving parts of the machine, including auxiliary parts?

   Yes ☐   No ☐

(continued)

Figure 10–14
Machine guarding checklist.
Source: CAW Health and Safety Department.

EDUCATION AND TRAINING

1. Do operators and skilled trades workers have the necessary education and training in how to use the guards?

   Yes ❏   No ❏

2. Does the education include examples of workers in your workplace or elsewhere who might have lost their life or their limbs from lack of machine guarding?

   Yes ❏   No ❏

3. Have production workers and skilled trades workers been trained in where the guards are located, how they provide protection, and what hazards they protect against?

   Yes ❏   No ❏

4. Have production workers and skilled trades workers been trained in how and under what circumstances guards can be removed?

   Yes ❏   No ❏

5. Have workers been trained in the procedure to follow if they notice guards that are damaged, missing or inadequate?

   Yes ❏   No ❏

6. Do skilled trades workers have the necessary education and training in how to build the safety aspects of guards?

   Yes ❏   No ❏

PROTECTIVE EQUIPMENT AND PROPER CLOTHING

1. Is protective equipment required?

   Yes ❏   No ❏

2. If protective equipment is required, is it appropriate for the job, in good condition, kept clean and sanitary, and stored carefully when not in use?

   Yes ❏   No ❏

3. Is the operator dressed safely for the job (no loose fitting clothing or jewelry)?

   Yes ❏   No ❏

MACHINE MAINTENANCE AND REPAIR

- Have skilled trades workers received up-to-date instruction on the machines they service?

   Yes ❏   No ❏

- Do skilled trades workers lock out the machine from all of its energy sources before beginning repairs?

   Yes ❏   No ❏

- Is the maintenance equipment itself properly guarded?

   Yes ❏   No ❏

These types of safeguards are especially important because robots can be deceptive. A robot that is not moving at the moment may simply be at a stage between cycles. Without warning, it might make sudden and rapid movements that could endanger any person inside the work envelope.

CONTROL OF HAZARDOUS ENERGY (LOCKOUT/TAGOUT SYSTEMS)

The specific requirements for lockout/tagout systems may be found in the industrial regulations for most jurisdictions in Canada. However, when prosecuting employers for failing to meet the health and safety requirements, the legal team will frequently refer to sections of the legislation dealing with "due diligence." Progressive companies will often adopt the standards of the CSA, ANSI (the American National Standards Institute), or other international agencies as a minimum requirement for lockout/tagout procedures. The lockout/tagout standards identify the proper procedures for shutting down machines and equipment and locking or tagging it out so that accidental or inadvertent activation does not occur.

Lockout/Tagout Language

The following terms and phrases are frequently used in the language of **lockout/tagout**. All health and safety professionals should know and understand these terms:

LOCKOUT/TAGOUT SYSTEM
A system for incapacitating a machine until it can be made safe to operate. "Lockout" means physically locking up the machine so that it cannot be used without removing the lock. "Tagout" means applying a tag that warns employees not to operate the machine in question.

Affected employee. Employees who perform their jobs in areas in which the procedure in question is implemented and in which serving or maintenance operations are performed. Affected employees do not implement energy control procedures unless they are *authorized*.

Authorized employee. Employees who perform service or maintenance on a machine and use lockout/tagout procedures for their own protection.

Energized. Machines, equipment, and tools are energized if they are connected to an energy source or when they still contain stored or residual energy even after being disconnected.

Capable of being locked out. A device is considered to be capable of being locked out if it meets one of the following requirements: (1) it has a hasp to which a lock can be attached; (2) it has another appropriate integral part through which a lock can be attached; (3) it has a built-in locking mechanism; or (4) it can be locked without permanently dismantling, rebuilding, or replacing the energy-isolating device.

Energy-isolating device. Any mechanical device that physically prevents the release or transmission of energy (e.g., circuit breakers, disconnect switches, blocks, etc.).

Energy source. Any source of power that can activate a machine or piece of equipment (e.g., electrical, mechanical, hydraulic, pneumatic, chemical, thermal, etc.).

Energy control procedure. A written document containing all of the information an authorized person needs to know in order to properly control hazardous energy when shutting down a machine or equipment for maintenance or service.

Energy control program. A systematic program for preventing the accidental or inadvertent energizing of machines or equipment during maintenance or servicing. This is sometimes called the organization's lockout/tagout program.

Lockout. Placing a lockout device such as a padlock on an energy-isolating device to prevent the accidental or inadvertent energizing of a machine during maintenance or servicing.

Lockout device. Any device (see Figure 10–15) that uses a positive means to keep an energy-isolation device in the *safe* position to prevent the accidental or inadvertent energizing of a machine or piece of equipment.

Tagout. Placing a tag (see Figure 10–16) on an energy-isolation device to warn people so that they do not accidentally or inadvertently energize a machine or piece of equipment.

Tagout device. Any prominent warning device such as a tag that can be affixed to an energy-isolation device to prevent the accidental or inadvertent energizing of a machine or piece of equipment.

Evaluating Lockout/Tagout Programs

Lockout/tagout violations are frequently cited during on-site inspections. The following questions can be used to evaluate an organization's lockout/tagout program:

- Are all machinery or equipment capable of movement required to be de-energized or disengaged and blocked or locked out during cleaning, servicing, adjusting, or setting up operations?

Figure 10–15
Lockout system.

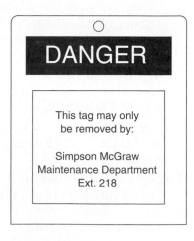

Figure 10–16
Tagout system.

Machines That Are Not Properly Locked Out Can Kill

Failure to properly lock out machines can be fatal. It was in the case of 18-year-old David Ellis, who was killed when he was pulled into an industrial dough mixer on the second day of his short term job in a bakery. Like too many young temporary employees, David had been given no safety training and was unaware of the potential hazards in his job. David's father Rob has become a well known ambassador in making workplaces safer, particularly for young workers.

- Where the power disconnect equipment does not disconnect the electrical control circuit, are the appropriate electrical enclosures identified?
- If the power disconnect for equipment does not disconnect the electrical control circuit, is a means provided to ensure that the control circuit can be disconnected and locked out?
- Is it required to lock out main power disconnects instead of locking out control circuits?
- Are all equipment control valve handles equipped with a means for locking out?
- Does the lockout procedure require that stored energy — whether it is mechanical, hydraulic, or air — be released or blocked before the equipment is locked out for repairs?
- Are appropriate employees provided with individually keyed personal safety locks?
- Are these employees required to keep personal control of their keys while they have safety locks in use?

What Is Your Opinion?

John Martin, Director of Manufacturing, is not happy with his colleague Pete Chang who is Director of Health and Safety at Robbins Engineering Corporation. Chang has ordered two machines in the Manufacturing Department *tagged out* until point-of-operation guards are replaced. The machining supervisor, in an attempt to increase output, had his machinists remove the guards. As a result, there have been several minor injuries and a couple of more serious near misses. The issue is short term productivity versus the health and safety of employees. What is your opinion on this issue?

- Is only the employee exposed to the hazard required to install or remove the safety lock?
- Are employees required to check the safety lockout by attempting a startup after making sure no one is exposed?
- After the safety is checked, does the employee again place the switch in the "off" position?
- Are employees instructed always to push the control circuit stop button before re-energizing the main power switch?
- Are all employees who are working on locked-out equipment identified by their locks or accompanying tags?
- Are enough accident prevention signs, tags, and safety padlocks provided for any reasonably foreseeable repair emergency?
- When machine operations, configuration, or size require the operator to leave his or her control station to install tools or perform other operations, is he or she required to lock or tag out separately any parts of the machine that could move if accidentally activated?
- If the equipment or lines cannot be shut down, locked out, and tagged, is a safe job procedure established and rigidly followed?
- Have employees been trained not to start machinery or equipment if it is locked out or tagged out?
- Are all workers notified when the machinery or equipment they usually use is shut down and locked out for maintenance or servicing purposes?
- After maintenance is completed, is the machinery checked to ensure that nonessential items have been removed and the machine is operationally intact?
- Before the machinery is activated, are employees removed from possible danger?
- When the machinery is fully operational, are employees notified?[9]

GENERAL PRECAUTIONS

The types of safeguards explained in this chapter are critical. In addition to these specific safeguards, there are also a number of general precautions that apply across the board in settings where machines are used. Some of the more important general precautions are as follows:

- All operators should be trained in the safe operation and maintenance of their machines.
- All machine operators should be trained in the emergency procedures to take when accidents occur.
- All employees should know how to activate emergency shutdown controls. This means knowing where the controls are and how to activate them.
- Inspection, maintenance, adjustment, repair, and calibration of safeguards should be carried out regularly.

- Supervisors should ensure that safeguards are properly in place when machines are in use. Employees who disable or remove safeguards should be disciplined appropriately.
- Operator teams (two or more operators) of the same system should be trained in coordination techniques and proper use of devices that prevent premature activation by a team member.
- Operators should be trained and supervised to ensure that they dress properly for the job. Long hair, loose clothing, neckties, rings, watches, necklaces, chains, and earrings can become caught in equipment and pull the employee into the hazard zone.
- Shortcuts that violate safety principles and practices should be avoided. The pressures of deadlines should never be the cause of unsafe work practices.
- Other employees who work around machines but do not operate them should be made aware of the emergency procedures to take when an accident occurs.

BASIC PROGRAM CONTENT

Machine safeguarding should be organized, systematic, and comprehensive. A company's safeguarding program should have at least the following elements:

- A safeguarding policy that is part of a broader companywide health and safety policy.
- Machine hazard analysis.
- Lockout/tagout (materials and procedures).
- Employee training.
- Comprehensive documentation.
- Periodic safeguarding audits (at least annually).

TAKING CORRECTIVE ACTION

What should be done when a mechanical hazard is observed? The only acceptable answer to this question is, take *immediate corrective action*. The specific action indicated will depend on what the problem is. Figure 10–17 shows selected examples of problems and corresponding corrective actions.

These are only a few of the many different types of problems that require corresponding corrective action. Regardless of the type of problem, the key to responding is immediacy. As shown in the examples given earlier in this chapter, waiting to take corrective action can be fatal.

Problem	Action
Machine is operating without the safety guard.	Stop machine immediately and activate the safety guard.
Maintenance worker is cleaning a machine that is operating.	Stop machine immediately and lock or tag it out.
Visitor to the shop is wearing a necktie as he observes a lathe in operation.	Immediately pull the visitor back and have him remove the tie.
An operator is observed disabling a guard.	Stop the operator, secure the guard, and take disciplinary action.
A robot is operating without a protective barrier.	Stop the robot and erect a barrier immediately.
A machine guard has a sharp, ragged edge.	Stop the machine and eliminate the sharp edge and ragged burrs by rounding it off.

Figure 10–17
Selected examples of problems and corresponding actions.

SUMMARY

1. The most common mechanical injuries are cutting and tearing, shearing, crushing, breaking, straining, spraining, and puncturing.

2. Safeguarding involves devices or methods that minimize the risk of accidents resulting from machine–operator contact. The contact may result from an individual making contact with a machine, flying metal chips, chemical or hot metal splashes, stock kickbacks, or mechanical malfunction.

3. All safeguards should prevent contact, be secure and durable, protect against falling objects, create no new hazards, create no interference, and allow safe maintenance.

4. Point-of-operation devices come in a variety of different types, including photoelectric, radio frequency, electromechanical, pullback, restraint, safety trip, two-hand controls, trips, and gates.

5. Feeding and ejection systems can be effective safeguards if properly designed and used. These systems come in two types: automatic and semi-automatic.

6. The main mechanical hazards associated with robots are as follows: (a) entrapment of a worker between a robot and a solid surface, (b) impact with a moving robot arm, and (c) impact with objects ejected or dropped by the robot. The best safeguard for a robot is a barrier around the perimeter of its work envelope. Sensitized doors or gates in the barrier can also decrease the hazard potential.

7. When hazards or hazardous behaviours are observed, corrective action should be taken immediately. Waiting to act can be fatal.

KEY TERMS AND CONCEPTS

Adjustable guards

Automatic ejection

Automatic feed

Crushing

Cutting

Electromechanical devices

Fixed guards

Gates

Interlocked guards

Lockout/tagout

Mechanical hazards

Mechanical injuries

Photoelectric devices

Point-of-operation guards

Pullback devices

Puncturing

Radio-frequency devices

Restraint devices

Risk assessment

Safety trip devices

Semiautomatic ejection

Semiautomatic feed

Shearing

Two-hand controls

Work envelope

REVIEW QUESTIONS

1. List and briefly explain the common types of mechanical injury hazards.

2. Explain the concept of safeguarding.

3. What are the requirements all safeguards should meet?

4. Describe the three types of point-of-operation guards.

5. Describe four types of point-of-operation devices.

6. What are the relative advantages and disadvantages of feeding and ejection systems?

7. Describe the primary hazards associated with robots.

8. Explain how to guard against the hazards associated with robots.

9. What is a lockout system?

10. What is a tagout system?

11. Explain the concept of risk assessment as it relates to machine operation.

12. Explain how to evaluate lockout/tagout programs.

WEBLINKS

Canadian Auto Workers

www.caw.ca/whatwedo/health&safety/pdf/blowing.pdf

This booklet, *Blowin' in the Wind,* provides a sobering look at the effects of poor machine guarding, along with lots of useful tips and tools for improving or implementing a machine guarding program in the workplace.

Canadian Occupational Safety Magazine
www.industrialsourcebook.com/cgi-bin/archivef.pl?id=147

The link above contains an article on historical machine guarding. Visit the home page for more interesting and informative articles on current safety issues.

Our Youth at Work
www.ouryouthatwork.com

On this site, we can see examples of the tireless work performed by Rob Ellis, father of David Ellis, the teenager who was killed by an unguarded machine. The site contains useful links and video clips.

ENDNOTES

1. Canadian Auto Workers. (no date). *Blowin' in the Wind,* "Machine Guarding Prevents Deaths." CAW Health and Safety Department. [Online]. Available: http://www.caw.ca/whatwedo/health&safety/pdf/blowing.pdf. (Retrieved March 3, 2005).
2. 954, Part I, "Safety of Machinery: Principles of Safety Related to Control Systems," *European Union,* 1997.
3. Canadian Auto Workers. (May/June 2000). *Health, Safety and Environment Newsletter* 8, no. 3. [Online]. Available: http://www.caw.ca/whatwedo/health&safety/newsletter/ 8.3may00.asp. (Retrieved March 3, 2005).
4. National Safety Council, *Guards: Safeguarding Concepts Illustrated,* 6th ed. (Chicago: National Safety Council, 1997), 2–3.
5. Ibid., 36.
6. Ibid., 38–39.
7. Retrieved from http://online.misu.nodak.edu/19577/BADM309 checklist.htm.
8. Ibid., 44.
9. L. Johnson, "The 'Red Flags' of LOTC," *Occupational Health & Safety* 68, no. 3: 55.

Falling, Impact, Acceleration, Lifting, and Vision Hazards

11
CHAPTER

LEARNING OBJECTIVES

- List the common causes of falls.
- Describe the four categories of falls.
- Explain how to increase traction to prevent slipping.
- List and briefly explain five strategies for preventing slips.
- List the key items found in a ladder safety inspection checklist.
- Describe head, eyes, face, and feet protection equipment for acceleration and impact hazards.
- Describe safe lifting techniques.
- Explain how hazards associated with standing are controlled.
- List common hand hazards and the corresponding glove materials used to protect the worker.
- Describe the role of personal protective equipment in the workplace.
- Identify the major hazards associated with forklift use.

Some of the most common accidents in the workplace happen as the result of slipping, falling, and improper lifting. **Impact** from a falling object is also a common cause of accidents. This chapter provides the information needed by modern health and safety professionals to prevent such accidents. It also provides specific information about head, hand, back, eye, face, and foot protection.

IMPACT ACCIDENTS
Involve a worker being struck by or against an object.

CAUSES OF FALLS

Falls represent about 15% of lost time injuries in Canada. About sixty thousand workers are injured each year due to fall accidents.[1] Clearly, falls are a major concern of health and safety professionals. The primary causes of falls are:

- A foreign object on the walking surface.
- A design flaw in the walking surface.
- Slippery surfaces.
- An individual's impaired physical condition.[2]

FOREIGN OBJECT
Any object that is out of place or in a position to trip someone or to cause a slip.

DESIGN FLAW
A defect in equipment or in the work space that can lead to an accident or injury.

A **foreign object** is any object that is out of place or in a position to trip someone or to cause a slip. There are an almost limitless number of **design flaws** that may cause a fall. A poorly designed floor covering, a ladder that does not seat properly, or a catwalk that gives way are all examples of design flaws that may cause falls. Slippery surfaces are particularly prevalent in industrial plants where numerous different lubricants and cleaning solvents are used.

Automobile accidents are often caused when a driver's attention is temporarily drawn away from the road by a visual distraction. This is also true in the workplace. Anything that distracts workers visually can cause a fall. When a person's physical condition is impaired for any reason, the potential for falls also increases. This is a particularly common problem among aging workers. Understanding these causes is the first step in developing fall prevention techniques.

KINDS OF FALLS

Workers who are at risk of falling 3 metres (10 feet) are required to wear fall protection equipment, such as safety belts and lanyards or full body harnesses, such as that seen in Figure 11–1. Fall arrest equipment should meet CSA standards Z259.1-95 for safety belts and lanyards and CSA standard Z259.10-M90 for full body harnesses. While 3 metres is generally the rule, numerous situations in various jurisdictions call for fall protection at lower elevations. For example, in Ontario, workers must be protected from falling from heights of more than 1.2 metres if the work area is used as a path for a wheelbarrow or similar equipment.

This section deals with the more common surface falls. According to Miller, such falls can be divided into the following four categories:

TRIP AND FALL
An accident that occurs when a worker encounters an unseen foreign object in his or her path.

STUMP AND FALL
An accident that occurs when a worker's foot suddenly meets a sticky surface or a defect in the walking surface.

STEP AND FALL
An accident that occurs when a person's foot encounters an unexpected step down.

SLIP AND FALL
Accidents that occur when the worker's centre of gravity is suddenly thrown out of balance.

- **Trip and fall** accidents occur when workers encounter an unseen foreign object in their path. When the employee's foot strikes the object, he or she trips and falls.
- **Stump and fall** accidents occur when a worker's foot suddenly meets a sticky surface or a defect in the walking surface. Expecting to continue at the established pace, the worker falls when his or her foot is unable to respond properly.
- **Step and fall** accidents occur when a person's foot encounters an unexpected step down (e.g., a hole in the floor or a floorboard that gives way). This can also happen when an employee thinks he or she has reached the bottom of the stairs when, in reality, there is one more step.
- **Slip and fall** accidents occur when the worker's centre of gravity is suddenly thrown out of balance (e.g., an oily spot causes a foot to shoot out from under the worker). This is the most common type of fall.[3]

▶ **Figure 11–1**
Personal fall arrest harness.
Source: Courtesy of Dalloz Safety (Miller Brand Products).

WALKING AND SLIPPING

Judging by the number of injuries that occur each year as the result of slipping, it is clear that walking can be hazardous to a worker's health. This is, in fact, the case when walking on an unstable platform. A stable platform for walking is any surface with a high degree of traction that is free of obstructions. It follows that an unstable platform is one lacking traction, one on which there are obstructions, or both.

Measuring Surface Traction

In order to understand *surface traction*, one must have a basis for comparison. An effective way for comparing the relative traction of a given surface is to use the **coefficient of friction**, which is a numerical comparison of the resistance of one surface (shoe or boot) against another surface (the floor).

COEFFICIENT OF FRICTION
A numerical correlation of the resistance of one surface against another surface.

Figure 11–2 is a continuum showing coefficient of friction ratings from very slippery to good traction. Surfaces with a coefficient of friction of 0.2 or less are very slippery and very hazardous. At the other end of the continuum, surfaces with a coefficient of friction of 0.4 or higher have good traction.

To gain a feel for what different coefficients actually mean, consider the following: (1) ice has a coefficient of friction of 0.10; (2) concrete has a coefficient of 0.43; (3) linoleum has a coefficient of 0.33; and (4) waxed white oak has a coefficient of 0.24. Compare these coefficients with Figure 11–2 to determine the degree of hazard and how the surfaces compare.

Factors That Decrease Traction

Good housekeeping can be a major factor in reducing slip and fall hazards. Water, oil, soap, coolant, and cleaning solvents left on a floor can decrease traction and turn an otherwise safe surface into a danger zone. For example, the friction coefficient of concrete (0.43) is reduced by almost 15% if the concrete is wet. Rubber-soled shoes can decrease slipping hazards somewhat, but changing the type of shoe is not enough to ensure safety. Additional precautions are needed.

Strategies for Preventing Slips

Modern health and safety professionals are concerned with preventing slips and falls, and slip prevention should be a part of the company's overall health and safety program. Here are some strategies that can be used to help prevent slipping:

1. **Choose the right material from the outset.** Where the walking surface is to be newly constructed or an existing surface is to be replaced, health and safety professionals should encourage the selection of surface materials that have the highest possible coefficient of friction. Getting it right from the start is the best way to prevent slipping accidents.

2. **Retrofit an existing surface.** If it is too disruptive or too expensive to replace a slippery surface completely, **retrofit** it with friction enhancement devices or materials. Such devices or materials include runners, skid strips, carpet, grooves, abrasive coatings, grilles, and textured coverings.

RETROFIT
Renovating rather than replacing.

Figure 11–2
Coefficients of friction and relative traction ratings.

3. **Practise good housekeeping.** Regardless of the type of surface, keep it clean and dry. Spilled water, grease, oil, solvents, and other liquids should be removed immediately. When the surface is intentionally made wet, as when cleaning or mopping, rope off the area and erect warning signs.

4. **Require nonskid footwear.** Employees who work in areas where slipping is likely to be a problem should be required to wear shoes with special nonskid soles. This is no different from requiring steel-toed boots to protect against falling objects. **Nonskid footwear** should be a normal part of a worker's personal protective equipment.

5. **Inspect surfaces frequently.** Employees who are working to meet production deadlines may be so distracted that they don't notice a wet surface, or they may notice it but feel too rushed to do anything about it. Consequently, health and safety professionals should conduct frequent inspections and act immediately when a hazard is identified.[4]

NONSKID FOOTWEAR Shoes that have special nonskid soles.

In addition to these generic strategies, safety experts were asked by *Occupational Hazards* magazine to give their top five strategies for preventing slips and falls. Their responses are summarized as follows.

Malcolm Robbins of Robbins & Associates recommends the following strategies:

1. Do not rely on cleanup and maintenance. Safety mats, slip-resistant safety shoes, and nonslip flooring are more reliable.

2. Ramps and sloped floor surfaces require higher friction values than level walking surfaces do.

3. Warning signs have limited value. Where used, however, they should warn of the dangerous condition, indicate what could happen, and show how to avoid the problem.

4. Focus on areas with open walking space such as large plants, warehouses, and supermarkets.

5. Use lighting and paint effectively to draw attention to steps, speed bumps, and other obstacles.[5]

Robert J. Brungraber, president of Slip-Test, Inc., recommends the following strategies:

1. Balance slip resistance against other needs. Floors in hospital operating rooms and kitchens, for example, must be smooth enough to be easy to clean and disinfect.

2. Accidents occur on wet floors. Clean and dry them as soon as possible.

3. Surprises lead to accidents. A wet floor on a rainy day is not as surprising (or as dangerous) as a wet floor from a spill on a sunny day.

4. Don't overlook workplace areas such as bathrooms and lunchrooms.

5. Slip, trip, and fall hazards put non-employees such as visitors and customers at risk. There is no exclusive remedy protection against non-employee suits.[6]

Foot Protection

The various regulations for most Canadian jurisdictions state that where a worker is exposed to foot injury hazards, appropriate foot protection shall be

Health and Safety Violations Can Result in Injuries and Big Fines

On September 16, 2002, while working on a theatre set in Burlington, Ontario, a carpenter fell a little more than 3 metres (10 feet) to the concrete floor below. The accident left the worker with two fractured heels and ankle injuries. The worker was not wearing any fall arrest equipment at the time of the accident. This was in contravention to Section 25(1)(c) of the Ontario Occupational Health and Safety Act, which states that the employer shall ensure that the measures and procedures as prescribed are carried out in the workplace. Those prescribed measures are found in Section 85 of Ontario's Regulations for Industrial Establishments, which require that a worker who is exposed to a hazard of falling more than 3 metres be equipped with fall arrest equipment.

On January 19, 2004, F & D Scene Changes Ltd. a Calgary, Alberta–based company, which operates Great Lakes Scenic Studios, was fined $60 000 for failing to comply with health and safety regulations.[7]

worn. Depending on the type of work being conducted, several types of foot injuries may be present. The major kinds of injuries to the foot and toes are from the following:

- Falls or impact from sharp or heavy objects (this type accounts for 60% of all injuries).
- Compression when rolled over by or pressed between heavy objects.
- Punctures through the sole of the foot.
- Conductivity of electricity or heat.
- Electrocution from contact with an energized, conducting material.
- Slips on unstable walking surfaces.
- Hot liquid or metal splashed into shoes or boots.
- Temperature extremes.[8]

The key to protecting workers' feet and toes is to match the protective measure with the hazard. This involves the following steps: (1) identify the various types of hazards present in the workplace, (2) identify the types of footwear available to counter the hazards, and (3) require that proper footwear be worn. Shoes selected should meet all applicable CSA standards and have the corresponding CSA markings. For the proper selection of safety footwear, the table in Figure 11–3 below shows the standard markings used to identify various safety features and their application.

Modern safety boots are available that provide comprehensive foot and toe protection. The best safety boots provide all of the following types of protection:

- *Steel toe* for impact protection.
- *Rubber or vinyl* for chemical protection.
- *Puncture-resistant soles* for protection against sharp objects.
- *Slip-resistant soles* for protection against slippery surfaces.
- *Electricity-resistant material* for protection from electric shock.

Protective Footwear Markings

Outside labels	Location	Criteria	Intended application
△® (green triangle)	The label shall appear at ankle height or on the tongue of the right shoe.	Green triangle indicates sole puncture protection with a Grade 1 protective toe to withstand impacts up to 125 joules.	For any industrial environment, especially that of construction, where sharp objects (such as nails) are present; heavy work environments.
△® (yellow triangle)	The label shall appear at ankle height or on the tongue of the right shoe.	Yellow triangle indicates sole puncture protection with a Grade 2 protective toe to withstand impacts up to 90 joules.	For light industrial work environments requiring puncture protection as well as toe protection.
Ω®	The label shall appear at ankle height or on the tongue of the right shoe.	White rectangle with orange Greek letter omega indicates soles that provide resistance to electric shock.	For any industrial environment where accidental contact with live electrical conductors can occur. **Warning:** *Electrical shock resistance deteriorates with wear and in a wet environment.*
SD ®	The label shall appear at ankle height or on the tongue of the right shoe.	Yellow rectangle with green "SD" and grounding symbol indicates soles are static-dissipative.	For any industrial environment where a static discharge can create a hazard for workers or equipment.
C ®	The label shall appear at ankle height or on the tongue of the right shoe.	Red rectangle with black "C" and grounding symbol indicates soles are electrically conductive.	For any industrial environment where low-power electrical charges may create a hazard for workers or equipment.
▲® (fir tree)	The label shall appear at ankle height or on the tongue of the right shoe.	White label with green fir tree symbol indicates chainsaw protective footwear.	For forestry workers and others exposed to hand-held chainsaws or other cutting tools.
® (blue rectangle)	The label shall appear on the outside of the right shoe.	Blue rectangle indicates a Grade 1 protective toe with no protective sole.	For industrial work environments not requiring puncture protection.
® (grey rectangle)	The label shall appear on the outside of the right shoe.	Grey rectangle indicates a Grade 2 protective toe with no protective sole.	For institutional and non-industrial work environments not requiring puncture protection.

Note: *The ® symbol indicates the preferred positioning for the registered identifying logo or mark of the certifying agency.*

Figure 11–3
Selection of safety footwear.
Source: CCOHS. (December 3, 2003). "Safety Footwear." [Online]. Available:
http://www.ccohs.ca/oshanswers/prevention/ppe/footwear.html. (Retrieved March 4, 2005).

Many employers and construction associations simply require that the worker wear Grade 1 CSA-certified footwear. The "grade," refers to the ability of the toe to withstand impact. Grade 1 withstands an impact of 125 joules (the equivalent of a 12.75 kilogram object dropped from a height of 1 metre).

LADDER SAFETY

Jobs that involve the use of ladders (see Figure 11–4) introduce their own set of safety problems, one of which is an increased potential for falls. Many accidents involving ladders result from improper use. Following a simple set of rules for the proper use of ladders can reduce the risk of falls and other ladder-related accidents. The Construction Safety Association of Ontario (CSAO) recommends the following checklist be considered before ladder use:

- Check ladder for defects before use.
- Clear scrap and material away from the base and the top of the ladder, since getting on and off the ladder is relatively hazardous.
- Secure the base against accidental movement. It is also a good idea to secure the top of the ladder as well.
- Set the ladder on a firm, level surface. On soft, uncompacted rough soil, use a mud sill.
- Single-width job-built ladders are only meant for one worker at a time. A double-width ladder can be used by two workers providing they are on opposite sides.
- Make sure the rails on the ladder reach at least 90 cm (three feet) above the landing. This allows for a secure grip while stepping on or off.
- Set straight or extension ladders 30 cm (one foot) out for every 90 to 120 cm (three to four feet) up. The base should be out one fourth to one third the height.
- Before setting up a ladder, always check for overhead powerlines.
- Do not position ladders against flexible or moveable surfaces.
- Always face the ladder while climbing or working on it.
- Maintain three point contact when climbing up or down.
- Keep your centre of gravity inside the side rails. Your belt buckle should never be outside the side rails.
- When climbing up or down never carry tools or materials in your hand. Use a hoist rope instead.
- Keep boots free of mud, grease, or any material that could cause a loss of footing.
- When working 3 metres (10 feet) or more above the ground or floor, wear a safety belt or harness with the **lanyard** tied off to the structure.
- Never straddle the space between the ladder and another object.
- Use fall-arrest equipment such as ladder climbing devices or lifelines when working from long ladders or vertical fixed ladders.
- Never use ladders horizontally as scaffold planks, runways, or any other service for which they were not designed.
- Stand no higher than the third or fourth rung from the top. Maintain knee contact for balance.
- Do not splice short ladders together to make a long ladder.

LANYARD
A flexible line for connecting the body belt or body harness to a deceleration device, lifeline, or anchorage.

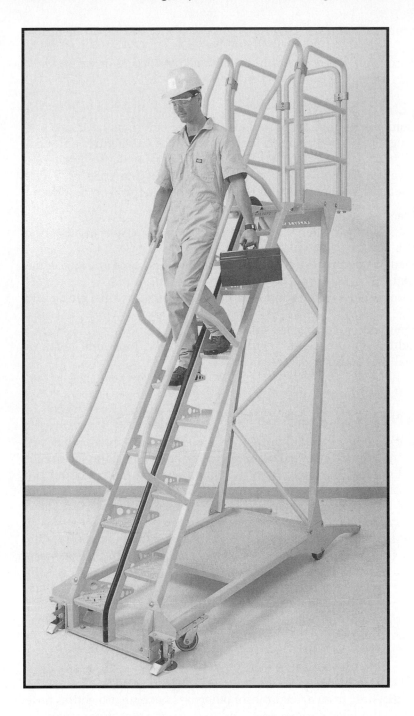

▶ **Figure 11–4**
Portable ladder/stair.
Source: Courtesy of Lapeyre
Stair, Inc.

- Do not use ladders for bracing.
- Do not set up ladders in doorways, passageways, or locations where they can be knocked over.
- Do not rest a ladder on its rungs. Ladders must rest on their side rails.
- Get help when erecting long, heavy, or awkward ladders to prevent overexertion.

- Before erecting, using, or working from ladders, always check for electrical hazards.
- Never use aluminum ladders near live electrical equipment or wires. [9]

Inspecting Ladders

Taking a few moments to look over a ladder carefully before using it can prevent a fall. It is a good starting point to look for visible manufacturer and CSA markings on all purchased ladders. For job-built ladders, specific details are given in the relevant regulations for each jurisdiction. The Construction Safety Association of Ontario recommends the following when inspecting a ladder:

- Inspect ladders for structural rigidity.
- Inspect nonskid feet for wear, embedded material, and proper pivot action on swivel feet.
- Replace frayed or worn ropes on extension ladders with type and size equal to original rope.
- Check aluminum ladders for dents and bends in the side rails, steps, and rungs.
- Check wooden ladders for cracks, splits, or rot.
- Check all ladders for grease, oil, caulking, embedded stone and metal, or other material that could make them unsafe.[10]

IMPACT AND ACCELERATION HAZARDS

An employee working on a catwalk drops a wrench. The falling wrench accelerates over the 5-metre drop and strikes an employee below. Had the victim not been wearing a hard hat he might have sustained serious injuries from the impact. A robot loses its grip on a part, slinging it across the plant and striking an employee. The impact from the part breaks one of the employee's ribs. These are examples of accidents involving **acceleration** and impact. So is any type of fall because, having fallen, a person's rate of fall accelerates (increases) until striking a surface (impact). Motor vehicle accidents are also examples of acceleration and impact.

Because falls were covered in the previous section, this section will focus on hazards relating to the acceleration and impact of objects. Approximately 25% of the workplace accidents that occur each year as the result of acceleration and impact involve objects that become projectiles.

ACCELERATION
Increase in the speed of a falling object before impact.

Protection from Falling or Accelerating Objects

Objects that fall, are slung from a machine, or otherwise become projectiles pose a serious hazard to the heads, faces, feet, and eyes of workers. Consequently, protecting workers from projectiles requires the use of appropriate personal protective equipment and strict adherence to safety rules by all employees.

Head Protection

People who sustain head injuries on the job account for less than 5% of all lost time accidents in Canada each year. However, due to the potential severity of these accidents, the safety practitioner should be aware of the risk of such injuries and the means to protect the worker. Falling objects are involved in many of these accidents. These injuries occur in spite of the fact that many of the victims were wearing hard hats. Such statistics have been the driving force behind the development of tougher, more durable hard hats.

Originally introduced in 1919, the hard hats first used for head protection in an industrial setting were inspired by the helmets worn by soldiers in World War I. Such early versions were made of varnished resin-impregnated canvas. As material technology evolved, hard hats were made of vulcanized fibre, then aluminum, and then fibreglass. Today's hard hats are typically made from the thermoplastic material polyethylene, using the injection-molding process. Basic hard hat design has not changed radically since before World War II. Hard hats are designed to provide limited protection from impact primarily to the top of the head, and thereby reduce the amount of impact transmitted to the head, neck, and spine.[11]

The Canadian Standards Association (CSA), American National Standards Institute (ANSI), and International Standards Organization (ISO) all have standards that define the minimum performance for hard hats along with other safety devices. While testing methods often vary among these organizations, the standards usually result in products of similar integrity.

The standard for hard hats used by jurisdictions from Newfoundland and Labrador to Yukon is the CSA Z94.1-92. This standard calls for testing hard hats for impact attenuation and penetration resistance as well as electrical insulation. Hard hats are also designed to limit penetration of sharp objects that may hit the top of the hard-hat shell and to provide some lateral penetration protection.[12]

Hard hats should be inspected regularly for cracks and deep scratches and replaced when any defects are found. Ensure that the replacement hat bears the CSA label, and do not paint hard hats, because paint can reduce impact resistance and hide other defects.

Hard hats can help reduce the risk associated with falling or projected objects, but only if they are worn. In addition to making the use of hard hats mandatory when appropriate and supervising to ensure compliance, Feuerstein recommends the use of incentives.[13] According to Feuerstein,

> It would seem that the sweetest offer a head-injury prevention program makes is a work environment free of injuries from falling objects. But sometimes this ultimate reward is too abstract to excite employees. They need to be led into safety for its own sake by concrete incentives, such as intra-department competition, monetary rewards for good suggestions, points toward prizes, and peer recognition for the most improved behavior.[14]

Eye and Face Protection

Eye and face protection are critical in the modern workplace. Eye injuries are a common and costly phenomenon. The Canadian National Institute for the Blind (CNIB) reports that thousands of workers sustain on-the-job eye injuries that result in permanent damage or blindness. The financial cost in lost production time, medical expenses, and workers' compensation is borne by all of society eventually, but the human cost borne by the injured workers and their families can be devastating. So why is this continuing to happen?

First, too many people are not wearing eye protection. And second, they are not wearing the right kind of eye protection.

Eye and face protection typically consist of safety glasses, safety goggles, or face shields. The standard generally adopted for face and eye protective devices in Canadian jurisdictions is CSA Z94.3-02. It requires that industrial eye and face protective devices protect against certain eye and face hazards to a specific level, but the standard does not include factors such as style, appearance, comfort, or service life.

Frequently seen in Canada along with the CSA logo is the ANSI Z78 marking for face and eye protective devices. The ANSI standard Z78.1-1989 and the newer Z78.1-2003 require that eye and face protective devices pass two impact tests: a high-mass, low-speed test and a low-mass, high-speed test. Figure 11–5 summarizes the purpose of the tests and their individual requirements concerning impact and penetration. Figures 11–6, 11–7, and 11–8 are examples of the types of devices available for eye and face protection.

The high-mass impact test determines the level of protection provided by face and eye protective devices from relatively heavy, pointed objects that are moving at low speeds. The high-velocity impact test determines the level of protection provided from low-mass objects moving at high velocity.

High-Mass Impact Test—Purpose

This test is intended to ensure the level of mechanical integrity of a protective device and a level of protection from relatively heavy, pointed objects travelling at low speeds. Frames shall be capable of resisting impact from a 500-gram (17.6-ounce) missile with a 30-degree conical heat-treated tip and a 1-mm (.039-inch) radius dropped from a height of 130 cm (51.2 inches). No parts or fragments shall be ejected from the protector that could contact an eye.

High-Velocity Impact Test—Purpose

This test is intended to ensure a level of protection from high-velocity, low-mass projectiles. Frames shall be capable of resisting impact from 6.35-mm (¼-inch) steel balls weighing 1.06 grams (.04 ounce) at 45.72 metres/second (150 feet per second [fps] from 0 degrees to 90 degrees for frames; 76.2 metres/second (250 fps) for goggles; 91.44 metres/second (300 fps) for face shields.

Impact Test—Drop Ball

A 25.4-mm (1-inch) steel ball, weighing 68 grams (2.4 ounces), free fall from 127 cm (50 inches).

Lens Thickness

Thickness is 3.0 mm (.118 inch) except lenses that withstand high velocity impact, then 2.0-mm (.079-inch) thickness is acceptable.

Impact Test—Penetration

Lens shall be capable of resisting penetration from a Singer needle on a holder weighing 44.2 g (1.56 ounces) dropped freely from 127 cm (50 inches).

Figure 11–5
ANSI Standard Z87.1–1989.

**Figure 11–6
Safety glasses that
wrap around for lateral
protection.**
Source: Courtesy of ELVEX
Corporation, Bethel, CT.

**Figure 11–7
Eye safety shield
combined with ear
and head protection.**
Source: Courtesy of ELVEX
Corporation, Bethel, CT.

DISCUSSION CASE

What Is Your Opinion?

Two health and safety professionals are debating an issue over lunch. "Hard hats don't really do any good because employees won't wear them. It's like dieting. The best diet in the world won't work if you don't follow it." "I don't agree," said the second safety professional. "Hard hats have prevented thousands of head injuries. If employees don't wear them, it's because managers don't enforce their own rules." Join this debate. What is your opinion?

**Figure 11–8
Huntsman® Model K
Facesaver® face
shield with 8154L
window attached.**
Source: Courtesy of Kedman
Company, Huntsman Products
Division.

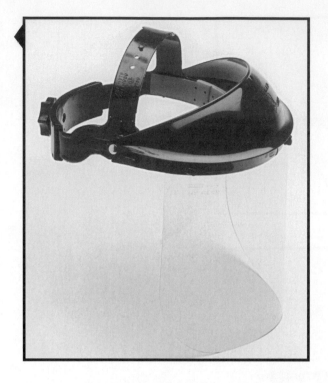

ASSESSING THE WORKPLACE FOR EYE HAZARDS The type of eye protection needed in a given setting depends on the type of work done in that setting and the corresponding hazards. Before establishing a vision protection program, it is necessary to assess the workplace. OSHA recommends using the following questions in making a workplace assessment:

- Do employees perform tasks that may produce airborne dust or flying particles?
- Do employees work near others who perform tasks that may produce airborne dust or flying particles?
- Do employees handle hazardous liquid chemicals or blood?
- Do employees work near others who handle hazardous liquid chemicals or blood?
- Do employees work in situations that may expose their eyes to chemical or physical irritants?
- Do employees work in situations that may expose their eyes to intense light or lasers?[15]

FIRST AID FOR EYE INJURIES Even with proper eye protection, there is still the risk that an employee may sustain an injury. Even the best vision protection program is not perfect. When this happens, the following guidelines for first aid apply:

- Be gentle with the employee. Don't add to the injury with rough treatment.
- Do not attempt to remove objects embedded in the eyeball.
- Rinse the eyes with copious amount of water for 15 to 30 minutes to remove the chemicals. Call for professional help. Cover both eyes after the rinsing has been completed.

SAFETY FACT

Selecting the Right Face Protection Device
Protection devices for . . .

- Flying particles, chips, sand, and so on — face shield

- Hot sparks — face shield

- Heat — reflective face shield

- Molten metal — face shield

- Chemical splash — face shield

- Ultraviolet light and infrared heat — welding helmet or welding shield with shaded lens

- Never press on an injured eye or put any pressure on it (as when covering the eyes).
- Do not allow the employee to rub his or her eyes.[16]

LIFTING HAZARDS

Back injuries that result from improper lifting are among the most common in an industrial setting. **Manual materials handling** (MMH) is the most common cause of occupational fatigue and low back pain. About three of every four Canadians whose job includes MMH suffer pain due to back injury at some time. Such back injuries account for about one third of all lost work and 40% of all compensation costs. More important than financial cost is human suffering. Each year about 8000 Canadian workers are permanently disabled by back injuries. Many others are unable to return to their former jobs. Their lives are profoundly disrupted.[17]

Back injuries in the workplace are typically caused by improper lifting, reaching, sitting, and bending. **Lifting hazards** such as poor posture, ergonomic factors, and personal lifestyles also contribute to back problems. Consequently, a company's overall health and safety program should have a back safety/lifting component.

Workers should be aware of the maximum load that can be safely lifted. The universally accepted standard for manual lifting weight limits is the *revised NIOSH equation for the design and evaluation of manual lifting tasks.* The NIOSH lifting equation takes into account the weight plus several other variables in lifting tasks that contribute to the risk of injury. For example, if the situation requires frequent lifts or lifting loads far away from the body, there is an increased risk of injury. Under these conditions, the weight limit would be reduced from a baseline weight or "load constant" (LC) to a recommended weight limit (RWL). A load constant (LC) of 23 kg (about 51 lbs.) was established by NIOSH as a load that, under ideal conditions, is safe for 75% of females and 90% of males.[18] For more information on the NIOSH lifting equation, see the web links at the end of this chapter.

MANUAL MATERIALS HANDLING
Moving goods or equipment without the aid of machinery.

LIFTING HAZARD
Any factor that if not properly dealt with may lead to an injury from lifting.

Back Safety/Lifting Program

Prevention is critical in back safety. Consequently, health and safety professionals need to know how to establish back safety programs that overcome the hazards of lifting and other activities. Dr. Alex Kaliokin recommends the following six-step program:

1. **Display poster illustrations.** Posters that illustrate proper lifting, reaching, sitting, and bending techniques should be displayed strategically throughout the workplace. This is as important in offices as in the plant. Clerical and office personnel actually sustain a higher proportion of back injuries than employees in general. Sitting too long without standing, stretching, and walking can put as much pressure on the back as lifting.

2. **Pre-employment screening.** Pre-employment screening can identify people who already have back problems when they apply. This is important because more than 40% of back injuries occur in the first year of employment and the majority of these injuries are related to pre-existing back problems.

3. **Regular safety inspections.** Periodic inspections of the workplace can identify potential problem areas so that corrective action can be taken immediately. Occasionally bringing a workers' compensation consultant in to assist with an inspection can help identify hazards that company personnel may miss.

4. **Education and training.** Education and training designed to help employees understand how to lift, bend, reach, stand, walk, and sit safely can be the most effective preventive measure undertaken. Companies that provide back safety training report a significant decrease in back injuries.

5. **Use external services.** A variety of external health care agencies can help companies extend their programs. Identify local health care providing agencies and organizations, what services they can provide, and a contact person in each. Maintaining a positive relationship with these external service contact people can increase the services available to employers.

6. **Map out the prevention program.** The first five steps should be written down and incorporated in the company's overall health and safety program. The written plan should be reviewed periodically and updated as needed.[19]

In spite of a company's best efforts, back injuries will still occur. Consequently, health and safety professionals should be familiar with the treatment and therapy that injured employees are likely to receive. Treatment for reconditioning addresses five goals: restoring function, reducing pain, minimizing deficits in strength, reducing lost time, and returning the body to pre-injury fitness levels.[20]

A concept that is gaining acceptance in bridging the gap between treatment or therapy and a safe return to work is known as *work hardening*.[21] Work hardening and its objectives are explained as follows: In specially designed "work centres," various work stations, exercise equipment, and aggressive protocols are used for work reconditioning. The objectives are:

- A return to maximum physical abilities as soon as possible;
- Improvement of general body fitness;
- Reducing the likelihood of re-injury;
- Work simulation that duplicates real work conditions.[22]

The work centres referred to above replicate in as much detail as possible the injured employee's actual work environment. In addition to undergoing carefully controlled and monitored therapy in the work centre, the employee is encouraged to use exercise equipment. Employees who undergo work centre therapy should have already completed a program of acute physical therapy and pain management, and they should be medically stable.[23]

Health and safety managers can help facilitate the fastest possible safe resumption of duties by injured employees by identifying local health care providers that use the work-hardening approach. Such services and local providers of them should be made known to higher management so that the company can take advantage of them.

Proper Lifting Techniques

One of the most effective ways to prevent back injuries is to teach employees proper lifting techniques. Following are lifting techniques that should be taught as part of an organization's safety program.

PLAN AHEAD

- Determine if you can lift the load. Is it too heavy or too awkward?
- Decide if you need assistance.
- Check your route to see whether it has obstructions and slippery surfaces.

LIFT WITH YOUR LEGS, NOT YOUR BACK

- Bend at your knees, keeping your back straight.
- Position your feet close to the object.
- Centre your body over the load.
- Lift straight up smoothly; don't jerk.
- Keep your torso straight; don't twist while lifting or after the load is lifted.
- Set the load down slowly and smoothly with a straight back and bent knees; don't let go until the object is on the floor.

PUSH, DON'T PULL

- Pushing puts less strain on your back; don't pull objects.
- Use rollers under the object whenever possible.

STANDING HAZARDS

Consider this statement by Roberta Carson, a certified professional ergonomist: "Prolonged standing or walking is common in industry and can be very painful. Low back pain, sore feet, varicose veins, swelling in the legs, general muscular fatigue, and other health problems have been associated with prolonged standing or walking."[24] Carson recommends the following precautions for minimizing standing hazards:[25]

Anti-Fatigue Mats

Anti-fatigue mats provide cushioning between the feet and hard working surfaces such as concrete floors (see Figure 11–9). This cushioning effect can

Figure 11–9
Padded mat.
Source: Courtesy of Tennessee Mat
Company, OH.

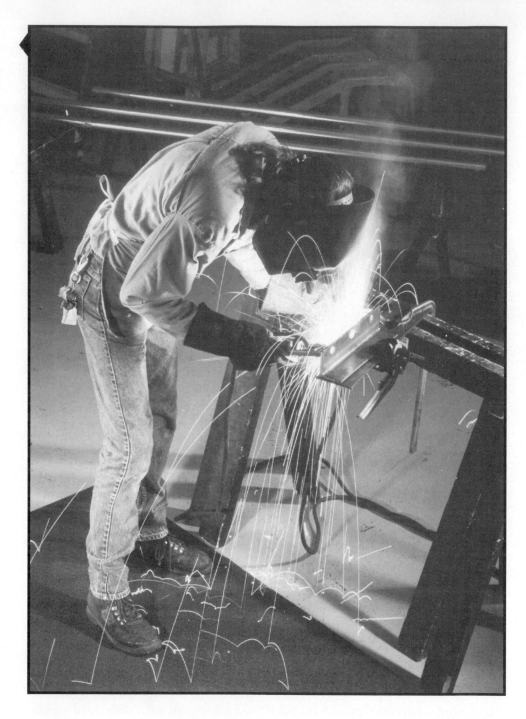

reduce muscle fatigue and lower back pain. However, too much cushioning can be just as bad as too little. Consequently, it is important to test mats on a trial basis before buying a large quantity. Mats that become slippery when wet should be avoided. In areas where chemicals are used, be sure to select mats that will hold up to chemicals.

Shoe Inserts

When anti-fatigue mats are not feasible because employees must move from area to area and, correspondingly, from surface to surface, shoe inserts may be the answer. Such inserts are worn inside the shoe and provide the same type of cushioning the mats provide. Shoe inserts can help reduce lower back, foot, and leg pain. It is important to ensure proper fit. If inserts make an employee's shoes too tight, they will do more harm than good. In such cases, employees may need to wear a slightly larger shoe size.

Foot Rails

Foot rails added to work stations can help relieve the hazards of prolonged standing. Foot rails allow employees to elevate one foot at a time about 10 cm (4 inches). The elevated foot rounds out the lower back, thereby relieving some of the pressure on the spinal column. Placement of a rail is important. It should not be placed in a position that inhibits movement or becomes a tripping hazard.

Workplace Design

A well-designed workstation can help relieve the hazards of prolonged standing. The key is to design workstations so that employees can move about while they work and can adjust the height of the workstation to match their physical needs.

Sit/Stand Chairs

Sit/stand chairs are higher-than-normal chairs that allow employees who typically stand while working to take quick mini-breaks and return to work without the hazards associated with getting out of lower chairs. They have the advantage of giving the employee's feet, legs, and back an occasional rest without introducing the hazards associated with lower chairs.

Proper Footwear

Proper footwear is critical for employees who stand for prolonged periods. Well-fitting, comfortable shoes that grip the work surface and allow free movement of the toes are best.

HAND PROTECTION

In Canada, the hand is the body part most frequently injured. Canadians suffer about 500 000 hand injuries every year. Hand injuries are both serious and costly for employers and for employees. The range of hazards include needlestick injuries, cuts, pinching, chemical exposure, vibration, and temperature extremes.

Where the risk of hand injuries is present in the workplace, an assessment of the control measures, including glove selection, should be completed to ensure that they are best suited for the individual situation. Selecting just the right gloves for the job is not a simple task. A poorly fitted pair of gloves, for example, cannot offer the degree of protection that a responsible employer or employee wants. Yet, because manufacturers have not developed a consistent set of metrics for sizing gloves, the only way to determine whether a pair fits properly is for the employee to try them on.

And fit is just one of the problems faced when selecting gloves. Other critical features include the protection capability, comfort, and tactile sensitivity of the gloves. Often, greater comfort and tactile sensitivity can mean less protection. Correspondingly, greater protection can mean less comfort and tactile sensitivity.

Common Glove Materials

Depending on the individual hazards available in a given situation, the right gloves for the application may be made of a variety of different materials (see Figures 11–10, 11–11, and 11–12). The most widely used materials in manufacturing gloves are as follows:

- **Leather.** Offers comfort, excellent abrasion resistance, and minimum cut resistance.

**Figure 11–10
Cut-resistant
work glove.**
Source: Courtesy of Best
Manufacturing Company.

- **Cotton.** Offers comfort, minimal abrasion resistance, and minimum cut resistance.
- **Aramids.** Offer comfort, good abrasion resistance, excellent cut resistance, and excellent heat resistance.
- **Polyethylene.** Offers comfort, excellent abrasion resistance, and minimal cut resistance. Gloves made of this material should not be subjected to high temperatures.
- **Stainless steel cord (wrapped in synthetic fibre).** Offers comfort, good abrasion resistance, and optimal cut resistance.
- **Chain link or metal mesh.** Offers very little comfort, but maximum abrasion and cut resistance.
- **Butyl rubber.** Offers little comfort, but has excellent resistance to heat, ozone, tearing, and certain chemicals including alcohols, aldehydes, ketones, esters, nitriles, gases, amides, acids, and nitro compounds.
- **Viton rubber.** Offers little comfort, but performs well with chemicals that butyl rubber cannot protect against, including aliphatics, halogenated compounds, and aromatics. Like butyl gloves, viton gloves also perform well in handling alcohols, gases, and acids.[26]

PERSONAL PROTECTIVE EQUIPMENT

Personal protective equipment (PPE) is a critical component in the safety program of most organizations. PPE, however, should be considered a last line of

**Figure 11–11
Synthetic fibre gloves reinforced with stain- less steel.**
Source: Courtesy of Best Manufacturing Company.

Figure 11–12
Natural rubber gloves.
Source: Courtesy of Best
Manufacturing Company.

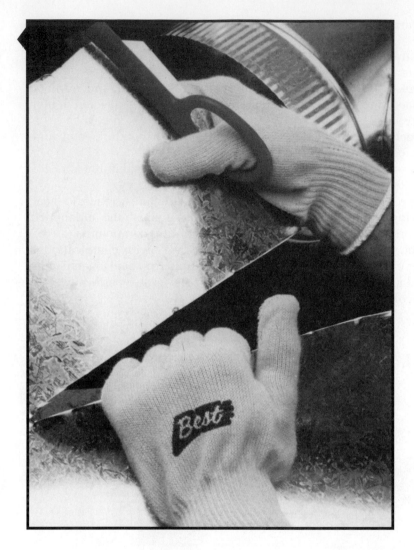

defence against injuries and employed only after all practical engineering and administrative controls have been used. Head, hand, back, eye, face, foot, skin, and breathing protection all involve the use of PPE. Unfortunately, it can be difficult to convince employees to wear PPE properly or, sometimes, to wear it at all. Employees often balk at the perceived "inconvenience" of PPE. They don't like the way it looks or how it feels. They find it cumbersome to work in or time consuming to put on and take off. Sometimes, they just forget.

Making employees comfortable with PPE is a serious and sometimes difficult challenge for health and safety professionals. The following strategies can be used to meet this challenge:

- **Make maximum use of engineering and administrative controls.** PPE should be the last line of defence in protecting employees from hazardous conditions. Before adopting PPE, organizations should first use every engineering and administrative control available to minimize potential hazards.

If employees see that the organization is doing its part by applying these controls, they will be less reluctant to do their part in properly using PPE.

- **Ensure the optimum choice of PPE by using risk assessment.** Employees know when there is a mismatch between the hazards they face and the PPE they are provided. PPE should be selected on the basis of a comprehensive risk assessment. This approach helps employers make the optimum choice when selecting PPE. Employees who know that the PPE provides adequate protection from hazards will be more likely to use it.
- **Involve employees in all aspects of the PPE program.** Always involve employees when making decisions that affect them. This is good policy for two reasons: (1) Employees may be able to provide input that will improve the quality of the decisions being made because they understand the work tasks being discussed; and (2) employees who are involved in the decision making are more likely to buy into and support the resulting decision.
- **Provide comprehensive education and training programs.** Employees need to understand why PPE is important and how to properly use it. Employers should never assume that employees understand the "why" or "how" of PPE. Training programs should begin with the why aspects, cover them thoroughly, and give employees ample opportunities to ask questions and voice concerns. Once employees understand why PPE is important, they should be given comprehensive training on how to use it properly. No employee should be expected to use PPE without first understanding why and how they should use it.
- **Reinforce the proper use of PPE and challenge its improper use.** Employers should never fall into the trap of taking PPE use for granted. Proper behaviour relating to PPE should be reinforced by supervisors and managers. Correspondingly, improper use should be challenged. Employers should use PPE properly themselves and reward employees who follow suit. Rewards need not be formal. Publicly complimenting an employee can be reward enough. Correspondingly, when an employee is seen failing to use the required PPE or using it improperly, that employee should be corrected. However, whereas compliments are given publicly, correction should be done in private.
- **Be sensitive to fit, comfort, and style issues.** Ill-fitting PPE poses a double problem: (1) it may not provide the necessary protection because of the improper fit; and (2) if it does not fit well, employees may be reluctant to wear it because it is uncomfortable. Style can also be a problem in that employees are often self-conscious about their appearance. All of these factors should be considered when choosing PPE.
- **Work to make PPE a normal part of the uniform.** By applying these strategies, employers can make PPE a normal part of the uniform. When this happens, using PPE will become standard operating procedure, and its proper use will cease to be an issue.[27]

FORKLIFT SAFETY (POWERED INDUSTRIAL TRUCKS)

Powered industrial truck or forklift safety is included here because forklift-related injuries often result from impact or acceleration hazards. Some jurisdictions in Canada have no specific requirements for forklift operators to be trained, however, all operators should meet any training and certification requirements. Lift trucks used in many workplaces are powerful and heavy machines that are potentially very hazardous when under the control of an incompetent operator.

Forklifts are different from cars and trucks in several ways. Employees who drive forklifts should understand how they are different. The primary differences are as follows:

- Forklifts are typically steered by the rear wheels.
- An empty forklift can be more difficult to steer than one with a load.
- Forklifts are frequently driven in reverse.
- Forklifts have three-point suspension so that the centre of gravity can move from the rear of the vehicle closer to the front when it is loaded.

Because of these differences, it is important to ensure that only properly trained employees drive forklifts and that these employees follow some basic rules of accident prevention. The rules fall into four categories: (1) general, (2) lifting, (3) travelling, and (4) placing.

GENERAL RULES The rules in this section are general and apply to all phases of forklift operation:

- Keep arms, hands, and legs inside the vehicle at all times.
- Face in the direction of travel at all times.
- If the load blocks your view, drive backward.
- Allow plenty of room for braking — at least three vehicle lengths.
- Make sure there is sufficient overhead clearance before moving a load.

RULES FOR PICKING UP A LOAD

- Make sure the load is within the capacity of the forklift.
- Make sure forks are positioned properly.
- Make sure the load is properly balanced.
- Make sure the load is secure.
- Raise the load to the proper height.
- Run the forks all the way into the pallet, and tilt the mast back to stabilize the load before moving.
- Back out and stop completely before lowering the load.

RULES FOR TRAVELLING WITH A LOAD

- Always give pedestrians the right-of-way.
- Never allow passengers on the forklift.
- Keep the forks low while moving.
- Keep the load tilted back slightly while moving.
- Drive slowly; a forklift is not a car.
- Slow down at all intersections; stop and sound the horn at blind intersections.
- Drive up and back down ramps and inclines.
- Never lift or lower the load when travelling.
- Keep to the right just as you do when driving a car.
- Watch for oil, grease, and wet spots, which could inhibit traction.

- Cross railroad tracks at a skewed angle, never at a right angle.
- Watch for edges on loading docks and other changes in elevation.

RULES FOR PLACING A LOAD

- Stop the forklift completely before raising or lowering the load.
- Move slowly and cautiously with the load raised.
- Never walk or stand under a raised load or allow anyone else to do so.
- Be certain the forks have cleared the pallet before turning and before changing height.
- Stack the load square and straight.
- Check behind and on both sides before backing up.

SAFETY FACT

Ambient Noise Can Increase Forklift Hazards

Part of safely operating forklifts is ensuring that pedestrians in the vicinity can hear the truck and thereby avoid it. If pedestrians in the workplace cannot hear a forklift, the results can be fatal. They were at Revere Copper Products, Inc. in Rome, New York. After an employee was killed by a forklift, the company's safety investigation revealed that ambient noise was making it difficult for pedestrians to hear forklifts in Revere's mill. To correct this problem, Revere's safety personnel installed high-intensity strobe lights on the forklift mast uprights. Because the flashing strobe lights of an approaching truck reflect off the surroundings, pedestrians can see a truck approaching even if they cannot hear it.

Source: "Tip of the Week," *Occupational Health & Safety*, [Online]. Available: http://stevenspub ca-14478352@process.request.com.

SUMMARY

1. The primary causes of falls are a foreign object on the walking surface, a design flaw in the walking surface, a slippery surface, and a person's impaired physical condition.

2. Most falls fit into one of four categories: trip and fall, stump and fall, step and fall, and slip and fall.

3. The coefficient of friction between surfaces is an effective method for comparing the traction of a walking surface. A coefficient of friction of 0.20 or less means the surface is very slippery and very hazardous. A coefficient of 0.40 or higher means there is good traction. Coefficients of friction decrease when a surface is wet.

4. Strategies for preventing slips include the following: choose the right material from the outset, retrofit an existing surface, practise good housekeeping, require nonskid footwear, and inspect surfaces frequently.

5. A slip and fall prevention program should have the following components: policy statement/commitment; review and acceptance of walkways; recon-

ditioning and retrofitting; maintenance standards and procedures; inspection, audits, tests, and records; employee footwear; legal defences; and measurement of results.

6. Dos and don'ts of ladder safety include checking for slipperiness, allowing only one person on the ladder at a time, securing the base and top on a level surface, applying the **four-to-one ratio**, facing the ladder when climbing, avoiding leaning, and always holding on with one hand.

7. Protection from impact injuries from falling or projected objects includes personal protective equipment to protect the head (hard hats), eyes and face (goggles or shields), and feet (footwear).

8. Back/lifting safety programs should have the following components: poster illustrations, pre-employment screening, regular safety inspections, education and training, external services, and a written map of the program.

9. Standing hazards can be minimized by using the following: anti-fatigue mats, shoe inserts, foot rails, improved workplace design, and sit/stand chairs.

10. The most widely used materials in manufacturing gloves for hand protection are leather, cotton, aramids, polyethylene, stainless steel cord, chain link, metal mesh, butyl rubber, and viton rubber.

11. Personal protective equipment should be the last line of defence protecting employees from hazards. Before using PPE, every feasible engineering and administrative control should be employed.

FOUR-TO-ONE RATIO
Base one foot away from the wall for every four feet between the ground and the top support point of a ladder.

KEY TERMS AND CONCEPTS

Acceleration	Manual materials handling
Coefficient of friction	Nonskid footwear
Design flaw	Retrofit
Foreign object	Slip and fall
Four-to-one ratio	Step and fall
Impact accident	Stump and fall
Lanyard	Trip and fall
Lifting hazards	

REVIEW QUESTIONS

1. List the primary causes of falls.

2. Explain briefly the most common kinds of falls.

3. Explain how surface traction is measured.

4. List and briefly explain five strategies for preventing slips.

5. Describe the various components of a slip and fall prevention program.

6. What is a lanyard?

7. Explain how to assess the workplace for eye hazards.

8. What topics should be covered in eye protection training?

9. What should an employee look for when inspecting a ladder?

10. List six major kinds of injuries to the foot and toes that occur in the workplace each year.

11. List four ways to minimize standing hazards.

12. Explain the strategies for proper lifting that should be taught as part of the safety program.

13. What are the critical factors to consider when selecting gloves?

14 What problems are created with PPE?

WEBLINKS

Canadian Centre for Occupational Health and Safety
www.ccohs.ca/oshanswers/ergonomics/niosh/calculating_rwl.html

An easy to use weight calculator based on the revised NIOSH lifting equation.

The Construction Safety Association of Ontario (CSAO)
www.csao.org

This CSAO website is a useful resource for the construction industry and deals with many of the subjects covered in this chapter.

Industrial Accident Prevention Association (IAPA)
www.iapa.ca

IAPA is Canada's largest health and safety organization and their website features interesting and informative articles weekly.

ENDNOTES

1. Canadian Centre for Occupational Health and Safety. (November 27, 1997). "OHS Answers". [Online]. Available: http://www.ccohs.ca/oshanswers/safety_haz/falls.html. (Retrieved March 4, 2005).
2. G. LaBar, "Standing Tall against Slips and Falls," *Occupational Hazards* (April 1998): 40–42.
3. Ibid.
4. Ibid., 42.
5. Ibid.
6. Ibid.
7. Ontario Ministry of Labour. (January 23, 2004). Ontario Newswire. [Online]. Available: http://ogov.newswire.ca/ontario/GPOE/2004/01/23/c2828.html?lmatch=&lang=_e.html. (Retrieved March 30, 2005).
8. C. Brickman, "Heart & Sole," *Occupational Health & Safety* 68, no. 4: 35.
9. Construction Safety Association of Ontario, *Health and Safety Manual,* rev. ed. (CSAO, 1999), 69.
10. Ibid., 72.

11. Retrieved from http://public.ansi.org/ansionline/portal/search, July 2003.

12. Ibid.

13. P. Feuerstein, "Head Protection Looks Up," *Safety & Health* 144, no. 3: 39.

14. Ibid.

15. J. Hensel, "Setting Up a Vision Program," *Occupational Health & Safety* 68, no. 10: 36.

16. Ibid.

17. Canadian Centre for Occupational Health and Safety. (November 27, 1997). "OHS Answers." [Online]. Available: http://www.ccohs.ca/oshanswers/ergonomics/mmh/hlth_haz.html. (Retrieved August 4, 2004).

18. Canadian Centre for Occupational Health and Safety. (November 27, 1997). "OHS Answers." [Online]. Available: http://www.ccohs.ca/oshanswers/ergonomics/niosh/ assessing.html.(Retrieved March 4, 2005).

19. A. Kaliokin, "Six Steps Can Help Prevent Back Injuries and Reduce Compensation Costs," *Safety & Health* 138, no. 4: 50.

20. B. Urborg, "How to Comply with OSHA's Ergonomic Standard," [Online]. Available: http://www.nsc.org/news/nr11601.htm. (Retrieved May 2003).

21. Ibid.

22. Ibid.

23. Ibid.

24. R. Carson, "Stand by Your Job," *Occupational Health & Safety* (April 1994): 38.

25. Ibid., 40–42.

26. T. Busshart, "A Cut Above," *Occupational Safety & Health* 67, no. 1: 36.

27. T. Andrews, "Getting Employees Comfortable with PPE," *Occupational Hazards* 62, no. 1: 35–38.

Hazards of Temperature Extremes

12

CHAPTER

LEARNING OBJECTIVES

- Describe the factors that influence thermal comfort.
- Define heat stress, heat strain, and heat exhaustion.
- Describe the physiological effect of exposure to extreme cold.
- Explain how the human body maintains a constant core temperature.
- List the functions of human skin.
- Compare thermal and chemical burns.

Part of providing a safe and healthy workplace is appropriately controlling the temperature, humidity, and air distribution in work areas. A work environment in which the temperature is not properly controlled can be uncomfortable. Extremes of either heat or cold can also be more than uncomfortable — they can be dangerous. Heat stress, cold stress, and burns are major concerns of modern health and safety professionals. This chapter provides the information that professionals need to know to overcome the hazards associated with extreme temperatures.

THERMAL COMFORT

Thermal comfort in the workplace is a function of a number of different factors.[1] Temperature, humidity, air distribution, personal preference, and acclimatization are all determinants of comfort in the workplace. However, determining optimum conditions is not a simple process.

To understand fully the hazards posed by temperature extremes, health and safety professionals must be familiar with several basic concepts related to thermal energy. The most important of these are summarized here:

CONDUCTION
The transfer of heat between two bodies that are touching or from one location to another within a body.

CONVECTION
The transfer of heat from one location to another by way of a moving medium.

METABOLIC HEAT
Produced within a body as a result of activity that burns energy.

ENVIRONMENTAL HEAT
Heat that is produced by sources outside the body.

RADIANT HEAT
The result of electromagnetic nonionizing energy that is transmitted through space without the movement of matter within that space.

- **Conduction** is the transfer of heat between two bodies that are touching, or from one location to another within a body. For example, if an employee touches a workpiece that has just been welded and is still hot, heat will be conducted from the workpiece to the hand. Of course, the result of this heat transfer is a burn.
- **Convection** is the transfer of heat from one location to another by way of a moving medium (a gas or a liquid). Convection ovens use this principle to transfer heat from an electrode by way of gases in the air to whatever is being baked.
- **Metabolic heat** is produced within a body as a result of activity that burns energy. All humans produce metabolic heat. This is why a room that is comfortable when occupied by just a few people may become uncomfortable when it is crowded. Unless the thermostat is lowered to compensate, the metabolic heat of a crowd will cause the temperature of a room to rise to an uncomfortable level.
- **Environmental heat** is produced by external sources. Gas or electric heating systems produce environmental heat, as do sources of electricity and a number of industrial processes.
- **Radiant heat** is the result of electromagnetic nonionizing energy that is transmitted through space without the movement of matter within that space.

The human body is constantly producing heat, equivalent to about 75 watts when sleeping and up to 700 watts while performing heavy work. The net heat exchange rate should maintain a core temperature of 37°C or 98.6°F. Including the factors mentioned above, a formula is given below to show that as work intensity (internal heat production) increases, so must the net heat exchange from the body.

$$H = S + E + R + C$$

Where

H = rate of internal heat production

S = rate of heat storage in the body

E = rate of loss by evaporation

R = rate of radiant energy exchange with surroundings

C = rate of loss by convection

HEAT STRESS AND STRAIN

The key question that must be answered by health and safety professionals concerning employees whose work may subject them to heat stress is:

> What are the conditions to which most adequately hydrated, unmedicated, healthy employees may be exposed without experiencing heat strain or any other adverse effects?

The American Conference of Governmental Industrial Hygienists (ACGIH) publishes a comprehensive manual to help health and safety professionals answer this question for the specific situations and conditions that they face. This manual, titled *TLVs and BEIs: Threshold Limit Values for Chemical Substances and Physical Agents and Biological Exposure Indices*, provides reliable guidance and should be in every health and safety professional's library. Most jurisdictions in Canada base their regulations, standards, or guidelines on these temperature exposure indices. In addition to using the information contained in this manual, all health and safety professionals should have a comprehensive heat stress management program in place and apply sound professional judgment where temperature extremes are an issue.[2]

Heat Stress Defined

Heat stress is the net heat load to which a worker may be exposed from the combined contributions of metabolic cost of work, environmental factors (i.e., air temperature, humidity, air movement, and radiant heat exchange), and clothing requirements. A mild or moderate heat stress may cause discomfort and may adversely affect performance and safety, but it is not harmful to health. As the heat stress approaches human tolerance limits, the risk of heat-related disorders increases.[3]

HEAT STRESS
The net heat load to which a worker is exposed.

Heat Strain Defined

Heat strain is the overall physiological response resulting from heat stress. The physiological adjustments are dedicated to dissipating excess heat from the body. **Acclimatization** is a gradual physiological adaptation that improves an individual's ability to tolerate heat stress.

HEAT STRAIN
The overall physiological response resulting from heat stress.

ACCLIMATIZATION
Process by which the body becomes gradually accustomed to heat or cold in a work setting.

Recognizing Heat Strain

Health and safety professionals, supervisors, and co-workers should know how to recognize heat strain. The following factors are signs of excessive heat strain. Exposure to heat stress should be stopped immediately for any employee experiencing any of these symptoms:

- A sustained rapid heart rate (180 beats per minute minus the employee's age in years). For example, a 40-year-old employee has a sustained heart rate of 150 beats per minute. This is a problem because the heart rate exceeds 140 (180 minus 40) beats per minute.
- Core body temperature is greater than 38.5°C or 101.3°F.
- Recovery rate one minute after a peak work effort is greater than 110 beats per minute.
- Sudden and severe fatigue, nausea, dizziness, or light-headedness.

These symptoms can be assessed on the spot at any given moment in time. In addition, other symptoms can be monitored only over a period of time. Employees are at greater risk of excessive heat strain if they experience any of the following:

- Profuse sweating that continues for hours.
- Weight loss of more than 1.5% of body weight during one work shift.
- Urinary sodium excretion of less than 50 moles (in a 24-hour period).

Symptoms of Heat Exhaustion

Employees need to be able to observe and recognize the symptoms of heat exhaustion in themselves and their co-workers. The following are observable symptoms of heat exhaustion:

- Fatigue
- Nausea and/or vomiting
- Headache
- Light-headedness
- Clammy, moist skin
- Pale or flushed complexion
- Fainting when trying to stand
- Rapid pulse

Clothing

Heat is most easily removed from the body when there is free movement of cool dry air over the skin's surface. This promotes the evaporation of sweat from the skin, which is the body's principal cooling mechanism. Clothing impedes this process, some types more than others. Encapsulating suits and clothing that is impermeable or highly resistant to the flow of air and water vapour increase the potential for heat strain.

When assessing heat stress hazards in the workplace, health and safety professionals should consider the added effect of clothing. For example, the *wet bulb globe temperature* (WBGT) of working conditions should be increased by 3.5°C for employees wearing cloth overalls. This factor increases to 5°C with double cloth overalls.

The basic instrumentation used to determine WBGT consists of three thermometers that are exposed to different conditions that affect the amount of heat exchange from the body. A wet sock covers the first thermometer and simulates the effect of sweat evaporating from the body. A second temperature reading takes into account the radiant heat load on the body, by placing the thermometer inside a black globe. Thirdly, the ambient temperature is measured and included in the WBGT calculation. However, this reading has the least effect on the final value.

Because the WBGT is influenced by air temperature, radiant heat, and humidity, it can be helpful in establishing a threshold for making judgments about working conditions. WBGT values can be calculated using the following formula:

EXPOSED TO DIRECT SUNLIGHT

$$WBGT = 0.7\ T_{nwb} \text{ to } 0.2\ T_g + 0.1\ T_{db}$$

T_{nwb} = Natural wet bulb temperature

T_g = Globe temperature

T_{db} = Dry bulb (air) temperature

NOT EXPOSED TO DIRECT SUNLIGHT

$$WBGT = 0.7\ T_{nwb} + 0.3\ T_g$$

These formulas for WBGT give health and safety professionals a beginning point for making judgments. The WBGT must be adjusted for clothing, work demands, and the employee's acclimatization state. The key is to ensure that employees never experience a core body temperature of 38°C or higher. Figures 12–1 and 12–2 provide screening criteria for heat stress exposure. Once the WBGT has been calculated and adjusted for clothing, these figures may be used for factoring in work demands and acclimatization. To use Figures 12–1 and 12–2, apply them to the following example:

Several acclimatized employees have a job to do that has a work demand of 75% work and 25% rest. The WBGT in the work area has been computed as 26°. The work is considered "heavy." Because the employees will wear long-sleeved shirts and long trousers made of woven material, however, an additional 3.5° must be added: 26° + 3.5° = 29.5°C. Using the proper column and row of Figure 12–1, we see that the allowable WBGT under those conditions is 27.5°. Because the calculated and adjusted WBGT is 29.5°, there is a problem. In order to work in these conditions, the employees should adjust the work demand to 25% work and 75% rest. We can see from Figure 12–1 that under the adjusted conditions the allowable WBGT is 30°, so 29.5° falls safely within that level.

Heat Stress Management

Health and safety professionals should continually emphasize the importance of paying attention to recognizable symptoms of heat stress. In addition, they should ensure that a comprehensive heat stress management program is in place. Such a program should consist of both general and specific controls.

GENERAL CONTROLS The ACGIH recommends the following general controls:

- Provide accurate verbal and written instructions, training programs, and other information about heat stress and strain.
- Encourage drinking small volumes (approximately 250 ml or 1 cup) of cool water about every 20 minutes.
- Permit self-limitation of exposure.
- Encourage co-worker observation to detect signs and symptoms of heat strain in others.
- Counsel and monitor those employees who take medications that may compromise normal cardiovascular, blood pressure, body temperature regulation, renal, or sweat gland functions, as well as those who abuse or who are recovering from the abuse of alcohol and other intoxicants.
- Encourage healthy lifestyles, ideal body weight, and electrolyte balance.

- Adjust expectations of those returning to work after absence from heat stress situations and encourage consumption of salty foods (with approval of the employee's physician if on a salt-restricted diet).
- Consider . . . medical screening to identify those susceptible to systemic heat injury.[4]

Screening Criteria (°C) Acclimatized Employees				
Work Demands	Light Work	Moderate Work	Heavy Work	Very Heavy Work
100% Work	29.5	27.5	26.0	—
75% Work 25% Rest	30.5	28.5	27.5	—
50% Work 50% Rest	31.5	29.5	28.5	27.5
25% Work 75% Rest	32.5	31.0	30.0	29.5

Figure 12–1
Criteria for determining the allowable work periods for acclimatized employees.
Source: American Council of Government Industrial Hygienists (ACGIH).

Screening Criteria (°C) Not Acclimatized Employees				
Work Demands	Light Work	Moderate Work	Heavy Work	Very Heavy Work
100% Work	27.5	25.0	22.5	—
75% Work 25% Rest	29.0	26.5	24.5	—
50% Work 50% Rest	30.0	28.0	26.5	25.0
25% Work 75% Rest	31.0	29.0	28.0	26.5

Figure 12–2
Criteria for determining the allowable work periods for employees who are not acclimatized.
Source: American Council of Government Industrial Hygienists (ACGIH).

SPECIFIC CONTROLS The ACGIH recommends the following specific controls:

- Establish engineering controls that reduce the metabolic rate, provide general air movement, reduce process heat and water-vapour release, and shield radiant heat sources, among others.
- Consider administrative controls that set acceptable exposure times, allow sufficient recovery, and limit physiological strain.
- Consider personal protection that has been demonstrated to be effective for the specific work practices and conditions at the location.[5]

ACCLIMATIZATION Acclimatization is the process of gradually enabling the body to better cope with temperature extremes. The process of acclimatization can take from one to three weeks depending on the general physical condition of the worker. Younger and physically fit people become acclimatized quicker. The worker will benefit from enhanced cardiovascular fitness, which keeps heart rate and core temperature lower during high temperature activities. Other benefits to the acclimatized worker include increased sweating efficiency and a decrease in electrolyte (salt) loss.

The benefits of acclimatization are lost more quickly than they are gained. In as few as two or three days a loss can occur. Workers returning from a break of as little as a couple of days should reduce their workload until their acclimatization has improved. Many Canadian workers who work outdoors are well versed in the annual ritual of acclimatization. In central areas of the country the

SAFETY FACT

Humidex and Wind Chill Warnings

When Canadians hear a weather forecast, along with the temperature, we often get humidex and wind chill numbers. The humidex indicates how hot we would feel in the summer. As the humidity of the air increases, the perceived temperature also rises because evaporation of our sweat is less efficient.

Environment Canada provides the following humidex guidelines:

Humidex level below 29°C – comfortable.
Humidex level 30°C to 39°C – some discomfort.
Humidex level 40°C to 45°C – uncomfortable, avoid exertion.
Humidex level over 45°C – dangerous, probable heat stroke.

In the winter, of course, we are more concerned with how cold it feels outside. Wind chill is the cooling sensation created by the temperature and the wind together. Moving air causes evaporation from our skin and a resulting increase in loss of body heat. So the wind chill provides a better indication of the risk of hypothermia and frostbite to those outside who are not dressed properly or sheltered from the wind than does the air temperature alone. In 2003 Environment Canada began using an improved index based on new wind chill research on precisely how long it takes for exposed skin to freeze. For example, with a wind chill index of –40, which is not uncommon for many parts of Canada, it would take from five to ten minutes for exposed skin to become frostbitten.

temperatures faced by many workers can range from −30°C in the winter to +30°C in summer. In many parts of our vast country, getting "used to" hot outdoor working conditions is not a problem. In most parts of Yukon, the Northwest Territories, and Nunavut, the mean daily temperature rarely exceeds 0°C for eight months of the year and the summertime high is normally less than 20°C.

COLD STRESS

HYPOTHERMIA
The condition that results when the body's core temperature drops to dangerously low levels (35°C or 95°F).

COLD STRESS
Physical or mental stress that results from working in cold conditions.

Excessive exposure to cold can lead to **hypothermia**, which can be fatal. The goal of health and safety professionals in protecting employees from **cold stress** is to prevent the deep body temperature from falling below 36°C (98.6°F) and to prevent cold injuries to body extremities, especially the hands, feet, and head. A fatal exposure to cold typically results from failure to remove the employee from a cold air environment or immersion in cold water.[6]

Excessive exposure to cold stress, even when not fatal, can result in impaired judgment, reduced alertness, and poor decision making. All of these factors increase the likelihood of accidents and injuries. Figure 12–3 shows the effects of allowing the core body temperature to fall to selected levels.

Whether employees are simply exposed to cold air or are immersed in cold water, wind can magnify the level of cold stress. Figure 12–4 shows the effect of wind on selected temperatures. To read this chart, locate the actual temperature in the row across the top (4, −7, −18, −29, −40), then, find the applicable wind speed in the column at the left, and the chart will give you the equivalent temperature. For example, if employees are working in an environment that is −18°C and has a wind speed of 24 kilometres per hour (km/h), the equivalent temperature is −36°C.

Figure 12–3
The body's response to reducing its core temperature.

Effects of Reducing the Core Body Temperature

Core Temperature

°C	°F	Body's Response
37.6	99.6	Normal rectal temperature
36.0	96.8	Metabolic rate increases
35.0	95.0	Pronounced shivering
33.0	91.4	Severe hypothermia
30.0	86.0	Progressive loss of consciousness begins
24.0	75.2	Pulmonary edema
20.0	68.0	Cardiac standstill

Wind Speed (in km/h)	Cooling Effect of Wind				
	Actual Temperature (°C) and Equivalent Temperatures (°C)				
	4	–7	–18	–29	–40
8	3	–9	–21	–32	–44
24	–6	–20	–36	–50	–65
40	–9	–26	–42	–59	–76
64	–2	–29	–47	–65	–82

Figure 12–4
Effect of wind on the actual temperature.
Source: US Army Research Institute of Environmental Medicine.

Preventing Cold Stress

When the equivalent air temperature reaches –32°C (or –25.6°F), continuous exposure of skin should not be allowed. At equivalent air temperatures of 2°C (or 35.6°F), employees who are immersed in water or whose clothing gets wet should be treated for hypothermia immediately. Figure 12–5 shows selected TLVs for employees who work in environments with temperature below freezing.

To use Figure 12–5, locate the applicable temperature in the left-hand column, then, reading across the top, locate the applicable wind speed. For example, employees working a four-hour shift in an environment with an air temperature of –32°C and an 8-km/h wind should be exposed for no longer than 55 minutes at a time and should warm up at least three times during the shift.

When work is to be performed in an environment with an air temperature of 4°C (or 39.2°F) or less, total body protective clothing is advisable. What follows are several strategies that can be used to decrease the hazards of cold stress:

- When working in a setting in which wind is a factor, reduce the effect of the wind by (1) erecting a windscreen; or (2) wearing wind-breaking clothing.
- When working in a setting in which clothing may get wet, apply one or more of the following strategies: (1) with light work, wear an outer layer of impermeable clothing; (2) with heavier work, wear an outer layer that is water repellent, but not impermeable (change outerwear as it becomes wet); (3) select outer garments that are ventilated to prevent internal wetting from sweat; (4) if clothing gets wet before going into the cold environment, change first; (5) change socks daily or more often to keep them dry; and (6) use vapour barrier boots to help keep the feet dry.
- If adequate protective clothing that is appropriate for the conditions in question is not available, the work should be modified or suspended until conditions change or the clothing is available.

| TLVs for a Four-Hour Shift | | | | | | |
| Air Temperature | | No Wind | | 8 km/h (5 mph) Wind | | 16 km/h (10 mph) Wind | |
C°	F°	Max. Work Time	No. of Breaks	Max. Work Time	No. of Breaks	Max. Work Time	No. of Breaks
−32 to −34	−25 to −29	75 min.	2	55 min.	3	40 min.	4
−35 to −37	−30 to −34	55 min.	3	40 min.	4	30 min.	5
−38 to −39	−35 to −39	40 min.	4	30 min.	5	Non–emergency Work Prohibited	

Note: This applies to workers properly dressed in dry clothing.

Figure 12–5
Partial table for determining TLVs in selected circumstances.
Source: American Council of Government Industrial Hygienists (ACGIH).

When work is to be performed in an environment with an air temperature of −12°C (or 10.4°F), the following additional strategies should be applied:

- Employees should be under continuous observation using either direct supervision or the buddy system.
- The work rate should be paced to avoid sweating. When heavy work is necessary, employees should take frequent warming breaks in heated shelters. If clothing becomes wet — internally or externally — it should be changed during a break.
- Do not allow new employees to work full time in these conditions until they have several days to become accustomed to the conditions and the necessary protective clothing.
- When determining the required work level for employees (light, heavy, or very heavy), consider the weight and bulkiness of protective clothing.
- Organize work in cold environments to minimize long periods of sitting or standing still. Never use unprotected metal chairs or seats.
- Before allowing employees to work in a cold environment, make sure they have been trained in health and safety procedures for working in cold environments. Figure 12–6 is a checklist of topics that should be covered as a minimum during employee training.
- When work in a refrigerated room is required, the air velocity should be minimized and maintained at one metre per second (200 fpm) or less.
- When work outdoors in snow is required, employees should be provided with special safety goggles that protect the eyes from ultraviolet light, glare, and blowing ice crystals.
- Employees who suffer from diseases or take medications that inhibit normal body functions or that reduce normal body tolerances should be prohibited from working in environments where temperatures are at −1°C or 30.2°F or less.

- Employees who are routinely exposed to the following conditions should be medically certified as being suitable for work in such conditions: (1) air temperatures of less than −24°C (or 211.2°F) with wind speeds less than 8 km/h (5 mph); and (2) air temperatures of less than −18°C (or 0°F) with wind speeds greater than 8 km/h (5 mph).

BURNS AND THEIR EFFECTS

One of the most common hazards associated with heat in the workplace is the burn. Burns can be especially dangerous because they disrupt the normal functioning of the skin, which is the body's largest organ and the most important in terms of protecting other organs. It is necessary first to understand the composition of, and purpose served by, the skin to understand the hazards that burns can represent.

Human Skin

Human skin is the tough, continuous outer covering of the body. It consists of the following two main layers: (1) the outer layer, which is known as the **epidermis**; and (2) the inner layer, which is known as the **dermis**, **cutis**, or **corium**. The dermis is connected to the underlying subcutaneous tissue.

The skin serves several important purposes, including protection of body tissue, sensation, secretion, excretion, and respiration (see Figure 12–7). Protection from **fluid loss**, water penetration, ultraviolet radiation, and infestation by microorganisms is a major function of the skin. The sensory functions of touching, sensing cold, feeling pain, and sensing heat involve the skin.

The skin helps regulate body heat through the sweating process. It excretes sweat that takes with it **electrolytes** and certain toxins. This helps keep the body's fluid level in balance. By giving off minute amounts of carbon dioxide and absorbing small amounts of oxygen, the skin also aids slightly in respiration.

What makes burns particularly dangerous is that they can disrupt any or all of these functions depending on their severity. The deeper the penetration, the more severe the burn.

EPIDERMIS
The outer layer of human skin.

DERMIS
The inner layer of human skin.

CUTIS
The inner layer of human skin.

CORIUM
The inner layer of human skin.

FLUID LOSS
Depletion of necessary body fluids, primarily through perspiration.

ELECTROLYTES
Minerals that are needed for the body to maintain the proper metabolism and for cells to produce energy.

Training Checklist for Employees Who Work in a Cold Environment
- ✓ Proper warming procedures
- ✓ Applicable first-aid procedures
- ✓ Protective clothing requirements and proper use of protective clothing
- ✓ Proper eating habits
- ✓ Proper drinking habits
- ✓ Recognizing cold stress and strain (e.g., impending frostbite, impending hypothermia, and so on)
- ✓ Safe work processes

Figure 12–6
Checklist for training employees who will work in a cold environment.

**Figure 12–7
Functions of the
human skin.**

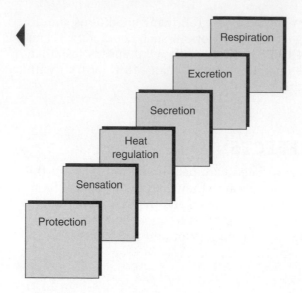

Severity of Burns

The severity of a burn depends on several factors. The most important of these is the depth to which the burn penetrates. Other determining factors include the location of the burn, the age of the victim, and the amount of burned area.

The most widely used method of classifying burns is by degree (i.e., first-, second-, or third-degree burns). Modern health and safety professionals should be familiar with these classifications and what they mean.

First-degree burns are minor and result only in a mild inflammation of the skin, known as *erythema*. Sunburn is a common form of first-degree burn. It is easily recognizable as a redness of the skin that makes the skin sensitive and moderately painful to the touch.

Second-degree burns are easily recognizable from the blisters that form on the skin. If a second-degree burn is superficial, the skin will heal with little or no scarring. A deeper second-degree burn will form a thin layer of coagulated, dead cells that feels leathery to the touch. A temperature of approximately 99°C (210°F) can cause a second-degree burn in as little as 15 seconds of contact.

Third-degree burns are very dangerous and can be fatal depending on the amount of body surface affected. A third-degree burn penetrates through both the epidermis and the dermis. A deep third-degree burn will penetrate body tissue. Third-degree burns can be caused by both moist and dry hazards. Moist hazards include steam and hot liquids; these cause burns that appear white. Dry hazards include fire and hot objects or surfaces; these cause burns that appear black and charred.

In addition to the depth of penetration of a burn, the amount of surface area covered is also a critical concern. This amount is expressed as a percentage of **body surface area (BSA)**. Figure 12–8 shows how the percentage of BSA can be estimated. Burns covering over 75% of BSA are usually fatal.

Using the first-, second-, and third-degree burn classifications in conjunction with BSA percentages, burns can be classified further as minor, moderate, or critical. According to Mertz, these classifications can be summarized as follows:[7]

FIRST-DEGREE BURN
Results in a mild inflammation of the skin known as erythema.

SECOND-DEGREE BURN
Results in blisters forming on the skin.

THIRD-DEGREE BURN
Penetrates through both the epidermis and the dermis. It may be fatal.

BODY SURFACE AREA (BSA)
When assessing the severity of burns, the amount of body surface area that is covered with burns is an important factor.

Right arm	9% of BSA
Left arm	9% of BSA
Head/neck	9% of BSA
Right leg	18% of BSA
Left leg	18% of BSA
Back	18% of BSA
Chest/stomach	18% of BSA
Perineum	1% of BSA

▶ **Figure 12–8**
Estimating percentage of body surface area (BSA) burned.

Minor Burns

All first-degree burns are considered **minor**. Second-degree burns covering less than 15% of the body are considered **minor**. Third-degree burns can be considered minor provided they cover only 2% or less of BSA.

Moderate Burns

Second-degree burns that penetrate the epidermis and cover 15% or more of BSA are considered moderate. Second-degree burns that penetrate the dermis and cover from 15 to 30% of BSA are considered **moderate**. Third-degree burns can be considered moderate provided they cover less than 10% of BSA and are not on the hands, face, or feet.

Critical Burns

Second-degree burns covering more than 30% of BSA or third-degree burns covering over 10% of BSA are considered **critical**. Even small-area third-degree burns to the hands, face, or feet are considered critical because of the greater potential for **infection** to these areas by their nature. In addition, burns that are complicated by other injuries (fractures, soft tissue damage, and so on) are considered critical.

CHEMICAL BURNS

Chemicals are widely used in modern industry even by companies that do not produce them as part of their product base. Many of the chemicals produced, handled, stored, transported or otherwise used in industry can cause burns similar to those caused by heat (i.e., first-, second-, and third-degree burns). The hazards of chemical burns are very similar to those of thermal burns.

Chemical burns, like thermal burns, destroy body tissue; the extent of destruction depends on the severity of the burn. However, chemical burns continue to destroy body tissue until the chemicals are washed away completely.

The severity of the burn produced by a given chemical depends on the following factors:

MINOR BURNS
All first-degree burns are considered minor as well as second-degree burns covering less than 15% of the body.

MODERATE BURNS
Second-degree burns covering less than 30% of the body and third-degree burns covering less than 10% are considered moderate.

CRITICAL BURNS
Second-degree burns covering more than 30% of the body and third-degree burns covering over 10% are considered critical.

INFECTION
The body's response to contamination by a disease-producing microorganism.

CHEMICAL BURNS
Burn damage to the skin caused by chemicals such as acids and alkalies.

- Corrosive capability of the chemical.
- Concentration of the chemical.
- Temperature of the chemical or the solution in which it is dissolved.
- Duration of contact with the chemical.[8]

Effects of Chemical Burns

Different chemicals have different effects on the human body. The harmful effects of selected widely used chemicals are summarized in Figure 12–9.[9] These are only a few of the many chemicals widely used in industry today. All serve an important purpose; however, all carry the potential for serious injury.

The primary hazardous effects of chemical burns are infection, loss of body fluids, and shock.[10]

INFECTION The risk of infection is high with chemical burns — as is it with heat-induced burns — because the body's primary defence against infection-causing microorganisms (the skin) is penetrated. This is why it is so important to keep burns clean. Infection in a burn wound can cause *septicemia* (blood poisoning).

FLUID LOSS Body fluid loss in second- and third-degree burns can be serious. With second-degree burns, the blisters that form on the skin often fill with fluid that seeps out of damaged tissue under the blister. With third-degree burns, fluids are lost internally and this can cause the same complications as a hemorrhage. If these fluids are not replaced properly, the burns can be fatal.

SHOCK
A depression of the nervous system.

SHOCK Shock is a depression of the nervous system. It can be caused by both physical and psychological trauma. In cases of serious burns, it may be caused

Chemical	Potential Harmful Effect
Acetic acid	Tissue damage
Liquid bromide	Corrosive effect on the respiratory system and tissue damage
Formaldehyde	Tissue hardening
Lime	Dermatitis and eye burns
Methylbromide	Blisters
Nitric/sulphuric acid mixture	Severe burns and tissue damage
Oxalic acid	Ulceration and tissue damage
White phosphorus	Ignites in air causing thermal burns
Silver nitrate	Corrosive/caustic effect on the skin
Sodium (metal)	Ignites with moisture causing thermal burns
Trichloracetic acid	Tissue damage

Figure 12–9
Harmful effects of selected widely used chemicals.

by the intense pain that can occur when skin is burned away, leaving sensitive nerve endings exposed. Shock from burns can come in the following two forms: (1) primary shock, which is the first stage and results from physical pain or psychological trauma; and (2) secondary shock, which comes later and is caused by a loss of fluids and plasma proteins resulting from the burns.

First Aid for Chemical Burns

There is a definite course of action that should be taken when chemical burns occur, and the need for immediate action cannot be overemphasized. Flooding the affected area with water, especially in the case of caustic chemicals, will reduce the severity of the damage. In the case of chemical burns to the eyes, the continuous flooding should continue for at least 15 minutes. The eyelids should be held open to ensure that chemicals are not trapped under them.

Clothing is another consideration when an employee comes in contact with a caustic chemical. If chemicals have saturated the employee's clothes, they must be removed quickly. The best approach is to remove the clothes while flooding the body or the affected area. If necessary for quick removal, clothing should be ripped or cut off.

The critical need to apply water immediately in cases of chemical burns means that water must be readily available. Health and safety professionals should ensure that special eye wash and shower facilities are available wherever employees handle chemicals.

SUMMARY

1. Important thermal-related terms include conduction, convection, metabolic heat, environmental heat, and radiant heat.

2. Heat stress is the net load to which a worker may be exposed from the combined contributions of metabolic cost of work, environmental factors, and clothing requirements.

3. The goal in protecting employees from cold stress is to prevent the deep body temperature from falling below 36°C (or 98.6°F).

4. Cold stress can be prevented by applying the following strategies: medical screening and supervision, orientation and training, proper work practices, and engineering and administrative controls.

5. Wind or air movement causes the body to sense coldness beyond what the thermometer registers. This phenomenon is known as the wind-chill factor. This should be considered when planning work schedules.

6. The most common form of cold stress is hypothermia.

7. The most widely used method of classifying burns is by degree: first-, second-, and third-degree burns. The amount of surface area covered by burns is expressed as a percentage of body surface area (BSA). Burns are also classified as minor, moderate, and critical.

8. The severity of chemical burns depends on the corrosive capability of the chemical, the concentration and temperature of the chemical, and the duration of contact.

9. The primary hazards associated with chemical burns beyond the damage to the body tissues are infection, fluid loss, and shock. The most important first aid for chemical burns is immediate and continual flushing with water.

KEY TERMS AND CONCEPTS

Acclimatization	First-degree burn
Body surface area (BSA)	Fluid loss
Chemical burn	Heat stress
Cold stress	Heat strain
Conduction	Hypothermia
Convection	Infection
Corium	Metabolic heat
Critical burn	Minor burn
Cutis	Moderate burn
Dermis	Radiant heat
Electrolytes	Second-degree burn
Environmental heat	Shock
Epidermis	Third-degree burn

REVIEW QUESTIONS

1. Define the following thermal comfort–related terms: *conduction, convection*, and *metabolic heat.*

2. What is heat stress?

3. What is heat strain?

4. What are the symptoms of heat exhaustion?

5. How can heat strain be recognized?

6. How does clothing affect the cooling process?

7. What factors influence the WBGT?

8. Describe the various general controls in heat stress management.

9. How can cold stress be prevented?

10. How does wind movement affect the way the body perceives temperature?

11. Describe the symptoms of cold stress and hypothermia.

12. Describe the various components of a cold stress prevention program.

13. Describe the various purposes served by the skin.

14. Describe and differentiate among first-, second-, and third-degree burns.

15. Describe and differentiate among minor, moderate, and critical burns.

16. List the factors that determine the severity of a chemical burn.

17. Explain the hazards of chemical burns besides tissue damage.

18. What should you do if an employee accidentally splashes a caustic chemical on himself or herself?

WEBLINKS

Canadian Centre for Occupational Health and Safety
www.ccohs.ca/oshanswers/phys_agents

CCOHS offers information for workers who are exposed to potentially harmful hot or cold environments, both indoors and out.

The Weather Office
www.weatheroffice.ec.gc.ca/canada_e.html

The Weather Office website from Environment Canada contains weather facts, trivia, and lots of great tips on working or playing in Canada's extreme temperatures.

ENDNOTES

1. American Conference of Governmental Industrial Hygienists (ACGIH), 2003 *TLVs and BEIs* (Cincinnati: 2003), 172–181.

2. Ibid., 180–188.

3. Ibid., 181.

4. Ibid., 187.

5. Ibid.

6. Ibid., 171–179.

7. Patricia M. Mertz, "Burn Study," unpublished paper, University of Miami School of Medicine, Department of Dermatology and Cutaneous Surgery, Miami, FL, October 2000, 2.

8. National Safety Council, "Chemical Burns," Data Sheet 1–523 Rev. 87 (Chicago: National Safety Council): 1.

9. Ibid., 3–4.

10. Ibid., 2.

13 CHAPTER

Pressure Hazards

LEARNING OBJECTIVES

- Define pressure hazard, bends, dysbarism, creeps, chokes, and aseptic necrosis.
- Describe pressure danger to humans.
- Describe the hazards associated with boilers, high-temperature water, unfired pressure vessels, and high-pressure systems.
- Describe cracking hazards in pressure vessels.
- List methods of nondestructive testing of pressure vessels.
- List and describe five symptoms of pressure hazards.
- Produce a checklist that may be used to reduce pressure hazards.

PRESSURE
The force exerted against an opposing fluid or thrust distributed over a surface.

HAZARD
A condition with the potential of causing injury to personnel, damage to equipment or structures, loss of material, or lessening of the ability to perform a prescribed function.

PRESSURE HAZARD
A hazard caused by a dangerous condition involving pressure.

PRESSURE HAZARDS DEFINED

Pressure is defined in physics as the force exerted against an opposing fluid or thrust distributed over a surface. This may be expressed in force or weight per unit of area, such as kilograms/centimetre squared (or psi [pounds per square inch]). Units of pressure are also commonly expressed as pascals or kilopascals (the air in your car tires is under about 200 kilopascals of pressure [30 psi] and the atmosphere is at approximately 101.3 kPa [14.7 psi]); a pascal is equal to one Newton per square metre (N/m). A **hazard** is a condition with the potential of causing injury to personnel, damage to equipment or structures, loss of material, or lessening of the ability to perform a prescribed function. Thus, a **pressure hazard** is a hazard caused by a dangerous condition involving pressure. Critical injury and damage can occur with relatively little pressure.

We perceive pressure in relation to the earth's atmosphere. Approximately 21% of the atmosphere is oxygen, with most of the other 79% being nitrogen. In addition to oxygen and nitrogen, the atmosphere contains trace amounts of several inert gases: argon, neon, krypton, xenon, and helium.

At sea level, the earth's atmosphere averages 101.3 kilopascals (101 325 N/m), or 1.013 millibars, or 760 mm Hg (29.92 inches), or 14.7 psi, depending on the measuring scale used.[1] The international system of measurement uses newtons per square metre (N/m) — that is, pascals. However, in human physiology studies, the typical unit is millimetres of mercury (mm Hg).

Atmospheric pressure is usually measured using a **barometer**. As the altitude above sea level increases, atmospheric pressure decreases in a nonlinear fashion. For example, at 5486.4 metres (18 000 feet) above sea level, the barometric pressure is equal to 390 mm Hg. Half of this pressure, around 195 mm Hg, can be found at 7010.4 metres (23 000 feet) above sea level.

Boyle's law states that the product of a given pressure and volume is constant with a constant temperature:

$$P_1 V_1 = P_2 V_2, \text{ when } T \text{ is constant}$$

Air moves in and out of the lungs because of a pressure gradient or difference in pressure. When atmospheric pressure is greater than pressure within the lungs, air flows down this pressure gradient from the outside into the lungs. This is called **inspiration**, inhalation, or breathing in, and occurs with greater lung volume than at rest (i.e., the lungs are expanded). When pressure in the lungs is greater than atmospheric pressure, air moves down a pressure gradient outward from the lungs to the outside. **Expiration** occurs when air leaves the lungs and the lung volume is less than the relaxed volume, increasing pressure within the lungs.

Gas exchange occurs between air in the lung alveoli and gas in solution in blood. The pressure gradients causing this gas exchange are called partial pressures. **Dalton's law of partial pressures** states that, in a mixture of theoretically ideal gases, the pressure exerted by the mixture is the sum of the pressures exerted by each component gas of the mixture:

$$P_A = P_O + P_N + P_{else}$$

Air entering the lungs immediately becomes saturated with water vapour. Water vapour, although it is a gas, does not conform to Dalton's law. The partial pressure of water vapour in a mixture of gases is not dependent on its fractional concentration in that mixture. Water vapour partial pressure, instead, is dependent on its temperature. From this exception to Dalton's law comes the fact that at the normal body temperature of 37°C (98.6°F), water vapour maintains a partial pressure of 47 mm Hg as long as that temperature is maintained. With this brief explanation of how pressure is involved in human breathing, we now focus on the various sources of pressure hazards.

BAROMETER
Scientific device for measuring atmospheric pressure.

BOYLE'S LAW
States that the product of a given pressure and volume is constant with a constant temperature.

INSPIRATION
When atmospheric pressure is greater than pressure within the lungs, air flows down this pressure gradient from the outside into the lungs.

EXPIRATION
When pressure within the lungs is greater than atmospheric pressure, air moves down a pressure gradient from the lungs to the outside.

DALTON'S LAW OF PARTIAL PRESSURES
States that in a mixture of theoretically ideal gases, the pressure exerted by the mixture is the sum of the pressures exerted by each component gas of the mixture.

SOURCES OF PRESSURE HAZARDS

There are many sources of pressure hazard — some natural, most created by humans. Because the human body comprises approximately 85% liquid, which is virtually incompressible, increasing pressure does not create problems by itself. Problems can result from air being trapped or expanded within body cavities.

When sinus passages are blocked so that air cannot pass easily from the sinuses to the nose, expansion of the air in the sinuses can lead to problems. The same complications can occur with air trapped in the middle ear's eustachian tube. As Boyle's law states, gas volume increases as pressure decreases. Expansion of the air in blocked sinus passages or the middle ear occurs with a rapid increase in altitude or a rapid ascent under water. This can cause pain and, if not eventually relieved, disease. Under extreme circumstances of rapid ascent from underwater diving or high-altitude decompression, lungs can rupture.

Nitrogen absorption into the body tissues can become excessive during underwater diving and breathing of nitrogen-enriched air. Nitrogen permeation of tissues occurs in proportion to the partial pressure of nitrogen taken in. If the nitrogen is permeating tissues faster than the person can breathe it out, bubbles of gas may form in the tissues.

Decompression sickness can result from the decompression that accompanies a rapid rise from sea level to at least 5500 metres (18 000 feet) or a rapid ascent from around 40 to 20 metres (132 to 66 feet) under water. Several factors influence the onset of decompression sickness:

- A *history* of previous decompression sickness increases the probability of another attack.
- *Age* is a component. Being over 30 increases the chances of an attack.
- *Physical fitness* plays a role. People in better condition have a reduced chance of the sickness. Previously broken bones and joint injuries are often the sites of pain.
- *Exercise* during the exposure to decompression increases the likelihood and brings on an earlier onset of symptoms.
- *Low temperature* increases the probability of the sickness.
- *Speed of decompression* also influences the sickness. A rapid rate of decompression increases the possibility and severity of symptoms.
- *Length of exposure* of the person to the pressure is proportionately related to the intensity of symptoms. The longer the exposure, the greater the chances of decompression sickness.

A reduction in partial pressure can result from reduced available oxygen and cause a problem in breathing known as **hypoxia**. Too much oxygen or oxygen breathed under pressure that is too high is called **hyperoxia**. Another partial pressure hazard, *nitrogen narcosis,* results from a higher-than-normal level of nitrogen pressure.

When breathed under pressure, nitrogen causes a reduction of cerebral and neural activity. Breathing nitrogen at great depths under water can cause a feeling of euphoria and loss of reality. At depths greater than 30 metres (100 feet), nitrogen narcosis can occur even when breathing normal air. The effects may become pathogenic at depths greater than 60 metres (200 feet), with motor skills threatened at depths greater than 90 metres (300 feet). Cognitive processes deteriorate quickly after reaching a depth of 100 metres (325 feet).

DECOMPRESSION SICKNESS
Can result from the decompression that accompanies a rapid rise from sea level to at least 5500 metres (18 000 feet) or a rapid ascent from around 40 to 20 metres (132 to 66 feet) under water.

HYPOXIA
Too little oxygen getting to body tissues.

HYPEROXIA
Too much oxygen or oxygen breathed under too high a pressure.

BOILERS AND PRESSURE HAZARDS

A boiler is a closed vessel in which water is heated to form steam, hot water, or high-temperature water under pressure.[2] Potential safety hazards associated with boilers and other pressurized vessels include the following:

- Design, construction, or installation errors.
- Poor or insufficient training of operators.

- Human error.
- Mechanical breakdown or failure.
- Failure or blockage of control or safety devices.
- Insufficient or improper inspections.
- Improper application of equipment.
- Insufficient preventive maintenance.[3]

Through years of experience, a great deal has been learned about how to prevent accidents associated with boilers. Union Gas Association recommends the daily, weekly, monthly, semi-annual, and annual boiler inspection schedule found in Figure 13–1.

HIGH-TEMPERATURE WATER HAZARDS

High-temperature water (HTW) is exactly what its name implies — water that has been heated to a very high temperature, but not high enough to produce steam.[4] In some cases, HTW can be used as an economical substitute for steam (e.g., in industrial heating systems). It has the added advantage of releasing less energy (pressure) than steam does.

In spite of this, there are hazards associated with HTW. Human contact with HTW can result in extremely serious burns and even death. The two most prominent sources of hazards associated with HTW are operator error and improper design. Proper training and careful supervision are the best guards against operator error.

The design of HTW systems is a highly specialized process that should be undertaken only by experienced engineers. Mechanical forces such as water hammer, thermal expansion, thermal shock, or faulty materials cause system failures more often than do thermodynamic forces. Therefore, it is important to allow for such causes when designing an HTW system.

The best designs are simple and operator-friendly. Designing too many automatic controls into an HTW system can create more problems than it solves by turning operators into mere attendants who are unable to respond properly to emergencies.

HAZARDS OF UNFIRED PRESSURE VESSELS

Not all pressure vessels are fired. Unfired pressure vessels include compressed air tanks, steam-jacketed kettles, digesters, and vulcanizers, as well as others that can create heat internally by various means rather than by external fire.[5] The various means of creating internal heat include (1) chemical action within the vessel, and (2) application of some heating medium (electricity, steam, hot oil, and so on) to the contents of the vessel. The potential hazards associated with unfired pressure vessels include hazardous interaction between the material of the vessel and the materials that will be processed in it; inability of the filled vessel to carry the weight of its contents and the corresponding internal pressure; inability of the vessel to withstand the pressure introduced into it plus pressure caused by chemical reactions that occur during processing; and inability of the vessel to withstand any vacuum that may be created accidentally or intentionally.

Recommended Gas/Oil Fired Boiler Inspection Schedules

It is very important that preventive maintenance be performed on an established schedule. Following are recommendations on schedules as well as suggestions to assist in maximizing the uptime of your boiler and associated equipment.

Daily*	Weekly	Monthly	Semi-Annually	Annually
Check water level	Check for tight closing of fuel valves	Inspect burner	Clean low water cut-off(s)	Clean fireside surfaces
Blowdown boiler	Check fuel and air linkage	Analyze combustion	Check oil preheater	Clean breeching
Blowdown water column	Check indicating lights and alarms	Check cams	Inspect refractory	Clean waterside surfaces
Check combustion visually	Check operating and limit controls	Inspect for flue gas leaks	Clean oil pump strainer and filter	Check oil storage tanks
Treat water according to the established program	Check safety and interlock controls	Inspect for hot spots	Clean air cleaner and air/oil separator	Check fluid levels on hydraulic valves
Record boiler operating pressure/temperature	Check low water cutoff(s) operation	Review boiler blowdown procedures	Check pump coupling alignment	Check gauge glass
Record feedwater pressure/temperature	Check for leaks, noise, vibration, unusual conditions	Check combustion air supply	Reset combustion	Remove and recondition safety valves
Record flue gas temperature	Check operation of all motors	Check all filter elements	Inspect mercury switches	Check oil pumps
Record oil pressure and temperature	Check general burner operation	Check fuel systems		Check boiler feed pumps
Record gas pressure	Check lubricating oil levels	Check belt drives		Check condensate receivers
Record atomizing pressure	Check flame scanner assembly	Check lubrication requirements		Check chemical feed systems
Check general boiler/burner operation	Check packing glands			Tighten all electrical terminals

*Daily items may be performed more than once daily.

Figure 13–1
Recommended gas/oil fired boiler inspection schedule.

Source: Union Gas. (2000–2004). "Recommended Gas/Oil Fired Boiler Inspection Schedule." [Online]. Available: http://www.uniongas.com/business/otherci/techsol/heating/boiler/inspection.asp. (Retrieved March 5, 2005).

The most effective preventive measure for overcoming these potential hazards is proper design. Specifications for the design and construction of unfired pressure vessels include requirements in the following areas: working pressure range, working temperature range, type of materials to be processed, stress relief, welding or joining measures, and radiography. Designs that meet the specifications set forth for unfired pressure vessels in such codes as the ASME (American Society of Mechanical Engineers) Code (Section VIII) will overcome most predictable hazards. ASME codes are internationally recognized and are available through the CSA. The CSA Boiler, Pressure Vessel and Pressure Piping Code can be found in CSA publication number is B51-03. Beyond proper design, the same types of precautions taken when operating fired pressure vessels can be used when operating unfired vessels. These include continual inspection, proper housekeeping, periodic testing, visual observation (for detecting cracks), and the use of appropriate safety devices.

HAZARDS OF HIGH-PRESSURE SYSTEMS

The hazards most commonly associated with high-pressure systems are leaks, pulsation, vibration, release of high-pressure gases, and whiplash from broken high-pressure pipe, tubing, or hose.[6] Strategies for reducing these hazards include limiting vibration through the use of vibration dampening (use of anchored pipe supports); decreasing the potential for leaks by limiting the number of joints in the system; using pressure gauges; placing shields or barricades around the system; using remote control and monitoring; and restricting access.

CRACKING HAZARDS IN PRESSURE VESSELS

One of the most serious hazards in pressure vessels is the potential for cracking.[7] Cracking can lead to either a complete rupture or to leaks. The consequences of a complete rupture include the following: (1) blast effects due to the sudden expansion of the contents of the vessel; and (2) possible injuries and damage from fragmentation. The consequences of a leak include the following: (1) suffocation or poisoning of employees depending on the contents of the vessel; (2) explosion and fire; and (3) chemical and thermal burns from contact with the contents of the vessel.

Pressure vessels are used in many different applications to contain many different types of substances ranging from water to extremely toxic chemicals. Leakage or rupture may occur in welded seams, bolted joints, or at nozzles. Figure 13–2 is a diagram of a typical pressure vessel showing the potential points of leakage and rupture. The types of vessels that are most susceptible to leakage and rupture, primarily because of the processes they are part of or their contents, are as follows:

Deaerator Vessels

Deaeration is the process of removing noncondensible gases, primarily oxygen, from the water used in steam generation. Deaerator vessels are used in such applications as power generation, pulp and paper processing, chemical pro-

Figure 13–2
Diagram of a typical pressure vessel showing potential points for leakage or rupture.

cessing, and petroleum refining. The most common failures associated with deaerator vessels are (1) cracks caused by water hammer at welded joints that were not postweld heat treated, and (2) cracks caused by corrosion fatigue.

Amine Vessels

The *amine process* removes hydrogen sulphide from petroleum gases such as propane and butane. It can also be used for removing carbon dioxide in some processes. Amine vessels are used in petroleum refineries, gas treatment facilities, and chemical plants. The most common failures associated with amine vessels are cracks in stressed or unrelieved welds.

Wet Hydrogen Sulphide Vessels

Any fluid that contains water and hydrogen sulphide is considered wet hydrogen sulphide. Many of the vessels used to contain wet hydrogen sulphide are made of steel. Hydrogen is generated when steel is exposed to such a mixture. Dissolved hydrogen can cause cracking, blistering, and embrittlement, particularly in high-strength steels. Consequently, low-strength steels are recommended for wet hydrogen sulphide vessels.

Ammonia Vessels

Vessels for the containment of ammonia are widely used in commercial refrigeration systems and chemical processes. Such ammonia vessels are typically constructed as spheres of carbon steel. The water and oxygen content in ammonia can cause carbon steel to crack, particularly near welds.

Pulp Digester Vessels

The process used to digest pulp in the manufacture of paper involves the use of a weak water solution of sodium hydroxide and sodium sulphide in a temperature range of 110°C to 140°C (230°F to 285°F). The most common failure in pulp digester vessels is cracking along welded seams due primarily to caustic stress corrosion.

NONDESTRUCTIVE TESTING OF PRESSURE VESSELS

To prevent leakage or rupture, it is necessary to examine pressure vessels periodically. There are five widely used nondestructive methods for testing: (1) visual examination, (2) liquid penetration test, (3) magnetic particle test, (4) gamma and X-ray radiography, and (5) ultrasonic test. Visual, liquid penetration, and magnetic particle tests can detect only those defects that are either on the surface or near it. Radiographic and ultrasonic tests can detect problems within the material. Consequently, the visual, liquid penetration, and magnetic particle tests are referred to as *surface tests*. Radiography and ultrasonic are called *volumetric tests*.

Visual Examination

A visual examination consists of taking a thorough look at the vessel to detect signs of corrosion, erosion, or hydrogen blistering. In order to conduct a dependable visual examination of a pressure vessel, it is necessary to have a clean surface and good lighting.

Liquid Penetration Test

This test involves placing a specially formulated liquid penetrant over an area and letting it seep in. When the penetrant is removed from the surface, some of it remains entrapped in the area of discontinuity. A developing agent is then applied, which draws out the entrapped penetrant and magnifies the discontinuity. The process can be enhanced by adding fluorescent chemicals to the penetrant to aid in the detection of problems.

Magnetic Particle Test

This test is based on the fact that discontinuities in or near the surface of a pressure vessel disturb magnetic flux lines that are induced in a ferromagnetic material. Disturbances are detected by applying fine particles of ferromagnetic material to the surface of the vessel. The necessary magnetic field is produced most frequently using the "prod" technique in which electric current is run through an area by applying opposing "prods" (contact probes). A drawback of this test is that corners and surface irregularities in the vessel material can produce the same disturbances as defects. Consequently, special care is needed when using this test in a region with corners or welded joints. Because this test works only with ferromagnetic material, its use is limited to vessels made of carbon and low-alloy steels.

Radiography Test

This test amounts to making an X-ray negative of a given portion of the vessel. The process works in the same way as those used by physicians and dentists. Irregularities such as holes, voids, or discontinuities produce a greater exposure (darker area) on the X-ray negative.

Ultrasonic Testing

ULTRASONIC TESTING
Use of acoustic waves for detecting foreign objects.

This test is similar to radar and other uses of electromagnetic and acoustic waves for detecting foreign objects. Short signals are induced into the material. Waves that are reflected back from discontinuities are detected by one or more transducers. **Ultrasonic testing** requires an electronic system for generating a signal, a transducer system for converting the electrical signal into mechanical vibrations and vice versa, and an electronic system for amplifying, processing, and displaying the return signal.

PRESSURE DANGERS TO HUMANS

The term *anoxia* refers to the rare case of a total lack of oxygen. Hypoxia, a condition that occurs when the available oxygen is reduced, can occur while ascending to a high altitude or when oxygen in air has been replaced with another gas, which may happen in some industrial situations.

ALTITUDE SICKNESS
A form of hypoxia associated with high altitudes.

Altitude sickness is a form of hypoxia associated with high altitudes. Ascent to an altitude of 3000 metres (10 000 feet) above sea level can result in a feeling of malaise, shortness of breath, and fatigue. A person ascending to 4300 to 4600 metres (14 000 to 15 000 feet) may experience euphoria, along with a reduction in powers of reason, judgment, and memory. Altitude sickness includes a loss of **useful consciousness** at 6100 to 7600 metres (20 000 to 25 000 feet). After approximately five minutes at this altitude, a person may lose consciousness. The loss of consciousness comes at approximately one minute or less at 9000 metres (30 000 feet). Over 11 500 metres (38 000 feet), most people lose consciousness within 30 seconds and may fall into a coma and possibly die.

USEFUL CONSCIOUSNESS
A state of consciousness in which a person is clear-headed and alert enough to make responsible decisions.

Hyperoxia, or an increased concentration of oxygen in air, is not a common situation. Hyperbaric chambers or improperly calibrated scuba equipment can create conditions that may lead to convulsions if pure oxygen is breathed for greater than three hours. Breathing air at a depth of around 100 metres (300 feet) can be toxic and is equivalent to breathing pure oxygen at a depth of 20 metres (66 feet).

At high pressures of oxygen, around 2000 to 5000 mm Hg, dangerous cerebral problems such as dizziness, twitching, vision deterioration, and nausea may occur. Continued exposure to these high pressures will result in confusion, convulsion, and eventual death.

Changes in total pressure can induce **trapped gas effects**. With a decrease in pressure, trapped gases will increase in volume (according to Boyle's law). Trapped gases in the body include air pockets in the ears, sinuses, and chest. Divers refer to the trapped gas phenomenon as the *squeeze*. Jet travel causes the most commonly occurring instance of trapped gas effects. Takeoff and landing may cause relatively sudden shifts in pressure, which may lead to discomfort and pain. With very rapid ascent or descent, injury can develop.

Lung rupture can be caused by a swift return to the surface from diving or decompression during high-altitude flight. This event is rare and happens only if the person is holding his or her breath during the decompression.

Evolved gas effects are associated with the absorption of nitrogen into body tissues. When breathed, nitrogen can be absorbed into all body tissues in concentrations proportional to the partial pressure of nitrogen in air. When a person is ascending in altitude, on the ground, in flight, or under water, nitrogen must be exhaled at a rate equal to or exceeding the absorption rate to avoid evolved gas effects.

If the nitrogen in body tissues such as blood is being absorbed faster than it is being exhaled, bubbles of gas may form in the blood and other tissues. Gas bubbles in the tissues may cause decompression sickness, which can be painful and occasionally fatal. Early symptoms of this disorder occur in body bends or joints such as elbows, knees, and shoulders. The common name for decompression sickness is the **bends**.

When the formation of gas bubbles is due to rapid ambient pressure reduction, it is called **dysbarism**.[8] The major causes of dysbarism are (1) the release of gas from the blood, and (2) the attempted expansion of trapped gas in body tissues. The sickness may occur with the decompression associated with rapidly moving from sea level (considered zero) to approximately 6100 metres (20 000 feet) above sea level. Dysbarism is most often associated with underwater diving or working in pressurized containers (such as airplanes). Obese and older people seem to be more susceptible to dysbarism and decompression sickness.

Dysbarism manifests itself in a variety of symptoms. The **creeps** are caused by bubble formation in the skin, which causes an itchy, crawling, rashy feeling in the skin. Coughing and choking, resulting from bubbles in the respiratory system, are called the **chokes**. Bubbles occurring in the brain, although rare, may cause tingling and numbing, severe headaches, spasticity of muscles, and in some cases, blindness and paralysis. Dysbarism of the brain is, however, rare. Rapid pressure change may also cause pain in the teeth and sinuses.[9]

Aseptic necrosis of bone is a delayed effect of decompression sickness. Blood in the capillaries supplying the bone marrow may become blocked with gas bubbles, which can cause a collection of platelets and blood cells to build up in a bone cavity. The marrow generation of blood cells can be damaged as a result, as well as the maintenance of healthy bone cells. Some bone areas may become calcified, with severe complications when the bone is involved in a joint. Employees who work in an environment that is under pressure must undergo decompression procedures before returning to a normal atmosphere.

MEASUREMENT OF PRESSURE HAZARDS

Confirming the point of pressurized gas leakage can be difficult. After a gas has leaked out to a level of equilibrium with its surrounding air, the symptoms

TRAPPED GAS EFFECTS
With a decrease in pressure, gases in the body increase in volume. These occurrences often cause pain or discomfort and may result in injuries if the pressure change is rapid.

EVOLVED GAS EFFECTS
Happens when gas is being absorbed faster than it is being exhaled. These bubbles of gas, which are often nitrogen, may form in the blood and other tissues.

BENDS
Common name for decompression sickness.

DYSBARISM
The formation of gas bubbles due to rapid ambient pressure reduction.

CREEPS
Caused by bubble formation in the skin, which causes an itchy, crawling, rashy feeling in the skin.

CHOKES
Coughing and choking, resulting from bubbles in the respiratory system.

ASEPTIC NECROSIS
A delayed effect of decompression sickness involving damage to marrow generation as well as to healthy bone cells.

of the leak may disappear. There are several methods of detecting pressure hazards:

- *Sounds* can be used to signal a pressurized gas leak. Gas discharge may be indicated by a whistling noise, particularly with highly pressurized gases escaping through small openings. Workers should not use their fingers to probe for gas leaks as highly pressurized gases may cut through tissue, including bone.
- *Cloth streamers* may be tied to the gas vessel to help indicate leaks. Soap solutions may be smeared over the vessel surface so that bubbles are formed when gas escapes. A stream of bubbles indicates gas release.
- *Scents* may be added to gases that do not naturally have an odour. For instance, the odour sometimes smelled in homes that cook or heat with natural gas is not the gas itself but a scent added to it.
- *Leak detectors* that measure pressure, current flow, or radioactivity may be useful for some types of gases.
- *Corrosion* may be the long-term effect of escaping gases. Metal cracking, surface roughening, and general weakening of materials may result from corrosion.

There are many potential causes of gas leaks. The most common of these are as follows:

- *Contamination* by dirt can prevent the proper closing of gas valves, threads, gaskets, and other closures used to control gas flow.
- *Overpressurization* can overstress the gas vessel, permitting gas release. The container closure can distort and separate from gaskets, leading to cracking.
- *Excessive temperatures* applied to dissimilar metals that are joined can cause unequal thermal expansion, loosening the metal-to-metal joint and allowing gas to escape. Materials can crack because of excessive cold, which can also result in gas escape. Thermometers are often used to indicate the possibility of gas release.
- *Operator errors* can lead to hazardous gas release from improper closure of valves, inappropriate opening of valves, or overfilling of vessels. Proper training and supervision can reduce operator errors.

NONDESTRUCTIVE TESTING
Testing by these methods does not harm the material being tested.

DESTRUCTIVE TESTING
Testing by these methods destroys the material being checked.

PROOF PRESSURE TESTS
Tests in which containers are "proofed" by subjecting them to specified pressures for specified periods.

Destructive as well as nondestructive methods may be used to detect pressure leaks and incorrect pressure levels. **Nondestructive testing** methods do not harm the material being tested. Nondestructive methods may include mixing dye penetrants and magnetic or radioactive particles with the gas and then measuring the flow of the gas. Ultrasonic and X-ray waves are another form of nondestructive testing and are often used to characterize materials and detect cracks or other leakage points.

Destructive testing methods destroy the material being checked. Proof pressures generate stresses to the gas container, typically 1.5 to 1.667 times the maximum expected operating pressure for that container. Strain measurements may also be collected to indicate permanent weakening changes to the container material that remain after the pressure is released. **Proof pressure tests** often call for the pressure to be applied for a specified time and released. Stress and strain tests are then applied to the material. Proof pressure tests may or may not result in the destruction of the container being tested.

REDUCING PRESSURE HAZARDS

The reduction of pressure hazards can often be achieved by improving the standard of maintenance and inspection of equipment that measures or uses high-pressure gases. Proper storage of pressurized containers can reduce many pressure hazards. Pressurized vessels should be stored in locations away from cold or heat sources, including the sun. Cryogenic compounds (those that have been cooled to unusually low temperatures) may boil and burst the container when not kept at the proper temperatures. The whipping action of pressurized flexible hoses can also be dangerous. Hoses should be firmly clamped at the ends when pressurized.

Gas compression can occur in sealed containers exposed to heat. For this reason, aerosol cans must never be thrown into or exposed to a fire. Aerosol cans may explode violently when exposed to heat, although most commercially available aerosols are contained in low–melting point metals that melt before pressure can build up.

Pressure should be released before working on equipment. Gauges can be checked to ensure that pressure has been released before any work on the pressurized system is begun. When steam equipment is shut down, liquid can condense within the system. This liquid (as well as any dirt in the system, which would make the problem worse) can become a propellant, which can strike bends in the system, causing loud noises and possibly doing damage.

Water hammer is a shock effect caused by liquid flow suddenly stopping. This shock effect can produce loud noises. In addition, the momentum of the liquid is conducted back upstream in a shock wave that can damage pipe fittings and valves. Using air chambers in the system and avoiding the use of quick-closing valves reduces this hazard.

Negative pressures or **vacuums** are pressures below atmospheric level. Negative pressures and vacuums can cause closed containers to collapse. Storage tanks and tanker trucks, for example, need to have makeup air enter as the contents are emptied, or a negative pressure will result inside the tank. (The gas tank in the cars we drive would collapse as we used its contents if the gas cap didn't have a "vacuum valve" incorporated into it.) A change in temperature can also create a negative pressure situation: For instance, as a tank cools

WATER HAMMER
A series of loud noises caused by liquid flow suddenly stopping.

NEGATIVE PRESSURES
Pressures below atmospheric level.

VACUUMS
Areas where there is little or no matter, creating an area of negative pressure (pressure below atmospheric level).

DISCUSSION CASE

What Is Your Opinion?

While visiting a friend, Mary Carpenter — safety director for a small manufacturer of pressurized metal containers — saw something that really bothered her. While cleaning up his yard, her friend threw all of his trash into a fire contained in a metal drum. Carpenter noticed two aerosol cans being thrown in the fire and quickly warned her friend of the danger of explosion. He laughed and shrugged off her warning, saying "There is no danger. The can will melt before it explodes." Who is right in this situation? What is your opinion?

**Figure 13–3
Reduction of pressure
hazards.**

- Install valves so that failure of a valve does not result in a hazard.
- Do not store pressurized containers near heat or sources of ignition.
- Train and test personnel dealing with pressurized vessels. Only tested personnel should be permitted to install, operate, maintain, calibrate, or repair pressurized systems. Personnel working on pressure systems should wear safety face shields or goggles.
- Examine valves periodically to ensure that they are capable of withstanding working pressures.
- Operate pressure systems only under the conditions for which they were designed.
- Relieve all pressure from the system before performing any work.
- Label pressure system components to indicate inspection status as well as acceptable pressures and flow direction.
- Connect pressure relief devices to pressure lines.
- Do not use pressure systems and hoses at pressure exceeding the manufacturer's recommendations.
- Keep pressure systems clean.
- Keep pressurized hoses as short as possible.
- Avoid banging, dropping, or striking pressurized containers.
- Secure pressurized cylinders by a chain to prevent toppling.
- Store acetylene containers upright.
- Examine labels before using pressurized systems to ensure correct matching of gases and uses.

in the evening after sitting all day in the sun, the pressure can drop to the point where collapse would be a real possibility if air were not allowed to enter. Vessel wall thickness must be designed to sustain the load imposed by the differential in pressure caused by negative pressure. Most vessels can easily handle the pressure from within for which they were designed, because the material from which they are constructed can not easily stretch, but the same container would collapse under the force of surprisingly little suction (vacuum or low pressure). A simple, everyday illustration of this physical fact is trying to blow up a two litre plastic bottle by breathing into it. No matter how hard you blow, you will not be able to do it. However, if you try to suck the air out of it, it collapses quite readily!

Figure 13–3 describes several methods to reduce the hazards associated with pressurized containers.

SUMMARY

1. Pressure is defined in physics as the force exerted against an opposing fluid or solid.

2. Pressure is perceived in relation to the earth's atmosphere.

3. Barometers are used to measure atmospheric pressure.

4. Boyle's law states that the product of a given pressure and volume is constant with constant temperature:

$$P_1 V_1 = P_2 V_2, \text{ when } T \text{ is constant}$$

5. Inspiration is breathing air into the lungs; this can only occur when the pressure inside the lungs is lower than the atmospheric pressure (i.e., when the lungs are expanded).

6. Expiration occurs when air leaves the lungs; this can only occur when the pressure inside the lungs is higher than the atmospheric pressure (i.e., when the lung space is contracted).

7. Dalton's law of partial pressures states that in a mixture of ideal gases, the pressure exerted by the mixture is the sum of the pressures exerted by each component gas of the mixture:

$$P_A = P_O + P_N + P_{\text{else}}$$

8. Water vapour, although a gas, does not conform to Dalton's law.

9. Increasing pressure on the body does not by itself create problems.

10. Decompression sickness can occur from the decompression involved with a rapid rise from sea level to 5500 metres (18 000 feet) or a rapid ascent from around 40 to 20 metres (132 to 66 feet) under water.

11. In extreme instances of rapid ascent from underwater diving or high-altitude decompression, lung rupture can occur.

12. Factors involved with decompression sickness include previous exposure history, age, physical fitness, exercise, low temperatures, speed of decompression, and length of exposure.

13. The bends are an example of decompression sickness.

14. Aseptic necrosis of bone can be a delayed effect of decompression sickness.

15. Hypoxia is a reduction of available oxygen.

16. Excessive nitrogen absorption into body tissues can occur from breathing nitrogen-enriched air and is called nitrogen narcosis.

17. Evolved gas effects are associated with the absorption of nitrogen into body tissues.

18. Altitude sickness is a form of hypoxia.

19. Altitude sickness may involve a loss of useful consciousness.

20. Hyperoxia is an increased concentration of oxygen in air and is not common.

21. Trapped gas effects can result from changes in total pressure.

22. Dysbarism is the rapid formation of gas bubbles in the tissue due to rapid ambient pressure reduction.

23. The creeps are caused by bubble formation in the skin.

24. Formation of bubbles in the respiratory tract is called the chokes.

25. Pressure vessels are of many types including deaerator, amine, wet hydrogen sulphide, ammonia, and pulp digester vessels.

26. Nondestructive testing of pressure vessels can be accomplished by visual examination, liquid penetration test, magnetic particle test, radiography test, and ultrasonic testing.

27. Several methods can be used to detect pressure hazards: sounds, cloth streamers, soap solutions, scents, leak detectors, and visual checks for corrosion or contamination.

28. Detection of pressure hazards includes destructive and nondestructive testing.

29. Proof pressures can be used to test container strength of containers designed to hold a pressurized gas.

30. Pressurized cylinders and other vessels should be stored away from cold or heat sources, including the sun.

31. Aerosol cans should not be discarded in fires or disposed of by any method using heat.

32. Water hammer is a series of loud noises caused by pressurized liquid flow suddenly stopping.

33. Negative pressures or vacuums are pressures below atmospheric level.

KEY TERMS AND CONCEPTS

Altitude sickness

Aseptic necrosis

Barometer

Bends

Boyle's law

Chokes

Creeps

Dalton's law of partial pressures

Decompression sickness

Destructive testing

Dysbarism

Evolved gas effects

Expiration

Hazard

Hyperoxia

Hypoxia

Inspiration

Negative pressures

Nondestructive testing

Pressure

Pressure hazard

Proof pressure

Trapped gas effects

Ultrasonic testing

Useful consciousness

Vacuums

Water hammer

REVIEW QUESTIONS

1. Against which references is pressure measured? How are these references measured?

2. Define *inspiration* and *expiration*.

3. Explain Dalton's law of partial pressures.

4. Does water vapour conform to Dalton's law?

5. Briefly discuss decompression sickness.

6. What do length of exposure, the bends, the chokes, and aseptic necrosis of bone have in common?

7. Define *hypoxia* and *hyperoxia.*

8. Explain nitrogen narcosis.

9. Discuss altitude sickness.

10. What is the relationship between trapped gas effects and dysbarism?

11. What is the difference between destructive and nondestructive testing?

12. Briefly explain proof pressures.

13. What causes vacuums?

14. Explain three ways to conduct nondestructive testing of pressure vessels.

WEBLINKS

American Society of Mechanical Engineers (ASME)
www.asme.org

ASME's standards for pressure vessels are accepted by most North American jurisdictions. These standards and codes and other news and articles can be found on their website.

National Energy Board of Canada
www.neb-one.gc.ca/ActsRegulations/divregs_e.htm

Diving operations are used extensively with the offshore oil industry. This site is a link to the draft Canada Oil and Gas Diving Regulations.

Technical Standards and Technical Authority (TSSA)
www.tssa.org

On this website TSSA, which regulates all pressure-retaining components manufactured or used in Ontario, provides information on training and standards for pressure vessels and other products.

ENDNOTES

1. Occupational Safety and Health Administration, "Pressure Vessel Guidelines," *OSHA Technical Manual* (Washington, DC: Occupational Safety and Health Administration, 2000), sec. IV, chap. 3, 30.
2. Ibid., 31.
3. Ibid.
4. Ibid.
5. Ibid.
6. Ibid., 38.
7. Ibid., 39.
8. Ibid., 39.
9. Ibid.

Electrical Hazards

LEARNING OBJECTIVES

- Explain what electricity is and how it is measured.
- List common sources of electrical hazards.
- Describe the effect of electrical current on humans.
- List seven means of reducing electrical hazards.
- Explain under which jurisdiction electrical standards fall.

ELECTRICITY
The flow of negatively charged particles called electrons through an electrically conductive material.

NEUTRONS
Particles that neutralize the negative charge of electrons. They act as temporary energy repositories between positively charged particles called protons and electrons.

PROTONS
Positively charged particles.

ELECTRONS
Negatively charged particles.

Contemplate the following scenario: An electrical worker was rewiring a junction box that powered a piece of machinery. He mistakenly thought he'd shut off the juice to the junction box. The circuits in the box were not properly labelled or marked. When he touched a 277-volt conductor inside the box with a pair of uninsulated pliers, he was electrocuted.[1] This scenario demonstrates the importance of electrical safety. Electrocution accounts for about 20% of all fatalities in the construction industry.[2]

ELECTRICAL HAZARDS DEFINED

Electricity is the flow of negatively charged particles called *electrons* through an electrically conductive material. Electrons orbit the nucleus of an atom, which is located approximately in the atom's centre. The negative charge of the electrons is neutralized by particles called **neutrons**, which act as temporary energy repositories for the interactions between positively charged particles, called **protons,** and **electrons**.

Figure 14–1 shows the basic structure of an atom, with the positively charged nucleus in the centre. The electrons are shown as energy bands of orbit-

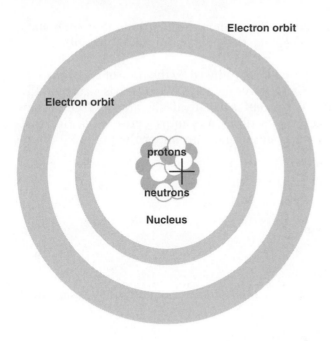

Electron orbit

Electron orbit

protons

neutrons

Nucleus

Figure 14–1
Basic structure of an atom.

ing negatively charged particles. Each ring of electrons contains a particular quantity of negative charges. The basic characteristics of a material are determined by the number of electron rings and the number of electrons in the outer rings of its atoms. A *positive charge* is present when an atom (or group of atoms) in a material has too many electrons in its outer shell. In all other cases, the atom or material carries a *negative charge.*

Electrons that are freed from an atom and are directed by external forces to travel in a specific direction produce *electrical current,* also called *electricity.* **Conductors** are substances that have many free electrons at room temperature and can conduct electricity. *Insulators* do not have a large number of free electrons at room temperature and do not conduct electricity. Substances that are neither conductors nor insulators can be called **semiconductors**. Pure conductors offer little **resistance** to the flow of electrons. Insulators, on the other hand, have very high resistance to electricity. Semiconductors have a medium-range resistance to electricity. The higher the resistance, the lower the flow of electrons. Resistance is measured in **ohms.**

The path of this flow of electrons is from a negative source to a positive point, because opposite charges attract one another. The *potential difference* between two points in a circuit is measured by **voltage**. The higher the voltage, the more likely it is that electricity will flow between the negative and positive points.

When a surplus or deficiency of electrons on the surface of a material exists, **static electricity** is produced. This type of electricity is called "static" because there is no positive material nearby to attract the electrons and cause them to move. Friction is not required to produce static electricity, although it can increase the charge of existing static electricity. When two surfaces of opposite static electricity charges are brought into close range, a discharge, or spark, will

CONDUCTORS
Substances that have many free electrons at room temperature and can conduct electricity.

SEMICONDUCTORS
Substances that are neither conductors nor insulators.

RESISTANCE
A tendency to block flow of electric current.

OHMS
Measure of resistance.

VOLTAGE
Measures the potential difference between two points in a circuit.

STATIC ELECTRICITY
A surplus or deficiency of electrons on the surface of a material.

occur. The spark from static electricity is often the first clue that such static exists. A common example is the sparks that come from rustling woollen blankets in dry heated indoor air.

Electrical current, as we have said, is produced by the flow of electrons. The unit of measurement for current is **amperes** (or amps). One amp is a current flow of 6.28×10 electrons per second. Current is usually designated by I. **Ohm's law** describes the relationship among volts, ohms, and amps. One ohm is the resistance of a conductor that has a current of one amp under the potential of one volt. Ohm's law is stated as

$$V = IR$$

where

V = potential difference in volts

I = current flow in amps

R = resistance to current flow in ohms

Power is measured in wattage (or **watts**) and can be determined from Ohm's law:

$$W = VI \text{ or } W = I^2R$$

where

W = power in watts

Most industrial and domestic use of electricity is supplied by **alternating current** (or AC current). In Canada, standard AC circuits cycle 60 times per second. (The same system is used in the United States and Mexico, but Europe uses a completely different system.) The number of cycles per second is known as **frequency** and is measured in hertz. Because voltage cycles in AC current, an effective current for AC circuits is computed that is slightly less than the peak current during a cycle.

A direct current (or DC current) has been found to generate as much heat as an AC current that has a peak current 41.4% higher than the DC. The ratio of effective current to peak current can be determined by

(Effective current)/(Peak current) = (100%)/(100% + 41.4%) = 0.707 or 70.7%

Effective voltages are computed using the same ratios as effective current. A domestic 110-volt circuit has an effective voltage of 110 volts, with peaks of voltage over 150 volts.

The path of electrical current must make a complete loop for the current to flow. This loop includes the source of electrical power, a conductor to act as the path, a device to use the current (called a **load**), and a path to the ground. The earth maintains a relatively stable electrical charge and is a good conductor. The earth is considered to have **zero potential** because of its massive size. Any electrical conductor pushed into the earth is said to have zero potential. The earth is used as a giant common conductor back to the source of power.

Electrical hazards occur when a person makes contact with a conductor carrying a current and simultaneously contacts the ground or another object that includes a conductive path to the ground. This person completes the circuit loop by providing a load for the circuit and thereby enables the current to

Margin glossary

AMPERE
The unit of measurement for electrical current.

OHM'S LAW
describes the relationship among volts, ohms, and amps. One ohm is the resistance of a conductor that has a current of one amp under the potential of one volt.

WATT
Measure of electrical power.

ALTERNATING CURRENT (AC)
Electrical current in which the direction of flow alternates from one direction to the other.

FREQUENCY
The number of cycles per second in hertz (Hz).

LOAD
A device that uses currents.

ZERO POTENTIAL
State of a neutral electrical charge.

ELECTRICAL HAZARDS
Potentially dangerous situations related to electricity (e.g., a bare wire).

**Figure 14–2
Typical three-wire
circuit.**

pass through his or her body. Electrical current passing through the human body causes a shock. The quantity and path of this current determines the level of damage to the body. People can be protected from this danger by insulating the conductors, insulating the people, or isolating the danger from the people.

Typical 110-volt circuit wiring has a hot wire carrying current, a neutral wire, and a ground wire. The neutral wire may be called a grounded conductor, with the ground wire being called a grounding conductor. Neutral wires usually have white insulation, hot wires have red or black insulation, and ground wires have green insulation or are bare. Figure 14–2 shows a typical three-wire circuit.

The hot wire carries an effective voltage of 110 volts with respect to the ground. The neutral wire carries nearly zero voltage with respect to the ground. If the hot wire makes contact with an unintended conductor, such as a metal equipment case, the current can bypass the load and go directly to the ground. With the load skipped, the ground wire is a low-resistance path to the earth and carries the highest current possible for that circuit.

When the load is bypassed, as we have just described, it is called a **short circuit**. Short circuits can be another source of electrical hazard if a human is the conductor to the ground, thereby bypassing the load.

SHORT CIRCUIT
A circuit in which the load has been removed or bypassed.

SOURCES OF ELECTRICAL HAZARDS

Short circuits are one of many potential electrical hazards that can cause electrical shock. Another hazard is water, which considerably decreases the resistance of materials, including humans. The resistance of wet skin can be as low as 450 ohms, whereas dry skin has an average resistance of 600 000 ohms. According to Ohm's law, the higher the resistance, the lower the current flow. When the current flow is reduced, the probability of electrical shock is also reduced.

The major causes of electrical shock are

- Contact with a bare wire carrying current. The bare wire may have deteriorated insulation or be normally bare.
- Working with electrical equipment that lacks the UL label for safety inspection.
- Electrical equipment that has not been properly grounded. Failure of the equipment can lead to short circuits.

- Working with electrical equipment on damp floors or other sources of wetness.
- Static electricity discharge.
- Using metal ladders to work on electrical equipment. These ladders can provide a direct line from the power source to the ground, again causing a shock.
- Working on electrical equipment without ensuring that the power has been shut off.
- Lightning strikes.

Figure 14–3 depicts some of these electrical shock hazards.

Electrostatic Hazards

ELECTROSTATIC HAZARDS
Shocks from static electricity discharge.

Electrostatic hazards are minor shocks caused by static electricity. These shocks can result from a single discharge or from multiple discharges of static. Instances of electrostatic discharge include the following:

- A nonconductive material briskly rubbed over a stationary surface can create an electrostatic charge. One common example of this is scuffing shoes

Figure 14–3
Electrical shock hazards.

across a wool or nylon carpet. Multilayered clothing can also cause static sparks (as the layers of fabric rub against each other).[3]

- Large sheets of plastic, when moved, can discharge sparks.
- Farm grain silos and mine shafts can accumulate a static charge; the resulting sparks can cause organic (e.g., grain) and metallic dusts to ignite causing fires or explosions..
- Conveyor belts. Depending on their constituent material, conveyor belts can rub the materials being transported and cause static sparks.
- Vehicle tires rolling across a road surface.
- Friction between a flowing liquid and a solid surface.[4]

The rate of discharge of electrical charges increases with lower humidity. Buildup of electrostatic charge is generally greater on cold, dry winter days. Adding humidity to the air is not commonly used to combat static discharge, however, because overly moist air can result in an uncomfortable working environment and can adversely affect equipment.[5]

Arcs and Sparks Hazards

When conductors are in close proximity or accidentally touch, an electrical arc can jump the air between the conductors to complete a circuit. This arc can ignite combustible gases or dusts causing a fire or an explosion. When the electric arc is a discharge of static electricity, it is called a spark. In a highly combustible atmosphere, sparks can also cause fires or explosions. A spark or arc may involve relatively little or a great deal of power and is usually discharged into a small space.

Combustible and Explosive Materials

High currents moving through contaminated liquids may cause the contaminants to expand rapidly and explode. This situation is particularly dangerous with contaminated oil-filled circuit breakers or transformers. A poor match between current or polarity and capacitors can also cause an explosion. In each of these cases, the conductor is not capable of carrying a current of such high magnitude. Overheating from high currents can also lead to short circuits, which in turn may generate fires or explosions.

Lightning Hazards

Lightning is static charges from clouds following the path of least resistance to the earth, involving very high voltage and current. If this path to the earth involves humans, serious disability can result, including electrocution. Lightning can also damage airplanes from intracloud and cloud-to-cloud flashes. Electrical equipment and building structures are commonly subject to lightning hazards. Lightning tends to strike the tallest object on the earth below the clouds, making trees a common natural path for lightning.

LIGHTNING
Static charges from clouds following the path of least resistance to the earth, involving very high voltage and current.

Improper Wiring

Improper wiring permits equipment to operate normally but can result in hazardous conditions. The section of this chapter on detection of electrical hazards discusses tests to identify unsafe wiring practices. One common mistake is to "jump" the ground wire to the neutral wire. In this case, the ground wire is actually connected to the neutral wire. Equipment usually operates in a customary way, but the hazard occurs when low voltages are generated on exposed parts of the equipment, such as the housing. If the neutral circuit becomes corroded or loose, the voltage on the ground wire increases to a dangerous level.

OPEN GROUND
Electrical wiring condition in which current has no path to ground.

Improper wiring (or miswiring) can cause other hazards. When the ground is connected improperly, the situation is referred to as an **open ground**. Usually the equipment with this miswiring will operate normally. But if a short occurs in the equipment circuitry without proper grounding, anyone touching that equipment may be severely shocked.

Reversed polarity occurs when the hot and neutral wires have been reversed. A worker who is not aware that the black lead (hot) and white lead (neutral) have been reversed could be injured or could cause further confusion by connecting the improperly wired circuit to another apparatus. If a short between the on/off switch and the load occurred as a result, the equipment might run indefinitely, regardless of the switch position. In a reversed polarity light bulb socket, the screw threads become conductors.[6]

Temporary wiring installations sometimes remain in place for years until an accident occurs. Flexible wiring should rarely be substituted for fixed wiring in permanent buildings. When using flexible cord, a loose knot should be tied in it when the plug is installed or replaced. The knot can prevent a pull on the cord from being transmitted to electrical connections such as the plug.

Insulation Failure

The degradation of insulation can cause a bare wire, resulting in a shock to anyone coming in contact with that wire. Most insulation failure is caused by environments toxic to insulation. These environments include the following:

- Direct sunlight or other sources of ultraviolet light, which can induce gradual breakdown of plastic insulation material.
- Sparks or arcs from discharging static electricity, which can result in burned-through holes in insulation.
- Repeated exposure to elevated temperatures, which can produce slow but progressive degradation of insulation material.
- Contact with abrasive surfaces, which can result in erosion of the material strength of the insulation.
- Substance incompatibility with the atmosphere around the insulation and the insulation material, which can induce chemical reactions. Such reactions may include oxidation or dehydration of the insulation and eventual breakdown.
- Animals such as rodents or insects chewing or eating the insulation material, leading to exposure of the circuit. Insects can also pack an enclosed area with their bodies so tightly that a short circuit occurs. This is a common occurrence with electrical systems near water, such as pump housings and television satellite dishes.
- Moisture and humidity being absorbed by the insulation material, which may result in the moisture on the insulation carrying a current.

Equipment Failure

There are several ways in which equipment failure can cause electrical shocks. Electrical equipment designers attempt to create devices that are explosion-proof, dust-ignition-proof, and spark-proof. Following are some of the more common types of equipment failure:

- Wet insulation can become a conductor and cause an electrical shock.
- Portable tool defects can result in the device's housing carrying an electric current. Workers do not expect tool housings to be charged and may be shocked when they touch a charged tool housing.
- Broken power lines carry great amperage and voltage and contact with them can cause severe disability or death.
- When equipment is not properly grounded or insulated, an unshielded worker can receive a substantial electrical shock.

Hazardous Locations for Electrical Equipment

Section 18 of the Canadian Electrical Code (CE Code), classifies hazardous locations for electrical equipment. There are three basic classes: Class I for flammable vapours and gases, Class II for combustible dusts, and Class III for ignitable fibres. There are also two divisions of hazard categories. Division I has more stringent requirements for electrical installation than does Division II. Figure 14–4 gives examples for each location category.[7]

		Division	
Class	**Group**	**I**	**II**
I. Flammable vapours and gases	A. Acetylene B. Hydrogen C. Ether D. Hydrocarbon fuels and solvents	Normally explosive; flammable paint spray areas	Not normally in explosive concentration; adjacent to paint spray area
II. Combustible dusts	E. Metal dusts F. Carbon dusts G. Flour, starch, grain, plastic, or chemical dusts	Conductive or ignitable dusts may be present; grain mills or processors	Not normally in ignitable concentration; grain storage areas
III. Ignitable fibres	Textiles, woodworking	Handled or used in manufacturing; cotton gins	Stored or handled in storage, not in manufacturing; excelsior storage

Figure 14–4
Hazardous electrical equipment location categories.

ELECTRICAL HAZARDS TO HUMANS

The greatest danger to humans suffering electrical shock results from current flow. The voltage determines whether a particular person's natural resistance to current flow will be overcome. Skin resistance can vary between 450 ohms and 600 000 ohms, depending on skin moisture.[8] Some levels of current **"freeze"** a person to the conductor; in that case the person cannot voluntarily release his or her grasp. **Let-go current** is the highest current level at which a person in contact with the conductor can release the grasp of the conductor. Figure 14–5 shows the relationship between amperage dosage and danger with a typical domestic 60-cycle AC current.

The severity of injury with electrical shock depends not only on the dosage of current, as shown in Figure 14–5, but also on the path taken through the body by the current. The path is influenced by the resistance of various parts of the body at the time of contact with the conductor. The skin is the major form of resistance to current flow. Current paths through the heart, brain, or trunk are generally much more injurious than paths through extremities.

FREEZE
The inability to release one's grip voluntarily from a conductor of electricity.

LET-GO CURRENT
The highest current level at which a person in contact with a conductor of electricity can release the grasp of the conductor.

Figure 14–5
Effects of electrical current on the human body (60-cycle AC current).

Dose in Current in Milliamps	Effect on Human Body
Less than 1	No sensation, no perceptible effect.
1	Shock perceptible, reflex action to jump away. No direct danger from shock but sudden motion may cause accident.
More than 3	Painful shock.
6	Let-go current for women.*
9	Let-go current for men.*
10–15	Local muscle contractions. Freezing to the conductor for 2.5% of the population.
30–50	Local muscle contractions. Freezing to the conductor for 50% of the population.
50–100	Prolonged contact may cause collapse and unconsciousness. Death may occur after three minutes of contact due to paralysis of the respiratory muscles.
100–200	Contact of more than a quarter of a second may cause ventricular fibrillation of the heart and death. AC currents continuing for more than one heart cycle may cause fibrillation.
Over 200	Clamps and stops the heart as long as the current flows. Heart beating and circulation may resume when current ceases. High current can produce respiratory paralysis, which can be reversed with immediate resuscitation. Severe burns to the skin and internal organs. May result in irreparable body damage.

*Difference between men and women is based on the relative body mass of the "average"-sized man and woman (60-cycle AC current).

DETECTION OF ELECTRICAL HAZARDS

Several items of test equipment can be used to verify electrical equipment safety. A **circuit tester** is an inexpensive piece of test equipment with two wire leads capped by probes and connected to a small bulb. Most circuit testers test at least a 110- to 220-volt range. This simple tester can ensure that power has been turned off before electrical maintenance begins. The tester can also be used to determine whether housings and other equipment parts are carrying a current. When one of the leads makes contact with a hot wire and the other lead connects to a grounded conductor, the bulb lights.

A **receptacle wiring tester** is a device with two standard plug probes for insertion into an ordinary 110-volt outlet and a probe for the ground. Indicator lights show an improperly wired receptacle (outlet). This tester will not indicate a properly wired outlet, but it will reveal an incorrectly wired one. However, there are several types of miswiring that are not disclosed by using this tester, including the ground wire to neutral wire mistake. Figure 14–6 shows the meaning of lit indicator lights on the receptacle wiring tester.

A **continuity tester** can be used to determine whether a conductor is properly grounded or has a break in the circuit. Continuity is checked on circuits that are disconnected from a power source. Continuity testers often have an alligator clip on one end of a wire and a bulb and probe on the other end of the same wire. One terminal of the tester can be connected to the equipment housing; the other terminal is connected to a known ground. If the bulb does not light, the equipment is shown to be improperly grounded. With a circuit, the bulb lights when a current is capable of passing through the complete circuit. The unlit bulb of a continuity tester indicates a break in the circuit.

CIRCUIT TESTER
An inexpensive piece of test equipment with two wire leads capped by probes and connected to a small bulb.

RECEPTACLE WIRING TESTER
A device with two standard plug probes for insertion into an ordinary 110-volt outlet and a probe for the ground.

CONTINUITY TESTER
May be used to determine whether a conductor is properly grounded or has a break in the circuit.

REDUCING ELECTRICAL HAZARDS

Grounding of electrical equipment is the primary method of reducing electrical hazards. The purpose of grounding is to safeguard people from electrical shocks, reduce the probability of a fire, and protect equipment from damage. Grounding ensures a path to the earth for the flow of excess current. Grounding also eliminates the possibility of a person being shocked by contact with a charged capacitor. The actual mechanism of grounding was discussed at the beginning of this chapter.

	Lights		
Situation	1	2	3
Correct wiring	On	On	Off
Ground jumped to neutral	On	On	Off
Neutral and ground reversed	On	On	Off
Reversed polarity	On	Off	On
Open ground	On	Off	Off

▶ Figure 14–6
Receptacle wiring tester indicator lights.

SAFETY FACT

Workplace Deaths from Electrocution in Ontario

There were ten workplace deaths from electrocution in Ontario in 2003; all were men. Sixty percent of all electrocutions involved contact with energized power lines. A lack of job planning, including hazard awareness, was deemed by the coroner to be responsible in 80% of these accidents. Aluminum ladders were the most common tool involved in these fatalities. These Ontario electrical fatality figures are proportional to the electrocution figures across Canada.

Source: Electrical Safety Authority of Ontario, *Ontario Electrical Safety Report 2003.* [Online]. Available: http:// www.esainspection.net/pdf/2003%20report.pdf. (Retrieved March 5, 2005).

ELECTRICAL SYSTEM GROUNDING
Achieved when one conductor of the circuit is connected to the earth.

BONDING
Used to connect two pieces of equipment by a conductor. Also, involves eliminating the difference in static charge potential between materials.

GROUND FAULT CIRCUIT INTERRUPTER (GFCI)
Can detect the flow of current to the ground and open the circuit, thereby interrupting the flow of current.

Electrical system grounding is achieved when one conductor of the circuit is connected to the earth. Power surges and voltage changes are attenuated and usually eliminated with proper system grounding. **Bonding** is used to connect two pieces of equipment by a conductor. Bonding can reduce potential differences in electrical charge between the pieces of equipment and thus reduce the possibility of sparking. Bonding and grounding together are used for entire electrical systems.

Separate equipment grounding involves connecting all metal frames of the equipment in a permanent and continuous manner. If an insulation failure occurs, the current should return to the system ground at the power supply for the circuit. The equipment ground wiring will be the path for the circuit current, enabling circuit breakers and fuses to operate properly. The exposed metal parts of the equipment shown in Figure 14–7 must be grounded or provided with double insulations.[9]

A **ground fault circuit interrupter (GFCI)**, also called a *ground fault interrupter (GFI),* can detect the flow of current to the ground and open the circuit, thereby interrupting the flow of current. When the current flow in the hot wire is greater than the current in the neutral wire (because instead of returning via the neutral wire the current has taken another route to the ground), a **ground fault** has occurred. The GFI provides a safety measure for a person who becomes part of the ground fault circuit (that is, the current is passing through them to

**Figure 14–7
Equipment requiring grounding or double insulation.**

Portable electric tools such as drills and saws.
Communication receivers and transmitters.
Electrical equipment in damp locations.
Television antenna towers.
Electrical equipment in flammable liquid storage areas.
Electrical equipment operated with over 150 volts.

the ground) by opening the circuit and thereby stopping the flow of electricity. The GFI cannot interrupt current passing between two circuits or between the hot and neutral wires of a three-wire circuit. To ensure safety, equipment must be grounded as well as protected by a GFI.

There are several options for reducing the hazards associated with static electricity. The primary hazard of static electricity is the transfer of charges to surfaces with lower potential. When the spark of static electricity jumps from one surface to another, it can deliver a shock; the spark can also ignite anything flammable (gas, dust, etc.) that is in the area. Bonding and grounding are two means of controlling static discharge. **Humidification** is another mechanism for reducing electrical static as was discussed in the section on sources of electrical hazards. Increased moisture in the air increases the conductivity of the air and also of any object around that absorbs the moisture, reducing the likelihood of a static charge building up. Raising the humidity above 65% substantially reduces charge accumulation.[10]

Antistatic materials have also been used effectively to reduce electrical static hazards. Such materials either increase the surface conductivity of the charged material or absorb moisture, which reduces resistance and the tendency to accumulate charges.

Ionizers and electrostatic neutralizers ionize the air surrounding a charged surface to provide a conductive path for the flow of charges. Radioactive neutralizers include a radioactive element that emits positive particles to neutralize collected negative electrical charges. Workers need to be safely isolated from the radioactive particle emitter.

Fuses consist of a metal strip or wire that melts if a current above a specific value is conducted through the metal. Melting the metal causes the circuit to open at the fuse, thereby stopping the flow of current. Some fuses are designed to include a time lag before melting to allow higher currents during startup of the system or as an occasional event.

Magnetic circuit breakers use a solenoid (a type of coil) to surround a metal strip that connects to a tripping device. When the allowable current is exceeded, the magnetic force of the solenoid retracts the metal strip, opening the circuit. Thermal circuit breakers rely on excess current to produce heat and bending in a sensitive metal strip. Once bent, the metal strip opens the circuit. Circuit breakers differ from fuses in that they are usually easier to reset after tripping and often provide a lower time lag or none at all before being activated.

Double insulation is another means of increasing electrical equipment safety. Most double-insulated tools have plastic nonconductive housings in addition to standard insulation around conductive materials.

There are numerous methods of reducing the risk of electrocution by lightning. Figure 14–8 lists the major precautions to take.[11]

Another means of protecting workers is isolating the hazard from the workers or vice versa. **Interlocks** automatically break the circuit when an unsafe situation is detected. For instance, elevator doors typically have interlocks to ensure that the elevator does not move when the doors are open. Interlocks can be used around high-voltage areas to keep personnel from entering the area. Warning devices to alert personnel about detected hazards can also be used and include lights, coloured indicators, on/off blinkers, audible signals, or labels.

It is better to design safety into the equipment and system than to rely on human behaviour such as reading and following labels. Figure 14–9 summarizes the many methods of reducing electrical hazards.

GROUND FAULT
When the current flow in the hot wire is greater than the current in the neutral wire.

HUMIDIFICATION
Adding moisture to the air to reduce electrical static.

IONIZER
Ionizes the air surrounding a charged surface to provide a conductive path for the flow of charges.

FUSES
Consist of a metal strip or wire that will melt if a current above a specific value is conducted through the metal.

DOUBLE INSULATION
A means of increasing electrical equipment safety.

INTERLOCKS
Automatically break the circuit when an unsafe situation is detected.

**Figure 14–8
Lightning hazard
control.**

- Place lightning rods so that the upper end is higher than nearby structures.
- Avoid standing in high places or near tall objects. Be aware that trees in an open field may be the tallest object nearby.
- Do not work with flammable liquids or gases during electrical storms.
- Ensure proper grounding of all electrical equipment.
- If inside an automobile, remain inside the automobile.
- If in a small boat, lie down in the bottom of the boat.
- If in a metal building, stay in the building and do not touch the walls of the building.
- Wear rubber clothing if outdoors.
- Do not work touching or near conducting materials, especially those in contact with the earth such as fences.
- Avoid using the telephone during an electrical storm.
- Do not use electrical equipment during the storm.
- Avoid standing near open doors or windows where lightning may enter the building directly.

**Figure 14–9
Summary of safety
precautions for
electrical hazards.**

- Ensure that power has been disconnected from the system before working with it. Test the system for de-energization. Capacitors can store current after power has been shut off.
- Allow only fully authorized and trained people to work on electrical systems.
- Do not wear conductive material such as metal jewelry when working with electricity.
- Screw bulbs securely into their sockets. Ensure that bulbs are matched to the circuit by the correct voltage rating.
- Periodically inspect insulation.
- If working on a hot circuit, use the buddy system and wear protective clothing.
- Do not use a fuse with a greater capacity than was prescribed for the circuit.
- Verify circuit voltages before performing work.
- Do not use water to put out an electrical fire.
- Check the entire length of electrical cord before using it.
- Use only explosion-proof devices and nonsparking switches in flammable liquid storage areas.
- Enclose uninsulated conductors in protective areas.
- Discharge capacitors before working on the equipment.
- Use fuses and circuit breakers for protection against excessive current.
- Provide lightning protection on all structures.
- Train people working with electrical equipment on a routine basis in first aid and cardiopulmonary resuscitation (CPR).

Dos and Don'ts of Extension Cords

Approximately 2500 workplace injuries annually are tied to improper use of extension cords. The following tips can help prevent accidents when extension cords are used in the workplace:

1. Never use an extension cord for an extended period — that is, more than a few weeks — even if it appears to be in perfect condition.

2. Never cover extension cords with rugs, mats, or carpet in an attempt to prevent tripping — this can hide shorts and bare spots in the cord that might set the rug on fire.

3. Never just unplug an extension cord that feels hot in order to let it cool down — get rid of it (extension cords that get hot have probably reached the end of their period of safe usage).

Source: "Extension Cord Do's and Don'ts," (October 1, 2002), *Facility Manager's Alert* 8, no. 175: 7.

CANADIAN ELECTRICAL STANDARDS

In Canada, the rules and regulations regarding installation, wiring and maintenance of electrical equipment are governed by the Canadian Electrical Code (CE Code). To accommodate differences in climate, geography, and industry, the provinces and territories make amendments to the Canadian code to deal with unique situations in their own jurisdiction. For example, the provinces in Atlantic Canada may include regulations in the code to deal with the corrosion from the salt air, whereas in Yukon, the Code covers the requirements for split receptacles at driveway locations, because of the need to "plug in" vehicles during the winter.[12]

On the municipal level, electrical standards are often incorporated into that town, city, or region's building code requirements. These regulations are enforced by local inspectors whose approval is required at various stages of the construction or renovation project. A competent electrician will know under which jurisdiction each project falls and will seek out and comply with the standards for that area.

SUMMARY

1. Electricity is the flow of negatively charged particles through an electrically conductive material.

2. Atoms have a centrally located nucleus that consists of protons and neutrons. Electrons orbit the nucleus.

3. Conductors are substances that have many free electrons at room temperature and can conduct electricity.

4. Insulators do not have a large number of free electrons at room temperature and do not conduct electricity.

5. When a surplus or deficiency of electrons on the surface of a material exists, static electricity is produced.

6. Resistance is measured in ohms.

7. Current flow is measured in amperes or amps.

8. Ohm's law is $V = IR$, where V = volts, I = amps, and R = ohms.

9. Power is measured in watts.

10. Watts (W) are calculated by $W = VI$ or $W = IR$.

11. Frequency is measured in hertz.

12. A load is a device that uses electrical current.

13. Common 110-volt circuits include a hot wire, a neutral wire, and a ground wire.

14. A short circuit is one in which the load has been removed or is bypassed.

15. Sources of electrical hazards include contact with a bare wire, deteriorated insulation, improper grounding of equipment, short circuits, dampness, static electricity discharge, metal ladders, power sources remaining on during electrical maintenance, and lightning strikes.

16. Electrostatic hazards can cause minor shocks.

17. A spark or arc involves little power and is discharged into a small space.

18. If the conductor is not capable of carrying a particular amperage of current, the material surrounding the conductor can become overheated and explode or burst into flame.

19. Lightning is a collection of static charges from clouds following the path of least resistance to the earth.

20. Lightning tends to strike the tallest object on the earth.

21. Jumping the ground wire to the neutral wire is unsafe wiring.

22. Open grounds are those with improperly connected ground wires.

23. Reversing the hot and neutral wires results in reversed polarity and an unsafe situation.

24. Most insulation failure is caused by an environment toxic to insulation.

25. Electrical equipment designers attempt to create devices that are explosion-proof, dust-ignition-proof, and spark-proof.

26. The CEC classifies hazardous locations for electrical equipment.

27. The level of danger to humans from electrical shock is determined by the amount of current flow and the path through the body that the current takes.

28. Above a particular amperage of current, people freeze to conductors and are unable to let go of the conductor.

29. Circuit testers can ensure that power has been turned off.

30. A receptacle wiring tester indicates improperly wired outlets.

31. A continuity tester can be used to check whether a conductor is properly grounded or has a break in the circuit.

32. Grounding ensures a path to the earth for the flow of excess current.

33. Bonding and grounding increase the safety for entire electrical systems.

34. A GFI can detect current flow to the ground and open the circuit.

35. A ground fault occurs when the current in the hot wire is greater than the current in the neutral wire.

36. Antistatic materials, ionizers, and radioactive neutralizers reduce electrical static buildup.

37. Fuses and circuit breakers open the circuit with excess amperage.

38. Double insulation increases electrical safety.

39. Lightning hazard control includes using lightning rods and avoiding tall objects and flammable materials, not touching conductive materials, not using the telephone, not touching the walls of metal buildings, and not standing near open doors and windows during electrical storms.

40. Interlocks automatically open the circuit when an unsafe condition is detected.

KEY TERMS AND CONCEPTS

Alternating current (AC)

Amperes (amps)

Bonding

Circuit tester

Conductors

Continuity tester

Double insulation

Electrical hazards

Electrical system grounding

Electricity

Electrons

Electrostatic hazards

Freeze

Frequency

Fuses

Ground fault

Ground fault circuit interrupter (GFCI)

Humidification

Interlocks

Ionizers

Let-go current

Lightning

Load

Neutrons

Ohms

Ohm's law

Open ground

Protons

Receptacle wiring tester

Resistance

Semiconductor

Short circuit

Static electricity

Voltage

Watt

Zero potential

REVIEW QUESTIONS

1. Define *zero potential*. Explain the relationship between zero potential and grounding.

2. Explain what each of the following terms measure: *volt, amp, ohm, hertz,* and *watt*.

3. Define *open ground*.

4. How do ionizers and antistatic materials work? Why does humidification work?

5. Discuss how bonding and grounding work together to increase electrical safety.

6. How do continuity testers, circuit testers, and receptacle wiring testers operate?

7. Explain freeze and let-go current.

8. Describe the structure of an atom.

9. Discuss the proper wiring of a three-wire circuit.

10. Who administers electrical safety in federal, provincial, and municipal jurisdictions?

WEBLINKS

Canadian Standards Association
www.csa.ca

The CSA website gives lists of standards that can be viewed and ordered. The CSA learning centre also posts training opportunities.

Electrical Safety Authority
www.esainspection.net

A comprehensive electrical safety resource for work and home.

International Brotherhood of Electrical Workers
www.ibew.org

On this site the viewer can find news, stories, and links to the latest developments in the Canada/US electrical industry.

ENDNOTES

1. "Worker Shocked to Death; Equipment Not Labeled," *Facility Manager's Alert* 8, no. 181 (January 16, 2003): 3.
2. Construction Safety Association of Ontario. (Spring 2000). "Electrocution." [Online]. Available: http://www.csao.org/uploadfiles/magazine/vol11no1/shock.htm. (Retrieved November 10, 2004).
3. National Fire Protection Association, *Electrical Safety in the Workplace* (Quincy, MA: National Fire Protection Association, 2000), 57.
4. Ibid., 59.
5. H. R. Kavianian and C. A. Wentz, Jr., *Industrial Safety* (New York: Van Nostrand Reinhold, 1990), 231.
6. C. Ray Asfahl, *Industrial Safety and Health Management* (Upper Saddle River, NJ: Prentice Hall, 1990), 347.
7. National Fire Protection Association, *Electrical Safety,* 103.

8. Kavianian and Wentz, *Industrial Safety,* 214.

9. Ibid., 218.

10. National Fire Protection Association, *Electrical Safety,* 109.

11. Kavianian and Wentz, *Industrial Safety,* 232.

12. William Graham. (February 2003). The Canadian Electrical Code, Part I. CLB Media Inc. [Online]. Available: http://www.ebmag.com/EBFEB03/feb03_contracting.html. (Retrieved November 10, 2004).

15

CHAPTER

Fire Hazards and Life Safety

LEARNING OBJECTIVES

- Describe the components necessary to sustain fire.
- List and describe the classes of fires.
- Explain the classifications of flammable and combustible liquids.
- Describe the NFPA hazard diamond.
- List four common types of fire detection systems.
- Describe the main features of the three main fire extinguishing systems.
- Explain how each class of fire extinguisher puts out fires.
- Describe which jurisdictions have authority over fire safety.
- Explain what is meant by "life safety" system.
- Describe hazards associated with explosive materials.
- List the key elements of a fire protection program self-assessment.

FIRE HAZARD
Conditions that favour the ignition and spread of fire

FIRE
A chemical reaction between oxygen and a combustible fuel.

COMBUSTION
A chemical reaction between oxygen and a combustible fuel.

IGNITION TEMPERATURE
The temperature at which a given fuel can burst into flame.

FIRE HAZARDS DEFINED

Fire hazards are conditions that favour fire development or growth. Three elements are required to start and sustain fire: (1) oxygen, (2) fuel, and (3) heat. Because oxygen is naturally present in most earth environments, fire hazards usually involve the mishandling of fuel or heat.

Fire, or **combustion**, is a chemical reaction between oxygen and a combustible fuel. Combustion is the process by which fire converts fuel and oxygen into energy, usually in the form of heat. By-products of combustion include light and smoke. For the reaction to start, a source of ignition, such as a spark or open flame, or a sufficiently high temperature is needed. Given a sufficiently high temperature, almost every substance will burn. The **ignition temperature** or **combustion point** is the temperature at which a given fuel can burst into flame.

Fire is a chain reaction. For combustion to continue there must be a constant source of fuel, oxygen, and heat. These three components have traditionally been represented by a *fire triangle* as seen in Figure 15–1. However, to sustain combustion, a fourth component is necessary: a chemical chain reaction. To include each four of these elements a four plane triangular figure is used in the pictorial representation. The three outer triangles of the *fire tetrahedron* represent the fuel, oxygen, and heat and the centre triangle represents the chemical chain reaction with which they interact — as seen in Figure 15–1. **Exothermic** chemical reactions create heat. Combustion and fire are exothermic reactions and can often generate large quantities of heat. **Endothermic** reactions consume more heat than they generate. An ongoing fire usually provides its own sources of heat. It is important to remember that cooling is one of the principal ways to control a fire or put it out.

All chemical reactions involve forming and breaking chemical bonds between atoms. In the process of combustion, materials are broken down into basic elements. Loose atoms form bonds with each other to create molecules of substances that were not originally present.

Carbon is found in almost every flammable substance. When a substance burns, the carbon is released and then combines with the oxygen that *must* be present to form either carbon dioxide or carbon monoxide.

Carbon dioxide is produced when there is more oxygen than the fire needs. It is not toxic, but it can be produced in such volumes that it seriously reduces the concentration of oxygen in the air surrounding the fire site. Carbon monoxide — a colourless, odourless, deadly gas — is the result of incomplete combustion of a fuel. It is produced when there is insufficient oxygen to burn the fuel present efficiently. In general, most fires have insufficient oxygen and therefore produce large quantities of carbon monoxide. It is important in any intentional

COMBUSTION POINT
The temperature at which a given fuel can burst into flame.

EXOTHERMIC
Chemical reactions that create heat.

ENDOTHERMIC
Reactions that consume more heat than they generate.

Fire Triangle

Fire Tetrahedron

Oxygen   Heat

Fuel

Heat

Chemical
Chain
Reaction

Oxygen   Fuel

▶ Figure 15–1
**Fire triangle
and fire tetrahedron.**

industrial fire that the fuel be consumed as completely as possible. This will reduce ash and minimize smoke and gases, including carbon monoxide.

Synthetic polymers, found in plastics and vinyls, often form deadly fumes when they are consumed by fire, or when they melt or disintegrate from being near fire or high heat. Burning, melting, or disintegrating plastic at a fire site should be presumed to be releasing toxic fumes.

Liquids and solids, such as oil and wood, do not burn directly but must first be converted into a flammable vapour by heat. Hold a match to a sheet of paper, and the paper will burst into flames. Look closely at the paper, and you will see that the paper is not burning. The flames reside in a vapour area just above the surface of the sheet.

Vapours will burn only at a specific range of mixtures of oxygen and fuel, determined by the composition of the fuel. At the optimum mixture, a fire burns, generates heat and some light, and produces no other by-products. In an unintentional fire, the mixture is constantly changing as more or less oxygen is brought into the flames and more or less heat is generated, producing more or less vapours and flammable gases.

Remove the fire's access to fuel or remove the oxygen, and the fire dies. Although a spark, flame, or heat may start a fire, the heat that a fire produces is necessary to sustain it. Therefore, a fire may be extinguished not only by removing the fuel source or starving it of oxygen but by cooling it below the combustion point. Even in an oxygen-rich, combustible environment, such as a hospital oxygen tent, fire can be avoided by controlling heat and eliminating sparks and open flames.

EXPLOSION
A very rapid, contained fire.

An **explosion** is a very rapid, contained fire. When the gases produced exceed the pressure capacity of the vessel, a rupture or explosion must result. The simplest example is a firecracker. The fuse, which usually contains its own source of oxygen, burns into the centre of a firecracker. The surrounding powder ignites, and the heat produced vaporizes the balance of the explosive material and ignites it. The tightly wrapped paper of the firecracker cannot contain the expanding gases. The firecracker explodes, in much less time than was required to read about it.

CONDUCTION
The transfer of heat between two bodies that are touching or from one location to another within a body.

Heat always flows from a higher temperature to a lower temperature, never from a lower temperature to a higher temperature without an outside force being applied. Fires generate heat, which in turn is necessary to sustain the fire. Excess heat is then transferred to surrounding objects, which may ignite, explode, or decompose. Heat transfer is accomplished by three means, usually simultaneously: (1) conduction, (2) radiation, and (3) convection.

KINETIC ENERGY
The energy resulting from a moving object.

Conduction is direct thermal energy transfer. On a molecular level, materials near a source of heat absorb the heat, raising their kinetic energy. **Kinetic energy** is the energy resulting from a moving object. Energy in the form of heat is transferred from one molecule to the next. Materials conduct heat at varying rates. Metals are very good conductors of heat. Concrete and plastics are poor conductors, hence good insulators. Nevertheless, a heat buildup on one side of a wall — even if it is made of a material like concrete that is a poor conductor — will eventually transfer to the other side of the wall by conduction.

RADIATION
Consists of energetic nuclear particles and includes alpha rays, beta rays, gamma rays, X-rays, neutrons, high-speed electrons, and high-speed protons.

Radiation is the electromagnetic wave transfer of heat to a solid. Waves travel in all directions from the fire and may be reflected off surfaces, as well as absorbed by them. Absorbed heat may raise the temperature beyond a material's combustion point, and then a fire erupts. Heat may also be conducted through a vessel to its contents, which will expand and may explode. An example is the spread of fire through an oil tank field. A fire in one tank can spread to nearby tanks through radiated heat, raising the temperature and pressure of the other tank contents.

Convection is heat transfer through the movement of hot gases. The gases may be the direct products of fire, the results of chemical reaction, or additional gases brought to the fire by the movement of air and heated at the fire surfaces by conduction. Convection determines the general direction of the spread of a fire. Convection causes fires to rise as heat rises and move in the direction of the prevailing air currents.

All three forms of heat transfer are present at a campfire. A metal poker left in a fire gets red hot at the flame end. Heat is conducted up the handle, which gets progressively hotter until the opposite end of the poker is too hot to touch. People around the fire are warmed principally by radiation, but only on the side of their body that is facing the fire. People farther away from the fire will be warmer on the side of their body facing the fire than the backs of people closer to the fire. Marshmallows toasted above the flames are heated by convection (see Figure 15–2).

Spontaneous combustion is rare, but it can happen. Organic compounds decompose through natural chemical processes. As they degrade, they release methane gas (natural gas), an excellent fuel. The degradation process — a chemical reaction — produces heat. In a forest, the concentrations of decomposing matter are relatively minimal, and both the gas and the heat vent naturally.

A classic example of spontaneous combustion is a pile of oil-soaked rags. A container of oil seldom ignites spontaneously. A collection of clean fabrics seldom bursts into flames. Rags soaking completely within oil are usually safe. One oil-soaked rag is unlikely to cause a problem. However, in a pile of oil-soaked rags — especially in a closed container — the chemistry is quite different.

The fibres of the rags expose a large surface area of oil to oxidation. The porous nature of rags allows additional oxygen to be absorbed, replacing the oxygen already consumed. When the temperature rises sufficiently, the surfaces of the oil on the rags vaporize.

CONVECTION
The transfer of heat from one location to another by way of a moving medium.

SPONTANEOUS COMBUSTION
Result of sufficient fuel and heat from decomposing organic material for ignition.

Convection

Radiation

(waves)

Conduction
(direct contact)

▶ **Figure 15–2
Campfire.**

HYPERGOLIC
Fuels that ignite sponta-
neously on contact with
an oxidizer.

Hypergolic reactions occur when mixing fuels. Oxidizers produce a rapid heat buildup, causing immediate combustion at room temperature with no apparent source of ignition. Although the term *hypergolic* originated with rocket propellants, the phenomenon has been around for a long time. *Pyrophor hypergolic* fuels are those that self-ignite in the presence of oxygen found at normal atmospheric concentrations. One example is white phosphorus, which is kept underwater. If it starts to dry out, the phosphorus erupts in flames.

SOURCES OF FIRE HAZARDS

Almost everything in an industrial environment can burn. Metal furniture, machines, plaster, and concrete block walls are usually painted. Most paints and lacquers will easily catch fire. Oxygen is almost always present. Therefore, the principal method of fire suppression is passive — the absence of sufficient heat. Within our environment, various conditions elevate the risk of fire and so are termed *fire hazards*.

For identification, fires are classified according to their properties, which relate to the nature of the fuel. The properties of the fuel directly correspond to the best means of combating a fire (see Figure 15–3).

Without a source of fuel, there is no fire hazard. However, almost everything in our environment can be a fuel. Fuels occur as solids, liquids, vapours, and gases.

Solid fuels include wood, building decorations and furnishings such as fabric curtains and wall coverings, and synthetics used in furniture. What would an office be without paper? What would most factories be without cardboard and packing materials such as Styrofoam moulds and panels, shredded or crumpled papers, bubble wrap, and shrink wrap? All of these materials easily burn.

Few solid fuels are, or can be made, fireproof. Even firewalls do not stop fires, although they are defined by their ability to slow the spread of fire. Wood and textiles can be treated with fire- or flame-retardant chemicals to reduce their flammability.

FLASH POINT
The lowest temperature
for a given fuel at which
vapours are produced in
sufficient concentrations
to flash in the presence of
a source of ignition.

Solid fuels are involved in most industrial fires, but mishandling flammable liquids and flammable gases is a major cause of industrial fires. Two often-confused terms applied to flammable liquids are *flash point* and *fire point*. The **flash point** is the lowest temperature for a given fuel at which vapours are pro-

**Figure 15–3
Classes of fire.**
Source: National Fire Association, *Fire Protection Handbook*, 18th ed. (Quincy, MA: NFPA, 1997).

Class A fires	Solid materials such as wood, plastics, textiles, and their products: paper, housing, clothing.
Class B fires	Flammable liquids and gases.
Class C fires	Electrical (referring to live electricity situations, not including fires in other materials started by electricity).
Class D fires	Combustible, easily oxidized metals such as aluminum, magnesium, titanium, and zirconium.
Special categories	Extremely active oxidizers or mixtures, flammables containing oxygen, nitric acid, hydrogen peroxide, and solid missile propellants.

duced in sufficient concentrations to flash in the presence of a source of ignition. The **fire point** is the minimum temperature at which the vapours continue to burn, given a source of ignition. The **auto-ignition temperature** is the lowest point at which the vapours of a liquid or solid self-ignite *without* a source of ignition.

Flammable liquids have a flash point below 100°F (37.7°C). **Combustible** liquids have a flash point at or higher than 100°F. Both flammable and combustible liquids are further divided into the three classifications shown in Figure 15–4.

As the temperature of any flammable liquid increases, the amount of vapour generated on the surface also increases. Safe handling, therefore, requires both a knowledge of the properties of the liquid and an awareness of ambient temperatures in the work or storage place. The **explosive range**, or *flammable range,* defines the concentrations of a vapour or gas in air that can ignite from a source. The auto-ignition temperature is the lowest temperature at which liquids spontaneously ignite.

Most flammable liquids are lighter than water. If the flammable liquid is lighter than water, water cannot be used to put the fire out.[1] The application of water floats the fuel and spreads a gasoline fire. Crude oil fires burn even while floating on fresh or sea water.

Unlike solids (which have a definite shape and location) and unlike liquids (which have a definite volume and are heavier than air), gases have no shape. Gases expand to fill the volume of the container in which they are enclosed, and they are frequently lighter than air. Released into air, gas concentrations are difficult to monitor due to the changing factors of air current direction and temperature. Gases may stratify in layers of differing concentrations but often collect near the top of whatever container in which they are enclosed. Concentrations found to be safe when sampled at workbench level may be close to, or exceed, flammability limits if sampled just above head height.

The products of combustion are gases, flame (light), heat, and smoke. Smoke is a combination of gases, air, and suspended particles, which are the products of incomplete combustion. Many of the gases present in smoke and at a fire site are toxic to humans. Other, usually nontoxic, gases may replace the oxygen normally present in air. Most fatalities associated with fire are from breathing toxic gases and smoke and from being suffocated because of lack of oxygen. Gases that may be produced by a fire include acrolein, ammonia, car-

FIRE POINT
The minimum temperature at which the vapours or gas in air can ignite from a source of ignition.

AUTO-IGNITION TEMPERATURE
The lowest temperature at which a vapour-producing substance or a flammable gas will ignite even without the presence of a spark or a flame.

FLAMMABLE SUBSTANCE
Any substance with a flash point below 37.8°C (100°F).

COMBUSTIBLE SUBSTANCE
Any substance with a flash point of 37.8°C (100°F) or higher.

EXPLOSIVE RANGE
Defines the concentrations of a vapour or gas in air that can ignite from a source.

Flammable Liquids

Class I–A	Flash point below 22.8°C (73°F), boiling point below 37.8°C (100°F).
Class I–B	Flash point below 22.8°C (73°F), boiling point at or above 37.8°C (100°F).
Class I–C	Flash point at or above 22.8°C (73°F), but below 37.8°C (100°F).

Combustible Liquids

Class II	Flash point at or above 37.8°C (100°F), but below 60°C (140°F).
Class III–A	Flash point at or above 60°C (140°F), but below 93.3°C (200°F).
Class III–B	Flash point at or above 93.3°C (200°F).

Figure 15–4
Classes of flammable and combustible liquids.

bon monoxide, carbon dioxide, hydrogen bromide, hydrogen cyanide, hydrogen chloride, hydrogen sulphide, sulphur dioxide, and nitrogen dioxide. Released gases are capable of travelling across a room and randomly finding a spark, flame, or adequate heat source, flashing back to the source of the gas.

The National Fire Protection Association (NFPA) has devised the NFPA 704 system for quick identification of hazards presented when substances burn (see Figure 15–5). The NFPA's red, blue, yellow, and white diamond is used on product labels, shipping cartons, and buildings. Ratings within each category are 0 to 4, where zero represents no hazard and four the most severe hazard level. The colours refer to a specific category of hazard:

Red = flammability

Blue = health

Yellow = reactivity

White = special information

Although we do not think of electricity as burning, natural and generated electricity play a large role in causing fires. Lightning strikes cause many fires every year. In the presence of a flammable gas or liquid mixture, one spark can produce a fire. Electrical lines and equipment can cause fires either by a short circuit that provides an ignition spark, by arcs, or by resistances generating a heat buildup. Electrical switches and relays commonly arc as contact is made or broken.

Another source of ignition is heat in the form of hot surfaces. It is easy to see the flame hazard present when cooking oil is poured on a very hot grill. The wooden broom handle leaning up against the side of a hot oven may not be as obvious a hazard. Irons used in textile manufacturing and dry-cleaning plants also pose a heat hazard.

Space heaters frequently have hot sides, tops, backs, and bottoms in addition to the heat-generating face. Hotplates, coffee pots, and coffee makers often create heated surfaces. Many types of electric lighting generate heat, which is transferred to the lamp housing.

Engines produce heat, especially in their exhaust systems. Compressors produce heat through friction, which is transferred to their housings. Boilers produce hot surfaces, as do steam lines and equipment using steam as power. Radiators, pipes, flues, and chimneys all have hot surfaces. Metal stock that has been cut by a blade heats up as does the blade. Surfaces exposed to direct sunlight become hot surfaces and transmit their heat by conduction to their other side. Heated surfaces are a potential source of fire.

FIRE DANGERS TO HUMANS

Direct contact with flame is obviously dangerous to humans. Flesh burns, as do muscles and internal organs. The fact that we are 80% water, by some estimations, does not mitigate the fact that virtually all of the other 20% burns. Nevertheless, burns are not the major cause of death in a fire.

National Fire Protection Association statistics show that most people die in fires from suffocating or breathing smoke and toxic fumes. Carbon dioxide can lead to suffocation because it can be produced in large volumes, depleting oxy-

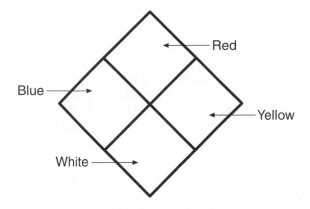

Flammability has a red background and is the top quarter of the diamond.

0   No hazard. Materials are stable during a fire and do not react with water.
1   Slight hazard. Flash point well above normal ambient temperature.
2   Moderate hazard. Flash point is slightly above normal ambient temperature.
3   Extreme fire hazard. Gases or liquids that can ignite at normal temperature.
4   Extremely flammable gases or liquids with very low flash points.

Health has a blue background and is the left quarter of the diamond.

0   No threat to health.
1   Slight health hazards. Respirator is recommended.
2   Moderate health hazard. Respirator and eye protection required.
3   Extremely dangerous to health. Protective clothing and equipment is required.
4   Imminent danger to health. Breathing or skin absorption may cause death. A fully encapsulating
       suit is required.

Reactive has a yellow background and is the right quarter of the diamond.

0   No hazard. Material is stable in a fire and does not react with water.
1   Slight hazard. Materials can become unstable at higher temperatures or react with water to
       produce a slight amount of heat.
2   Moderate or greater hazard. Materials may undergo violent chemical reaction, but will not
       explode. Materials react violently with water directly or form explosive mixtures with water.
3   Extreme hazard. Materials may explode given an ignition source or have violent reactions
       with water.
4   Constant extreme hazard. Materials may polymerize, decompose, explode, or undergo other
       hazardous reactions on their own. Area should be evacuated in event of a fire.

Special information has a white background and is the bottom quarter of the diamond.

This area is used to note any special hazards presented by the material.

Figure 15–5
Identification of fire hazards.

gen from the air. Many fire extinguishers use carbon dioxide because of its ability to starve the fire of oxygen while simultaneously cooling the fire. The number one killer in fires is carbon monoxide, which is produced in virtually all fires involving organic compounds. Carbon monoxide is produced in large volumes and can quickly reach lethal dosage concentrations.

Figure 15–6 shows the major chemical products of combustion. Other gases may be produced under some conditions. Not all of these gases are present at any particular fire site. Many of these compounds will further react with other substances often present at a fire. For example, sulphur dioxide will combine with water to produce sulphuric acid. Oxides of nitrogen may combine with water to produce nitric acid. Sulphuric acid and nitric acid can cause serious acid burns.

DETECTION OF FIRE HAZARDS

Many automatic fire detection systems are used in industry today. These systems can warn of the presence of smoke, radiation, elevated temperature, or increased light intensity. *Thermal expansion detectors* use a heat-sensitive metal link that melts at a predetermined temperature to make contact and ultimately sound an

Product	Fuels	Pathology
Acrolein	Cellulose, fatty substances, woods, and paints	Highly toxic irritant to eyes and respiratory system.
Ammonia (NH_3)	Wool, silk, nylon, melamine, refrigerants, hydrogen-nitrogen compounds	Somewhat toxic irritant to eyes and respiratory system.
Carbon dioxide (CO_2)	All carbon and organic compounds	Not toxic, but depletes available oxygen.
Carbon monoxide (CO)	All carbon and organic compounds	Can be deadly.
Hydrogen chloride (HCN)	Wool, silk, nylon, paper, polyurethane, rubber, leather, plastic, wood	Quickly lethal asphyxiant.
Hydrogen sulphide (H_2S)	Sulphur-containing compounds, rubber, crude oil	Highly toxic gas. Strong odour of rotten eggs, but quickly destroys sense of smell.
Nitrogen dioxide (NO_2)	Cellulose nitrate, celluloid, textiles, other nitrogen oxides	Lung irritant, causing death or damage.
Sulphur dioxide (SO_2)	Sulphur and sulphur-containing compounds	Toxic irritant.

Figure 15–6
Major chemical products of combustion.

alarm. Heat-sensitive insulation can be used, which melts at a predetermined temperature, thereby initiating a short circuit and activating the alarm.

Photoelectric fire sensors detect changes in infrared energy that is radiated by smoke, often by the smoke particles obscuring the photoelectric beam. A relay is open under acceptable conditions and closed to complete the alarm circuit when smoke interferes.

Ionization or radiation sensors use the tendency of a radioactive substance to ionize when exposed to smoke. The substance becomes electrically conductive with smoke exposure and permits the alarm circuit to be completed.

Ultraviolet or *infrared detectors* sound an alarm when the radiation from fire flames is detected. When rapid changes in radiation intensities are detected, a fire alarm signal is given.

REDUCING FIRE HAZARDS

The best way to reduce fires is to prevent them. A major cause of industrial fires is hot, poorly insulated machinery and processes. One means of reducing a fire hazard is the isolation of the three triangle elements: fuel, oxygen, and heat. In the case of fluids, closing a valve may stop the fuel element.

Fires may also be prevented by the proper storage of flammable liquids. Liquids should be stored as follows:

- In flame-resistant buildings that are isolated from places where people work. Proper drainage and venting should be provided for such buildings.
- In tanks below ground level.
- On the first floor of multi-storey buildings.

Substituting less flammable materials is another effective technique for fire reduction. A catalyst or fire inhibitor can be employed to create an endothermic energy state that eventually smothers the fire. Several ignition sources can be eliminated or isolated from fuels:

- Prohibit smoking near any possible fuels.
- Store fuels away from areas where electrical sparks from equipment, wiring, or lightning may occur.
- Keep fuels separate from areas where there are open flames. These may include welding torches, heating elements, or furnaces.
- Isolate fuels from tools or equipment that may produce mechanical or static sparks.

Other strategies for reducing the risk of fires are as follows:

- Clean up spills of flammable liquids as soon as they occur. Properly dispose of the materials used in the cleanup.
- Keep work areas free from extra supplies of flammable materials (e.g., paper, rags, boxes, and so on). Have only what is needed on hand with the remaining inventory properly stored.
- Run electrical cords along walls rather than across aisles or in other heavy traffic areas. Cords that are walked on can become frayed and dangerous.
- Turn off the power and completely de-energize equipment before conducting maintenance procedures.

- Don't use spark- or friction-prone tools near combustible materials.
- Routinely test fire extinguishers.

Fire Extinguishing Systems

In larger or isolated industrial facilities, an employee fire brigade may be created. **Standpipe and hose systems** provide the hose and pressurized water for firefighting. Hoses for these systems usually vary from 25 mm (1 inch) to 63 mm (2.5 inches) in diameter.[2]

Automatic sprinkler systems are an example of a fixed extinguishing system, so called because the sprinklers are fixed in position. There are two types of sprinkler systems: wet and dry. Wet systems are most common; they are water filled and discharge water as soon as a sprinkler head is opened. A dry system is used where the chance of freezing exists; in a dry system the pipes contain air or nitrogen gas and when a sprinkler opens, the air escapes and water enters the system. Both systems are triggered when a predetermined heat threshold is breached.

Portable fire extinguishers are classified by the types of fire they can most effectively reduce. Figure 15–7 describes the four major fire extinguisher classifications. Blocking or shielding the spread of fire can include covering the fire with an inert foam, inert powder, nonflammable gas, or water with a thickening agent added. The fire may suffocate under such a covering. Flooding a liquid fuel with nonflammable liquid can dilute the fuel to the point where it will not burn. Figures 15–8, 15–9, and 15–10 are photographs of effective fire prevention equipment.

Fire Class	Extinguisher Contents	Mechanism	Disadvantages
A	Foam, water, dry chemical	Chain-breaking cooling, smothering, and diluting	Freezing if not kept heated.
B	Dry chemical, bromotrifluoromethane, and other halogenated compounds, foam, CO_2, dry chemical	Chain-breaking smothering, cooling, and shielding	Halogenated compounds are toxic.
C	Bromotrifluoromethane, CO_2, dry chemical	Chain-breaking smothering, cooling, and shielding	Halogenated compounds are toxic; fires may ignite after CO_2 dissipates.
D	Specialized powders such as graphite, sand, limestone, soda ash, sodium chloride	Cooling, smothering	Expensive; cover of powder may be broken with resultant reignition.

Figure 15–7
Fire extinguisher characteristics.

Figure 15–9
Fire-protective drums on a poly spill pallet.
Source: Courtesy of JUSTRITE®.

Figure 15–8
Fireproof storage cabinet.
Source: Courtesy of JUSTRITE®.

Figure 15–10
Fire-protective drums stored in an outside storage cabinet.
Source: Courtesy of JUSTRITE®.

Disaster Preparations

Training employees may be the most successful life-saving preparation for a fire disaster. Company fire brigade members should be trained and tested at least quarterly. Disaster preparation initially requires management commitment and planning and continued response and recovery practice by the fire brigade on a regular basis. Also necessary are regular, but less frequent, fire drills for all personnel.

Disaster preparations also include the integration of company planning with community plans. Community disaster relief agencies such as the police, fire department, Red Cross, and hospitals should be consulted and informed of company disaster preparation plans.

Preventing Office Fires

The shop floor is not the only part of the plant where fire hazards exist. Offices are also susceptible to fires. The following strategies are helpful in preventing office fires:

- Periodically check electrical circuits and connections. Replace frayed or worn cords immediately.
- Make sure that extension cords and other accessories are UL- or CSA-approved and used only as recommended.
- Make sure there is plenty of air space left around copying machines and other office machines that can overheat.
- Locate heat-producing appliances away from the wall or anything else that can ignite.
- Frequently inspect personal appliances such as hotplates, coffee pots, and cup warmers. Assign responsibility for turning off such appliances every day to a specific person.
- Keep aisles, stairwells, and exits clear of paper, boxes, and other combustible materials.[3]

DEVELOPMENT OF FIRE SAFETY STANDARDS

The purpose of modern fire safety standards is the protection of life and the prevention of property damage. However, the impetus for developing standards has always been and continues to be the occurrence of major disasters. Typically, standards are developed after a major tragedy occurs in which property is damaged on a large scale and lives are lost. Public shock turns into an outcry for action. A flurry of political activity follows, and agencies and organizations that develop standards are called on to develop new standards.

The trend in fire safety standards is toward performance-based standards and away from the traditional specification-based approach. An example of each type of standard will help to illustrate the difference. A specification-based standard may require that brick, concrete, or steel material be used in a given type of building. A performance-based standard may specify that materials used have a one-, two-, or four-hour fire resistance rating.[4] Advances in the testing of engineering materials will help overcome most of the barriers to full development and implementation of performance-based standards.

A. E. Cote summarizes his views on the future of fire safety standards as follows:

> Codes and standards will survive in the 21st century. They may, however, be considerably different from the codes and standards we now have. They certainly will be based more on standardized fire tests, models, data, and related science and engineering than on consensus judgment. How much more will depend on the extent to which there is widespread acceptance of the anticipated breakthroughs in fire science and in related modeling and calculation methods.[5]

FIRE REGULATIONS IN CANADA

Jurisdiction over fire protection in Canada remains with the provinces and territories. While a national fire code exists (Canada's National Fire Code or NFC), most provinces have developed their own fire code, which is usually modelled after the NFC. The NFC was developed to provide national consistency among various provincial, territorial, and municipal jurisdictions, but modifications are frequently made to account for geographical, social, and economic variations. One must also consider that the NFC is only one component of the total life safety system incorporated into the design and construction of buildings. The NFC works in conjunction with other codes such as electrical, building, and plumbing codes. Below is a list of the relationships between the National Fire Code and of the code in each jurisdiction:

Yukon, Northwest Territories, Nunavut, Saskatchewan, and Manitoba Territory/province–wide adoption of the National Fire Code with some modifications and additions.

Nova Scotia and Quebec No province-wide fire code. Some municipalities adopt the National Fire Code.

Alberta and British Columbia Province-wide fire code substantially the same as national code, but with variations that are primarily additions.

Ontario Province-wide fire code based on national code but with significant variations in content and scope. The Ontario Fire Code differs more from the National Fire Code than do the codes of other provinces/territories.

New Brunswick Province-wide adoption of the National Fire Code.

Prince Edward Island Province-wide fire code not based on the National Fire Code.

Newfoundland and Labrador Province-wide adoption of the National Fire Code and aspects of the National Building Code pertaining to fire and life safety that are cross-referenced in the National Fire Code.[6]

Figure 15–11 summarizes fire prevention and suppression strategies.

LIFE SAFETY

Life safety involves protecting the vehicles, vessels, and lives of people in buildings and structures from fire. The primary reference source for life safety is the *Life Safety Code*, published by the National Fire Protection Association.

Figure 15–11
Fire prevention and
suppression summary.

- Use the least flammable materials whenever possible.
- Analyze the company to determine types of potential fires and provide appropriate sprinklers and/or extinguishers.
- Develop a database of the flammability of materials available in the company.
- Store containers or flammable materials away from sources of heat or sparks and away from humans.
- Do not permit smoking near flammable materials.
- Include a venting mechanism in storage containers and locate them near a drain.
- Minimize fuel storage container size to reduce the size of the fire that may involve those fuels.
- Isolate fuels from sources of heat.
- Include a smoke detection system and portable fire extinguishers in the facility. Extinguishers should be easily available to every workstation.
- Make sure sources of heat have controlling mechanisms and are near fire detection equipment.
- Check fire extinguishing equipment regularly.
- Perform periodic inspections for new fire hazards and reappraisal of existing fire hazards.
- Train plant personnel in basic fire prevention, which should include periodic fire drills.
- Make sure fire brigade personnel are well trained, tested, and regularly practise fire control.
- Stress cleanliness and an organized method of disposal of flammable materials.

The code applies to new and existing buildings. It addresses the construction, protection, and occupancy features necessary to minimize the hazards of fire, smoke, fumes, and panic. A major part of the code is devoted to the minimum requirements for design of egress necessary to ensure that occupants can quickly evacuate a building or structure.

Basic Requirements

In this section, the term *structure* refers to a structure or building.

MEANS OF EGRESS
A route for exiting a building or other structure.

- Every structure, new and existing, that is to be occupied by people must have a **means of egress** and other fire protection safeguards that, together, meet the following criteria: (1) ensure that occupants can promptly evacuate or be adequately protected without evacuating; and (2) provide sufficient backup safeguards to ensure that human life is not endangered if one system fails.
- Every structure must be constructed or renovated, maintained, and operated in such a way that occupants are (1) protected from fire, smoke, or fumes; (2) protected from fire-related panic; (3) protected long enough to allow a reasonable amount of time for evacuation; and (4) protected long enough to defend themselves without evacuating.
- In providing structures with means of egress and other fire protection safeguards, the following factors must be considered: (1) character of the occupancy; (2) capabilities of occupants; (3) number of occupants; (4) available

fire protection; (5) height of the structure; (6) type of construction; and (7) any other applicable concerns.

- No lock or other device may be allowed to obstruct egress in any part of a structure at any time that it is occupied. The only exceptions to this requirement are mental health detention and correctional facilities. In these, the following criteria are required: (1) responsible personnel must be available to act in the case of fire or a similar emergency; and (2) procedures must be in place to ensure that occupants are evacuated in the event of an emergency.
- All exits in structures must satisfy the following criteria: (1) be clearly visible or marked in such a way that an unimpaired individual can readily discern the route of escape; (2) all routes to a place of safety must be arranged or clearly marked; (3) any doorway and passageway that may be mistaken as a route to safety must be arranged or clearly marked in such a way as to prevent confusion in an emergency; and (4) all appropriate steps must be taken to ensure that occupants do not mistakenly enter a dead-end passageway.
- Egress routes and facilities must be included in the lighting design wherever artificial illumination is required in a structure.
- Fire alarm systems must be provided in any facility that is large enough or so arranged that a fire itself may not adequately warn occupants of the danger. Fire alarms should alert occupants to initiate appropriate emergency procedures.
- In any structure or portion of a structure in which a single means of egress may be blocked or overcrowded in an emergency situation, at least two means of egress must be provided. The two means of egress must be arranged in such a way as to minimize the possibility of both becoming impassable in the same emergency situation.
- All stairs, ramps, and other means of moving from floor to floor must be enclosed (or otherwise protected) to afford occupants protection when used as a means of egress in an emergency situation. These means of vertical movement should also serve to inhibit the spread of fire, fumes, and smoke from floor to floor.
- Compliance with the requirements summarized herein does not eliminate or reduce the need to take other precautions to protect occupants from fire hazards, nor does it permit the acceptance of any condition that could be hazardous under normal occupancy conditions.[7]

The information in this section is a summary of the broad fundamental requirements of the *Life Safety Code* of the National Fire Protection Association. More specific requirements relating to means of egress and features of fire protection are explained in the following sections.

Means of Egress

This section explains some of the more important issues in the *Life Safety Code* relating to means of egress. Students and practitioners who need more detailed information are encouraged to refer to the *Life Safety Code*.

1. **Doors.** Doors that serve as exits must be designed, constructed, and maintained in such a way that the means of egress is direct and obvious. Windows that could be mistaken for doors in an emergency situation must be made inaccessible to occupants.

2. **Capacity of means of egress.** The means of egress must have a capacity sufficient to accommodate the occupant load of the structure calculated in accordance with the requirements of the *Life Safety Code*.

3. **Number of means of egress.** Any component of a structure must have a minimum of two means of egress (with exceptions as set forth in the code). The minimum number of means of egress from any storey or any part of a storey is three for occupancy loads of 500 to 1000 and four for occupancy loads of more than 1000.

4. **Arrangement of means of egress.** All exits must be easily accessible at all times in terms of both location and arrangement.

5. **Measurement of travel distance to exits.** The travel distance to at least one exit must be measured on the walking surface along a natural path of travel beginning at the most remote occupied space and ending at the centre of the exit. Distances must comply with the code.

6. **Discharge from exits.** All exits from a structure must terminate at a public way or at yards, courts, or open spaces that lead to the exterior of the structure.

7. **Illumination of means of egress.** All means of egress shall be illuminated continuously during times when the structure is occupied. Artificial lighting must be used as required to maintain the necessary level of illumination. Illumination must be arranged in such a way that no area is left in darkness by a single lighting failure.

8. **Emergency lighting.** Emergency lighting for all means of egress must be provided in accordance with the code. In cases where maintaining the required illumination depends on changing from one source of power to another, there shall be no appreciable interruption of lighting.

9. **Marking of means of egress.** Exits must be marked by readily visible, approved signs in all cases where the means of egress is not obviously apparent to occupants. No point in the exit access corridor shall be more than 100 feet [30.5 metres] from the nearest sign.

10. **Special provisions for high hazard areas.** If an area contains contents that are classified as highly hazardous, occupants must be able to exit by travelling no more than 75 feet [22.9 metres]. At least two means of egress must be provided, and there shall be no dead-end corridors.[8]

SAFETY MYTH

Fire Ratings for Doors, Walls, and Floors

A three-hour fire wall will provide protection for three hours. Right? Not necessarily. In fact, any relationship between a fire rating and the reality of fire resistance may be little more than coincidental. The problem is that the factors used to determine fire ratings are outdated. They are based on materials that were in use many years ago and no longer have any relevance. The materials used for constructing and furnishing buildings today are radically different from those upon which fire ratings are based. Consider fire ratings overvalued, and plan for less time than they allow.

The requirements summarized in this section relate to the fundamental specifications of the *Life Safety Code* relating to means of egress. For more detailed information concerning general requirements, means of egress, and other factors such as fire protection and fire protection equipment, refer to the actual code.

EXPLOSIVE HAZARDS

Many chemical and toxic substances used in modern organizations are flammable or combustible. Consequently, under certain conditions, they can explode. Working in these conditions involves hazards that require special precautions for handling, storing, transporting, and using such substances.

Health Hazards of Explosive Materials

The health hazards associated with explosions and fires are well known. The potential for serious injury or death from the force of a blast or from burns is very high. However, there are other hazards associated with explosive and combustible materials. These include skin irritation, intoxication, and suffocation.

Irritation can occur when the skin comes in contact with hazardous substances. The degree of irritation can range from minor to severe, depending on the type of substance, its concentration, and the duration of contact. Intoxication can occur when an employee breathes the vapours of combustible substances. This can cause impaired judgment, performance, and reaction time, which can, in turn, result in an accident. Finally, the vapours from combustible materials can accumulate in confined spaces. When this happens, the air becomes contaminated and is both toxic and explosive. In such cases, the hazard of suffocation must be added to those associated with explosives.[9]

SELF-ASSESSMENT IN FIRE PROTECTION

Health and safety personnel cannot be everywhere at the same time. Consequently, it is wise to enlist the assistance of supervisors and employees in fire protection. An excellent way to do this is to provide them with a self-assessment checklist that will guide them in scanning their areas of responsibility for fire hazards. Such checklists should contain at least the following questions:

1. Are portable fire extinguishers properly mounted, readily accessible, and available in adequate number and type?

2. Are fire extinguishers inspected monthly for both operability and general condition with appropriate notation made on their respective tags?

3. Are fire extinguishers recharged regularly and are the dates noted on their tags?

4. Are interior standpipes and valves inspected regularly?

5. Is the fire alarm system tested regularly?

6. Are employees trained in the proper use of fire extinguishers?

7. Are employees trained concerning under what conditions they should help fight fires and under what conditions they should evacuate?

8. Are the nearest fire hydrants flushed annually?

9. Are the nearest fire hydrants maintained regularly?

10. Are avenues and ingress and egress clearly marked?

11. Are all avenues of ingress and egress kept free of clutter and other types of obstructions?

12. Are fire doors and shutters in good working condition?

13. Are fusible links in place and readily accessible?

14. Is the local fire department familiar with the facility and any specific hazards?

15. Is the automatic sprinkler system in good working order, maintained on a regular basis, given the proper overhead clearance, and protected from inadvertent contact damage?[10]

SUMMARY

1. Fire hazards are conditions that favour fire development or growth.

2. The elements required to start and sustain a fire in the smouldering mode are heat, fuel, oxygen, and a chemical chain reaction.

3. The elements required to start and sustain a fire in the flaming mode are heat, an oxidizing agent, a reducing agent, and a chemical chain reaction.

4. The product of combustion is energy in the form of heat.

5. By-products of combustion include light and smoke.

6. For a fire to start, there must be either a source of ignition or a sufficiently high temperature for the fuel.

7. Fire is an exothermic chemical reaction. Exothermic reactions generate heat. Endothermic reactions consume more heat than they generate.

8. Chemical reactions in a fire break down materials into basic elements.

9. Loose atoms bond with each other to create substances that were not originally present.

10. Cooling is one of the principal ways to control a fire or extinguish it.

11. Carbon is found in almost every flammable substance.

12. In a fire, released carbon atoms combine with oxygen to form either carbon dioxide or carbon monoxide.

13. Carbon dioxide can deplete oxygen concentrations in the air near the fire.

14. Carbon monoxide is a colourless, odourless, deadly gas.

15. Synthetic polymers in plastics and vinyls often form deadly toxic fumes when they are consumed, melted, or disintegrated in the presence of fire or high heat.

16. Liquid and solid fuels are first converted to a vapour before they burn.

17. The trend with regard to safety standards is away from the traditional specifications-based approach to a performance-based approach.

18. Removing the fuel, starving the fire of oxygen, or cooling it below the combustion point may extinguish a fire.

19. An explosion is a very rapid, contained fire.

20. Heat always travels from a higher temperature to a lower one.
21. Excess heat is transferred to other objects by conduction, radiation, or convection.
22. Conduction is direct thermal energy heat transfer, molecule to molecule, through solids and liquids.
23. Radiation is electromagnetic wave heat transfer through air in a straight line to surrounding solids.
24. Convection is heat transfer through the movement of molecules in a fluid.
25. Spontaneous combustion is rare, but not impossible.
26. Almost everything in the industrial environment can burn.
27. Fires are classified according to their properties, which relate to the fuels.
28. Class A fires involve solid fuels.
29. Class B fires involve flammable liquids and gases.
30. Class C fires involve live electricity.
31. Class D fires involve combustible metals.
32. Special categories include extremely active oxidizers and flammables containing oxygen.
33. All common packing materials burn easily.
34. Fire walls are defined by their ability to slow the spread of fire.
35. Wood and textiles can be treated to reduce their flammability.
36. The flash point is the lowest temperature at which vapours are produced in sufficient concentration to burn, given a source of ignition.
37. The fire point is the lowest temperature at which vapours will continue to burn, given a source of ignition.
38. The auto-ignition temperature is the lowest point at which the vapours of a liquid or solid self-ignites without a source of ignition.
39. Flammable liquids have a flash point below 37.8°C (100°F).
40. Combustible liquids have a flash point at or above 37.8°C.
41. Flammable and combustible liquids are each divided into three classifications.
42. Most flammable liquids are lighter than water; therefore, water cannot be used to put out these fires.
43. Most gases are lighter than air.
44. Many of the gases present in smoke and at a fire site are toxic to humans.
45. Most fatalities from fire result from breathing toxic gases and smoke, or from suffocating because of a lack of oxygen.
46. A red, blue, yellow, and white diamond label is used to identify hazards present when a substance burns.
47. Natural and generated electricity play a major role in causing fires.
48. Heat, in the form of hot surfaces, can be a source of ignition.
49. Automatic fire detection systems employ different means of detecting a fire.
50. The best way to reduce fires is to prevent their occurrence.
51. A comprehensive fire safety program should have at least the following elements: assessment, planning, awareness and prevention, and response.

KEY TERMS AND CONCEPTS

Auto-ignition temperature	Fire point
Combustible substance	Flammable range
Combustion	Flammable substance
Combustion point	Flash point
Conduction	Hypergolic
Convection	Ignition temperature
Endothermic	Kinetic energy
Exothermic	Means of egress
Explosion	Radiation
Explosive range	Spontaneous combustion
Fire	Standpipe and hose systems

REVIEW QUESTIONS

1. What are the four elements of the fire tetrahedron?

2. Fire is a chemical reaction. What is going on?

3. Where is carbon found?

4. Compare and contrast carbon monoxide and carbon dioxide.

5. How is combustion of liquids and solids different from gases?

6. What are the three methods of heat transfer? Describe each.

7. What can happen to a pile of oil-soaked rags in a closed container? Describe the process.

8. In which direction does a fire normally travel?

9. Name something in this room that will not burn.

10. What are the classes of fires?

11. What property do almost all packing materials share?

12. What are the differences among flash point, fire point, and auto-ignition temperature?

13. Which are more stable: combustible liquids or flammable liquids?

14. Which way do gases usually travel?

15. Describe the NFPA hazards identification system.

16. In what four ways can electricity cause a fire?

17. What are the leading causes of fire-related deaths?

18. What are some of the toxic chemicals often produced by fires?

19. What are some of the systems utilized by smoke detectors?

20. What is the most successful life-saving preparation for a fire disaster?

21. Explain the best ways to prevent an office fire.

22. What is the trend with regard to future fire safety standards?

23. Define the term *life safety*.

24. Summarize the key components of a fire safety program.

WEBLINKS

Canadian Association of Fire Chiefs
www.cafc.ca

The latest trends in fire safety can be found on this site, with links to provincial associations and other useful resources.

Canadian Fire Safety Association
www.canadianfiresafety.com

The Canadian Fire Safety Association's website shows how they promote fire safety through the use of seminars, safety training courses, informative newsletters, scholarships, and regular meetings.

National Fire Protection Association
www.nfpa.org

NFPA's website has interesting and informative articles for home and the workplace, along with links to international standards for fire and building safety, on which Canadian jurisdiction standards and codes are based.

National Research Council and the Institute for Research in Construction
www.nrc.ca/irc

Links to and information on the National Fire and Building codes can be found here.

ENDNOTES

1. National Fire Protection Association, *Fire Protection Handbook*, 18th ed. (Quincy, MA: NFPA, 1997), 112.
2. Ibid., 132.
3. C. Vogel, "Fires Can Raze Office Buildings," *Safety & Health* 144, no. 3: 26–27.
4. A. E. Cote, "Will Fire Safety Standards Survive in the 21st Century?" *NFPA Journal* 85, no. 5: 42.
5. Ibid.
6. National Research Council of Canada. (June 15, 2001). *Construction Innovation* 6, no. 2 (Spring 2001). [Online]. Available: http://irc.nrc-cnrc.gc.ca/newsletter/v6no2/code_e.html. (Retrieved December 14, 2004).
7. National Fire Protection Association, *Life Safety Code* (NFPA 101) (Quincy, MA: NFPA, 2000), 101–119.
8. Ibid., 101-26–101-50.
9. Ibid.
10. Retrieved from http://online.misu.nodak.edu/19577/BADM309checklist.htm.

16 CHAPTER

Radiation Hazards

LEARNING OBJECTIVES

- Define key terms and concepts used in discussing ionizing radiation.
- Explain the effects of exposure to ionizing radiation.
- Describe the common types of personal monitoring devices used.
- Describe the caution signs and symbols used for radiation.
- List the information and instruction nuclear workers are required to receive.
- Describe common methods of storage and disposal of radioactive material.
- List the requirements for the employer when the allowable dose of radiation is exceeded.
- Compare ionizing radiation to nonionizing radiation.
- Explain the effect of worker exposure to electromagnetic fields in the workplace.

IONIZING RADIATION
Radiation that becomes electrically charged or changed into ions.

RADIATION
Consists of energetic nuclear particles and includes alpha rays, beta rays, gamma rays, X-rays, neutrons, high-speed electrons, and high-speed protons.

RADIOACTIVE MATERIAL
Material that emits corpuscular or electro-magnetic emanations as the result of spontaneous nuclear disintegration.

The widow of a construction worker who helped build the British Nuclear Fuels (BNF) Sellafield plant was awarded $286 500 when it was determined that his death from chronic myeloid leukemia was the result of overexposure to radiation. Sellafield was constructed for the purpose of separating uranium from used fuel rods. Working at the plant for approximately nine months, the victim received a total cumulative dose of almost 52 millisieverts of radiation, which exceeded the established limit for an entire 12-month period. BNF compensated the victim's wife and the families of 20 additional workers who died from causes related to radiation.

Radiation hazards in the workplace fall into one of two categories: ionizing or nonionizing. This chapter provides prospective and practising health and safety professionals with the information they need concerning radiation hazards in both categories.

IONIZING RADIATION: TERMS AND CONCEPTS

An *ion* is an electrically charged atom (or group of atoms) that becomes charged when a neutral atom (or group of atoms) loses or gains one or more electrons as a result of a chemical reaction. If an electron is lost during this process, a positively charged ion is produced; if an electron is gained, a negatively charged ion is produced. To *ionize* is to become electrically charged or to change into ions. Therefore, **ionizing radiation** is radiation that becomes electrically charged or changed into ions. Types of ionizing radiation, as shown in Figure 16–1, include alpha particles, beta particles, neutrons, X-radiation, gamma radiation, high-speed electrons, and high-speed protons.

To understand the hazards associated with radiation, health and safety professionals need to understand the basic terms and concepts summarized in the following paragraphs:

- **Radiation** consists of energetic nuclear particles and includes alpha rays, beta rays, gamma rays, X-rays, neutrons, high-speed electrons, and high-speed protons.
- **Radioactive material** is material that emits corpuscular or electromagnetic emanations as the result of spontaneous nuclear disintegration.
- A **restricted area** is any area to which access is restricted in an attempt to protect employees from exposure to radiation or radioactive materials.
- An **unrestricted area** is any area to which access is not controlled because there is no radioactivity hazard present.
- A **dose** is the amount of ionizing radiation absorbed per unit of mass by part of the body or the whole body.
- **Rad** is a measure of the dose of ionizing radiation absorbed by body tissues stated in terms of the amount of energy absorbed per unit of mass of tissue. One rad equals the absorption of 100 ergs per gram of tissue.
- **Rem** is a measure of the dose of ionizing radiation to body tissue stated in terms of its estimated biological effect relative to a dose of 1 roentgen (r) of X-rays.

RESTRICTED AREA

Any area to which access is restricted in an attempt to protect employees from exposure to radiation or radioactive materials.

UNRESTRICTED AREA

Any area to which access is not controlled because no radioactivity hazard is present.

DOSE

The amount of ionizing radiation absorbed per unit of mass by part of the body or the whole body.

RAD

A measure of the dose of ionizing radiation absorbed by body tissue stated in terms of the amount of energy absorbed per unit of mass of tissue.

► **Figure 16–1**
Types of ionizing radiation.

- **Sievert** is a single unit used to indicate the effective dose absorbed by various organs or tissue.

$$1 \text{ sievert (Sv)} = 100 \text{ rem (rem)}$$

- **Air dose** is the dose measured by an instrument in the air at or near the surface of the body in the area that has received the highest dosage of radiation.
- **Personal monitoring devices** are devices worn or carried by individuals to measure radiation doses received. Widely used devices include film badges, pocket chambers, pocket dosimeters, and film rings.
- A **radiation area** is any accessible area in which radiation hazards exist that could deliver doses as follows: (1) within one hour, a major portion of the body could receive more than 5 millirem; or (2) within five consecutive days, a major portion of the body could receive more than 100 millirem.
- A **high-radiation area** is any accessible area in which radiation hazards exist that could deliver a dose in excess of 100 millirem within one hour.

EXPOSURE OF EMPLOYEES TO RADIATION

The exposure of employees to ionizing radiation must be carefully controlled and accurately monitored. The Canadian Nuclear Safety Commission (CNSC), formerly the Atomic Energy Control Board of Canada, regulates the use of all radioactive material in Canada. In its legislation, the Nuclear Safety and Control Act, exposure limits to ionizing radiation are given. Figure 16–2 shows the maximum doses for individuals. Employers are responsible for ensuring that these dosages are not exceeded.

The energy absorbed by living tissue can cause biological changes that may lead to genetic or reproductive health effects. These effects of exposure are cumulative so the prescribed exposure levels in Figure 16–2 are for periods of one and five years. The units used in the Canadian Nuclear Safety Commission Radiation Protection Regulations, sieverts (Sv), represent a large dosage that would have serious health effects if the worker suffered acute exposure of a similar magnitude. For example, 100 millisieverts (100 mSv) would increase the risk of developing cancer later in life to 5 in 1000. One sievert (1 Sv) would increase that risk to 5 in 100 and 10 Sv would likely cause death within days or weeks.[1]

CNSC is not the only agency that regulates radiation exposure. Health Canada has published Safety Code 6 — Limits of Human Exposure to Radiofrequency Electromagnetic Fields in the Frequency Range from 3 kHz to 300 GHz. Safety Code 6 has been adopted by many organizations across Canada and referred to in a number of regulations, including the Canada Occupational Safety and Health Regulations. Industry Canada, which licenses radiocommunication equipment, approves where cell phone base stations are located, and conducts compliance assessments on cell phones and base stations, has also adopted Safety Code 6.[2]

PERSONAL MONITORING

Personal monitoring precautions are important for employees of companies that produce, use, release, dispose of, or store radioactive materials or any other

Person	Period	Effective Dose (mSv)
Nuclear energy worker, including a pregnant nuclear energy worker (before she knows she's pregnant)	(a) One-year dosimetry period	50
	(b) Five-year dosimetry period	100
Pregnant nuclear energy worker (after she knows she's pregnant)	Balance of pregnancy	4
A person who is not a nuclear energy worker	One calendar year	1

> **Figure 16–2**
> **Ionizing radiation exposure limits.**
> *Source:* Based on *Radiation Protection Regulations.* (May 31, 2000). *Canada Gazette Part II* 134, no. 13: 1177–1178, 1183. Reproduced with the permission of the Minister of Public Works and Government Services, 2005.

Personal monitoring is done with special radiation detection equipment that is de-signed to detect radiation from the different pathways:

- **Dosimeters** measure the external dose from nearby sources of radiation. They are not effective for monitoring skin contamination or radioactive dust that may have been inhaled into the body. There are three types of dosimeters:
  - *Badge dosimeters* record, but do not display, the dose; they are processed at a laboratory.
  - *Pencil dosimeters* display the dose and can be read by the user.
  - *Electronic dosimeters* display the dose on a digital readout.
- *Survey meters* measure external dose, and give an immediate reading of the strength and extent of the radiation around radioactive sources.
- *Hand-held contamination monitors* are portable units that are used to monitor surface contamination: radioactive particles on skin, hair, clothing, vehicles, or other objects that could be covered with radioactive dust.
- *Portal monitors* scan a person for surface contamination of the skin, hair, and clothing. The portal monitor looks like a door frame. The person being monitored stands inside the frame for a few seconds until a reading has been registered.

> **Figure 16–3**
> **Personal monitoring equipment.**
> *Source:* Health Canada. (October 6, 2003). "Monitoring Radiation Exposure." [Online]. Available: http://www.hc-sc.gc.ca/hecs-sesc/neprd/related-topics/monitoring-radiation.htm. (Retrieved December 29, 2004).

source of ionizing radiation. Personal monitoring is routinely carried out by radiation workers in licensed nuclear facilities and by hospital employees who work with radioactive diagnostic equipment. During nuclear emergencies, mon-itoring equipment would be distributed by National Dosimetry Services to track and measure worker radiation exposure. National Dosimetry Services is licensed by CNSC and provincial regulatory authorities to provide dosimetry services throughout Canada. Various types of personal monitoring equipment are explained in Figure 16–3.

DOSIMETER
Measures the external dose from nearby sources of radiation.

CAUTION SIGNS AND LABELS

Caution signs and labels have always been an important part of health and safety programs. This is particularly true in companies where radiation hazards exist. The universal colour scheme for caution signs and labels warning of radiation hazards is black or magenta superimposed on a yellow background.

Figure 16–4 shows the universal symbol for radiation. Along with the appropriate warning words, this symbol should be used on signs and labels. Figure 16–5 shows a warning sign and label that may be used in various radioactive settings. On containers, labels should also include the following information: (1) quantity of radioactive material, (2) kinds of radioactive materials, and (3) date on which the contents were measured.[3]

Figure 16–4
Universal radiation symbol.

Source: *Radiation Protection Regulations.* (May 31, 2000). *Canada Gazette Part II* 134, no. 13: 1177–1178, 1183. Reproduced with the permission of the Minister of Public Works and Government Services, 2005.

Figure 16–5
Sample warning sign.

RAYONNEMENT - DANGER - RADIATION

INSTRUCTING AND INFORMING PERSONNEL

It is critical that companies involved in producing, using, storing, handling, or transporting radioactive materials keep employees informed concerning radiation hazards and the appropriate precautions for minimizing them. Consequently, CNSC in its Radiation Protection Regulations has established specific requirements along these lines. Section 7 of these regulations is shown below:

> **7.** (1) Every licensee shall inform each nuclear energy worker, in writing, (*a*) that he or she is a nuclear energy worker; (*b*) of the risks associated with radiation to which the worker may be exposed in the course of his or her work, including the risks associated with the exposure of embryos and foetuses to radiation; (*c*) of the applicable effective dose limits and equivalent dose limits prescribed by sections 13, 14 and 15; and (*d*) of the worker's radiation dose levels. (2) Every licensee shall inform each female nuclear energy worker, in writing, of the rights and obligations of a pregnant nuclear energy worker under section 11 and of the applicable effective dose limits prescribed by section 13. (3) Every licensee shall obtain from each nuclear energy worker who is informed of the matters referred to in paragraphs (1)(*a*) and (*b*) and subsection (2) a written acknowledgement that the worker has received the information.[4]

STORAGE AND DISPOSAL OF RADIOACTIVE MATERIAL

Radioactive materials that are stored in restricted areas must be appropriately labelled, as described earlier in this chapter. Radioactive materials that are stored in unrestricted areas must be secured against unauthorized removal from the place of storage. This requirement precludes the handling and transport, intentional or inadvertent, of radioactive materials by persons who are not qualified to move them safely.

A danger inherent in storing radioactive materials in unrestricted areas is that an employee, such as a maintenance worker, may unwittingly attempt to move the container and damage it in the process. This could release doses that exceed prescribed acceptable limits. Low-level nuclear waste is often sent to the Chalk River Laboratories run by Atomic Energy of Canada. Medium-level waste from nuclear power plants is usually stored on site in water-filled pools for years and then transferred to more permanent concrete bunkers or silos.

The storage and disposal of high-level radioactive waste is the topic of great controversy in Canada. Because of the massive volume of waste in existence and expected to be generated in the next four to five decades, permanent storage solutions are needed. Some of these materials will remain radioactive for thousands of years, so storage has to be very long term. At the heart of this debate is the proposal to store nuclear waste deep underground in stable geological structures of the Canadian Shield.

REPORTS AND RECORDS OF OVEREXPOSURE

During the control of an emergency or the consequent immediate remedial work, the dose may exceed the limits prescribed in sections 13 and 14 of the regulations. When a licensee becomes aware that a dose of radiation received by and committed to a person or an organ or tissue may have exceeded an applicable dose limit prescribed by section 13, 14 or 15, the licensee shall

> (*a*) immediately notify the person and the Commission of the dose; (*b*) require the person to leave any work that is likely to add to the dose; (*c*) conduct an investigation to determine the magnitude of the dose and to establish the causes of the exposure; (*d*) identify and take any action required to prevent the occurrence of a similar incident; and (*e*) within 21 days after becoming aware that the dose limit has been exceeded, report to the Commission the results of the investigation or on the progress that has been made in conducting the investigation.[5]

NONIONIZING RADIATION

NONIONIZING RADIATION
Radiation on the electromagnetic spectrum that has a frequency of 10 or less and a wavelength in metres of 3×10 or less.

Nonionizing radiation is that radiation on the electromagnetic spectrum that has a frequency (hertz, cycles per second) of 10 or less and a wavelength in metres of 3 Hz 10⁻ or less. This encompasses visible, ultraviolet, infrared, microwave, radio, and AC power frequencies. Radiation at these frequency levels does not have sufficient energy to shatter atoms and ionize them.[6] However, such radiation can cause blisters and blindness. In addition, there is mounting evidence of a link between nonionizing radiation and cancer.

DISCUSSION CASE

What Is Your Opinion?

"We are moving out of this house today!" said the wife to her husband.

"What are you talking about? You love this house."

"Yes, I do," said the wife. "But I love our kids more, and I don't intend to stay here and see them die of cancer."

"Cancer? What do you mean?" asked the husband, feeling increasingly lost.

"It's the power lines that run along our back lot line," said the wife. "I read an article today that says power lines cause cancer."

"I've heard that," said the husband. "But I don't believe it. That's just a myth."

Who is correct in this discussion? What is your opinion?

The greatest concerns about nonionizing radiation relate to the following sources: visible radiation, ultraviolet radiation, infrared radiation, radio frequency and microwave radiation, extremely low frequency radiation, lasers, and video display terminals. The main concerns in each of these areas are explained in the following paragraphs. The following section deals specifically with electromagnetic radiation (EMR) from power lines and other sources.

1. **Visible radiation** comes from light sources that create distortion. This can be a hazard to employees whose jobs require colour perception. For example, 8% of the male population is red colour-blind and cannot properly perceive red warning signs.[7]

2. The most common source of **ultraviolet radiation** is the sun. Potential problems from ultraviolet radiation include sunburn, skin cancer, and cataracts. Precautionary measures include special sunglasses treated to block out ultraviolet rays and protective clothing. Other sources of ultraviolet radiation include lasers, welding arcs, and ultraviolet lamps.[8]

3. **Infrared radiation** creates heat. Consequently, the problems associated with this kind of nonionizing radiation involve heat stress and dry skin and eyes. Primary sources of infrared radiation are high-temperature processes such as the production of glass and steel.[9]

4. *Radio frequency (RF)* and *microwave (MW) radiation* are electromagnetic radiation in the frequency range of 3 kilohertz (kHz) to 300 gigahertz (GHz). Usually MW radiation is considered a subset of RF radiation, although an alternative convention treats RF and MW radiation as two spectral regions. Microwaves occupy the spectral region between 300 GHz and 300 MHz, whereas RF or radio waves include 300 MHz to 3 kHz. RF and MW radiation are nonionizing in that there is insufficient energy (less than 10 electron volts [eV]) to ionize biologically important atoms. The primary health effects of RF and MW energy are considered to be thermal. The absorption of RF and MW energy varies with frequency. Microwave frequencies produce a skin effect — you can literally sense your skin starting to feel warm. RF radiation may penetrate the body and be absorbed in deep body organs without the skin effect that can warn an individual of danger.

   Research has revealed other nonthermal effects. All of the standards of Western countries have, so far, based their exposure limits solely on preventing thermal problems. In the meantime, research continues. Use of RF and MW radiation includes aeronautical radios, citizen's (CB) radios, cellular phones, processing and cooking of foods, heat sealers, vinyl welders, high-frequency welders, induction heaters, flow solder machines, communications transmitters, radar transmitters, ion implant equipment, microwave drying equipment, sputtering equipment, glue curing, and power amplifiers used in EMC and metrology (calibration).[10]

5. *Extremely low frequency (ELF) radiation* includes alternating current (AC) fields and nonionizing radiation from 1 Hz to 300 Hz. Because ELF frequencies are low (wavelengths are on the order of 1000 km), static electromagnetic fields are created. ELF fields are considered as separate, independent, nonradiating electric and magnetic fields. Electric and magnetic fields (EMFs) at 60 Hz are produced by power lines, electrical wiring, and electrical equipment. Electric fields are produced by voltage and increase in strength as the voltage increases. Electric field strength is measured in units of volts per metre (V/m). Magnetic fields are from the flow of current through wires or electrical devices and increase in strength as the current increases. Magnetic fields are measured in units of gauss (G) or tesla (T).

   Electrical equipment usually must be turned on for a magnetic field to be produced. However, electric fields are present even when equipment is turned off, as long as it is plugged in. Current research has focused on potential

VISIBLE RADIATION
Radiation that distorts light, making it visible.

ULTRAVIOLET RADIATION
Electromagnetic radiation with a frequency between visible violet light and X rays.

INFRARED RADIATION
Electromagnetic radiation with a frequency less than that of visible light and greater than that of most radio waves.

health effects of magnetic fields. Some inconclusive epidemiological studies have suggested increased cancer risk associated with estimates of magnetic field exposure. No similar associations have been reported for electric fields. Exposure to EMFs depends on the strength of the magnetic field sources, the distance from those sources, and the time spent in the magnetic field. The American Conference of Governmental Industrial Hygienists (ACGIH) has established occupational threshold limit values (TLVs) for static magnetic fields, sub-radio-frequency (30 kHz and below) magnetic fields, and sub-radio-frequency (30 kHz and below) static electric fields.[11]

LASER
Light amplification by stimulated emission of radiation.

6. **Lasers** are being used increasingly in modern industry. The hazards of lasers consist of a thermal threat to the eyes and the threat of electrocution from power sources. In addition, the smoke created by lasers in some processes can be toxic.[12]

VIDEO DISPLAY TERMINAL (VDT)
A device on which computer data or graphics can be displayed.

7. **Video display terminals (VDTs)** are widely used in the modern workplace. They emit various kinds of nonionizing radiation. Typically, the levels are well below established standards. However, concerns persist about the long-term effects of prolonged and continual exposure to VDT-based radiation.[13] The National Institute for Occupational Health and Safety (NIOSH) undertook a study of this issue in 1984. NIOSH specifically looked into the potential impact of VDT use on pregnant users. The study found that "women who work with VDTs have no greater risk of miscarriage than those who do not."[14]

ELECTROMAGNETIC FIELDS IN THE WORKPLACE

The first studies of the potential effects on worker health of occupational exposure to electric and magnetic fields were published in the literature of the former Soviet Union in the mid-1960s. In these studies, electric switchyard workers reported a variety of subjective complaints, including problems with their cardiovascular, digestive, and central nervous systems.[15] Since then, numerous studies of the effects of **electromagnetic fields (EMF)** on humans have been done. Although much of the research has been inconclusive in establishing a clear cause-and-effect relationship between EMF and health problems, the case for a link between EMF and a variety of health problems is strong. Consequently, health and safety professionals must be prepared to take appropriate precautions in the workplace.

ELECTROMAGNETIC FIELD (EMF)
Form of nonionizing radiation produced as electrical current flows.

According to Savitz, "associations reported between electric occupations and leukemia and brain cancer seem too consistent to be attributable to chance."[16] Occupations with a higher-than-normal incidence of leukemia and brain cancer are as follows:

- Telephone operators
- Electrical manufacturing workers
- Power plant workers
- Telecommunication workers
- Electrical engineers
- Electrical line workers

SAFETY FACT

Cell Phone Hazard

The debate continues over the health effects of cell phone use. Some research support a correlation between electromagnetic fields and brain cancer or leukemia, while some scientists strongly dispute these claims. One hazard that is disputed by few and supported by most Canadian jurisdictions is cell phone use while driving. In December 2002, Newfoundland and Labrador was the first province to pass legislation to ban cell phone use while driving and it is likely that several provinces will follow suit in the near future.

- Power station operators
- Electricians
- Cable splicers

The health problems most frequently associated with EMF exposure are brain cancer, acute myeloid leukemia, leukemia, and lymphatic leukemia.

EMFs and Health Problems

Studies have shown that some employees exposed to high magnetic fields have increased cancer rates. However, such associations do not necessarily show that EMF exposures cause cancer (any more than the springtime association of robins and daffodils shows that one causes the other). Scientists have looked carefully at all of the EMF evidence, but they still disagree on the health effects of EMFs, except to say that better information is needed.[17]

Many studies report small increases in the rate of leukemia or brain cancer in groups of people living or working in high magnetic fields. Other studies have found no such increases. The most important data come from six recent studies of workers wearing EMF monitors to measure magnetic fields. All but one study found significantly higher cancer rates for men with average workday exposures above 4 milligauss. However, the results of these studies disagree in important ways, such as the type of cancer associated with EMF exposures. Consequently, scientists cannot be sure whether the increased risks are caused by EMFs or by other factors. A few preliminary studies have also associated workplace EMFs with breast cancer, and one study has reported a possible link between occupational EMF exposure and Alzheimer's disease. The data from all of these studies are too limited for scientists to draw conclusions.

An Appropriate Response for Safety Professionals

The research into the possible cause-and-effect relationship between EMF and health problems is inconclusive. On the other hand, the anecdotal and circumstantial evidence strongly suggests a link. How, then, is the health and safety professional to respond? According to William E. Feero,

The emergence of new electrical technologies has produced an extremely complex electric and magnetic field environment in which we must live and work. Although there presently exist no universally accepted human exposure guidelines, current biological research may someday produce such limits. It is in anticipation of these exposure limits that electric and magnetic field management techniques are being investigated. At low frequencies, two categories of field management exist: cancellation and shielding. The particular class of control used will depend on several functions of the field and its source, and will be determined finally on a case-by-case basis.[18]

Cancellation Approach

Cancellation is an attenuation technique in which the magnetic fields produced by sources of electricity are, in effect, cancelled out. It works as follows: Phase currents flowing through a given conductor are cancelled out or drastically reduced by phase currents flowing in the opposite conductors. The cancellation approach can be used for both single-phase and balanced multiphase systems.

According to Feero,

Cancellation fields can be set up in some cases with very little cost penalty. In many cases, a principal source of magnetic fields is found to be the conductor systems leading to tools or power apparatus. In such relatively simple cases, these fields could be canceled via compaction of the conductor systems. For example, a low voltage device, either a 120 or 240V service, is typically supplied by a power cord and the fields any distance from the cord are rapidly attenuated. In the situation where the cords or leads have to be very close to the worker, the added precaution of twisting or interleaving of these leads with each other will further reduce the field. The net effect of twisting a pair of conductors is that each individual conductor appears to occupy the same space. Therefore, the fields are much more effectively canceled because the spacing between the conductors is reduced to nearly zero.

Electrical apparatus that consume considerable energy would generally be supplied by three-phase cables rather than single-phase cables. If single-phase cables are used, care in bundling of the cables within cable trays and the routing of the cable trays can be a very effective control technology. In many instances where strong fields have been found near transformer vaults in buildings, the source of the magnetic field is the cable system leading to and from the transformer vault.

The magnetic field produced directly from most apparatus exhibits the characteristics of loop current source fields. Therefore, a simple control technique may be to move the device, i.e., a compressor motor in a refrigeration unit, to the back of the unit's housing. If the device's function does not permit it to be moved (hand held

SAFETY FACT

TLVs and Personal Medical Devices

Routine exposures to static magnetic fields should not exceed 60 millitesla (mT) or the equivalent 600 gauss (G) for the whole body or 600 mT (6000 G) to the limbs on a daily time-weighted average basis. Wearers of cardiac pacemakers and other personal electronic medical devices should be exposed to no more than 0.5 mT (5 G) on a daily time-weighted average basis.

Reducing EMF Exposure in the Workplace

Employees are often exposed to electromagnetic fields in the workplace without even knowing it. It is important to inform employees about EMF and the associated hazards and to take steps to reduce exposure levels. Strategies for reducing exposure include the following:

- Because magnetic fields drop off significantly approximately three feet from the source, increase the distance between employees and sources of EMF.

- Substitute low-EMF-producing equipment (power supplies) wherever possible.

- Reduce the amount of time that employees are exposed to EMF sources.

tools, for instance) then more sophisticated and possibly expensive techniques must be employed.[19]

Shielding Approach

Shielding is another approach available for decreasing exposure to EMF. According to Feero,

> Shielding of magnetic fields requires either that the magnetic fields be diverted around the volume considered to be sensitive to the magnetic fields, or the magnetic fields be contained within the device that produces the fields. Effectively accomplishing shielding at either the source or the subject requires extreme care in choosing the shielding material. The electrical properties of ferromagnetic materials are very complex functions of magnetic field frequencies and magnitudes. For strong magnetic fields, the highly non-linear saturation characteristics of ferromagnetic materials have been widely recognized and reasonably adjusted to achieve source shielding. However, only a few engineers and physicists are aware of the effects of coerciveness at very low magnetizing forces. Subject shielding invariably involves weak magnetic fields. Ferromagnetic materials that are normally considered to have very high permeability may exhibit quite low permeability if being used to attempt to shield milligauss field levels. Thus, the problem of dynamic range encountered when trying to apply cancellation techniques reappears in a different form when attempting to utilize shielding techniques.[20]

Both cancellation and shielding are highly technical approaches requiring specialized knowledge. Health and safety professionals who are not specialists in electromagnetic fields may find it necessary to consult with EMF experts before attempting to implement either approach.

SUMMARY

1. Widely used terms relating to ionizing radiation are *radiation, radioactive material, restricted area, unrestricted area, dose, rad, rem, sievert, air dose, personal monitoring devices, radiation area*, and *high-radiation area*.

2. Exposure of individuals to radiation must be carefully controlled and accurately monitored. Doses are typically measured in rems or sieverts.

3. Employers must require the use of personal monitoring devices such as film badges, pocket chambers, pocket dosimeters, and film rings. Employers are also required to conduct comprehensive surveys to identify and evaluate radiation hazards present in the workplace.

4. Employees must be informed and instructed regarding potential radiation hazards, precautions that they should take, and records of exposure.

5. Radioactive materials that are stored in restricted areas must be appropriately labelled. Materials stored in unrestricted areas must be secured against unauthorized removal.

6. Radiation incidents that involve exposure beyond prescribed limits must be reported immediately to the Commission and investigated and the results or the status of the investigation reported within 21 days.

7. Nonionizing radiation is radiation on the electromagnetic spectrum that lacks sufficient energy to ionize atoms. This encompasses visible, ultraviolet, infrared, radio, microwave, and AC power frequencies.

8. Electromagnetic fields, or EMFs, encompass radiation from power lines and a long list of electrical appliances. Concerns about, and evidence of, a link between EMFs and cancer exist.

KEY TERMS AND CONCEPTS

Air dose

Dose

Dosimeter

Electromagnetic field (EMF)

High-radiation area

Infrared radiation

Ionizing radiation

Lasers

Nonionizing radiation

Personal monitoring devices

Rad

Radiation

Radiation area

Radioactive material

Rem

Restricted area

Sievert

Ultraviolet radiation

Unrestricted area

Video display terminals (VDTs)

Visible radiation

REVIEW QUESTIONS

1. Define the following terms relating to ionizing radiation: *radiation, restricted area, dose, rem, sievert,* and *radiation area.*

2. What is the maximum dose of radiation allowed to the whole body during one and five year period for a nuclear energy worker? For a member of the public?

3. Describe the types of personal monitoring devices used.

4. How should radioactive material be treated when stored in a nonrestricted area?

5. Describe the requirements in the case of radiation overexposure.

6. Where is nuclear waste stored?

7. Define the term *nonionizing radiation*.

8. What are the primary sources of concern regarding nonionizing radiation?

9. Describe the anecdotal and scientific evidence linking EMF to cancer.

WEBLINKS

Canadian Nuclear Safety Commission
www.nuclearsafety.gc.ca/eng

CNSC, the former Atomic Energy Control Board, has available on its website information on issues facing nuclear energy in Canada and links to nuclear energy legislation.

Health Canada
www.hc-sc.gc.ca/english/iyh/products/cellphones.htm

In this article, Health Canada provides information on cell phone hazards and their safe use. www.hc-sc.gc.ca/hecs-sesc/ccrph/publication/99ehd237/toc.htm. On this Health Canada site, Safety Code 6, Limits of Human Exposure to Radiofrequency Electromagnetic Fields in the Frequency Range from 3 kHz to 300, can be found.

ENDNOTES

1. Canadian Centre for Occupational Health and Safety. (May 23, 1999). "OHS Answers." [Online]. Available: http://www.ccohs.ca/oshanswers/phys_agents/ionizing.html. (Retrieved December 29, 2004).

2. Health Canada. (December 3, 2002). "It's Your Health, Safety and the Safe Use of Cell Phones." [Online]. Available: http://www.hc-sc.gc.ca/english/iyh/products/cellphones.htm. (Retrieved December 29, 2004).

3. Canadian Nuclear Safety Commission. (June 21, 2000). Radiation Protection Regulations. The Queen's Printer of Canada. [Online]. Available: http://www.nuclearsafety.gc.ca/eng/ regulatory_information/pdf/sor203.pdf. (Retrieved December 29, 2004).

4. Ibid.

5. Ibid.

6. American Conference of Governmental Industrial Hygienists, *TLVs and BEIs* (Cincinnati: ACGIH, 2001), 147.

7. Ibid., 42.

8. Ibid., 43.

9. Ibid.

10. OSHA, "Technical Links," [Online]. Available: http://www.osha-slc.gov. (Retrieved June 2003), 1.

11. Ibid.

12. Ibid.

13. Ibid.

14. J. Castelli, "NIOSH Releases Results of VDT Study," *Safety & Health* (June 1991): 69.

15. William E. Murray Jr. and Robert M. Patterson, "Electric and Magnetic Fields: What Do We Know?" *American Industrial Hygiene Association Journal* 54, no. 4 (April 1997): 164.

16. David A. Savitz, "Overview of Epidemiologic Research on Electric and Magnetic Fields and Cancer," *American Industrial Hygiene Journal* 54, no. 4 (April 1993): 202.

17. NIOSH, "Fact Sheet," [Online]. Available: http://www.cdc.gov/niosh/emf2. html. (Retrieved May 2001), 3.

18. William E. Feero, "Electric and Magnetic Field Management," *American Industrial Hygiene Journal* 54, no. 4: 205.

19. Ibid., 207–208.

20. Ibid., 208–209.

Noise and Vibration Hazards

17

CHAPTER

LEARNING OBJECTIVES

- Define terms commonly used with hearing loss protection.
- Describe the physical properties of sound.
- Explain how sound is measured.
- Compare standards and regulations among Canadian jurisdictions.
- Describe how workers' compensation boards can measure hearing loss.
- List four components involved in identifying and assessing hazardous noise conditions.
- Provide examples of three noise control strategies.
- Describe the injuries associated with vibration hazards.
- Explain how noise can have nonauditory effects on the worker.
- List five items to include when evaluating hearing loss prevention programs.

The modern industrial work site can be a noisy place. This poses two health- and safety-related problems. First, there is the problem of distraction. Noise can distract workers, disrupt their concentration, and mask audible warnings, which can lead to accidents. Second, there is the problem of hearing loss. Exposure to noise that exceeds prescribed levels can result in permanent hearing loss.

Modern health and safety professionals need to understand the hazards associated with noise and vibration, how to identify and assess these hazards, and how to prevent injuries related to them. This chapter provides the necessary information for prospective and practising health and safety professionals to do so.

HEARING LOSS PREVENTION TERMS

There are certain terms common to hearing loss prevention that must be understood by health and safety professionals. The reader may find the definitions in this section helpful when trying to understand the content of this chapter.

- **Baseline audiogram.** A valid audiogram against which subsequent audiograms are compared to determine if hearing thresholds have changed. The baseline audiogram is preceded by a quiet period to obtain the best estimate of the person's hearing at that time.
- **Continuous noise.** Noise of a constant level measured over at least one second using the "slow" setting on a sound level meter. Note that an intermittent noise (e.g., on for over a second and then off for a period) is both variable *and* continuous.
- **dB (decibel).** The unit used to express the intensity of sound. The decibel was named after Alexander Graham Bell. The decibel scale is a logarithmic scale in which 0 dB approximates the threshold of hearing in the midfrequencies for young adults and in which the threshold of discomfort is between 85 and 95 dB and the threshold for pain is between 120 and 140 dB.
- **Dosimeter.** When applied to noise, the instrument that measures sound levels over a specified interval, stores the measures, and calculates the sound as a function of sound level and sound duration. It describes the results in terms of dose, time-weighted average, and other parameters such as peak level, equivalent sound level, sound exposure level, and so on.
- **Exchange rate.** The relationship between intensity and dose. The federal government uses a 3-dB exchange rate. Thus, if the intensity of an exposure increases by 3 dB, the dose doubles. This may also be referred to as the *doubling rate.* While some provinces use a 5-dB exchange rate, others use a 3-dB exchange rate that provides a greater degree of protection.
- **Hazardous noise.** Any sound for which any combination of frequency, intensity, or duration is capable of causing permanent hearing loss in a specified population.
- Hearing loss is often characterized by the area of the auditory system responsible for the loss. For example, when injury or a medical condition affects the *outer ear* or *middle ear* (i.e., from the pinna, ear canal, and eardrum to the cavity behind the eardrum — which includes the ossicles), the resulting hearing loss is referred to as a *conductive* loss. When an injury or medical condition affects the *inner ear* or the auditory nerve that connects the inner ear to the brain (i.e., the cochlea and the VIIIth cranial nerve), the resulting hearing loss is referred to as a *sensorineural* loss. Thus, a welder's spark that damages the eardrum causes a conductive hearing loss. And because noise can damage the tiny hair cells located in the cochlea, noise causes a sensorineural hearing loss.
- **HTL (hearing threshold level).** The hearing level, above a reference value, at which a specified sound or tone is heard by an ear in a specified fraction of the trials. Hearing threshold levels have been established so that dB HTL reflects the best hearing of a group of persons.
- **Hz (hertz).** The unit measurement for audio frequencies. The frequency range for human hearing lies between 20 Hz and approximately 20 000 Hz. The sensitivity of the human ear drops off sharply below about 500 Hz and above 4000 Hz.
- **Impulsive noise.** Generally used to characterize impact or impulse noise typified by a sound that rapidly rises to a sharp peak and then quickly fades. The sound may or may not have a "ringing" quality (such as striking a ham-

mer on a metal plate or a gunshot in a reverberant room). Impulsive noise may be repetitive, or may be a single event (as with a sonic boom). *Note*: If impulses occur in very rapid succession (e.g., some jackhammers), the noise is not described as impulsive.

- **Noise.** Any unwanted sound.
- **Noise dose.** The noise exposure expressed as a percentage of the allowable daily exposure. For example; if 85 dB(A) is the maximum permissible level, an eight-hour exposure to a continuous 85-dB(A) noise equals a 100% dose. If a 3-dB exchange rate is used in conjunction with an 85-dB(A) maximum permissible level, a 50% dose equals a two-hour exposure to 88 dB(A) or an eight-hour exposure to 82 dB(A).
- **Noise-induced hearing loss.** A sensorineural hearing loss that is attributed to noise and for which no other etiology can be determined.
- **STS (significant threshold shift).** NIOSH uses this term to describe a change from baseline levels of 15 dB or more at any frequency from 400 through 6000 Hz that is present on a retest in the same ear and at the same frequency. NIOSH recommends a confirmation audiogram within 30 days with the confirmation audiogram preceded by a quiet period of at least 14 hours.
- **TWA (time-weighted average).** A value, expressed in dB(A), computed so that the resulting average is equivalent to an exposure resulting from a constant noise level over an eight-hour period.
- **Lex.** This is an abbreviation for average exposure level adjusted for an eight hour day. For example, when describing the Ontario regulations, the allowable noise limit is 90 dB(A) Lex.

CHARACTERISTICS OF SOUND

Sound is any change in pressure that can be detected by the ear. Typically, sound is a change in air pressure. However, it can also be a change in water pressure or any other pressure-sensitive medium. **Noise** is unwanted sound. Consequently, the difference between noise and sound is in the perception of the person hearing it (e.g., loud rock music may be considered "sound" by a rock fan but "noise" by a shift worker trying to sleep). Olishifski describes what occurs physiologically with sound:

> The generation and propagation of sound are easily visualized by means of a simple model. Consider a plate suspended in midair. When struck, the plate vibrates rapidly back and forth. As the plate travels in either direction, it compresses the air, causing a slight increase in pressure. When the plate reverses direction, it leaves a partial vacuum, or rarefaction, of the air. These alternate compressions and rarefactions cause small but repeated fluctuations in the atmospheric pressure that extend outward from the plate. When these pressure variations strike an eardrum, they cause it to vibrate in response to the slight changes in atmospheric pressure. The disturbance of the eardrum is translated into a neural sensation in the inner ear and is carried to the brain where it is interpreted as sound.[1]

Sound and vibration are very similar. Sound typically relates to a sensation that is perceived by the inner ear as hearing. **Vibration**, on the other hand, is inaudible and is perceived through the sense of touch. Sound can occur in any

SOUND
Any change in pressure that can be detected by the ear.

NOISE
Unwanted sound.

VIBRATION
Oscillations of solid or semi-solid objects that can be perceived by the sense of touch.

DECIBEL
The unit applied when measuring sound. One-tenth of a bel. One decibel is the smallest difference in the level of sound that can be perceived by the human ear.

THRESHOLD OF HEARING
The weakest sound that can be heard by a healthy human ear in a quiet setting.

THRESHOLD OF PAIN
The maximum level of sound that can be perceived without experiencing pain.

WIDE BAND NOISE
Noise that is distributed over a wide range of frequencies.

NARROW BAND NOISE
Noise that is confined to a narrow range of frequencies.

IMPULSE NOISE
Consists of transient pulses that can occur repetitively or nonrepetitively.

medium that has both mass and elasticity (air, water, and so on). It occurs as elastic waves that cross over (above and below) a line representing normal atmospheric pressure (Figure 17–1).

Normal atmospheric pressure is represented in Figure 17–1 by a straight horizontal line. Sound is represented by the wavy line that crosses above and below the line. The more frequently the sound waves cross the normal atmospheric pressure line (the shorter the cycle), the higher the pitch of the sound. The greater the vertical distance above and below the atmospheric pressure line (distance X), the louder or more intense the sound.

The unit of measurement used for discussing the level of sound and, correspondingly, what noise levels are hazardous is the **decibel**, or one-tenth of a *bel*. One decibel represents the smallest difference in the level of sound that can be perceived by the human ear. Figure 17–2 shows the decibel levels for various common sounds. The weakest sound that can be heard by a healthy human ear in a quiet setting is known as the **threshold of hearing** (1 dB(A)). The maximum level of sound that can be perceived without experiencing pain is known as the **threshold of pain** (140 dB(A)).

The human ear is more sensitive at higher frequencies, so two sounds of equal magnitude, but of different frequencies, will not seem equally as loud. The A-weighted sound pressure level, abbreviated dB(A), represents a single number indicator of the relative loudness as perceived by the human ear. Sound level meters attenuate frequencies by different amounts so that the sound pressure level shown represents relative loudness as perceived by the human ear. While people typically judge a 10 dB increase in sound level to be doubling of its intensity, a 6 dB increase is actually twice as loud. Most people can detect a change in sound levels as small as 2 to 3 dB.

The three broad types of industrial noise are described by McDonald as follows:

> **Wide band noise** is noise that is distributed over a wide range of **frequencies**. Most noise from manufacturing machines is wide band noise. **Narrow band noise** is noise that is confined to a narrow range of frequencies. The noise produced by power tools is narrow band noise. Finally, **impulse noise** consists of transient pulses that can occur repetitively or nonrepetitively. The noise produced by a jackhammer is repetitive impulse noise.[2]

**Figure 17–1
Sound waves.**

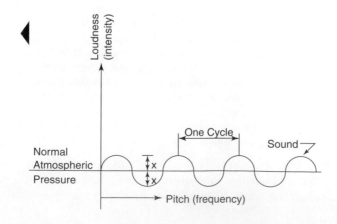

Source	Decibels (dB(A))
Whisper	20
Quiet library	30
Quiet office	50
Normal conversation	60
Vacuum cleaner	70
Noisy office	80
Power saw, lawn mower	90
Chain saw	90
Grinding operations	100
Passing truck	100
Gunshot blast	140
Jet aircraft	150
Rocket launching	180

▶ **Figure 17–2**
Selected sound levels.

HAZARD LEVELS AND RISKS

The fundamental hazard associated with excessive noise is hearing loss. Exposure to excessive noise levels for an extended period can damage the inner ear so that the ability to hear high-frequency sound is diminished or lost altogether. Additional exposure can increase the damage until even lower frequency sounds cannot be heard.[3]

A number of different factors affect the risk of hearing loss associated with exposure to excessive noise. The most important of these are

- Intensity of the noise (sound pressure level).
- Type of noise (wide band, narrow band, or impulse).
- Duration of daily exposure.
- Total duration of exposure (number of years).
- Age of the individual.
- Coexisting hearing disease.
- Nature of environment in which exposure occurs.
- Distance of the individual from the source of the noise.
- Position of the ears relative to the sound waves.[4]

Of these various factors, the most critical are the sound level, frequency, duration, and distribution of noise (Figure 17–3). The unprotected human ear is at risk when exposed to sound levels exceeding 115 dB(A). Exposure to sound levels below 80 dB(A) is generally considered safe. Prolonged exposure to noise levels higher than 80 dB(A) should be minimized through the use of appropriate personal protective devices.

To decrease the risk of hearing loss, exposure to noise should be limited to a maximum eight-hour time-weighted average of 85 dB(A). The following general rules should be applied for dealing with noise in the workplace:

- Exposures of less than 80 dB(A) may be considered safe for the purpose of risk assessment.

Figure 17–3
Critical noise
risk factors.

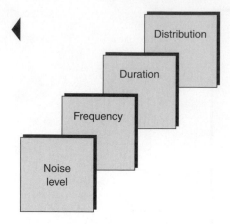

**Figure 17–3
Critical noise
risk factors.**

- A time-weighted average (threshold) of 85 dB(A) should be considered the maximum limit of continuous exposure over eight-hour days without protection.[5]

In noisy work environments, the primary concern for the health and safety practitioner is with the auditory effects on the worker, such as loss of hearing acuity or sensitivity. However, noise, like other environmental stressors, may have adverse effects on health, such as cardiovascular function (hypertension, changes in blood pressure and/or heart rate) and changes in breathing, annoyance, sleep, physical and mental health.[6]

STANDARDS AND REGULATIONS

Since hearing loss is a factor of both the level and duration of exposure to loud noise, standards and regulations relating to noise hazards include limiting worker exposure level and duration. The noise exposure limits for each Canadian jurisdiction, which are often based on National Institute for Occupational Safety and Health (NIOSH) or American Conference of Governmental Industrial Hygienists (ACGIH) standards, are summarized in Figure 17–4. The maximum permitted exposure levels are based on an eight hour day. When the magnitude of the noise exceeds these levels, some form of control is required to lower the sound level or duration of exposure to a point below the prescribed standard or regulation.

EXCHANGE RATE
Indicates the increase in sound level that is permitted as the time of exposure is halved.

As the duration of the exposure is decreased, the permissible level is increased. The **exchange rate** indicates the increase in sound level that is permitted as the time of exposure is halved. In Ontario, for example, the maximum permitted exposure level for an eight hour workday is 90 dB(A). With an exchange rate of 5 dB, the limit would be 95 dB(A) for four hours, 100 dB(A) for two hours and so on until 115 dB(A) is reached for 15 minutes, after which point no exposure without protection is permitted. Saskatchewan has a three dB(A) exchange rate that begins at 85 dB(A) for an eight hour day, but also limits the maximum level to 115 dB(A). The federal Occupational Health and Safety Regulations also have a three dB(A) exchange rate, but start at 87 dB(A)

Jurisdiction (Federal, Provincial, Territorial)	Continuous Noise		Impulse / Impact Noise	
	Maximum Permitted Exposure Level for 8 Hours: dB(A)	Exchange Rate dB(A)+	Maximum Peak Pressure Level dB(peak)	Maximum Number of Impacts
Canada (Federal)	87	3	-	-
British Columbia	85	3	140	-
Alberta	85	3	-	-
Saskatchewan	85	3	-	-
Manitoba	85	3	-	-
Ontario	90	5	-	-
Quebec	90	5	140	100
New Brunswick	85	5	140	100
Nova Scotia	85	3	140	100
Prince Edward Island (references ACGIH TLVs)	85	3	-	-
Newfoundland and Labrador	85	3	-	-
Northwest Territories	85	5	140	100
Nunavut	85	5	140	100
Yukon Territory	85	3	140	90

Figure 17–4
Noise exposure limits for Canadian jurisdictions.
Source: Canadian Centre for Occupational Health and Safety. (January 28, 2005). "Physical Agents, Noise." [Online]. Available: http://www.ccohs.ca/oshanswers/phys_agents/exposure_can.html. (Retrieved March 6, 2005).

SAFETY FACT

Muff the Machine, Not Just the Worker.

Experts on noise and hearing loss have expressed concern about the leniency of these regulations and the inadequacy of ear plugs, ear muffs, and yearly hearing tests to protect hearing in a noisy workplace. Noise reduction, rather than ear protection, is the best way to prevent occupational noise-induced hearing loss. In other words, muff the machine, not just the worker. Improved legislation could require the erection of acoustical barriers around noise sources in the workplace or the installation of effective mufflers on industrial equipment.

Source: Canadian Hearing Society. (2003). "Workplace and Industrial Noise." [Online]. Available: http://www.chs.ca/info/noise/book2.html. (Retrieved March 6, 2005).

for eight hours. Of the three examples described, the Saskatchewan regulations provide the greatest degree of hearing protection for the worker.

Hearing Hazards Monitoring

As with any health hazard, it is important to determine accurately the nature of the hearing hazard and to identify the affected employees. Those responsible for this aspect of the program must ensure that the exposures of all employees have been properly evaluated and that re-evaluations are conducted when changes in equipment or operations significantly alter working conditions. Recent evidence has indicated that aromatic solvents, metals, and petrochemicals may be associated with occupational hearing loss. Although studies are exploring the relationship between hearing loss and chemical exposures, there is insufficient information about this relationship to speculate on potential risk factors. Therefore, this section focuses on monitoring noise exposure, the major factor associated with occupational hearing losses. Hearing hazard exposure monitoring is conducted for various purposes, including

- Determining whether hazards to hearing exist.
- Determining whether noise presents a safety hazard by interfering with speech communication or the recognition of audible warning signals.
- Identifying employees for inclusion in the hearing loss prevention program.
- Classifying employees' noise exposures for prioritizing noise control efforts and defining and establishing hearing protection practices.
- Evaluating specific noise sources for noise control purposes.
- Evaluating the success of noise control efforts.

Various kinds of incrementation and measurement methods may be used, depending on the type of measurements being conducted. The most common measurements are area surveys, dosimetry, and engineering surveys.

In an area survey, environmental noise levels are measured using a sound level meter to identify work areas where exposures are above or below hazardous levels and where more thorough exposure monitoring may be needed. The result is often plotted in the form of a "noise map," showing noise level measurements for the different areas of the workplace.

Dosimetry involves the use of body-worn instruments (dosimeters) to monitor an employee's noise exposure over the work shift. Monitoring results for one employee can also represent the exposures of other workers in the area with similar noise exposures. It may also be possible to use task-based exposure methods to represent the exposures of other workers in different areas whose exposures result from having performed the same tasks.

Engineering surveys typically employ more sophisticated acoustical equipment in addition to sound level meters. These may include octave-band analyzers and sound level recorders that furnish information on the frequency–intensity composition of the noise being emitted by machinery or other sound sources in various modes of operation. These measurements are used to assess options for applying engineering controls.

Engineering and Administrative Controls

Engineering and administrative controls are essential to achieve an effective hearing loss prevention program. Engineering and administrative controls represent the first two echelons in the hierarchy of controls: (1) remove the hazard; and (2) remove the worker. The use of these controls should reduce hazardous exposure to the point where the risk to hearing is eliminated or at least more manageable. Engineering controls are technologically feasible for most noise sources, but their economic feasibility must be determined on a case-by-case basis. In some instances, the application of a relatively simple noise control solution reduces the hazard to the extent that the other elements of the program, such as audiometric testing and the use of hearing protection devices, are no longer necessary. In other cases, the noise reduction process may be more complex and must be accomplished in stages over a period of time. Even so, with each reduction of a few decibels, the hazard to hearing is reduced, communication is improved, and noise-related annoyance is reduced as well.

It is especially important that organizations specify low noise levels when purchasing new equipment. Many types of previously noisy equipment are now available in noise-controlled versions. Consequently, a "buy quiet" purchasing policy should not require new engineering solutions in many cases.

For hearing loss prevention purposes, engineering controls are defined as any modification or replacement of equipment or related physical change at the noise source or along the transmission path (with the exception of hearing protectors) that reduces the noise level at the employee's ear. Typical engineering controls involve:

- Reducing noise at the source (e.g., installing a muffler).
- Interrupting the noise path (e.g., erecting acoustical enclosures and barriers).
- Reducing reverberation (e.g., installing sound-absorbing material).
- Reducing structure-borne vibration (e.g., installing vibration mounts and providing proper lubrication).

Administrative controls, defined as changes in the work schedule or operations that reduce noise exposure, may also be used effectively. Examples include operating a noisy machine on the second or third shift when fewer people are exposed, or shifting an employee to a less noisy job once a hazardous daily noise dose has been reached. Generally, administrative controls have limited use in industry because employee contracts seldom permit shifting from one job to another. Moreover, the practice of rotating employees between quiet and noisy jobs, although it may reduce the risk of substantial hearing loss in a few workers, may actually increase the risk of small hearing losses in many workers. A more practical administrative control is to provide for quiet areas where employees can gain relief from workplace noise. Areas used for work breaks and lunch rooms should be located away from noise.

Audiometric Evaluation

Audiometric evaluation is crucial to the success of the hearing loss prevention program in that it is the only way to determine whether occupational hearing loss is being prevented. When the comparison of audiograms shows temporary threshold shift (a temporary hearing loss after noise exposure), early permanent threshold shift, or progressive occupational hearing loss, it is time to take swift action to halt the loss before additional deterioration occurs. Because occupational hearing loss occurs gradually and is not accompanied by pain, the affected employee may not notice the change until a large threshold shift has accumulated. However, the results of audiometric tests can trigger changes in the hearing loss prevention program more promptly, initiating protective measures, and motivating employees to prevent further hearing loss.

As shown in Figure 17–5, audiometric testing requirements vary throughout Canadian jurisdictions. However, for maximum protection of employees, audiograms should be performed on employees who work in noisy environments, on the following occasions:

- Pre-employment.
- Prior to initial assignment in a hearing hazardous work area.
- Annually as long as the employee is assigned to a noisy job (a time-weighted average exposure level equal to or greater than 85 dB(A)).
- At the time of reassignment out of a hearing hazardous job.
- At the termination of employment.

In addition, it is suggested that employees who are not exposed be given periodic audiograms as part of the organization's health care program. The audiograms of these employees can be compared to those of the exposed employees whenever the overall effectiveness of the hearing loss prevention program is evaluated. In an optimally effective program, the two employee groups show essentially the same amount of audiometric change.

Personal Hearing Protection Devices

A personal hearing protection device (or "hearing protector") is anything that can be worn to reduce the level of sound entering the ear. Earmuffs, ear canal

Figure 17–5
Audiometric test requirements for Canadian jurisdictions.

Jurisdiction	Audiometric Testing Requirements
Canada (Federal)	No testing required.
British Columbia	Every 12 months.
Alberta	Every 24 months. Initial test within 6 months. Second within 12 months of employment.
Saskatchewan	Every 24 months.
Manitoba	Every 12 months.
Ontario	No testing required.
Quebec	Testing required, but time interval is not specified.
New Brunswick	No testing required.
Nova Scotia	Every 12 months.
Prince Edward Island	Every 12 months.
Newfoundland and Labrador	No testing required.
Northwest Territories and Nunavut	Every 12 months.
Yukon Territory	Every 12 months.

caps, and earplugs are the three principal types of devices. Each employee reacts individually to the use of these devices, and a successful hearing loss prevention program should be able to respond to the needs of each employee. Ensuring that these devices protect hearing effectively requires the coordinated effort of management, the hearing loss prevention program operators, and the affected employees.

Education and Motivation

Training is a critical element of a good hearing loss prevention program. In order to obtain sincere and energetic support by management and active participation by employees, it is necessary to educate and motivate both groups. A hearing loss prevention program that overlooks the importance of education and motivation is likely to fail because employees will not understand why it is in their best interest to cooperate, and management will fail to make the necessary commitment. Employees and managers who appreciate the precious sense of hearing and understand the reasons for, and the mechanics of, the hearing loss prevention program will be more likely to participate for their mutual benefit, rather than viewing the program as an imposition.

Record Keeping

Records quite often get the least attention of any of the program's components. However, audiometric comparisons, reports of hearing protector use, and the analysis of hazardous exposure measurements all involve the keeping of records. Unfortunately, records are often kept poorly because there is no organized system in place, and in many cases, those responsible for maintaining the records do not understand their value. People tend to assume that if they merely place records in a file or enter them into a computer, adequate record-keeping procedures are being followed.

Many companies have found that their record-keeping system is inadequate only when they discover that they need accurate information. This sometimes occurs during the processing of compensation claims. Problems can be avoided by implementing an effective record-keeping system, in which (1) management encourages that the system be kept active and accessible; (2) hearing loss prevention program implementers make sure that all of the information entered is accurate and complete; and (3) employees validate the information.

Hearing loss prevention program records should include all items for each phase of the program: (1) hearing loss prevention audit, (2) monitoring hearing hazards, (3) engineering and administrative controls, (4) audiometric evaluation, (5) personal hearing protective devices, (6) education and motivation, (7) record keeping, and (8) program evaluation. Each phase must be considered in order to evaluate the effectiveness of the hearing loss prevention program.

Program Evaluation

The primary goal of any hearing loss prevention program must be to reduce, and eventually eliminate, hearing loss due to workplace exposures. Although management may have the best intentions of implementing this goal and a company's hearing loss prevention program may have the appearance of being complete and complying with the legislative requirements, the program still may not achieve this goal. A thorough evaluation of the effectiveness of all of the program's components is necessary to determine the extent to which the hearing loss prevention program is really working.

Management and program implementers should conduct periodic program evaluations to assess compliance with federal and provincial/territorial regulations and to ensure that hearing is being conserved. There are two basic approaches to following program evaluation: (1) assess the completeness and quality of the program's components; and (2) evaluate the audiometric data.

IDENTIFYING AND ASSESSING HAZARDOUS NOISE CONDITIONS

HAZARDOUS NOISE
Any sound for which any combination of frequency, intensity, or duration is capable of causing permanent hearing loss in a specified population.

Identifying and assessing **hazardous noise** conditions in the workplace involves (1) conducting periodic noise surveys, (2) conducting periodic audiometric tests, (3) record keeping, and (4) follow-up action. Each of these components is covered in the following sections.

Noise Surveys

SOUND LEVEL METER
Produces an immediate reading that represents the noise level at a specific instant in time.

Conducting *noise surveys* involves measuring noise levels at different locations in the workplace. The devices that are most widely used to measure noise levels are sound level meters and dosimeters. A **sound level meter** produces an immediate reading that represents the noise level at a specific instant in time. A **dosimeter** provides a time-weighted average over a period of time such as one complete work shift. A dosimeter also calculates the sound as a function of sound level and duration and describes the results in terms of dose, peak level, equivalent sound level, sound exposure level, and time-weighted average.[7] The dosimeter is the most widely used device because it measures total exposure. Using a dosimeter in various work areas and attaching a personal dosimeter to one or more employees is the recommended approach to ensure dependable, accurate readings.

DOSIMETER
Provides a time-weighted average over a period such as one complete work shift.

Audiometric Testing

AUDIOMETRIC TESTING
Measures the hearing threshold of employees.

Audiometric testing measures the hearing threshold of employees. Tests conducted can detect changes in the hearing threshold of the employee. A negative change represents hearing loss within a given frequency range. The initial **audiogram** establishes a baseline hearing threshold. After that, audiometric testing should occur at least annually. Testing should not be done on an employee who has a cold or an ear infection or who has been exposed to noise levels exceeding 80 dB(A) within 14 to 16 hours prior to a test. Such conditions can produce invalid results.[8] When even small changes in an employee's hearing threshold are identified, more frequent tests should be scheduled.

AUDIOGRAM
The results of an audiometric test to determine the noise threshold at which a subject responds to different test frequencies.

Record Keeping

Figure 17–6 is an example of an audiometric form that can be used to record test results for individual employees. Such forms should be completed and kept on file to allow for sequential comparisons. It is also important to retain records

Audiometric Test Results
Johnson-Jones, Inc.

Employee Name _____   SIN _____

Test Location _____   Date _____ Cert. No. _____

Tested By _____   Date _____ Cert. No. _____

Left Ear	Right Ear

Hearing Threshold in Decibels

-10
0
10
20
30
40
50
60
70
80
90

1000 500 1000 2000 3000 4000 6000 8000

1000 500 1000 2000 3000 4000 6000 8000

-10
0
10
20
30
40
50
60
70
80
90

Hearing Threshold in Decibels

Frequency in Hertz

Figure 17–6
Sample audiometric test form.

containing a worker's employment history, including all past positions and the working conditions in those positions.

Follow-Up

Follow-up is critical. Failure to take prompt corrective action at the first sign of hearing loss can lead to permanent debilitating damage.

Hearing loss can occur without producing any evidence of physiological damage. Therefore, it is important to follow up on even the slightest evidence of a change in an employee's hearing threshold.

Follow-up can take a number of different forms. The following would all be appropriate follow-up responses:

- Administering a retest to verify the hearing loss.
- Changing or improving the type of personal protection used.
- Conducting a new noise survey in the employee's work area to determine if engineering controls are sufficient.
- Testing other employees to determine if the hearing loss is isolated to the one employee in question or if other employees have been affected.

NOISE CONTROL STRATEGIES

Figure 17–7 illustrates the three components of a noise hazard. Noise can be reduced by engineering and administrative controls applied to one or more of

Figure 17–7
Three parts of a noise hazard.

these components. The most desirable noise controls are those that reduce noise at the source. The second priority is to reduce noise along its path. The last resort is noise reduction at the receiver using personal protective devices. The latter approach should never be substituted for the two former approaches.

The following paragraphs explain widely used strategies for reducing workplace noise at the source, along its path, and at the receiver:

- Noise can be reduced at its *source* by enclosing the source, altering the acoustical design at the source, substituting equipment that produces less noise, making alterations to existing equipment, or changing the process so that less noisy equipment can be used.
- Noise can be reduced along its *path* by moving the source farther away from receivers and improving the acoustical design of the path so that more sound is absorbed as it travels toward receivers.
- Noise can be reduced at the *receiver* by enclosing the worker, using personal protective devices, and changing job schedules so that exposure time is reduced.

Some of the noise reduction strategies explained in the preceding paragraphs are engineering controls; others are administrative controls. For example, enclosing a noise source and substituting less noisy equipment are both examples of engineering controls. Changing job schedules is an example of an administrative control. Health and safety professionals should be familiar with both types of controls.

Engineering Controls

"*Engineering controls* are steps taken, other than administrative or personal protection procedures, to reduce the sound level at the source or within the hearing zone of the workers."[9] Following are some commonly used engineering controls. All of these controls are designed to reduce noise at the source, along its path, or at the receiver. They focus primarily on the noise rather than the employees who are exposed to it.

MAINTENANCE

- Replacement or adjustment of worn, loose, or unbalanced parts of machines.
- Lubrication of machine parts and use of cutting oils.
- Use of properly shaped and sharpened cutting tools.

SUBSTITUTION OF MACHINES

- Larger, slower machines for smaller, faster ones.
- Step dies for single-operation dies.
- Presses for hammers.
- Rotating shears for square shears.
- Hydraulic presses for mechanical presses.
- Belt drives for gears.

SUBSTITUTION OF PROCESSES

- Compression riveting for impact riveting.
- Welding for riveting.
- Hot working for cold working.
- Pressing for rolling or forging.

REDUCE THE DRIVING FORCE OF VIBRATING SURFACES BY

- Reducing the forces.
- Minimizing rotational speed.
- Isolating.

REDUCE THE RESPONSE OF VIBRATING SURFACES BY

- Damping.
- Additional support.
- Increasing the stiffness of the material.
- Increasing the mass of vibrating members.
- Changing the size to change resonance frequency.

REDUCE THE SOUND RADIATION FROM THE VIBRATING SURFACES BY

- Reducing the radiating area.
- Reducing overall size.
- Perforating surfaces.

REDUCE THE SOUND TRANSMISSION THROUGH SOLIDS BY USING

- Flexible mounting.
- Flexible sections in pipe runs.
- Flexible-shaft couplings.
- Fabric sections in ducts.
- Resilient flooring.

REDUCE THE SOUND PRODUCED BY GAS FLOW BY

- Using intake and exhaust mufflers.
- Using fan blades designed to reduce turbulence.

- Using large, low-speed fans instead of smaller, high-speed fans.
- Reducing the velocity of fluid flow (air).
- Increasing the cross-section of streams.
- Reducing the pressure.
- Reducing the air turbulence.

REDUCE NOISE BY REDUCING ITS TRANSMISSION THROUGH AIR BY

- Using sound-absorptive material on walls and ceiling in work areas.
- Using sound barriers and sound absorption along the transmission path.
- Completely enclosing individual machines.
- Using baffles.
- Confining high-noise machines to insulated rooms.[10]

Administrative Controls

Administrative controls are controls that reduce the exposure of employees to noise rather than reducing the noise. Administrative controls can be described as follows:

> There are many operations in which the exposure of employees to noise can be controlled administratively, that is, production schedules can simply be changed or jobs can be rotated so that exposure times are reduced. This includes such measures as transferring employees from a job location with a high noise level to a job location with a lower one if this procedure would make the employee's daily noise exposure acceptable.[11]

Administrative controls should be considered a second-level approach, with engineering controls given top priority. Smaller companies that cannot afford to reduce noise through engineering measures may use administrative controls instead. However, this approach should be avoided if at all possible.

Hearing Protection Devices

In addition to engineering and administrative controls, employees should be required to use appropriate *hearing protection devices (HPDs)*. It should be noted, however, that such devices are effective only if worn properly. Enforcement of the proper use of HPDs is difficult in some settings. The following four classifications of HPDs are widely used: enclosures, earplugs, superaural caps, and earmuffs.

Enclosures are devices that completely encompass the employee's head, much like the helmets worn by motorcycle riders. *Earplugs* (also known as *aurals*) are devices that fit into the ear canal. Custom-moulded earplugs are designed and molded for the individual employee. Premoulded earplugs are generic in nature, are usually made of a soft rubber or plastic substance, and can be reused. *Formable earplugs* can be used by anyone. They are designed to be formed individually to a person's ears, used once, and then discarded.

Superaural caps fit over the external edge of the ear canal and are held in place by a headband. Earmuffs, also known as *circumaurals*, cover the entire ear with a cushioned cup that is attached to a headband. Earplugs and earmuffs are able to reduce noise by 20 to 30 dB. By combining earplugs and earmuffs, an additional 3 to 5 dB of blockage can be gained.

Figures 17–8 through 17–11 are examples of various types of HPDs. Figure 17–8 illustrates ear, face, and head protection combined into one comprehensive device. Figure 17–9 contains two types of superaural caps. Figure 17–10 shows an earmuff-style HPD equipped with FM radio capability. Figure 17–11 displays soft, mouldable earplugs.

The effectiveness of HPDs can be enhanced through the use of technologies that reduce noise levels. These active noise reduction (ANR) technologies reduce noise by manipulating sound and signal waves. Such waves are manipulated by creating an electronic mirror image of sound waves that tends to cancel out the unwanted noise in the same way that negative numbers cancel out positive numbers in a mathematical equation. Using ANR in conjunction with enclosure devices or earmuffs can be an especially effective strategy.

Traditional, or passive, HPDs can distort or muffle sounds at certain frequencies, particularly high-pitched sounds. *Flat-attenuation HPDs* solve this problem by using electronic devices to block all sound frequencies equally. This eliminates, or at least reduces, the distortion and muffling problems. Flat-attenuation HPDs are especially helpful for employees in settings where high-pitched sound is present that they should be able to hear, as well as for employees who have already begun to lose their ability to hear such sounds.

The ability to hear high-pitched sounds is significant because warning signals and human voices can be high-pitched.

**Figure 17–8
Earmuff-style HPD.**
Source: Courtesy of ELVEX Corporation.

A benefit of ANR technologies is *optimization*. The amount of noise protection can be adjusted so that employees can hear as much as they should, but not too much. Too much noise can cause employees to suffer hearing loss. Too little noise can mean that they may not hear warning signals.

VIBRATION HAZARDS

Vibration hazards are closely associated with noise hazards because tools that produce vibration typically also produce excessive levels of noise. The strategies for protecting employees against the noise associated with vibrating tools are the same as those presented so far in this chapter. This section focuses on the other health and safety hazards associated with vibration.

Eastman explains the problems associated with vibration:

> Vibration related problems are not only serious, they are widespread. Donald Wasserman, author of *Human Aspects of Occupational Vibration*, says that up to 8 million workers are exposed to some type of vibration hazard. Of these, it has been estimated that more than half will show some signs of injury.[12]

**HAND-ARM
VIBRATION (HAV)
SYNDROME**
A form of Raynaud's
syndrome that afflicts
workers who use vibrating power tools frequently over time.

The types of injuries associated with vibration depend on its source. For example, workers who operate heavy equipment often experience vibration over the whole body. This can lead to problems ranging from motion sickness to spinal injury. However, the most common vibration-related problem is known as **hand-arm vibration syndrome (HAV)**. Eastman describes HAV as follows:

> The condition, a form of Reynaud's Syndrome, strikes an alarming number of workers who use vibrating power tools day in and day out as part of their jobs. For HAV sufferers, . . . the sensations in their hands are more than just minor, temporary dis-

Figure 17–10
Earmuff-style HPDs with FM radio capability.
Source: Courtesy of ELVEX Corporation.

Figure 17–11
Earplug-style HPDs.
Source: Courtesy of ELVEX Corporation.

comforts. They are symptoms of the potentially irreversible damage their nerves and blood vessels have suffered. As the condition progresses, it takes less and less exposure to vibration or cold to trigger the symptoms, and the symptoms themselves become more severe and crippling.[13]

Environmental conditions and worker habits can exacerbate the problems associated with vibration. For example, working with vibrating tools in a cold environment is more dangerous than working with the same tools in a warm environment. Gripping a vibrating tool tightly will lead to problems sooner than using a loose grip. Smoking and excessive noise also increase the potential for HAV and other vibration-related injuries. What all of these conditions and habits have in common is that they constrict blood vessels, which in turn restricts blood flow to the affected part of the body.[14]

Injury Prevention Strategies

Modern health and safety professionals should know how to prevent vibration-related injuries. Prevention is especially important with HAV because the disease is thought to be irreversible. This does not mean that HAV cannot be treated. It can, but the treatments developed to date only reduce the symptoms. They do not cure the disease.

Following are prevention strategies that can be used by health and safety professionals in any company regardless of its size:

PURCHASE LOW-VIBRATION TOOLS Low-vibration tools are becoming more commonplace. Pneumatic tools are very popular in most industrial settings because of their high power, low cost, and low maintenance, but have historically produced excessive noise and vibration. By implementing low vibration technology into the design of high quality power tools, vibration hazards have dramatically been reduced. Vibration abatement may be achieved through the design incorporated into the tool or through energy absorbing handles, counterweights or gloves. While energy absorbing tools are generally more expensive, most trades workers choose this superior equipment for overall comfort and job satisfaction.

LIMIT EMPLOYEE EXPOSURE Although a correlation between cumulative exposure to vibration and the onset of HAV has not been scientifically quantified, there is strong suspicion in the health and safety community that such a link exists. For example, NIOSH recommends that companies limit the exposure of their

---

SAFETY FACT

Do You Have a Noise Problem?

Taking measurements is an effective way to determine if a noise problem exists in the workplace, but there are also other ways. Health and safety professionals can learn a great deal by simple observation. Walk through the workplace at different times during the day. Do employees have to raise their voices to hear each other? If so, noise control and hearing protection strategies are in order. At the end of an eight-hour shift, do employees have trouble distinguishing among similar-sounding words? If so, workers should be using HPDs, and both engineering and administrative controls should be adopted, as appropriate.

employees to no more than four hours per day, two days per week.[15] Until the correlation between cumulative exposure and HAV has been quantified, health and safety professionals are well advised to apply the NIOSH recommendation.

CHANGE EMPLOYEE WORK HABITS Employees can play a key role in protecting themselves if they know how. Health and safety professionals should teach employees who use vibration-producing tools the work habits that will protect them from HAV and other injuries. These work habits include the following: (1) wearing properly fitting thick gloves that can partially absorb vibration; (2) taking periodic breaks (at least 10 minutes every hour); (3) using a loose grip on the tool and holding it away from the body; (4) keeping tools properly maintained (i.e., replacing vibration-absorbing pads regularly); (5) keeping warm; and (6) using vibration-absorbing floor mats and seat covers as appropriate.[16]

Modern health and safety professionals should also encourage higher management to require careful screening of applicants for jobs involving the use of vibration-producing tools and equipment. Applicants who smoke or have other conditions that constrict blood vessels should be guided away from jobs that involve excessive vibration.

OTHER EFFECTS OF NOISE HAZARDS

Hearing loss is the principal concern of health and safety professionals relating to noise hazards. However, hearing loss is not the only detrimental effect of excess noise. Noise can also cause communication problems, isolation, and productivity problems. According to S. L. Smith,

> Workers in noisy environments, even those where the noise is not loud enough to require hearing protection, often have trouble communicating with co-workers and supervisors. It is difficult for them to hear warning bells and signals, and they generally can't hold conversations with co-workers.[17]

Noise can also be detrimental to productivity by interfering with an employee's ability to think, reason, and solve problems. Not all employees respond to noise in this way, but many do. Can you concentrate on your studies in a noisy room? Some students can, whereas others cannot. If excessive noise makes it difficult for you to study, you will probably have the same problem on the job.

Isolation is another problem for some employees in a noisy environment. According to Smith, "While some workers benefit from the isolation provided by noise, it can have a significantly negative impact on employees who must act as a group or who must communicate frequently with supervisors or co-workers."[18] They can begin to feel left out and uninformed, the antithesis of the goal of a modern teamwork-oriented organization.

EVALUATING HEARING LOSS PREVENTION PROGRAMS

Hearing loss prevention programs should be evaluated periodically to ensure their effectiveness.[19] Such evaluations should have at least the following

DISCUSSION CASE

What Is Your Opinion?

The father and son have had this argument before. The son wants to go to a rock concert in which four different bands will play. The *Megablast* concert will last eight hours. It is being held in the civic auditorium in a nearby city. The father is happy that his son is attending the concert but wants him to wear earplugs to guard against excess noise. According to the father, "Eight hours of continuous loud music can damage your hearing." However, the son is adamant in refusing to wear earplugs. "I'm going to hear the music." Is the father in this case overreacting? What is your opinion?

components: (1) training and education; (2) supervisor involvement; (3) noise measurement; (4) engineering and administrative controls; (5) monitoring and record keeping; (6) referrals; (7) hearing protection devices; and (8) administration. Following are checklists for each of these components.

Training and Education

Failures or deficiencies in hearing conservation programs (hearing loss prevention programs) can often be traced to inadequacies in the training and education of noise-exposed employees and those who conduct elements of the program.

- Has training been conducted at least once a year?
- Was the training provided by a qualified instructor?
- Was the success of each training program evaluated?
- Is the content revised periodically?
- Are managers and supervisors directly involved?
- Are posters, regulations, handouts, and employee newsletters used as supplements?
- Are personal counselling sessions conducted for employees having problems with hearing protection devices or showing hearing threshold shifts?

Supervisor Involvement

Data indicate that employees who refuse to wear hearing protectors or who fail to show up for hearing tests frequently work for supervisors who are not totally committed to the hearing conservation programs.

- Have supervisors been provided with the knowledge required to supervise the use and care of hearing protectors by subordinates?
- Do supervisors wear hearing protectors in appropriate areas?
- Have supervisors been counselled when employees resist wearing protectors or fail to show up for hearing tests?
- Are disciplinary actions enforced when employees repeatedly refuse to wear hearing protectors?

Noise Measurement

Noise measurements, to be useful, should be related to noise exposure risks or the prioritization of noise control efforts, rather than merely filed away. In addition, the results should be communicated to the appropriate personnel, especially when follow-up actions are required.

- Were the essential or critical noise studies performed?
- Was the purpose of each noise study clearly stated? Have noise-exposed employees been notified of their exposures and apprised of auditory risks?
- Are the results routinely transmitted to supervisors and other key individuals?
- Are results entered into health or medical records of noise-exposed employees?
- Are results entered into shop folders?
- If noise maps exist, are they used by the proper staff?
- Are noise measurement results considered when contemplating procurement of new equipment? Modifying the facility? Relocating employees?
- Have there been changes in areas, equipment, or processes that have altered noise exposure? Have follow-up noise measurements been conducted?
- Are appropriate steps taken to include (or exclude) employees in the hearing loss prevention programs whose exposures have changed significantly?

Engineering and Administrative Controls

Controlling noise by engineering and administrative methods is often the most effective means of reducing or eliminating the hazard. In some cases, engineering controls will remove requirements for other components of the program, such as audiometric testing and the use of hearing protectors.

- Have noise control needs been prioritized?
- Has the cost effectiveness of various options been addressed?
- Are employees and supervisors apprised of plans for noise control measures?
- Are they consulted on various approaches?
- Will in-house resources or outside consultants perform the work?
- Have employees and supervisors been counselled on the operation and maintenance of noise control devices?
- Are noise control projects monitored to ensure timely completion?
- Has the full potential for administrative controls been evaluated? Are noisy processes conducted during shifts with fewer employees? Do employees have sound-treated lunch or break areas?

Monitoring Audiometry and Record Keeping

The skills of audiometric technicians, the status of the audiometer, and the quality of audiometric test records are crucial to hearing loss prevention program success. Useful information may be ascertained from the audiometric records as well as from those who actually administer the tests.

- Has the audiometric technician been adequately trained, certified, and re-certified as necessary?

- Do on-the-job observations of the technicians indicate that they perform a thorough and valid audiometric test, instruct and consult the employee effectively, and keep appropriate records?
- Are records complete?
- Are follow-up actions documented?
- Are hearing threshold levels reasonably consistent from test to test? If not, are the reasons for inconsistencies investigated promptly?
- Is the annual incidence of standard threshold shift greater than a few percent? If so, are problem areas pinpointed and remedial steps taken?
- Are audiometric trends (deteriorations) being identified, both in individuals and in groups of employees? (NIOSH recommends no more than 5% of workers showing 15 dB significant threshold shift, same ear, same frequency.)
- Do records show that appropriate audiometer calibration procedures have been followed?
- Is there documentation showing that the background sound levels in the audiometer room were low enough to permit valid testing?
- Are the results of audiometric tests being communicated to supervisors and managers as well as to employees?
- Has corrective action been taken if the rate of no-shows for audiometric test appointments is more than about 5%?
- Are employees incurring STS (significant threshold shift) notified in writing within at least 21 days? (NIOSH recommends immediate notification if retest shows 15 dB significant threshold shift, same ear, same frequency.)

Referrals

Referrals to outside sources for consultation or treatment are sometimes in order, but they can be an expensive element of the hearing loss prevention program and should not be undertaken unnecessarily.

- Are referral procedures clearly specified?
- Have letters of agreement between the company and consulting physicians or audiologists been executed?
- Have mechanisms been established to ensure that employees needing evaluation or treatment actually receive the service (e.g., transportation, scheduling, reminders)?
- Are records properly transmitted to the physician or audiologist, and back to the company?
- If medical treatment is recommended, does the employee understand the condition requiring treatment, the recommendation, and methods of obtaining such treatment?
- Are employees being referred unnecessarily?

Hearing Protection Devices

When noise control measures are not feasible, or until such time as they are installed, hearing protection devices are the only way to prevent hazardous levels of noise from damaging the inner ear. Making sure that these devices are worn effectively requires continuous attention on the part of supervisors and program implementers as well as noise-exposed employees.

- Have hearing protectors been made available to all employees whose daily average noise exposures are 85 dB(A) or above? (NIOSH recommends requiring HPD use if noises equal or exceed 85 dB(A) regardless of exposure time. To reduce the nonauditory effects of noise exposure, HPDs should be used any time the sound level is uncomfortable.)
- Are employees given the opportunity to select from a variety of appropriate protectors?
- Are employees fitted carefully with special attention to comfort?
- Are employees thoroughly trained, not only initially but at least once a year?
- Are the protectors checked regularly for wear or defects and replaced immediately if necessary?
- If employees use disposable hearing protectors, are replacements readily available?
- Do employees understand the appropriate hygiene requirements?
- Have any employees developed ear infections or irritations associated with the use of hearing protectors? Are there any employees who are unable to wear these devices because of medical conditions? Have these conditions been treated promptly and successfully?
- Have alternative types of hearing protectors been considered when problems with current devices are experienced?
- Do employees who incur noise-induced hearing loss receive intensive counselling?
- Are those who fit and supervise the wearing of hearing protectors competent to deal with the many problems that can occur?
- Do workers complain that protectors interfere with their ability to do their jobs? Do they interfere with spoken instructions or warning signals? Are these complaints followed promptly with counselling, noise control, or other measures?
- Are employees encouraged to take home their hearing protectors if they engage in noisy nonoccupational activities?
- Are potentially more effective protectors considered as they become available?
- Is the effectiveness of the hearing protector program evaluated regularly?
- Have at-the-ear protection levels been evaluated to ensure that either over- or underprotection has been adequately balanced according to the anticipated ambient noise levels?
- Is each hearing protector user required to demonstrate that he or she understands how to use and care for the protector? Are the results documented?

Administration

Keeping organized and current on administrative matters will help the program run smoothly.

- Have there been any changes in federal or provincial/territorial regulations? Have hearing loss prevention programs' policies been modified to reflect these changes?
- Are copies of company policies and guidelines regarding the hearing loss prevention program available in the offices that support the various program

elements? Are those who implement the program elements aware of these policies? Do they comply?

- Are necessary materials and supplies being ordered with a minimum of delay?
- Are procurement officers overriding the hearing loss prevention program implementer's requests for specific hearing protectors or other hearing loss prevention equipment? If so, have corrective steps been taken?
- Is the performance of key personnel evaluated periodically? If such performance is found to be less than acceptable, are steps taken to correct the situation?
- Has the failure to hear warning shouts or alarms been tied to any accidents or injuries? If so, have remedial steps been taken?

SUMMARY

1. Sound is any change in pressure that can be detected by the ear. Typically, sound is a change in air pressure. However, it can also be a change in water pressure or any other pressure-sensitive medium. The unit of measurement for sound is the decibel, or one-tenth of a bel.

2. The threshold of hearing is the weakest sound that can be detected by the human ear. The maximum sound that can be perceived without experiencing pain is known as the threshold of pain.

3. Noise is excessive sound. Industrial noise is classified as wide band noise, narrow band noise, and impulse noise.

4. Several different factors affect the risk of hearing loss from excessive noise: (a) intensity of the noise, (b) type of noise, (c) duration of daily exposure, (d) total duration of exposure, (e) age of the individual, (f) coexisting disease, (g) nature of the environment, (h) distance of the receiver from the noise source, and (i) position of the ears relative to the sound waves.

5. Noise levels of less than 80 dB(A) are considered safe. A level of 85 dB(A) should be considered the maximum limit of continuous exposure over eight hours without protection.

6. With workers' compensation claims for hearing loss on the rise, the medical profession has established a procedure for identifying causal relationships between industrial noise and hearing loss. The procedure requires that physicians consider the following factors: (a) onset and progress of hearing loss, (b) the employee's complete work history, (c) results of otological examination, (d) results of hearing studies, and (e) ruling out hearing loss from sources outside of the workplace.

7. Methods for identifying and assessing hazardous noise conditions include the following: (a) noise surveys, (b) audiometric tests, (c) record keeping, and (d) follow-up.

8. Noise reduction strategies are of three types: those that reduce noise at the source, those that reduce noise along its path, and those that reduce noise at the receiver.

9. Noise can be reduced by applying either engineering or administrative controls. Engineering controls attempt to reduce noise. Administrative controls limit human exposure to noise.

10. Vibration can cause physical problems ranging from motion sickness to spinal injury to hand-arm vibration syndrome (HAV). HAV is the most widespread of these problems. Because the physical damage associated with HAV may be irreversible, prevention is especially important.

11. HAV prevention strategies include purchasing low-vibration tools, limiting employee exposure, and changing employee work habits.

12. Organizations with the most successful programs adopt comprehensive corporate policies relating to hearing loss prevention.

13. Hearing loss prevention programs should be evaluated periodically in the following areas: (a) training and education, (b) supervisor involvement, (c) noise measurement, (d) engineering and administrative controls, (e) monitoring and record keeping, (f) referrals, (g) hearing protection devices, and (h) administration.

KEY TERMS AND CONCEPTS

Audiogram

Audiometric testing

Decibel (dB)

Dosimeter

Exchange rate

Frequency

Hand-arm vibration syndrome (HAV)

Hazardous noise

Impulse noise

Narrow band noise

Noise

Sound

Sound level meter

Threshold of hearing

Threshold of pain

Vibration

Wide band noise

REVIEW QUESTIONS

1. Define the term *sound*.

2. What is the difference between sound and noise?

3. Differentiate between sound and vibration.

4. Describe the relationship between the pitch of sound and the cycle of sound waves.

5. List and briefly explain the three broad types of industrial noise.

6. Describe the various physiological problems associated with excessive noise.

7. List four factors that affect the risk of hearing loss from exposure to excessive noise.

8. At what sound level is it necessary to begin using some type of personal protection?

9. What factors do medical professionals consider in determining causal relationships of hearing loss?

10. Define the following terms: *follow-up, noise survey*, and *audiometric testing*.

11. List three appropriate follow-up activities when an audiometric test reveals hearing loss in an employee.

12. Differentiate between engineering and administrative controls.

13. What is HAV? How can it be prevented?

14. Explain the four classifications of HPDs that are widely used.

15. Explain the main components of an evaluation of a hearing loss prevention program.

WEBLINKS

Canadian Centre for Occupational Health and Safety
www.ccohs.ca/oshanswers/phys_agents

This CCOHS site has information to assist employers and workers in the recognition, assessment, and control of noise in the workplace.

Canadian Hearing Society
www.chs.ca

The Canadian Hearing Society provides services for those who are deaf, deafened, or hard of hearing. This website contains information on hearing and hearing loss prevention.

Noise Pollution Clearinghouse
www.nonoise.org

On this website you can find news and articles on different noise sources and links to those who control, monitor, and study noise pollution.

ENDNOTES

1. J. B. Olishifski (revised by J. J. Standard), *Fundamentals of Industrial Hygiene* (Chicago: National Safety Council, 1996), 165–166.
2. National Institute for Occupational Safety and Hearing (NIOSH), *A Practical Guide to Preventing Hearing Loss*, Publication 96–110 (Washington, DC: NIOSH, 1999), 2. [Online]. Available: http://www.cdc.gov/niosh/96–110a.html.
3. Ibid.
4. Olishifski, *Fundamentals of Industrial Hygiene*, 171.
5. NIOSH, *A Practical Guide*, 4.
6. Canadian Centre for Occupational Health and Safety. (June 3, 1999). "OHS Answers." [Online]. Available: http://www.ccohs.ca/oshanswers/phys_agents/non_auditory.html. (Retrieved December 28, 2004).
7. NIOSH, *A Practical Guide*, 8.
8. Ibid., 12.
9. Olishifski, *Fundamentals of Industrial Hygiene*, 178–179.
10. Ibid., 179.

11. Ibid.

12. M. Eastman, "Vibration Shakes Workers," *Safety & Health* 143, no. 5: 32.

13. Ibid.

14. Ibid., 32–33.

15. Ibid., 33.

16. Ibid., 35.

17. S. L. Smith, "The 'Other' Effects of Noise," *Occupational Hazards* (January 1997): 79.

18. Ibid.

19. NIOSH, *A Practical Guide*, Appendix B, 1–6.

18 Safety Analysis and Prevention

CHAPTER

LEARNING OBJECTIVES

- Define the term hazard.
- Explain the purpose of preliminary hazard analysis.
- Explain the importance of cost–benefit analysis.
- List common hazard prevention strategies.
- Describe the purpose and key elements of risk assessment.
- List examples of best safety management practices that may be adopted by organizations.

There is a saying that an ounce of prevention is worth a pound of cure. This is certainly the case with workplace health and safety. Every accident that can be prevented should be. Every hazard that can be identified should be corrected or at least minimized through the introduction of appropriate safeguards. Careful analysis of potential hazards in the workplace has led to many of today's widely used safety measures and practices.

The key to preventing accidents is identifying and eliminating hazards. A **hazard** may be defined as follows:

HAZARD
A condition with the potential of causing injury to personnel, damage to equipment or structures, loss of material, or lessening of the ability to perform a prescribed function.

> A hazard is a condition or combination of conditions that, if left uncorrected, may lead to an accident, illness, or property damage.

This chapter provides prospective and practising health and safety professionals with the information they need to analyze the workplace, identify hazards that exist there, and take the preventive measures necessary to neutralize the hazards.

HAZARD ANALYSIS
A systematic process for identifying hazards and recommending corrective action.

OVERVIEW OF HAZARD ANALYSIS

If a hazard is a condition that could lead to an injury or illness, **hazard analysis** is a systematic process for identifying hazards and recommending corrective action. There are two approaches to hazard analysis: preliminary and detailed (Figure 18–1). A **preliminary hazard analysis (PHA)** is conducted to identify potential hazards and prioritize them according to the (1) likelihood of an accident or injury being caused by the hazard; and (2) severity of injury, illness, or property damage that could result if the hazard caused an accident.

The Society of Manufacturing Engineers has this to say about preliminary hazard analysis:

> Each hazard should be ranked according to its probability to cause an accident and the severity of that accident. The ranking here is relative. Some hazards identified might be placed into a category for further analysis. A useful practice for early sorting is to place catastrophic severities together, followed by critical, marginal, and nuisance hazards, respectively. Then, with each item, indicate the probability of occurrence — considerable, probable, or unlikely. Rate the correction of these hazards next by cost.[1]

Key terms in this quote are those that describe the likelihood of an accident occurring (*considerable, probable,* or *unlikely*) and those that rate the probable level of injuries that could occur (*catastrophic, critical, marginal,* and *nuisance*). A key step is rating the cost of correcting hazards. All of these concepts are covered later in this chapter.

Whereas a preliminary analysis might involve just observation or pilot testing of new equipment and systems, the *detailed hazard analysis* involves the application of analytical, inductive, and deductive methods. Figure 18–2 lists some of the more widely used methods for conducting a detailed hazard analysis. Each of these methods is covered at length later in this chapter.

PRELIMINARY HAZARD ANALYSIS (PHA)
Conducted to identify potential hazards and prioritize them according to (1) the likelihood of an accident or injury being caused by the hazard; and (2) the severity of injury, illness, or property damage that could result if the hazard caused an accident.

Figure 18–1
Two approaches to hazard analysis.

- Failure mode and effects analysis (FMEA)
- Fault tree analysis (FTA)
- Hazard and operability review (HAZOP)
- Human error analysis (HEA)
- Risk analysis
- Technic of operations review (TOR)

Figure 18–2
Detailed hazard analysis methods.

PRELIMINARY HAZARD ANALYSIS

It is not always feasible to wait until all the data are compiled from a detailed analysis before taking steps to identify and eliminate hazards. For example, when a new system or piece of equipment is installed, management probably wants to bring it on line as soon as possible. In such cases, a preliminary hazard analysis is in order. The PHA can serve two purposes: (1) it can expedite bringing the new system on line, but at a substantially reduced risk of injuring workers; and (2) it can serve as a guide for a future detailed analysis.

Preliminary hazard analysis amounts to forming an ad hoc team of experienced personnel who are familiar with the equipment, material, substance, or process being analyzed. *Experience and related expertise* are important factors in conducting a preliminary review. For example, say, a new piece of equipment, such as a computer numerically controlled (CNC) machining centre, is installed. The health and safety professional could form a team that includes an experienced machinist, an electrician, a materials expert, and a computer control specialist.

All members of the team are asked to look over the machining centre for obvious hazards relating to their respective areas of expertise. Then they work together as a group to play devil's advocate. Each team member asks the others a series of "what if" questions: What if a cutting bit breaks? What if the wrong command is entered? What if the material stock is too long? Depending on the nature of the process being analyzed, personnel from adjacent or related processes should be added to the team.

Figure 18–3 is an example of a job hazard analysis survey adapted from one developed by the National Institute for Occupational Safety and Health

Operation:			Form (Type of hazard)						Route of Entry		Control Methods					
Number of Employees	Job Title	Exposure Substance	Dust	Liquid	Vapour	Gas	Fume	Mist	Skin	Inhaled	Local Ventilation	General Ventilation	Respirator	Gloves	Face Protection	Other Protection

Date:

Figure 18–3
Sample job hazard analysis survey.

Source: Adapted from survey instrument in NIOSH, *Safety Guide for Textile Machinery Manufacturers* (Cincinnati, OH: US Department of Health, Education, and Welfare, January 1978), 11.

CHAPTER 18   Safety Analysis and Prevention

(NIOSH). A preliminary analysis team would use this form to identify potential hazards associated with a spray-painting process. Key elements include the substances to which workers will be exposed, the form that those substances will take, the probable route of entry, and recommended hazard control strategies. A similar form can be developed for any process or operation that could be the focus of a preliminary hazard analysis.

Cost–Benefit Factors in Hazard Analysis

Every hazard typically has several different remedies. Every remedy has a corresponding **cost** and corresponding **benefit**. Management is not likely to want to apply $10 solutions to $1 problems. Therefore, it is important to factor in cost when recommending corrective action regarding hazards. This amounts to listing all of the potential remedies along with their respective costs and then estimating the extent to which each will reduce the hazard (its benefit).

COST–BENEFIT
The relationship between the cost of a remedy and the benefit it produces.

Going back to the earlier example of the CNC machining centre, assume that the analysis team identified the following potential hazards:

- Lubricants sprayed on the machine operator or floor.
- Flying metal chips hitting the operator or other workers.
- Jammed metal stock kicking back into the operator.

Figure 18–4 is a matrix that can be developed by the analysis team to illustrate the cost of each hazard versus the benefit of each remedy. After examining this matrix, the remedy that makes the most sense from the perspective of both cost and impact on the hazards is the Plexiglas™ door. It eliminates two of the hazards and reduces the third. The flexible curtain costs less but does not have a sufficient impact on the hazards. The third and fourth options cost more and have less impact on the hazards.

		Cost–Benefit Analysis Matrix		
		Impact on Hazard		
Possible Remedy	Estimated Cost	Spraying Lubricants	Metal Chips	Jammed Stock
Plexiglas™ door	$250	E	E	R
Flexible curtain	$75	R	R	N
Acme chip/jam guard	$260	N	E	E
Acme spray guard	$260	E	N	N

R = Reduces the hazard
E = Eliminates the hazard
N = No effect on the hazard
I = Increases the hazard
C = Creates new hazard

Figure 18–4
Sample cost–benefit analysis matrix.

DETAILED HAZARD ANALYSIS

RISK ANALYSIS
An analytical methodology normally associated with insurance and investments.

Typically, a preliminary hazard analysis is sufficient. However, in cases where the potential exists for serious injury, multiple injuries, or catastrophic illness, a detailed hazard analysis is conducted. A number of different methods can be used for conducting detailed analyses. The **risk analysis** method is a simple and effective method of detailed hazard analysis. The risk analysis method will be explained below. However, other common methods of detailed hazard analysis that may be used in various settings would include the following:

- Failure mode and effects of analysis (FMEA).
- Hazard and operability review (HAZOP).
- Technic of operations review (TOR).
- Human error analysis (HEA).
- Fault tree analysis (FTA).

DISCUSSION CASE

What Is Your Opinion?

Mike Chinchar is the new safety director at MicroTel Corporation. He completed his college degree just six weeks ago. At the moment, he is wishing he could transport himself back in time and be a college student again. He is on the hot seat. "Chinchar, you seem to think that this company should simply stop functioning every time you identify a hazard. This situation you are proposing will be expensive! Isn't there some other way to solve the problem? Did you do a cost–benefit analysis before arriving at this recommendation?" What types of factors should Chinchar have considered before recommending a solution to a hazardous situation? What is your opinion?

Risk Analysis

Where are we at risk? Where are we at greatest risk? These are important questions for health and safety professionals involved in analyzing the workplace for the purpose of identifying and overcoming hazards. Risk analysis is an analytical methodology normally associated with insurance and investments. However, risk analysis can be used to analyze the workplace, identify hazards, and develop strategies for overcoming these hazards. The risk analysis process focuses on two key questions:

FREQUENCY
The number of events in a given time.

SEVERITY
The magnitude of the results of an event of action.

- How *frequently* does a given event occur?
- How *severe* are the consequences of a given event? The fundamental rule-of-thumb of risk analysis is that risk is decreased by decreasing the frequency and severity of hazard-related events.

Health and safety professionals should understand the relationship that exists between the **frequency** and **severity** factors relating to accidents. Historical data on accidents, injuries, and illness show that the less severe an injury or illness, the more frequently it is likely to occur. Correspondingly, the more severe an injury or illness, the less frequently it is likely to occur. For example, there are many more minor scrapes, bumps, and abrasions experienced in the workplace than major debilitating injuries such as amputations or broken bones.

A number of different approaches can be used in conducting a risk analysis. One of the most effective is that developed by Chapanis.[2] Chapanis's approach to risk analysis considers both **probability** and **impact**.

Probability levels and corresponding frequency of occurrence ratings are as follows: 1 = Impossible (frequency of occurrence: 10^{-8}/day); 2 = Extremely unlikely (frequency of occurrence: 10^{-6}/day); 3 = Remote (frequency of occurrence: 10^{-5}/day); 4 = Occasional (frequency of occurrence: 10^{-4}/day); 5 = Reasonably probable (frequency of occurrence: 10^{-3}/day); 6 = Frequent (frequency of occurrence: 10^{-2}/day).[3]

The lowest rating (1) means it is impossible that a given error will be committed or a given failure will occur. The highest rating (6) means it is very likely that a given error will be committed frequently or a given failure will occur frequently. Notice the quantification of frequency levels for each level of probability. For example, the expected frequency of occurrence for a probability level of "remote" is 10 to the negative fifth power per day.

Severity levels can also be rated according to the likely consequence of an accident or failure event. The least severe incidents (1) are not likely to cause an injury or damage property. The most severe incidents (4) are almost certain to cause death or serious property damage. Critical accidents (3) may cause severe injury or major loss. Marginal accidents (2) may cause minor injury, minor occupational illness, or minor damage.[4]

PROBABILITY
The statistical likelihood of an action or event taking place.

IMPACT
The consequences of an action or event.

HAZARD PREVENTION AND DETERRENCE

All of the methods and procedures discussed in this chapter have been concerned with identifying potential hazards. This section deals with using the information learned during analysis to prevent accidents and illnesses. The Society of Manufacturing Engineers recommends the following hazard control methods:

- Eliminate the source of the hazards.
- Substitute a less hazardous equivalent.
- Reduce the hazards at the source.
- Remove the employee from the hazard (e.g., substitute a robot or other automated system).
- Isolate the hazards (e.g., enclose them in barriers).
- Dilute the hazard (e.g., ventilate the hazardous substance).
- Apply appropriate management strategies.
- Use appropriate personal protective equipment.
- Provide employee training.
- Practise good housekeeping.[5]

For every hazard identified during the analysis process, one or more of these hazard control methods will apply. Figure 18–5 shows the steps involved in implementing hazard control methods. The first step involves selecting the

Figure 18–5
Steps for implementing hazard control measures.

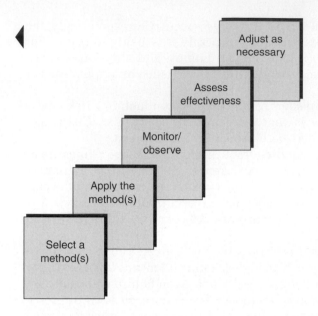

method or methods that are most likely to produce the desired results. Once selected, the method is applied and monitored to determine if the expected results are being achieved.

Monitoring and observing are informal procedures. They should be followed by a more formal, more structured assessment of the effectiveness of the method. If the method selected is not producing the desired results, adjustments should be made. This may mean changing the way in which the method is applied or dropping it and trying another.

The example of Crestview Container Corporation's (CCC) problems with toxic paint illustrates how the process works: CCC produces airtight aluminum containers for transporting electromechanical devices. The containers must be painted as the last step in the production process. Although the specified paint was supposed to be only slightly toxic — a problem that should have been resolved by using personal protective equipment — paint station operators complained frequently of various negative side effects.

The CCC health and safety professional, working with management, solved the problem by applying the following steps:

1. **Select a method.** Of the various methods available, the one selected involved eliminating the source of the hazard (the toxic paint). CCC personnel were tasked with testing various nontoxic paints until one was found that could match the problem paint in all categories (e.g., ease of application, drying time, quality of surface finish, etc.). After 40 different paints were tested, a nontoxic substitute was found.

2. **Apply the method.** The new paint was ordered and used on a partial shipment of containers.

3. **Monitor/observe.** The health and safety professional, along with CCC's painting supervisors, monitored both employee performance and employee complaints concerning the paint.

4. **Assess effectiveness.** To assess effectiveness, employee complaints were tabulated. The number of complaints was down to a negligible amount and not serious in nature. Productivity was also assessed. It was found that the new paint had no noticeable effect on productivity, negative or positive.

5. **Adjust as necessary.** CCC found that no adjustments were necessary.

RISK ASSESSMENT

Risk assessment in this context is the process of quantifying the level of risk associated with the operation of a given machine.[6] It should be a structured and systematic process that answers the following four specific questions:

- How *severe* are potential injuries?
- How *frequently* are employees exposed to the potential hazards?
- What is the *possibility* of avoiding the hazard if it does occur?
- What is the *likelihood* of an injury should a safety control system fail?

The most widely used risk-assessment technique is the decision tree, coupled with codes representing these four questions and defined levels of risk.

Figure 18–6 is an example of a risk-assessment decision tree. In this example, the codes and their associated levels of risk are as follows:

S = Severity

Question 1: Severity of potential injuries

S1   Slight injury (bruise, abrasion)
S2   Severe injury (amputation or death)

RISK ASSESSMENT
The process of quantifying the level of risk.

SAFETY FACT

What to Include in a Hazards Inventory

An excellent tool for getting the work of health and safety personnel organized, prioritized, and properly focused is the *hazards inventory*. Such an inventory is a comprehensive list of all hazards associated with all processes and work tasks in a company. A hazards inventory should include at least the following information:

- Process descriptions.
- Associated hazards.
- Controls relating to the hazards.
- Department location of each process.
- Names of supervisors of all personnel who work on each process (including telephone numbers).
- Number of employees who work on each process.
- Medical information relating to the hazards.
- Historical information about the process and related hazards.

F = Frequency

Question 2: Frequency of exposure to potential hazards

F1 Infrequent exposure
F2 From frequent to continuous exposure

P = Possibility

Question 3: Possibility of avoiding the hazard if it does occur

P1 Possible
P2 Less possible to not impossible

L = Likelihood

Question 4: Likelihood that the hazard will occur

L1 Highly unlikely
L2 Unlikely
L3 Highly likely

Risk Levels

Associated risk factors ranging from lowest (B) to highest (4)

By applying the decision tree in Figure 18–6 or a similar device, the risk associated with the operation of a given machine can be quantified. This allows safety personnel to assign logical priorities for machine safeguarding and hazard prevention.

BEST PRACTICES IN SAFETY MANAGEMENT

Health and safety texts necessarily focus on what can go wrong in the workplace and cause accidents and injuries. This is because health and safety professionals must be able to identify hazardous conditions and take the appropriate steps to keep them from harming people. However, it is also helpful for health and

**Figure 18–6
Risk-assessment
decision tree.**

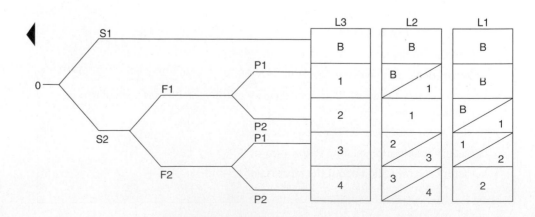

safety personnel to study the other side of the coin — outstanding practices that make the workplace safer. Most jurisdictions in Canada have available to employers and workers resources on best practices. One such resource is a document called *Business Results through Health & Safety* from Ontario's WSIB. The document may be found at http://www.wsib.on.ca/wsib/wsibsite.nsf/public/BusinessResultsHealthSafety. An example of the best safety management practices for one company are found below.[7]

Best Practices at Deere & Company

Deere & Company manufactures agricultural, forest harvesting, construction, lawn care, and diesel engine products. The company operates facilities in 17 countries and employs 40 000 people. Best safety management practices at Deere & Co. include the following:

1. Each unit within the company establishes safety goals annually. Progress toward accomplishing these goals is monitored carefully, and the results are reported to employees.

2. The corporate leadership commits to providing the resources and support necessary to ensure a safe and healthy workplace in all of its facilities. For example, the company employs 175 health and safety professionals.

3. The company implements safety management systems in all of its facilities that ensure compliance with all applicable laws and regulations.

4. Appropriate engineering and administrative controls are established in all facilities and monitored closely.

5. Line managers and supervisors are made part of the "safety team" and are expected to make this role a high priority.

6. Safety performance is included in performance appraisals of all employees.

SUMMARY

1. A hazard is a condition or combination of conditions that, if left uncorrected, may lead to an accident, illness, or property damage.

2. Hazard analysis is a systematic process for identifying hazards and recommending corrective action. There are two approaches to hazard analysis: preliminary and detailed.

3. Hazards can be ranked as potentially catastrophic, critical, marginal, and nuisance.

4. A preliminary hazard analysis involves forming an ad hoc team of experienced personnel who are familiar with the equipment, material substance, and process being analyzed. Experience and related expertise are critical in conducting a preliminary hazard analysis.

5. Risk analysis can be used for hazard and safety analysis. The process revolves around answering two questions: How frequently does a given event occur? How severe are the consequences of a given event? The fundamental rule of thumb of risk analysis is that risk is decreased by decreasing the frequency and severity of hazard-related events.

6. The fundamentals of hazard prevention and deterrence include the following strategies: eliminate the source of the hazard, substitute a less hazardous substance, reduce the hazard at the source, remove the employee from the hazard, isolate the hazard, dilute the hazard, apply appropriate management strategies, use personal protective equipment, provide employee training, and practise good housekeeping.

7. Risk assessment should answer four questions: (a) How severe are potential injuries? (b) How frequently are employees exposed to potential hazards? (c) What is the possibility of avoiding the hazard if it does occur? (d) What is the likelihood of an injury if a safety control system fails?

KEY TERMS AND CONCEPTS

Cost–benefit	Preliminary hazard analysis (PHA)
Frequency	Probability
Hazard	Risk analysis
Hazard analysis	Risk assessment
Impact	Severity

REVIEW QUESTIONS

1. Define the term *hazard*.

2. What is the purpose of preliminary hazard analysis?

3. Explain why experience and related expertise are so important when conducting a preliminary hazard analysis.

4. Why is cost–benefit analysis such a critical part of hazard analysis and prevention?

5. Name five widely applicable hazard prevention strategies.

6. What is risk assessment? How is it used?

WEBLINKS

Industrial Accident Prevention Association
www.iapa.ca/resources/resources_links.asp

IAPA has lots of downloads and links to helpful safety resources for accident recognition, assessment, and control.

Workplace Safety and Insurance Board of Ontario
www.wsib.on.ca/wsib/wsibsite.nsf/public/BusinessResultsHealthSafety

From this link you can download a PDF version of WSIB's *Business Results through Health & Safety*. This guidebook has information on various aspects of workplace safety and is loaded with tips and tools for the business person or the safety professional.

ENDNOTES

1. Society of Manufacturing Engineers (SME), *Tool and Manufacturing Engineers Handbook* 6 (Dearborn, MI: Society of Manufacturing Engineers, 1998), 12–17.

2. A. Chapanis, "To Err Is Human, to Forgive, Design," proceedings of the ASSE Annual Professional Development Conference, New Orleans, 1986, 6.

3. Ibid.

4. Ibid.

5. SME, *Tool and Manufacturing*, 12–20.

6. "Safety of Machinery — Principles of Safety Related to Control Systems," EN 954, Part I, *European Union*, 1997.

7. S. Smith, "America's Safest Companies," *Occupational Hazards* 64, no. 10 (October 2002): 47–62.

Accident Investigation and Reporting

LEARNING OBJECTIVES

- Explain the purpose of conducting accident investigations.
- Expand on the *who, what, when, where,* and *why* questions of accident investigation.
- List the five steps for conducting the investigation.
- Describe the elements of an effective witness interview.
- Explain why some accidents are not reported.

Dan Hartshorn defines an accident as "any unplanned event that causes injury, illness, property damage or harmful disruption of work process."[1]

When an accident occurs, it is important that it be investigated thoroughly. The results of a comprehensive accident report can help health and safety professionals pinpoint the cause of the accident. This information can then be used to prevent future accidents, which is the primary purpose of accident investigation.

The Society of Manufacturing Engineers describes the importance of thoroughly investigating accidents:

> The primary reason for investigating an accident is not to identify a scapegoat, but to determine the cause of the accident. The investigation concentrates on gathering factual information about the details that led to the accident. If investigations are conducted properly, there is the added benefit of uncovering problems that did not directly lead to the accident. This information benefits the ongoing effort of reducing the likelihood of accidents. As problems are revealed during the investigation, action items and improvements that can prevent similar accidents from happening in the future will be easier to identify than at any time.[2]

This chapter gives prospective and practising health and safety professionals the information they need to conduct thorough, effective accident investigations and prepare comprehensive accident reports.

TYPES OF ACCIDENT INVESTIGATIONS

There are *accident reports* and there are *accident-analysis reports*. An **accident report** is completed when the accident in question represents only a minor incident. It answers the following questions: *who, what, where,* and *when*. However, it does not answer the *why* question.[3] An accident report can be completed by a person with very little formal investigation and reporting training or experience. Supervisors often complete accident reports which, in turn, might be used later as part one of a more in-depth accident report.

An **accident-analysis report** is completed when the accident in question is serious. This level of report should answer the same questions as the regular accident report plus one more — *why*. Consequently it involves a formal accident analysis. The analysis is undertaken for the purpose of determining the root cause of the accident. Accident analysis requires special skills and should be undertaken only by an individual with those skills. There are two reasons for this: First, the accident analysis must identify the actual root cause or the company will expend resources treating only symptoms or, even worse, solving the wrong problem. Second, serious accidents are always accompanied by the potential for litigation. If there might be legal action as a result of an accident, it is important to have a professional conduct the investigation even if it means bringing in an outside consultant.

How can health and safety professionals determine when an accident report is sufficient and when an accident-analysis report is called for? Accident reports are called for when the accident in question is a minor incident that did *not* result in any of the following circumstances: death, loss of consciousness, medical treatment beyond first aid, more than one additional day of lost work beyond the day of the accident, or any kind of modifications to the injured employee's work duties beyond those that might occur on the day of the accident.

Accident-analysis reports are called for when any of the following circumstances result from the accident in question: death, loss of consciousness, professional medical treatment beyond first aid, one or more days of lost work over and above any time lost the day of the accident, or any modifications to the injured employee's work duties beyond those that might occur on the day of the injury.

WHEN TO INVESTIGATE

Of course, the first thing to do when an accident takes place is to implement emergency procedures. This involves bringing the situation under control and caring for the injured worker. As soon as all emergency procedures have been accomplished, the accident investigation should begin. Waiting too long to complete an investigation can harm the results. This is an important rule of thumb to remember. Another is that *all* accidents, no matter how small, should be investigated. Evidence suggests that the same factors that cause minor accidents cause major accidents.[4] Further, a near miss should be treated like an accident and investigated thoroughly.

There are several reasons why it is important to conduct investigations immediately. First, immediate investigations are more likely to produce accurate

ACCIDENT REPORT
Records the findings of an accident investigation, the cause or causes of an accident, and recommendations for corrective action.

ACCIDENT-ANALYSIS REPORT
Report identifying the root cause of an accident.

information. Conversely, the longer the time span between an accident and an investigation, the greater the likelihood of important facts becoming blurred as memories fade. Second, it is important to collect information before the accident scene is changed and before witnesses begin comparing notes. Human nature encourages people to change their stories to agree with those of other witnesses.[5] Finally, an immediate investigation is evidence of management's commitment to preventing future accidents. An immediate response shows that management cares.[6]

WHAT TO INVESTIGATE

ACCIDENT INVESTIGATION
The process of collecting facts to determine the cause of an accident.

The purpose of an **accident investigation** is to collect facts. It is not to find fault. It is important that health and safety professionals make this distinction known to all involved. Fault finding can cause reticence among witnesses who have valuable information to share. Causes of the accident should be the primary focus. The investigation should be guided by the following words: *who, what, when, where, why,* and *how*.

This does not mean that mistakes and breaches of precautionary procedures by workers are not noted. Rather, when these things are noted, they are recorded as facts instead of faults. CCOHS takes this approach:

> A difficulty that has bothered many investigators is the idea that one does not want to lay blame. However, when a thorough worksite accident investigation reveals that some person or persons among management, supervisor, and the workers were apparently at fault, then this fact should be pointed out. The intention here is to remedy the situation, not to discipline an individual.
>
> Failing to point out human failings that contributed to an accident will not only downgrade the quality of the investigation. Furthermore, it will also allow future accidents to happen from similar causes because they have not been addressed.[7]

In attempting to find the facts and identify causes, certain questions should be asked, regardless of the nature of the accident. The Society of Manufacturing Engineers recommends using the following questions when conducting accident investigations:

- What type of work was the injured person doing?
- Exactly what was the injured person doing or trying to do at the time of the accident?
- Was the injured person proficient in the task being performed at the time of the accident? Had the worker received proper training?
- Was the injured person authorized to use the equipment or perform the process involved in the accident?
- Were there other workers present at the time of the accident? If so, who are they, and what were they doing?
- Was the task in question being performed according to properly approved procedures?
- Was the proper equipment being used, including personal protective equipment?
- Was the injured employee new to the job?
- Was the process, equipment, or system involved new?
- Was the injured person being supervised at the time of the accident?

- Are there any established safety rules or procedures that were clearly not being followed?
- Where did the accident take place?
- What was the condition of the accident site at the time of the accident?
- Has a similar accident occurred before? If so, were corrective measures recommended? Were they implemented?
- Are there obvious solutions that would have prevented the accident?[8]

The answers to these questions should be carefully and copiously recorded. You may find it helpful to dictate your findings into a microcassette or digital recorder. This approach allows you to focus more time and energy on investigating and less on taking written notes.

Regardless of how the findings are recorded, it is important to be thorough. What may seem like a minor unrelated fact at the moment could turn out to be a valuable fact later when all of the evidence has been collected and is being analyzed.

Common Causes of Accidents

Hartshorn places many of the common causes of accidents in the following categories: personal beliefs and feelings, decision to work unsafely, mismatch or overload, systems failures, traps, unsafe conditions, and unsafe acts.[9] The common causes in each of these categories can help investigators determine the root cause of an accident.

Personal beliefs and feelings. Causes in this category include the following: individual did not believe the accident would happen to him or her; individual was working too fast, showing off, or being a know-it-all; individual ignored the rules out of contempt for authority and rules in general; individual gave in to peer pressure; and individual had personal problems that clouded his or her judgment.

Decision to work unsafely. Some people, for a variety of reasons, feel it is in their best interests or to their benefit to work unsafely. Hence, they make a conscious decision to do so.

Mismatch or overload. Causes in this category include the following: individual is in poor physical condition; individual is fatigued; individual has a high stress level; individual is mentally unfocused or distracted; the task required is too complex or difficult; the task required is boring; the physical environment is stressful (e.g., excessive noise, heat, dust, or other factors); the work in question is very demanding — even for an individual in good physical condition; and individual has a negative attitude (e.g., hostile, uncooperative, apathetic, etc.).

Systems failure. Causes in this category consist of the various errors management makes that are not grossly negligent or *serious and willful*. Common causes in this category include lack of a clear policy; lack of rules, regulations, and procedures; poor hiring procedures; inadequate monitoring and inspections; failure to correct known hazards; insufficient training for employees; rules that are in place but are not enforced; no rewarding or reinforcement of safe behaviour; inadequate tools and equipment provided; production requirements set too high; inadequate communication to employees of safety concerns, statistics, and rules; poor safety management; no or insufficient job safety analysis; and insufficient management support for safety.

Traps. Poor design of workstations and processes can create *traps* that, in turn, lead to unsafe behaviour. Common causes in this category include defective equipment; failure to provide, maintain, and replace proper personal protective equipment; failure to train employees in the proper use of their personal protective equipment; overly complicated and confusing controls; poorly laid out work area; mechanical lifting equipment that is inadequate for the jobs required of it; uncontrolled hazards that might lead to slips and falls; excessive reaching, bending, stooping, and twisting; excessive contact pressure, vibration, or force; awkward postures that result from poor workstation or tool design; excessive temperature extremes; insufficient lighting; and insufficient ventilation.

Unsafe conditions. Common causes in this category include the following: unsafe condition created by the person injured in the accident; unsafe condition created by a fellow employee; unsafe condition created by a third party; unsafe condition created by management; unsafe condition knowingly overlooked by management; and unsafe condition created by the elements (e.g., rain, sun, snow, ice, wind, darkness, etc.).

Unsafe acts. Common causes in this category include the following: individual chooses to ignore the rules; people are involved in horseplay or fighting; individual uses drugs or alcohol; individual uses unauthorized tools or equipment; individual chooses an improper work method; individual fails to ask for information or other resources needed to do the job safely; individual forgets a rule, regulation, or procedure; individual does not pay proper attention; and individual uses improper body mechanics.

WHO SHOULD INVESTIGATE

Who should conduct the accident investigation? Should it be the responsible supervisor? The health and safety professional? A higher-level manager? An outside specialist? There is no simple answer to this question and there is disagreement among professional people of goodwill.

The legal requirements for participation in an accident investigation vary slightly throughout each jurisdiction. Ontario, for example, requires that a designated committee member or worker representative investigate all accidents that result in a **critical injury** or fatality. In some companies, the supervisor of the injured worker conducts the investigation. In others, a health and safety professional performs the job. Some companies form an investigative team; others bring in outside specialists. There are several reasons for the various approaches used. Factors considered in deciding how to approach accident investigations include:

CRITICAL INJURY
Injuries where a specified degree of seriousness has been reached. The specific requirements for classifying an injury as "critical" are provided in the statutes of some jurisdictions.

- Size of the company.
- Structure of the company's health and safety program.
- Type of accident.
- Seriousness of the accident.
- Technical complexity.
- Number of times that similar accidents have occurred.

- Company's management philosophy.
- Company's commitment to health and safety.

CONDUCTING THE INVESTIGATION

The questions in the previous section summarize what to look for when conducting accident investigations. Figure 19–1 lists five steps to follow in conducting an accident investigation.[10] These steps are explained in the following paragraphs.

Isolate the Accident Scene

You may have seen a crime scene that was sealed off by the police. The entire area surrounding such a scene is typically blocked off by barriers or heavy yellow tape. This is done to keep curious onlookers from removing, disturbing, or unknowingly destroying vital evidence. This same approach should be used when conducting an accident investigation. As soon as emergency procedures have been completed and the injured worker has been removed, the accident scene should be *isolated* until all pertinent evidence has been collected or observed and recorded. Further, nothing but the injured worker should be removed from the scene. If necessary, a security guard should be posted to maintain the integrity of the **accident scene**. The purpose of isolating the scene is to maintain as closely as possible the conditions that existed at the time of the accident.

ACCIDENT SCENE
The area where an accident occurred.

Record All Evidence

It is important to make a permanent record of all *pertinent evidence* as quickly as possible. There are three reasons for this: (1) certain types of evidence may be

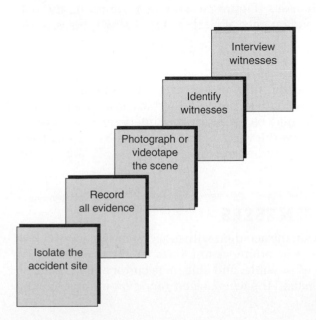

▶ **Figure 19–1**
Steps in conducting an accident investigation.

perishable; (2) the longer an accident scene must be isolated, the more likely it is that evidence will be disturbed, knowingly or unknowingly; and (3) if the isolated scene contains a critical piece of equipment or a critical component in a larger process, pressure will quickly mount to get it back in operation. Evidence can be recorded in a variety of ways including written notes, sketches, photography, videotape, dictated observations, and diagrams. In deciding what to record, a good rule of thumb is *if in doubt, record it*. It is better to record too much than to skip evidence that may be needed later after the accident scene has been disturbed.

Photograph or Videotape the Scene

This step is actually an extension of the previous step. Modern photographic and videotaping technology has simplified the task of observing and recording evidence. Health and safety professionals should be proficient in the operation of a camera, even if it is just an instant camera and a video camera.

The advent of the digital camera has introduced a new meaning for the concept of "instant photographs." Using a digital camera in conjunction with a computer, photographs of accident scenes can be viewed immediately and transmitted instantly to numerous different locations. Digital camera equipment is especially useful when photographs of accident scenes in remote locations are needed.

Both still and video cameras should be on hand, loaded, and ready to use immediately should an accident occur. As with the previous step, a good rule of thumb in photographing and videotaping is *if in doubt, shoot it*. When recording evidence, it is better to have more shots than necessary than to risk missing a vital piece of evidence.

Identify Witnesses

In identifying witnesses, it is important to compile a witness list. Names on the list should be recorded in three categories: (1) **primary witnesses**, (2) **secondary witnesses**, and (3) **tertiary witnesses** (Figure 19–2). When compiling the witness list, ask employees to provide names of all three types of witnesses.

PRIMARY WITNESS
An eyewitness to an accident.

SECONDARY WITNESS
Someone who was present at the scene of an accident but did not actually see the accident.

TERTIARY WITNESS
Someone who may have information that is relevant to an accident investigation although they were not present when the accident happened.

Interview Witnesses

Every witness on the list should be interviewed, preferably in the following order: primary witnesses first, secondary next, and tertiary last. After all witnesses have been interviewed, it may be necessary to reinterview witnesses for clarification or corroboration. Interviewing witnesses is such a specialized process that the next major section is devoted to it.

INTERVIEWING WITNESSES

The techniques used for interviewing accident witnesses are designed to ensure that the information is objective, accurate, as untainted by the personal opinions and feelings of witnesses as possible, and able to be corroborated. For this reason, it is important to understand the *when, where,* and *how* of interviewing the accident witnesses.

- Primary witnesses are eyewitnesses to the accident.
- Secondary witnesses are witnesses who did not actually see the accident happen, but were in the vicinity and arrived on the scene immediately or very shortly after the accident.
- Tertiary witnesses are witnesses who were not present at the time of the accident nor afterward but may still have relevant evidence to present (e.g., an employee who had complained earlier about a problem with the machine involved in the accident).

▶ **Figure 19–2**
Categories of accident witnesses.

When to Interview

Immediacy is important. Interviews should begin as soon as the witness list has been compiled and, once begun, should proceed expeditiously. There are two main reasons for this. First, a witness's recollections will be best right after the accident. The more time that elapses between the accident and the interview, the more blurred the witness's memory will become. Second, immediacy avoids the possibility of witnesses comparing notes and, as a result, changing their stories. This is just human nature, but it is a tendency that can undermine the value of testimony given and, in turn, the facts collected. Recommendations based on questionable facts are not likely to be valid. Also, witnesses should be interviewed individually and separately, preferably before they have talked to each other.

Where to Interview

The best place to interview is at the accident scene. If this is not possible, interviews should take place in a private setting elsewhere. It is important to ensure that all distractions are removed, interruptions are guarded against, and the witness is not accompanied by other witnesses. All persons interviewed should be allowed to relate their recollections without fear of contradiction or influence by other witnesses or employees. It is also important to select a neutral location in which witnesses will feel comfortable. Avoid the **"principal's office syndrome"** by selecting a location that is not likely to be intimidating to witnesses.

How to Interview

The key to getting at the facts is to put the witness at ease and to listen. Listen to what is said, how it is said, and what is not said. Ask questions that will get at the information listed earlier in this chapter, but phrase them in an **open-ended** format. For example, instead of asking, "Did you see the victim pull the red lever?" phrase your question as follows: "Tell me what you saw." Don't lead witnesses with your questions or influence them with gestures, facial expressions,

PRINCIPAL'S OFFICE SYNDROME
When an accident witness is unable to communicate freely about what they saw because he or she is intimidated or uncomfortable in the interview situation.

OPEN-ENDED
Questions that do not lead the witness to give certain answers or suggest any prejudgment of the answers.

Where to Conduct Accident Interviews

To ensure that employees are willing to give accurate information, health and safety professionals should conduct accident interviews in the privacy of their office. Right? Not necessarily. Experience has shown that the best way to promote accuracy is to interview witnesses at the site of the accident. This puts the accident interview *in context* in a setting that will help stimulate the memory. To ensure privacy and confidentiality, interview witnesses one at a time, at the accident site.

tone of voice, or any other form of nonverbal communication. Interrupt only if absolutely necessary to seek clarification on a critical point. Remain nonjudgmental and objective.

The information being sought in an accident investigation can be summarized as *who, what, when, where, why,* and *how* (Figure 19–3). As information is given, it may be necessary to take notes. If you can keep your note-taking to a minimum during the interview, your chances of getting uninhibited information are increased. Note-taking can distract and even frighten a witness.

Figure 19–3
Questions to ask when interviewing witnesses.

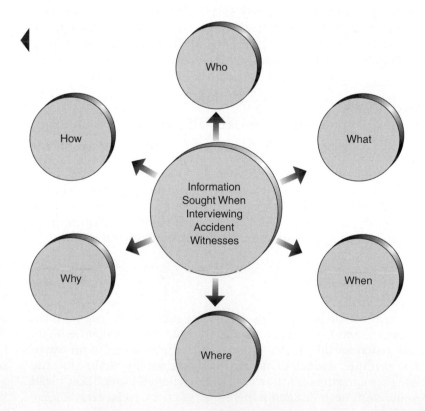

An effective technique is to listen during the interview and make mental notes of critical information. At the end of the interview, summarize what you have heard and have the witness verify your summary. After the witness leaves, develop your notes immediately.

A question that sometimes arises is, "Why not tape the interview?" Health and safety professionals disagree on the effectiveness and advisability of taping. Those who favour taping claim it allows the interviewer to concentrate on listening without having to worry about forgetting a key point or having to interrupt the witnesses to jot down critical information. It also preserves everything that is said for the record as well as the tone of voice in which it is said. A complete transcript of the interview also ensures that information is not taken out of context.

Those opposed to taping say that taping devices tend to inhibit witnesses so that they are not as forthcoming as they would be without taping. Taping also slows down the investigation while the taped interview is transcribed and the interviewer wades through voluminous testimony trying to separate critical information from irrelevant information.

In any case, if the interview is to be taped, the following rules of thumb should be applied:

- Use the smallest, most unobtrusive taping device available, such as a microcassette or digital recorder.
- Inform the witness that the interview will be taped.
- Make sure the taping device is working properly and that the tape it contains can run long enough so that you don't have to interrupt the witness to change it.
- Take time at the beginning of the interview to discuss unrelated matters long enough to put the witness at ease and overcome the presence of the taping device.
- Make sure that personnel are available to transcribe the tapes immediately.
- Read the transcripts as soon as they are available and highlight critical information.

An effective technique to use with eyewitnesses is to ask them to reenact the accident for you. Of course, the effectiveness of this technique is enhanced if the reenactment can take place at the accident site. However, even when this is not possible, an eyewitness reenactment can yield valuable information.

In using the **reenactment** technique, a word of caution is in order. If an eyewitness does exactly what the victim did, there may be another accident. Have the eyewitnesses explain what they are going to do before letting them do it. Then, have them *simulate* rather than actually perform the steps that led up to the accident.

REPORTING ACCIDENTS

An accident investigation should culminate in a comprehensive *accident report*. The purpose of the report is to record the findings of the accident investigation, the cause or causes of the accident, and recommendations for corrective action.

REENACTMENT A technique in which a witness to an accident goes through the same set of actions as the accident victim in order to demonstrate what happened to the investigator. The witness should simulate the actions rather than actually performing them or there may be another accident.

Management Is the Cause

One of the most difficult situations that a health and safety professional will face is when an investigation reveals that management — through action or inaction — is the root cause of an accident. How does the safety professional look his or her boss in the eye and say, "You are at fault"? Remember two things when facing such a situation. First, focus on the *condition* that led to the accident rather than whose action or inaction caused the condition. You want the condition corrected, and you don't want a higher manager wasting time and effort covering up. Second, be tactful. Remember, tact means "driving in the nail without breaking the board." By handling such situations in this way, you may achieve two things, both of which are good: (1) a hazardous condition will be corrected; and (2) you will win an important ally.

LOST TIME INJURY
An injury or illness due to a work-related accident or exposure to a noxious substance that results in an employee missing work and for which the employee receives compensation for lost income.

The accident report has to be submitted to the WSIB (Workplace Safety and Insurance Board of Ontario) Director within 48 hours. Where a **lost time injury** occurs, the director, committee, and trade union, if one exists, must be notified of the occurrence within four days. All injuries and illnesses should be recorded, regardless of severity, if they result in the worker seeking medical help or being unable to perform their usual work.

Accident report forms vary from company to company. However, the information contained in them is fairly standard. Regardless of the type of form used, an accident report should contain at least the information needed to meet the record-keeping requirements set forth by the local statutes.

In addition to these items, you may want to record such additional information as the list of witnesses; dates, times, and places of interviews; historical data relating to similar accidents; information about related corrective

DISCUSSION CASE

What Is Your Opinion?

"Find out who is at fault and get rid of him," demanded the CEO. "I'm not going to have a careless employee running up our health care costs. It's tough enough trying to make a profit without some careless employee causing accidents. There will be a lawsuit, just you wait and see. We are going to be sued!" Gordon Jasperton, Clark Processing Company's safety director, bit his tongue and just listened. He had learned to let his boss vent before making a counterproposal. When the time seemed right, Jasperton said, "Sir, if we focus on finding an employee to blame, it's just going to make matters worse. I'll never get to the root of it that way." Whose approach is best in this case? What is your opinion?

actions that were made previously but had not yet been followed up on; and any other information that might be relevant. Figure 19–4 is an example of a generic accident report form from the Industrial Accident Prevention Association (IAPA).

Why Some Accidents Are Not Reported

In spite of the legal requirements and the benefits of statistical data that is accumulated, there are several reasons why some accidents go unreported. Be familiar with these reasons so that you can do your part to overcome them. Cunningham and Kane list the main reasons as follows:

1. **Red tape.** Some people see the paperwork involved in accident reporting as red tape and, therefore, don't report accidents just to avoid paperwork.
2. **Ignorance.** Not all managers and supervisors are as knowledgeable as they should be about the reasons for accident reporting.
3. **Embarrassment.** Occasionally, people do not report an accident because they are embarrassed by their part in it. A supervisor who did not properly supervise or a manager who has not provided the proper training for employees may be embarrassed to file a report.
4. **Record-spoiling.** Some accidents go unreported just to preserve a safety record, such as the record for days worked without an accident.
5. **Fear of repercussions.** Some accidents go unreported because the people involved are afraid of being found at fault, being labelled accident prone, and being subjected to other negative repercussions.
6. **No feedback.** Some accidents go unreported because those involved feel filing a report is a waste of time. This typically happens when management does not respond to recommendations made in earlier accident reports.[11]

Clearly, these reasons for not reporting accidents present health and safety professionals with a challenge. To overcome these inhibitors, it is necessary to develop a simple reporting system that will not be viewed as too much bureaucratic paperwork to have to do. Health and safety professionals must educate personnel at all levels concerning the purpose of accident reporting and why it is important. An important step is to communicate the fact that fault finding is not the purpose. Another important step is to follow up to ensure that recommendations are acted on or that employees are made aware of why they aren't. This helps to ensure the integrity of the process.

Discipline and Accident Reporting

Fault finding is not the purpose of an accident investigation. However, an investigation sometimes reveals that an employee has violated or simply overlooked safety regulations. Should such violations be condoned? According to Kane and Cunningham,

> Many companies condone nonconformance to safety rules as long as no injury results. However, if the nonconformance results in an accident involving an injury, the disciplinary boom is promptly lowered. This inconsistency inevitably leads to resentment and failure to report accidents and a hiding of accident problems.[12]

Figure 19–4
Accident investigation report form.

Accident / Incident Investigation Report

Identification

Name: _____ Department: _____ Position: _____

Address: _____

Description of Accident

Date of Incident: _____ Time of incident: _____ Location of Incident: _____.

Classification of Injury: ___ Hazard Only ___No Injury ___ First Aid ___ Health Care ___ Lost Time

Type of Accident: 1. ___ Struck Against   2. ___ Struck By   3. ___ Caught In, On or Between   4. ___ Slip, Trip or Fall

5. ___ Strain / Sprain   6. ___ Exposure   7. ___ Explosion   8. ___ Other _____

Describe the Event: _____

_____

_____

_____

_____

_____

_____

Employee's Signature _____   Supervisor's Signature _____

Cause Analysis

Describe the immediate cause of the accident. E.g., what actions or conditions caused the accident?

_____

_____

_____

Describe the root cause of the accident. E.g., what personal, environmental, personal or job factors contributed to the accident?

_____

_____

_____

Corrective Action

What remedial actions are required to control the conditions listed above, and to prevent similar events from occurring?

_____

_____

_____

There is a built in dilemma here that modern health and safety professionals must be prepared to handle. On the one hand, it is important that fault finding not be seen as the purpose of an accident investigation. Such a perception limits the amount of information that can be collected. On the other hand, if those workers whose behaviour leads to accidents are not disciplined, the credibility of the safety program is undermined. Kane and Cunningham recommend the following procedures for handling this dilemma: *Never* discipline an employee because he or she had an accident. *Always* discipline employees for noncompliance with safety regulations.[13]

Such an approach applied with consistency will help maintain the integrity of both the accident investigation process and the overall safety program.

SUMMARY

1. Accidents are investigated for the purpose of identifying causal factors that could lead to other accidents if not corrected. The purpose is not to assign blame.

2. There are accident reports and accident-analysis reports. The latter attempt to determine *why* and should be completed by a professional.

3. It is important to begin an accident investigation as soon as possible after an accident occurs so that evidence and the memories of witnesses are still fresh.

4. Facts to be uncovered in an accident investigation can be summarized as *who, what, when, where, why*, and *how*.

5. Common causes of accidents fall into the following categories: personal beliefs and feelings, decision to work unsafely, mismatch or overload, systems failure, traps, unsafe conditions, and unsafe acts.

6. Who conducts the accident investigation can vary according to circumstances. However, regardless of how it is done, the health and safety professional should play an active role in the process.

7. Steps for conducting an accident investigation are as follows: (a) isolate the accident scene, (b) record all evidence, (c) photograph or videotape the accident scene, (d) identify witnesses, and (e) interview witnesses.

8. Witnesses to accidents fall into one of three categories: primary (eyewitnesses); secondary (were present at the scene, but did not see the accident); and tertiary (were not present but have information that may be relevant).

9. Interviews should take place at the accident site whenever possible. When this isn't practical, interviews should take place at a neutral location that is private and where the witness is comfortable.

10. The keys to getting at the facts in an interview are (a) put the witness at ease, (b) ask open-ended questions, and (c) listen. Interrupt only if absolutely necessary.

11. When possible, let eyewitnesses reenact the accident through simulation at the job site. Do not let them actually perform the tasks that led up to the accident.

12. The purpose of an accident report is to record the findings of the accident investigation, the cause or causes of the accident, and recommendations for corrective action.

KEY TERMS AND CONCEPTS

Accident-analysis report	Critical injury
Accident investigation	Lost time injury
Accident report	Open-ended
Accident scene	Primary witness

Principal's office syndrome   Secondary witness
Reenactment   Tertiary witness

REVIEW QUESTIONS

1. Explain the rationale for investigating accidents.

2. When should an accident be reported? Why?

3. Explain the difference between an accident report and an accident-analysis report.

4. List the categories of the most common causes of accidents.

5. What are the terms that should guide the conduct of an accident investigation?

6. What role should the health and safety professional play in the conduct of an accident investigation?

7. List and explain the steps for conducting an accident investigation.

8. Why is it important to record all pertinent evidence relating to an accident immediately after an accident has occurred?

9. List and differentiate among the three categories of witnesses to an accident.

10. Briefly explain the *when* and *where* of interviewing witnesses.

11. Briefly explain the *how* of interviewing witnesses.

12. What is the purpose of an accident report?

WEBLINKS

Canadian Auto Workers
www.caw.ca/whatwedo/health&safety/factsheet/hsfsissueno1.asp

The CAW website is not only an informative resource for union members, but also for anyone looking for information on specific health and safety topics such as accident investigation.

Canadian Centre for Occupational Health and Safety
www.ccohs.ca/oshanswers/hsprograms/investig.html

CCOHS's website is an essential resource for health and safety professionals. At this link, common questions and answers on accident investigation can be found.

Industrial Accident Prevention Association
www.iapa.ca

The Industrial Accident Prevention Association is dedicated to reducing workplace illness and injuries. The resources and services they provide can be found on this website.

ENDNOTES

1. D. Hartshorn, "Solving Accident Investigation Problems," *Occupational Hazards* 65, no. 1 (January 2003): 57.
2. Society of Manufacturing Engineers (SME), *Tool and Manufacturing Engineers Handbook* 6 (Dearborn, MI: Society of Manufacturing Engineers, 1998), 12–21.
3. Hartshorn, "Solving Problems," 57–58.
4. SME, *Tool and Manufacturing,* 12–21.
5. Ibid.
6. Ibid.
7. Canadian Centre for Occupational Health and Safety. (April 9, 1998). "OHS Answers, Accident Investigation." [Online]. Available: http://www.ccohs.ca/oshanswers/hsprograms/investig.html. (Retrieved January 23, 2005).
8. SME, *Tool and Manufacturing,* 12–21.
9. Hartshorn, "Solving Problems," 58–59.
10. National Safety Council, *Supervisor's Safety Manual* (Chicago: National Safety Council, 1991), 71.
11. J. Cunningham and A. Kane, "Accident Reporting — Part I: Key to Prevention," *Safety & Health* 139, no. 4: 70–71.
12. A. Kane and J. Cunningham, "Accident Reporting — Part II: Consistent Discipline Is Vital," *Safety & Health* 139, no. 5: 78.
13. Ibid.

20

CHAPTER

Health and Safety Promotion and Training

LEARNING OBJECTIVES

- Explain the importance of a company safety policy.
- Describe how participation in the following programs enhances safety:
  - safety committees
  - suggestion programs
  - visual awareness tools
  - incentive programs
  - competitions
- Describe the benefits of a company sponsored wellness program.
- Explain the importance of worker safety training.
- List the key features of the various safety training resources and tools available to workers and employers.
- Describe the issues to consider when training workers for whom English is a second language.
- List the different professionals that often make up the modern health and safety team.
- Describe the roles of various health and safety professionals.

One of the best ways to promote safety is to design it into the tools, machines, and technologies with which people interact in the workplace. Safety analysis can also be effective by eliminating hazards before they cause accidents and illnesses. However, even the best design or analysis cannot completely eliminate the potential for accidents. For this reason, it is important to have accident prevention procedures and make sure that employees follow them.

The purpose of safety promotion is to keep employees focused on doing their work the safe way, every day. This chapter provides prospective and practising health and safety professionals with information that will enable them to promote safety effectively.

COMPANY SAFETY POLICY

Promoting safety begins with having a published company **safety policy**. The policy should make it clear that safe work practices are expected of all employees at all levels at all times. The safety policy serves as the foundation upon which all other promotional efforts are built.

Figure 20–1 is an example of a company safety policy. This policy briefly and succinctly expresses the company's commitment to safety. It also indicates clearly that employees are expected to perform their duties with safety foremost in their minds. With such a policy in place and clearly communicated to all employees, other efforts to promote safety will have solid backing.

A company's safety policy need not be long. In fact, a short and simple policy is better. Regardless of its length or format, a safety policy should convey at least the following messages:

- The company and its top managers are committed to health and safety.
- Employees are expected to perform their duties in a safe and healthy manner.
- The company's commitment extends beyond the walls of its plant to include customers and the community.

SAFETY POLICY
A written description of an organization's commitment to maintaining a safe and healthy workplace.

Promoting Safety by Example

After a safety policy has been implemented, its credibility with employees will be determined by the example set by management, from supervisors through executives. It is critical that managers follow the company safety policy in both letter and spirit. Managers who set a poor example undermine all of the company's efforts to promote safety. The "do as I say, not as I do" approach will not work with employees today.

Mont Tremblant Springs, Inc.

2667 rue Cascades

Ste-Madeline, Québec

Safety Policy

It is the policy of this company and its top management to ensure a safe and healthy workplace for employees, a safe and healthy product for its customers, and a safe and healthy environment for the community. MTS, Inc. is committed to safety on the job and off. Employees are expected to perform their duties with this commitment in mind.

**Figure 20–1
Sample company safety policy.**

SAFETY FACT

Safety Rules and Regulations

It is not adequate for a company to rely on the Act and Regulations as the only set of rules to guide workers. The Act and Regulations provide only the legal minimum standards for the protection of workers. For an employer to exercise due diligence, the specific hazards presented in each particular workplace have to be factored into their own safety rules. Once the safety rules have been created, they must be enforced with **objectivity** and **consistency**. Objectivity means that rules are enforced without bias. Consistency means that the rules are enforced in the same manner every time with no regard to any outside factors.

OBJECTIVITY
Rules are enforced equally regardless of who commits an infraction, from the newest employee to the chief executive officer.

CONSISTENCY
The rules are enforced in the same manner every time with no regard to any outside factors.

Positive examples tend to break down most frequently under the pressure of deadlines. To meet a deadline, supervisors may encourage their team members to take shortcuts or, at least, look the other way when they do. This type of behaviour conveys the message that safety is not really important — something we talk about, but not something we believe in. The issue of setting a positive example is discussed further in the next section.

EMPLOYEE PARTICIPATION IN PROMOTING SAFETY

One of the keys to promoting safety successfully is to involve employees. They usually know better than anyone where hazards exist. In addition, they are the ones who must follow safety rules. A fundamental rule of management is *if you want employees to make a commitment, involve them from the start*. One of the most effective strategies for getting employees to commit to the safety program is to involve them in the development of it. Employees should also be involved in the implementation, monitoring, and follow-up. In all phases, employees should be empowered to take action to improve safety. The most effective safety program is one that employees view as *their* program.

The *internal responsibility system* and the *right to participate* that we employ in Canada lend themselves very well to employee empowerment. Through joint occupational health and safety committees, which are a major component of employees' right to participate, both workers and management are provided with the tools to reach agreements on safety issues, and the employee is given the power to influence the safety measures taken by the company.

Another excellent way to promote safety is to secure the cooperation of management and labour. For a company's safety program to succeed, *employee–management participation* and support is critical. Fortunately, employee–management agreement on workplace safety is commonplace.

When disagreement over a safety procedure does surface, the issue at the heart is usually money. Employees are likely to favour procedures that enhance workplace safety regardless of cost. Management, on the other hand, is likely to want to weigh the costs versus the benefits of safety improvement strategies. However, sometimes it is employees rather than managers who question safety strategies.

GAINING A PERSONAL COMMITMENT

If every employee is committed to working safely every day, workplace safety will take care of itself. But how does a company gain this type of personal commitment from its employees? One way is to have employees commit themselves to safety by signing on the bottom line, as A. Fettig describes here:

> Most safety superstars have formal safety programs — teams, committees, whatever the personal term. Many of these organizations also have signed commitments from their employees. They have their people's signatures on the dotted line indicating that they bought into the safety program. A signature on the dotted line is serious business. When our founding fathers signed the Declaration of Independence, they pledged their lives, their fortunes, and their sacred honor. How do you sell safety? One way is to get that signature on the dotted line.[1]

Fettig's approach to gaining a personal commitment from employees has merit. Ours is a society that revolves around the written signature. We sign countless documents in our lives, from credit statements to bank loans to home mortgages to college registration forms. In each of these cases, our signature is a written pledge of our commitment to meet certain responsibilities.

According to Fettig, companies gain the following three advantages from making signing on the dotted line part of their program to promote safety:

- By their signature, employees make a personal commitment.
- By their signature, employees promise to interact positively with fellow workers when they see them ignoring safety precautions.
- By their signature, employees give fellow workers permission to correct them when they ignore safety precautions.[2]

DISCUSSION CASE

What Is Your Opinion?

"I want our management team to develop a program to promote better safety practices in this company," said the CEO. "If we develop the program, it will show employees that we are committed to safety."

"I like the idea of showing executive-level commitment," said the vice president for engineering. "But the program may be more readily accepted if we involve employees in developing it."

Executive commitment and employee involvement. Which is the better approach? What is your opinion?

SUGGESTION PROGRAMS

Suggestion programs, if properly handled, promote health and safety. Well-run suggestion programs offer two advantages: (1) they solicit input from the people most likely to know where hazards exist; and (2) they involve and empower employees, which, in turn, gives them ownership of the safety program.

Suggestion programs must meet certain criteria to be effective:

- All suggestions must receive a formal response.
- All suggestions must be answered immediately.
- Management must monitor the performance of each department in generating and responding to suggestions.
- System costs and savings must be reported.
- Recognition and awards must be handled promptly.
- Good ideas must be implemented.
- Personality conflicts must be minimized.[3]

Suggestion programs that meet these criteria are more likely to be successful than those that don't. Figure 20–2 is an example of a suggestion form that may be used as part of a company's safety program. Note that all of the following must be recorded: the date that the suggestion was submitted, the date that the suggestion was logged in, and the date that the employee received a response.

This form satisfies the formal response and immediate response criteria. It also makes it easier to monitor response. Jones Petroleum Products (the company whose suggestion form we are looking at in Figure 20–2) also publishes system costs and savings in its monthly newsletter for employees, implements

**Figure 20–2
Sample safety
suggestion form.**

Jones Petroleum Products, Inc.

**5113 Crowchild Trail SW
Calgary, AB T3E 1T9**

Suggestion Form

Name of employee: _____ Date of suggestion: _____

Department: _____

Suggested improvement: _____

_____

_____

_____

Date logged in: _____ Time: _____

Logged in by: _____

Action taken: _____

_____

Current status: _____

Date of response to employee: _____

Person responding: _____

(Signature)

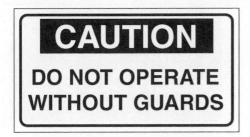

good ideas, and recognizes employees with a variety of awards ranging from certificates to cash at a monthly recognition ceremony. This company's suggestion program is an example of one that promotes not just safety, but continual improvements in quality, productivity, and competitiveness.

VISUAL AWARENESS

We tend to be a visual society. This is why television and billboards are so effective in marketing promotions. Making a health and safety message *visual* can be an effective way to get the message across. Figure 20–3 is a sign that gives machine operators a visual reminder to use the appropriate machine guards.

Such a sign is placed on or near the machine in question. If operators cannot activate their machines without first reading this sign, they will be reminded to use the safe way every time they operate the machine.

Figure 20–4 may be placed on the door leading into the hard hat area or on a stand placed prominently at the main point of entry if there is no door. Such a sign helps prevent inadvertent slip-ups when employees are in a hurry or are thinking about something else. Figures 20–5, 20–6, and 20–7 are additional examples of signs and posters that make a safety message visual.

Several rules of thumb can help ensure the effectiveness of efforts to make safety visual:

- Change signs, posters, and other visual aids periodically. Visual aids left up too long begin to blend into the background and are no longer noticed.

SAFETY FACT

Supervisor's Role in Safety

Research and experience show that the first-line supervisor plays a critical role in promoting safe and healthy work practices. The supervisor has the most frequent face-to-face contact with employees and provides the example they are most likely to follow. If supervisors are committed to safety, those who report directly to them will probably be equally committed. Therefore, time spent by health and safety professionals gaining the support, cooperation, and commitment of supervisors is time well spent.

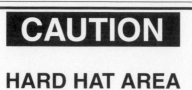

▼

Figure 20–4
Sample safety reminder sign.

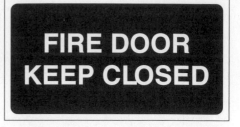

▼

Figure 20–5
Sample safety reminder sign.

CAUTION

**WEAR EYE PROTECTION
WHILE OPERATING**

▼

Figure 20–6
Sample safety reminder sign.

NOTICE
SAFETY SHOES ARE
REQUIRED
IN THIS AREA

▼

Figure 20–7
Sample safety reminder sign.

- Involve employees in developing the messages that are displayed on signs and posters. Employees are more likely to notice and heed their own messages than those of others.
- Keep visual aids simple and the messages brief.
- Make visual aids large enough to be seen easily from a reasonable distance.
- Locate visual aids for maximum effect. For example, the sign in Figure 20–3 should be located on the machine in question, preferably near the on/off switch so that the operator cannot activate the machine without seeing it.
- Use colour whenever possible to attract attention to the visual aid.

INCENTIVES

INCENTIVES
Rewards for desirable performance.

If properly used, **incentives** can help promote safety. However, the proper use of incentives is a widely misunderstood concept. Tim Puffer has this to say about the use of incentives in the modern workplace:

Most companies have no problem developing incentive programs for their sales forces. . . . But with the shift toward a service economy, a growing number of companies are becoming just as concerned with non-sales performance issues such as productivity and customer service.[4]

Safety is another issue that is being confronted using incentives. To promote safety effectively, incentives must be properly structured. Puffer recommends the following strategies for enhancing the effectiveness of incentive programs:

1. **Define objectives.** Begin by deciding what is supposed to be accomplished by the incentive program.

2. **Develop specific criteria.** On what basis will the incentives be awarded? This question should be answered during the development of the program. Specific criteria define the type of behaviour and level of performance that is to be rewarded as well as guidelines for measuring success.

3. **Make rewards meaningful.** For an incentive program to be effective, the rewards must be meaningful to the recipients. Giving an employee a reward that he or she does not value will not produce the desired results. To determine what types of rewards will be meaningful, it is necessary to involve employees.

4. **Recognize that only employees who will participate in an incentive program know what incentives will motivate them.** In addition, employees must feel it is *their* program. This means that employees should be involved in the planning, implementation, and evaluation of the incentive program.

5. **Keep communications clear.** It is important for employees to understand fully the incentive program and all of its aspects. Communicate with employees about the program, ask for continual feedback, listen to the feedback, and act on it.

6. **Reward teams.** Rewarding teams can be more effective than rewarding individuals. This is because work in the modern industrial setting is more likely to be accomplished by a team than an individual. When this is the case, other team members may resent the recognition given to an individual member. Such a situation can cause the incentive program to backfire.[5]

Effectiveness of Incentive Programs

When handled properly, incentive programs can be an effective way to promote safety in the workplace. But how effective are incentive programs? The answer to this question is: *it depends*. According to Sandy Smith, the following statistics show the effectiveness of incentive programs on workplace safety in selected circumstances:

1. Incentive programs that target individuals improve performance by 27%.

2. Incentive programs that target teams improve performance by 45%.

3. Incentive programs have an equally positive effect on both the quality and quantity of employee performance.

4. Incentive programs work best when they are structured with employee input.

5. Long-term incentives are more effective than short-term (44% improvement in performance compared with 20%, respectively).[6]

Potential Problems with Incentive Programs

Clearly, incentive programs are an excellent way to promote safety in the workplace. However, there are potential problems that, if ignored, can undermine the effectiveness of the programs. Bill Sims states these problems as follows:

Employee taxes. Taxes must be paid on incentives provided to employees. This means either the employer pays or the employee will be stuck with an added tax bill. In either case, taxes increase the cost of cash incentives to employers and decrease the net amount for employees.

Injury hiding. Incentive programs that are based on statistics can undermine the real effectiveness of the safety program as opposed to the apparent effectiveness. When departments and units hide (fail to report) injuries to win incentive rewards, the integrity of the safety program is at risk. OSHA frowns on statistics-based programs because the agency thinks they cause organizations to cheat on reporting requirements.

Unfair programs. Programs that award incentives based on yearly or quarterly improvements can undermine employee morale and support of the safety program when an accident occurs the day before the end of the period. Employees can maintain a safe working record for 364 days only to lose out on incentives when an accident occurs on day 365. It is better to base incentives on daily observation of safe behaviour and work practices.

Insufficient budget. Companies typically budget too little for safety incentives. A realistic budget would be in the range of $100 per employee per year. Less will have insufficient impact to be worth the time and effort an incentive program requires.[7]

Employer Incentive Programs

EXPERIENCE RATING
The recent safety performance of the company is reflected in the premiums charged.

Most workers' compensation boards in Canada offer some form of reduced premium for those employers who keep accident rates and their associated cost low. Commonly referred to as **experience rating**, these programs that reward good safety performance are one very effective tool used by these agencies to increase workplace safety. Ontario's Workplace Safety and Insurance Board offers various incentives to large and small employers to reduce accidents, increase worker awareness, and expedite injured workers' return to work.

COMPETITION

Competition is another strategy that can be used to promote safety. However, if this approach is not used wisely, it can backfire and do more harm than good. To a degree, most people are competitive. A child's competitive instinct is nurtured through play and reinforced by sports and school activities. Health and safety professionals can use the adult's competitive instinct when trying to motivate employees, but competition on the job should be carefully organized, closely monitored, and strictly controlled. Competition that is allowed to get out of hand can lead to cheating and hard feelings among co-workers.

Competition can be organized between teams, shifts, divisions, or even plants. Here are some tips that will help health and safety professionals use competition in a positive way while ensuring that it does not get out of hand:

- Involve the employees who will compete in planning programs of competition.
- Where possible, encourage competition among groups rather than individuals, while simultaneously promoting individual initiative within groups.
- Make sure that the competition is fair by ensuring that the resources available to competing teams are equitably distributed and that human talent is as appropriately spread among the teams as possible.

The main problem with using competition to promote safety is that it can induce competing teams to cover up or fail to report accidents just to win. Health and safety professionals should be particularly attentive to this situation and watch carefully for evidence that accidents are going unreported. If this occurs, the best approach is to confront the situation openly and frankly. Employees should be reminded that improved safety is the first priority and winning the competition is second. Failing to report an accident should be grounds for eliminating a team from competition.

WELLNESS PROGRAMS

Faced with mounting health care and workers' compensation costs, some employers are looking for innovative ways to keep their workers safe and healthy. One innovation that is gaining in popularity as a way to promote health and safety is the wellness program. A **wellness program** is any program designed to help and encourage employees to adopt a healthier lifestyle. These programs, which are sponsored by companies and various government agencies, benefit all parties by reducing the number of accidents, their severity, and associated cost and suffering.

A typical wellness program includes diet and exercise under the supervision of an appropriately qualified professional; stress management activities; and special activities designed to help high-risk employees overcome such lifestyle-related behaviours as smoking and overeating.

Company sponsored wellness programs often have some very beneficial outcomes, as pointed out by Dianne Dyck in a *Benefits Canada* magazine article:

- Canada Life, based in Toronto, developed a health promotion program in 1978 which was independently evaluated over a 10-year period. The program showed a return of $6.85 on each corporate dollar invested based on reduced employee turnover, greater productivity and decreased medical claims by participating employees.
- A review of worldwide wellness studies by Dr. Ray Shephard for the Canadian government found that workplace wellness programs have a return on investment of between $1.95 to $3.75 per employee, per dollar spent.
- A 1997 Labour Canada study showed that employees who smoke cost companies between $2308 to $2613 more per year than non-smoking employees. This is due to increased absenteeism, lost productivity, and increased health and life insurance premiums.

WELLNESS PROGRAM
Any program designed to help and encourage employees to adopt a healthier lifestyle.

- According to a Government of Ontario report called "The High Cost of a Sedentary Lifestyle," up to half of the burden of medical costs could be prevented by changes in personal lifestyle. Physical activity, in particular, has the potential to reduce both acute and chronic demands on the healthcare system, with a reduction in employee turnover and absence, an increase in productivity, a reduction in absenteeism and a decreased risk of industrial injury.[8]

SAFETY TRAINING

One of the best ways to promote safety in the workplace is to provide all employees with ongoing safety training. Initial safety training should be part of the orientation process for new employees. Subsequent safety training should be aimed at developing new, more specific, and more in-depth knowledge and at renewing and updating existing knowledge. Training serves a dual purpose in the promotion of safety. First, it ensures that employees know how to work safely and why doing so is important. Second, it shows that management is committed to safety.

Education and training have been recognized as important components of organized safety programs for many years. In today's rapidly changing high-tech workplace, they are more important than ever. Modern health and safety professionals have a key role to play in ensuring that all employees at all levels receive the appropriate types and amounts of training. They must also be prepared to play an active role in preparing, presenting, arranging for the application of, and evaluating health and safety training.

RATIONALE FOR HEALTH AND SAFETY TRAINING

Consider the following example. The management team at Will-Burt Company, a steel fabrication and parts manufacturer, was in financial trouble. According to Gregg LaBar,

> Low profits, too many product defects, and steep workers' compensation and medical costs were hurting the company. That's when new President and Chief Executive Officer Harry E. Featherstone stepped up and instituted an employee training and education program. . . . Naturally employees get their share of safety training, including lift truck operation, hazard communication, hearing protection, and lockout/tagout, as part of Will-Burt's overall commitment to education.[9]

The employee training program, including the safety components, helped turn Will-Burt's fortunes around. Today, the company is prosperous and competitive. In the words of Jack Bednarowski, director of human resources for Will-Burt, "Our overall attitude toward education, including safety training, is that we can't afford not to do it."[10]

Legal and Ethical Reasons for Training

The Occupational Health and Safety Act, for each jurisdiction, mandates that employers provide health and safety training to its workers. Although the various statutes throughout Canada present these training requirements in different formats, the general requirements include the following:

- Workers must be informed of any hazards in the workplace.
- Workers must be trained in the proper use of any safety devices used on the job.
- Workers must be trained in the safe handling of any "controlled products" used on the job through the WHMIS program.

In Ontario, where joint health and safety committees are required in workplaces that regularly employ 20 or more employees, certification training is mandatory. At least two members of the committee, one representing the workers and the other representing the employer, require certification training. This training teaches the members about health and safety law, and the identification, assessment, and control of hazards. Part one of the training provides overall knowledge of health and safety while part two focuses on hazards specific to the member's workplace.[11]

Beyond the legal reasons for providing health and safety training, there are also ethical reasons. No amount of legislation can properly regulate every hazardous substance or every potentially hazardous situation. Chemicals and technologies are developed and put in place much more rapidly than is legislation. Clearly, the only way to guarantee that employees are well informed about the health and safety aspects of their jobs is for companies to fulfill their moral obligations along these lines. According to Spencer and Simonowitz,

> If the sick person has rights to information and determination regarding his or her body, should the well, healthy employee or working person have any less right to the same consideration when there are health implications of exposure on the job? If the sick person is entitled to know about procedures and prognosis, discomforts and inconveniences, risk, and experience of proposed treatment, surely working persons should have similar rights to information about the nature and toxicity of the substances with which they work, controls and their effectiveness, personal discomforts and inconvenience of both hazards and controls, morbidity and mortality data, and the relative risk.[12]

DISCUSSION CASE

What Is Your Opinion?

"I don't need my employees wasting any more time in training," said the production supervisor. "I need them on the production line operating their machines."

The safety director, who had heard this argument many times before, countered, "They won't be able to operate their machines from a hospital bed, and if they don't complete their safety training, the hospital is probably their next stop!"

Both of these managers are interested in the same thing — productivity. The production supervisor is interested in his unit's productivity today. The safety director is interested in the unit's long-term productivity. Who is right in this argument? What is your opinion?

HEALTH AND SAFETY TRAINING RESOURCES

The safety practitioner should be aware of the numerous health and safety resources that are available for workers and employers. Regardless of the size or type of business being conducted, training is available through private trainers, industry associations, and various government agencies. The internet offers thousands of helpful sites, ranging from free information to complete online courses. Some of these useful resource websites are listed at the end of this chapter.

Supervisors

Supervisors play a key role in the maintenance of a safe and healthy workplace. Consequently, health and safety professionals need to ensure that supervisors have had the training they need to be positive participants in the process. A *Safety & Health* survey revealed that only 53% of the companies responding provide health and safety training for their supervisors.[13] This is an unfortunate statistic because supervisors are the health and safety professional's link with employees. In the words of Peter Minetos, "Supervisors . . . are the ones who have to teach employees the safe way to conduct their jobs. With proper training, they can spot and eliminate risks that are waiting to create havoc for their workers."[14]

Orientation

Perhaps the most important aspect of safety training is orientation for new and transferred employees. Consider the following quote from *Today's Supervisor*:

> The confusion and stress that accompany the first day of any job are often the reasons that new employees are more than twice as likely to have accidents as experienced workers. A lack of experience, a strong desire to please and a hesitation to ask for help all cause one in eight new employees to be involved in some type of accident the first year on the job. The first month is the most critical.[15]

The early training provided for new and transferred employees should have at least the following components: orientation, job-specific procedures, and follow-up. These components are discussed in the following paragraphs.

Orientation is critical. Too often, companies hand over new employees to an experienced employee who is supposed to "show them the ropes." This is a dangerous practice that can have the effect of minimizing, rather than emphasizing, the importance of safety. Orientation should be structured, and it should involve the new worker's supervisor as well as other personnel as appropriate. A good orientation program should teach the following at a minimum:

- Management is sincerely interested in preventing accidents.
- Accidents may occur, but it is possible to prevent them.
- Safeguarding equipment and the workplace has been done, and management is willing to go further as needs and methods are discovered.
- Each employee is expected to report to the supervisor any unsafe conditions encountered at work.
- The supervisor will give job instructions. No employee is expected to undertake a job before learning how to do it and being authorized to do it by a supervisor.

- The employee should contact the supervisor for guidance before undertaking a job that appears to be unsafe.
- If an employee suffers an injury, even a slight one, it must be reported at once.

In addition to these points, any safety rules that are a condition of employment, such as wearing eye protection or safety hats, should be understood and enforced from the first day of employment.[16]

ENGLISH AS A SECOND LANGUAGE TRAINING ISSUES

To enjoy the gains that come with a safe and healthy workplace, organizations that have employees who either speak only limited English or for whom English is a second language must take steps to accommodate their special needs in terms of both training and cultural perspectives. There is little question that a language barrier can magnify the potential for accidents and injuries in the workplace. In addition to increasing the likelihood of accidents, language problems can also result in lower productivity and higher turnover.[17]

Modifying Training Methods

Traditional training methods — videos, lectures, handouts, and other *classroom*-oriented methods — will not work well with employees who do not speak English as their principal language. *Hands-on* training that requires more doing and less listening, reading, and writing is the better approach with limited-English-speaking audiences. In other words, when working with a diverse group of employees in which language might be a barrier, don't use training methods that rely heavily on understanding the language. Instead of *telling* employees how to work safely, *show* them. Set up demonstrations that replicate the actual situation in question and let employees do what they are supposed to do on the job rather than just watching a video of someone else doing it.

SAFETY FACT

Safety Training Is a Must

Too many business executives take the MBA (management by accounting) approach to their jobs. They will accept only dollars on the bottom line as proof of the value of an activity or function. Although the value of training *can* be shown in dollars and cents, the ubiquitous MBA mentality that persists in business and industry is hard to understand, and even harder to overcome.

   The same executives who question the value of safety training have no problem understanding that professional football teams train all week to play just one game. Military units train constantly for the eventuality of a deployment. Training is fundamental to most professions and occupations. It should be fundamental to all.

According to Halcarz, the best way to overcome language, culture, and literacy barriers is to provide safety training programs that have the following attributes:

1. Bilingual training materials that address cultural issues.
2. Training materials that recognize the dignity of all employees regardless of their background.
3. Training materials that minimize literacy requirements.[18]

Considering Cultural Concerns

We tend to think of cultural issues in terms of language and national origin, and many of them are. However, even people who speak the same language and come from the same country can have cultural differences. An employee's attitude toward reporting an injury can have cultural implications. For example, an employee from one culture might be quick to report an injury, whereas an employee from another culture might see filing a report as making trouble or showing weakness.

An effective way to identify the various cultural barriers that might have a negative effect on an employee's ability to fully grasp the training provided is to arrange facilitated brainstorming sessions. In these sessions, a third-party facilitator helps employees discuss freely, openly, and without attribution any concerns they might have about the training they need and any barriers that might inhibit their progress in completing the training. A third-party facilitator, especially one who speaks the principal language of the employees in question, is more likely to bring out employee concerns than can their supervisor or manager.

THE ROLE OF MODERN HEALTH AND SAFETY PROFESSIONALS

It would be unreasonable to expect one person to be an expert in all of the many complex and diverse issues faced in the modern workplace. For this reason, the management and promotion of health and safety in the age of high technology has become a team sport. Figure 20–8 illustrates the types of positions that may comprise a health and safety team. The various members of the team are discussed below.

Safety Manager

The job of the health and safety manager is complex and diverse. Figure 20–9 is an example of a job description for such a position. The description attests to the diverse nature of the job. Duties range from hazard analysis to accident reporting to standards and compliance to record keeping to training to emergency planning and so on.

Engineers

Engineers can make a significant contribution to safety. Correspondingly, they can cause, inadvertently or through incompetence, accidents that result in seri-

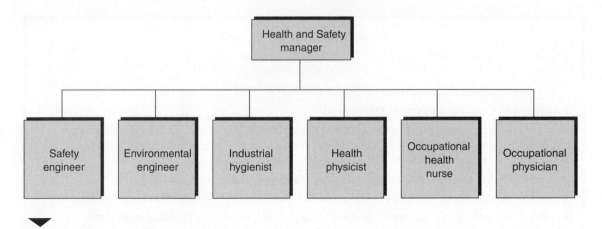

Figure 20–8
A modern health and safety team.

ous injury and property damage. The engineer has more potential to affect safety in the workplace than does any other person.

The engineer's greatest opportunity for both good and bad comes during the design process. The process is basically the same regardless of whether the product being designed is a small toy, an industrial machine, an automobile, a nuclear power plant, a ship, a jumbo jetliner, or a space vehicle. Health and safety professionals should be familiar with the design process so that they can more fully understand the role of engineers in regard to workplace safety.

Not all engineers are design engineers. Other engineers who would have a broad knowledge of their fields and may be useful on a health and safety committee are safety and environmental engineers.

Industrial Hygienists

Industrial hygienists are highly trained professionals dedicated to the health, well being, and productivity of the worker and the community, through anticipation, recognition, evaluation, and control of occupational and environmental hazards. The Certified Industrial Hygienist (CIH) is certified by an internationally respected organization, the ABIH (American Board of Industrial Hygienists). This certification is an important means for identifying the professional with the right credentials to solve your occupational and environmental health problems.[19]

Health Physicists

Health physicists are concerned primarily with radiation in the workplace. Consequently, they are employed by companies that generate or use nuclear power. Their primary duties include the following: monitoring radiation inside and outside the facility, measuring the radioactivity levels of biological samples, developing the radiation components of the company's emergency

---

POULTRY PROCESSING, INC.
2306 Industrial Avenue
Toronto, ON   M4W 1L5
Vacancy Announcement

Position Title: Health and Safety Manager

Position Description: The Health and Safety Manager for PPI is responsible for establishing, implementing, and managing the company's overall health and safety program. The position reports to the local plant manager. Specific duties include the following:

- Establish and maintain a comprehensive companywide health and safety program.
- Assess and analyze all departments, processes, and materials for potential hazards.
- Work with appropriate personnel to develop, implement, monitor, and evaluate accident prevention and hazard control strategies.
- Ensure companywide compliance with all applicable laws, standards, and codes.
- Coordinate the activities of all members of the company's health and safety program.
- Plan, implement, and broker, as appropriate, health and safety–related training.
- Maintain all required health and safety–related records and reports.
- Conduct accident investigations as necessary.
- Develop and maintain a companywide emergency action plan (EAP).
- Establish and maintain an ongoing safety promotion effort.
- Analyze the company's products from the perspectives of safety, health, and liability.

Qualifications Required: The following qualifications have been established by the PPI management team with input from all levels and all departments.

- *Minimum Education.* Applicants must have at least a one-year community college certificate or an associate of science or applied science degree in industrial safety or a closely related degree (A.S. holders will begin work at a salary 15 percent higher than a certificate graduate).
- *Preferred Education.* Applicants with a baccalaureate degree in any of the following major fields of study will be given first priority: industrial health and safety, industrial technology, industrial management, manufacturing technology, engineering technology, and related. Degree programs in these fields must include at least one three-semester or five-quarter-hour course in industrial or occupational health and safety.

Figure 20–9
Health and safety manager job description.

action plan, and supervising the decontamination of workers and the workplace when necessary.

Nuclear engineering and nuclear physics are the two most widely pursued fields of study for health physicists.

Occupational Health Nurses

Occupational health nurses have long been important members of corporate health and safety programs. According to the American Association of Occupational Health Nurses,

Occupational health nursing is the application of nursing principles in conserving the health of workers in all occupations. It involves prevention, recognition, and treatment of illness and injury, and requires special skills and knowledge in the areas of health education and counselling, environmental health, rehabilitation, and human relations.[20]

Like occupational physicians, today's occupational health nurses have seen their profession evolve over the years. The shift in emphasis is away from after-the-fact treatment to prevention-related activities such as analysis, monitoring, counselling, and education.

Occupational Physician

Occupational medicine as a specialized field dates back to World War II, when production of manufactured goods skyrocketed, and workplace-related medical needs followed suit.

Occupational physicians are fully degreed and licensed medical doctors. In addition they must have completed postgraduate work in the following areas of safety:

biostatistics and epidemiology, industrial toxicology, work physiology, radiation (ionizing and nonionizing), noise and hearing conservation, effects of certain environmental conditions such as high altitude and high pressures (hyperbaric and hypobaric factors), principles of occupational safety, fundamentals of industrial hygiene, occupational aspects of dermatology, psychiatric and psychological factors, occupational respiratory diseases, biological monitoring, ergonomics, basic personnel management functions, record and data collection, governmental regulations, general environmental health (air, water, ground pollution, and waste management control).[21]

Bernardino Ramazzini is widely thought of as being the first occupational physician. This reputation is primarily the result of his study of the work-related problems of workers in Modena, Italy, and a subsequent book he authored titled *The Diseases of Workers* (1700).[22]

Ergonomists

Ergonomists are an important element of the safety team. Ergonomics is the study of the relationship between humans and their interaction with the work environment and its objects. The role of ergonomists is to apply their broad knowledge to the workplace to ensure that the machines, tools, facilities, and environment are efficient, comfortable, and safe for the worker.

Certification of Health and Safety Professionals

Professional certification is an excellent way to establish credentials in the health and safety profession. Some of the most widely pursued Canadian accreditations are

- Certified Registered Safety Professional
- Certified Industrial Hygienist
- Canadian Certified Professional Ergonomist
- Certified Occupational Health Nurse

Professional Associations

Professional associations benefit both the members and the public by ensuring that their members have obtained the professional standard required by the association. Although membership in some associations is voluntary, it is a required credential for employment in many workplaces. Information on some Canadian safety related associations may be found at the following websites:

American Industrial Hygiene Association, BC and Yukon Section
www3.telus.net/aiha/

Association for Canadian Registered Safety Professionals
www.acrsp.ca/

Association of Canadian Ergonomists
www.ace-ergocanada.ca/

Canadian Association of Occupational Therapists
www.caot.ca

Canadian Occupational Health Nurses Association
www.cohna-aciist.ca/

Canadian Registration Board of Occupational Hygienists
www.crboh.ca

Canadian Society of Safety Engineering (CSSE)
www.csse.org

Electrical & Utilities Safety Association
www.eusa.on.ca

Health Canada's Health Information Network
www.hc-sc.gc.ca

Ontario Occupational Health Nurses Association
www.oohna.on.ca

SUMMARY

1. A company's safety policy should convey the following messages: (a) a companywide commitment; (b) the expectation that employees will perform their duties in a safe manner; and (c) the inclusion of customers and the community in the company's safety commitment.

2. From a legal perspective, an employer's obligations regarding safety rules can be summarized as follows: (a) employers must have rules that ensure a safe and healthy workplace; (b) employers must ensure that all employees are knowledgeable about the rules; and (c) employers must ensure that safety rules are enforced objectively and consistently.

3. A fundamental rule of management is: If you want employees to make a commitment, involve them from the start. This is especially important when formulating safety rules.

4. Safety training should be a fundamental part of any effort to promote safety. Safety training ensures that employees know how to work safely. In addition, it shows that management is committed to safety.

5. Well-run suggestion programs promote safety by (a) soliciting input from the people who are most likely to know where hazards exist; and (b) involving employees in a way that lets them feel ownership in the safety program.

6. Safety committees can help promote safety if they are properly structured. The composition of the committee can be a major factor in the committee's success. The most effective committees are composed of a broad cross-section of workers representing all departments.

7. Employee–management agreement is important in promoting safety. Fortunately, safety is an issue on which employees and management can usually agree.

8. Incentives can promote safety if they are properly applied. To enhance the effectiveness of incentives, the following steps should be followed: (a) define objectives, (b) lead by example, (c) develop specific criteria, (d) make rewards meaningful, (e) keep communications clear, (f) involve employees in planning the incentives, and (g) reward teams. However, cash incentives can create tax problems, and poorly designed incentives can lead to injury hiding, unfair circumstances, and morale problems.

9. Competition can promote safety, but it can also get out of hand and do more harm than good. To keep competition positive, involve employees in planning programs of competition and encourage competition between teams rather than individuals.

10. Employers may have to apply specific solutions to address various ethnic or cultural differences in today's mobile labour market.

11. Modern health and safety teams may consist of a safety manager, engineers, industrial hygienists, health physicists, occupational health nurses, an occupational physician, and ergonomists.

KEY TERMS AND CONCEPTS

Consistency	Objectivity
Experience rating	Safety policy
Incentives	Wellness program

REVIEW QUESTIONS

1. What messages should a company's safety policy convey?

2. Explain why promoting safety by example is so important.

3. What are the employer's obligations regarding safety rules and regulations?

4. Explain the concept of due diligence as it relates to a company's safety.

5. What is the significance of objectivity and consistency when enforcing safety rules?

6. Why is employee participation and involvement so critical in the promotion of safety?

7. List three benefits that companies gain from asking employees to sign a declaration of safety.

8. What are the steps for ensuring that incentives actually promote safety?

9. What problems can be caused by poorly designed incentives?

10. Explain briefly the rationale for providing safety training.

11. What legal obligations does an employer have to provide health and safety training?

12. What moral obligations does an employer have to provide health and safety training?

13. Explain how an employer can accommodate the training needs of workers with limited English-speaking ability.

14 Describe the roles of various professionals on a modern health and safety team.

WEBLINKS

Canada's National Occupational Health and Safety Web Site
www.canoshweb.org

This website has links to health and safety agencies and resources from all Canadian jurisdictions.

Canadian Centre for Occupational Health and Safety (CCOHS)
www.ccohs.ca

An essential health and safety resource for Canadians.

Institute for Work and Health (IWH)
www.iwh.on.ca

The Institute for Work and Health provides information and conducts scientific research on the cause, cure, and prevention of soft tissue injuries.

Listed below are the names and websites of the provincial and territorial agencies that enforce occupational health and safety legislation. Health and safety practitioners and the public can benefit from the information available from each jurisdiction:

WorkSafe BC, Workers' Compensation Board of BC
www.worksafebc.com

Alberta Human Resources and Employment
www3.gov.ab.ca/hre/whs/index.asp

Saskatchewan Labour
www.labour.gov.sk.ca/safety/

Manitoba Labour and Immigration, Workplace Health and Safety Division
www.gov.mb.ca/labour/safety/index.html

Workplace Safety and Insurance Board / Ontario
www.wsib.on.ca

Commission de la santé et de la sécurité du travail / Quebec
www.csst.qc.ca/portail/fr/

Workplace Health, Safety and Compensation Commission of New Brunswick
www.whscc.nb.ca

Department of Environment and Labour / Nova Scotia
www.gov.ns.ca/enla

Workers Compensation Board of Prince Edward Island
www.wcb.pe.ca

Workplace Health, Safety and Compensation Commission of Newfoundland and Labrador
www.whscc.nf.ca

Yukon Workers' Compensation Health and Safety Board
www.wcb.yk.ca

Workers' Compensation Board, Northwest Territories and Nunavut
www.wcb.nt.ca

ENDNOTES

1. A. Fettig, "Sign Up for Safety," *Safety & Health* 144, no. 1: 26.
2. Ibid.
3. B. McDermott, "Employees Are Best Source of Ideas for Constant Improvement," *Total Quality Newsletter* 1, no. 4: 5.
4. T. Puffer, "Eight Ways to Construct Effective Service Reward Systems," *Reward &Recognition Supplement, Training* (August 1990): 8–12.
5. Ibid.
6. S. Smith, "Safety Incentives: It's Not Just a Breakfast Anymore," *Occupational Hazards* 64, no. 6 (June 2002): 58.
7. B. Smith, as quoted in Smith, "Safety Incentives," 58.
8. Dianne Dyck. (January 1999). "The Wellness Package." *Benefits Canada Magazine*. [Online]. Available: http://www.benefitscanada.com/content/legacy/Content/1999/01-99/ben46.html. (Retrieved November 15, 2004).

9. G. LaBar, "Worker Training: An Investment in Safety," *Occupational Hazards* (August 1991): 25.

10. Ibid.

11. Workplace Safety and Insurance Board of Ontario. (October 21, 2004). "Incentive and Training Programs." [Online]. Available: http://www.wsib.on.ca/wsib/wsibsite.nsf/public/CertificationTraining. (Retrieved November 15, 2004).

12. J. A. Spencer and J. A. Simonowitz, "Employee Education," in *Introduction to Occupational Health and Safety,* ed., Joseph LaDon (Chicago: National Safety Council, 1986), 277–278.

13. P. Minetos, "Supervisors: Teach Them Well," *Safety & Health* 140, no. 4: 64.

14. Ibid.

15. K. Knowles, ed., "Start Safety Training Early," *Today's Supervisor* 55, no. 7: 4.

16. National Safety Council, *Accident Prevention Manual for Industrial Operations: Administration and Programs,* 9th ed. (Chicago: National Safety Council, 1988), 199.

17. Joseph E. Halcarz, "Safety Training for Diverse Worker Population," *Occupational Hazards* 65, no. 2 (February 2003): 26–28.

18. Ibid., 28.

19. American Industrial Hygiene Association. (2005). [Online]. Available: http://www.aiha.org/TheAcademy/html/cihbrochure.htm. (Retrieved February 8, 2005).

20. American Association of Occupational Health Nurses (AAOHN), *A Guide for Establishing an Occupational Health Nursing Service* (New York: AAOHN, 1977), 78.

21. C. Zenz, "The Occupational Physician," in *Fundamentals of Industrial Hygiene* (Chicago: National Safety Council, 1988), 607.

22. National Safety Council, "Occupational Physicians: What Is Their New Role?", *Safety & Health* 141, no. 4 (April 1990): 37.

Safety Management in a Global Marketplace

LEARNING OBJECTIVES

- Explain the effect of global competition on health and safety in the workplace.
- Define the terms *competitiveness*, *productivity*, and *value added*.
- List the common characteristics of the most competitive companies.
- Explain the relationship between productivity and quality as it relates to competitiveness.
- Define QM and TSM.
- Explain the rationale for QM and TSM.
- Explain how environmental concerns are changing the role of health and safety professionals?
- Describe the purpose of environmental management systems.
- List five potential benefits of an EMS.
- Describe the purpose of ISO 14000 standards.

One of the most frequently heard terms in the language of modern business and industry is **competitiveness**. To survive and prosper in today's global marketplace, industrial companies must be competitive. Companies that used to compete only with neighbouring firms now find themselves competing against companies from the United States, Japan, Germany, Taiwan, Korea, France, Great Britain, China, and many other countries throughout the world.

COMPETITIVENESS
The ability to succeed and prosper consistently in the marketplace whether it is local, regional, national, or global.

GLOBAL COMPETITION

The global marketplace is intensely competitive. It is like a sports contest that never ends. You may win today, but the race begins again tomorrow. Competing in the global marketplace has been described as the equivalent of running in a race that has no finish line.

The need to achieve peak performance levels day after day puts intense pressure on companies, and pressure runs downhill. This means that all employees from executive-level managers to workers on the shop floor feel it. It is not uncommon for this pressure to create a harried atmosphere that can increase the likelihood of accidents. It can also lead to shortcuts that increase the potential for health hazards (e.g., improper storage, handling, and use of hazardous materials).

This is unfortunate because the most competitive companies typically are also the safest and healthiest. It is critical that health and safety professionals understand the positive relationship between health and safety and competitiveness. Global competition is enhanced if companies meet established international standards for business management and environmental protection. It is also extremely important that they be able to articulate that connection effectively.

Competitiveness Defined

The Institute for Corporate Competitiveness defines *competitiveness* as "the ability to consistently succeed and prosper in the marketplace whether it is local, regional, national, or global."[1] The most competitive companies are those that do the following: (1) consistently outperform their competitors in the key areas of quality, productivity, response time, service, cost, and corporate image (Figure 21–1); and (2) continually improve all of these areas. The two key concepts associated with competitiveness are peak performance and continual improvement.

Competing in the **global marketplace** is difficult to do but easy to understand. One need only think of Olympic athletes to gain a perspective on the concept. Olympic athletes train continually to improve their performance to world-class levels. Their goal is to improve continually in practice so that they can achieve peak performance levels in competition. Those who do this consistently win.

Of the various factors influencing a company's competitiveness, the two most important are productivity and quality. The other factors are, to a large extent, functions of these two. Therefore, health and safety managers should be knowledgeable about these two concepts and be able to discuss them on an equal footing with production managers, supervisors, and representatives of higher management.

GLOBAL MARKETPLACE
The worldwide economic market in which many companies must compete for business.

Productivity and Competitiveness

Productivity is the concept of comparing output of goods or services to the input of resources needed to produce or deliver them. Productivity is typically expressed as the ratio of output to input in the following manner:

$$\text{Output/Input} = \text{Productivity}$$

To fully understand productivity, it is necessary to understand the concept of value added. Converting raw materials into useable products adds value to the materials. **Value added** is the difference between what it costs to produce a product and what it costs to purchase it (Figure 21–2). This difference represents the value that has been added to the product by the production process. Value added is increased when productivity is increased.

In Figure 21–2, Company A and Company B manufacture the same product. Each is able to sell their product for $1300. However, Company B can manufacture the product for $400 because it is more productive than Company A,

PRODUCTIVITY
The concept of comparing output of goods or services to the input of resources needed to produce or deliver them.

VALUE ADDED
The difference between what it costs to produce a product and the value the marketplace puts on it.

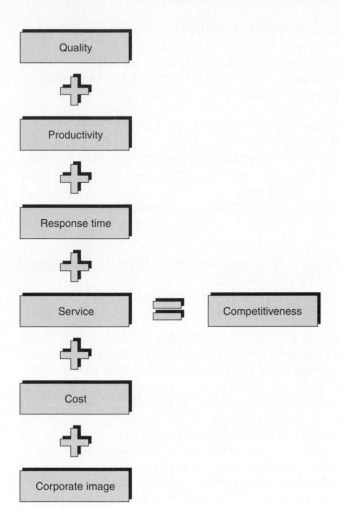

▶ **Figure 21–1**
Key areas that result in competitiveness.

▶ **Figure 21–2**
The value-added concept.

which produces the same product at a cost of $700. The productivity difference gives Company B at least two competitive advantages: (1) It can lower its price for the product below that of Company A and still make a profit; and (2) its greater profit margin gives Company B more capital to reinvest in upgrading its facilities, equipment, and personnel, which will, in turn, improve its competitiveness even more.

This productivity difference is important because all competing companies that produce a given product probably pay approximately the same for the raw materials. Consequently, the winner most likely is the one that adds the most value to the materials, which means the one that is the most productive (produces the most output with the least input).

Following are some rules of thumb that production managers use to monitor productivity in their plants. Health and safety managers should be familiar with these rules.

- Productivity is declining when (1) output declines and input is constant; or (2) output is constant but input increases.
- Productivity is improving when (1) output is constant but input decreases; or (2) output increases and input is constant.

In considering the concept of productivity, remember that it represents only half of the equation. Nothing has been gained if productivity is improved to the detriment of quality. When productivity is improved, quality must also improve or at least remain constant.

In the community of industrialized nations, Canada has historically been among the most productive. The perception that Canadian productivity in the industrial sector has declined steadily since World War II, actually, is not true. The problem is that productivity in other industrialized countries, particularly Japan, increased even more during this same period (Figure 21–3).

Pressure to increase productivity often results in actions that are detrimental to the health and safety of workers. In their rush to meet deadlines or quotas, workers may disassemble safeguards, stop taking the time to use appropriate personal protective gear, ignore safety rules, neglect equipment maintenance duties, improperly handle or store toxic substances, and take chances that they wouldn't take under normal conditions.

Such efforts occasionally result in short-term productivity improvements, but they invariably do more harm than good in the long run. The inevitable result is that productivity ultimately suffers, and the company finds that it won a battle only to lose the war.

Quality and Competitiveness

Quality goes hand in hand with productivity in the competitiveness equation. Today's production company must have both. Quality without productivity results in costs that are too high to be competitive. Productivity without quality results in a shabby product that quickly tarnishes the corporate image.

QUALITY
A measure of the extent to which a product or service meets or exceeds customer expectations.

Quality is a measure of the extent to which a product or service meets or exceeds customer expectations. According to Peters, it is important to define quality in terms of customer expectations.[2]

Whereas the pressure to increase productivity can be detrimental to health and safety, the pressure to improve quality generally supports health and safety.

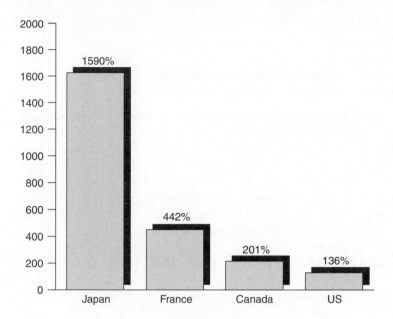

▶ Figure 21–3
Increases in output per hour of workers (1950–2003).

In the next section, prospective and practising health and safety professionals will see how to use productivity and quality to gain a commitment to health and safety or to increase a commitment that already exists.

HOW SAFETY AND HEALTH CAN IMPROVE COMPETITIVENESS

When the pressures of competing become intense, it is not uncommon for health and safety to be given a lower priority. Not only is this wrong from an ethical standpoint, it is also wrong from the perspective of competitiveness and profitability. In the days when a worker's most important qualifications were physical strength and stamina, there were always plenty of applicants in the labour pool. If a worker was injured, several equally qualified applicants were waiting to replace him or her.

However, with the dawning of the age of high technology and the advent of global competition, this situation changed. Mental ability became more important than physical ability; suddenly, the number of qualified applicants got smaller. In fact, whereas the workplace is becoming increasingly technical and complex, the literacy level of the labour pool is actually declining. While Goetsch refers to the US marketplace, consider the implications of the following statement for Canadian global competitiveness:

> The basic skills necessary to be productive in a modern industrial setting are increasing steadily. At the same time the national high school dropout rate continues to increase as does the number of high school graduates who are functionally illiterate in spite of their diploma. This means that while the number of high-skilled jobs in modern industry is increasing, the number of people able to fill them is on the decline. The impact this will have on industry in the United States can be summarized as follows:

1. Difficulty in filling high-skill jobs.
2. Lower levels of productivity and, as a result, a lower level of competitiveness.
3. Higher levels of waste.
4. Higher potential for damage to sophisticated technological systems.
5. Greater numbers of dissatisfied employees in the workplace.[3]

The illiteracy problem, coupled with rapid and continual technological change, has serious implications for global competitiveness. Modern industrial companies are like modern sports teams. To compete, they must recruit, employ, and develop the best possible personnel. Having done so, they must keep them safe and healthy to derive the benefits of their talents. Talented people working in a safe and healthy environment will be more competitive than equally talented people who are constantly distracted by concerns for their health and safety. In addition, the most talented employees cannot help a company compete if they are slowed by injuries.

The aging workforce also has serious implications for global competitiveness. They bring invaluable experience and a positive work ethic to the job, but they also have special needs that introduce a whole new set of health and safety concerns.

The people side of the competitiveness equation is only part of it. There is also the technology side. With technological change occurring so rapidly, reinvestment in modern equipment is essential. Today's industrial firm must invest a higher percentage of its profits in equipment upgrades and do so more frequently. Money that must be diverted to workers' compensation, medical claims, product liability litigation, and environmental cleanups is money that could have been invested in technological upgrades.

If they are able to convey these facts effectively, health and safety professionals should be able to secure a strong commitment to health and safety in the workplace. Naturally, they should still use the ethics and compliance arguments as well, because these are proper and compelling. However, health and safety professionals must not stop there. They must convince companies that committing to health and safety is not just the right thing to do ethically or the smart thing to do legally, it is also the profitable thing to do in terms of competitiveness.

Nothing will help health and safety managers make this point more than the competitiveness equation: productivity, quality, response time, cost, service, and corporate image. Each of these ingredients relies directly in some way on having a safe and healthy workplace. Some of the more direct ways are summarized in the following paragraphs.

COST
The amount of money needed to produce a product, not to be confused with "price," which is the amount of money needed to purchase a product after the cost has been marked up.

Productivity and Cost

Productivity is a function of people, technology, and management strategies. Health and safety have a direct effect on the first two. Companies with a reputation for providing a safe and healthy workplace will find it easier to attract and keep the best people. Correspondingly, these talented employees will be able to focus their skills more intently on being productive rather than worrying about accidents or health problems. On the **cost** side of the issue, companies with a record of safe and healthy practices will be better able to reinvest in equipment upgrades than those who must divert funds into such nonproductive costs as medical claims, environmental cleanups, and health- and safety-related litigation. The more productive a company, the more competitive it can be in setting prices for its products.

Quality

Quality is essential to competitiveness. Fortunately, those practices that enhance quality also tend to enhance health and safety. Quality requires strict adherence to established production practices, attention to detail, and a commitment to doing things the right way. So do health and safety. For this reason, health and safety professionals should also be advocates of quality.

Response Time

Response time is like productivity in that it is a function of people, technology, and management strategies. Therefore, the same arguments that apply to productivity apply to response time. This is particularly important in the age of global competition because response time and quality, taken together, are becoming more important than the old "low bid" approach when it comes to winning contracts. The ability to deliver a quality product on demand is a prerequisite to participating in just-in-time contracts. These are contracts in which suppliers provide their products just in time to be used in the production process. This allows manufacturers to produce their products while carrying little or no inventory, a characteristic of today's most competitive companies.

RESPONSE TIME
The amount of time between when an order is placed and when the product is delivered.

Service

Service is an important ingredient in competitiveness. With industrial companies, service typically means in-field or after-delivery service. The most common example is service provided to people who purchase an automobile.

Service is important because it can have a significant impact on customer satisfaction and, in turn, on corporate image. Service is not closely associated with health and safety and is, therefore, not a component to be used when trying to gain a commitment to health and safety.

SAFETY MYTH

Safety and Global Competitiveness

Maintaining a safe and healthy workplace cannot be shown to enhance a company's global competitiveness. Right? Not necessarily. Productivity is a measurement of how well various factors, when taken together, perform. These factors include employees, material, money, and motivation. All four of these factors are affected by the work environment. In fact, more than 90% of employees identify *quality of the work environment* as critical in terms of their motivation and performance.

Source: Institute for Corporate Competition, *Employee Perceptions: Impact of Work Factors on Job Performance*, Report 2003-11 (Niceville, FL: Institute for Corporate Competition, June 2003).

DISCUSSION CASE

What Is Your Opinion?

"Explain this to me again. You say that making all of these modifications to our work-stations and implementing these new procedures will make us more competitive. How? These workstation modifications are expensive, and it seems to me that some of these new procedures will just slow down production."

This wasn't the first time that Garner Baxter, an independent health and safety consultant, had been asked to explain the strategic advantages of a safe and healthy workplace. Can the quality of the work environment really make an organization more competitive? What is your opinion?

Image

CORPORATE IMAGE
How a company is perceived to interact with its workers, customers, and community.

In a competitive world, industrial companies must be concerned about their **corporate image**. An image of being concerned about employee health and safety will help companies attract and keep the best people. An image of being concerned about product safety will help companies market their products. An image of being concerned about the environment will make a company a welcome neighbour in any community. Correspondingly, a poor image in any of these areas can undermine a company's competitiveness. A product safety problem that becomes a media story can cause a company's sales of a given product to plummet overnight. This happened to a major automobile manufacturer when it was discovered that one of its economy models had a tendency to ignite and explode in rear-end collisions. It also happened to pharmaceutical manufacturers when various headache relief products were tampered with and found to have been laced with poison. Had these manufacturers not shown their concern by immediately recalling all containers that may have been affected and quickly developing tamper-proof substitutes, they could have suffered irreparable damage in the marketplace.

Image problems are not limited to product liability issues. Companies that are not careful about protecting the environment may find themselves the subject of protest demonstrations on the nightly news. Such negative publicity can harm the corporate image and translate very quickly into market losses. As corporate decision makers become more sensitive to these facts, health and safety professionals can use them to gain a commitment to their programs.

QUALITY MANAGEMENT (QM)
A way of managing a company that revolves around a total and willing commitment of all personnel at all levels to quality.

SAFETY MANAGEMENT IN A QUALITY MANAGEMENT SETTING

Quality management (QM) is an approach to doing business that began to gain wide acceptance in the late 1980s and early 1990s, and was originally called Total Quality Management, or TQM. Various individual components of this concept had been used by forward-looking organizations for years. However, not until the 1990s were these components pulled together into a cohesive philosophy of how to do business in a competitive global environment.

The health and safety professional of today is likely to work in an organization that practises the QM philosophy. Consequently, students of health and safety should understand QM and how to apply its principles to the management of an organization's health and safety programs. **Total safety management (TSM),** is the management of workplace health and safety according to the principles of QM.

What Is QM?

The QM concept goes by several different names. It is has been called TQL for *total quality leadership*, TQC for *total quality control*, TQ for *total quality* or TQM for *total quality management*. Regardless of the name used, the concept can be defined as follows:

> Quality management (QM) is an approach to doing business that maximizes the competitiveness of an organization through continuous improvement of its products, services, people, processes, and environments.[4]

How Does QM Relate to Safety?

QM has proven itself to be an effective way to maximize an organization's long term competitiveness. It is also an excellent approach for maximizing the effectiveness of an organization's health and safety programs. QM can solve the same problem for safety managers that it solves for quality managers — the problem of *isolation.*

Often in a traditionally managed organization, quality is viewed as the sole responsibility of the quality department or the quality manager. The weaknesses of this approach became evident when organizations wedded to it began losing market share to foreign competition in the 1970s and 1980s. QM solved this problem by making quality everybody's job and casting the quality manager in the role of facilitator and catalyst.[5]

The same type of isolation often occurs with health and safety managers. Management and employees sometimes view safety as the responsibility of the safety department or the safety manager. In the case of quality, isolation is a prescription for failure. In the case of safety, it is a prescription for disaster. QM principles can solve the problem of isolation by making safety everybody's job and casting the safety manager in the role of facilitator and catalyst.

The isolation issue is not the only tie between QM and safety management. To fully understand how QM relates to safety, one must examine each of the distinguishing characteristics of QM from a health and safety perspective. These characteristics, as viewed from this perspective, are as follows:

1. **Customer focus.** In addition to soliciting input and feedback about the quality of its products, organizations should also collect customer data about the health and safety features of the products. After all, these features have a significant bearing on the perceived quality of a product. An unsafe product is not a quality product regardless of the attractiveness of its other characteristics. In the same way, it is important to collect input and feedback

TOTAL SAFETY MANAGEMENT (TSM)
The principles of total quality management (TQM) applied to safety management.

from internal customers (i.e., the employees) concerning the safety of work processes and environments. Internal customer data are the most effective data available for continually improving health and safety procedures.

2. **Obsession with quality.** In addition to being obsessed with quality, organizations should become obsessed with safety. The two concepts are actually inseparable. An organization with unsafe processes or products will eventually pay too high a price to be able to keep up in a competitive marketplace.

3. **Scientific approach.** When dealing with accidents and incidents, it is critical to identify root causes rather than symptoms. Future accidents cannot be prevented when the action taken in response to a current accident is based on symptoms rather than the root cause. The same scientific tools used to identify root causes of quality problems can be used to identify root causes of health and safety problems.

4. **Long term commitment.** The long term commitment of top management is as essential to safety as it is to quality. Executive-level managers show their commitment to health and safety in the same way that they show it to quality — by making safety an organizational priority.

5. **Teamwork.** Part of making safety everybody's responsibility is taking a teamwork approach to the continuous improvement of work processes and the work environment from a safety perspective. Just as cross-functional teams are assigned specific quality improvement projects, similar teams should be formed to tackle specific health and safety issues.

6. **Continual process improvements.** QM organizations structure themselves to improve work processes continually from the perspective of quality. This can and should be done simultaneously from a safety perspective. The continual improvement of safety can be achieved in the same way as the continual improvement of quality.

7. **Education and training.** Quality and safety don't just happen. In both cases, employees at all levels develop the knowledge, skills, and attitudes needed to make a difference. This is accomplished in both cases through ongoing education and training for employees at all levels.

8. **Freedom through control.** Too often, safety precautions are viewed as unwanted inhibitors of productivity. Actually, the safe way is not always the fastest way in the short run. However, over the long run, when factoring in the downtime and expenses associated with injured employees and damaged machines, the safe way is typically the most productive way. Maximum productivity can be achieved by giving employees the freedom to apply their own initiatives in improving both quality and safety within the guidelines and parameters prescribed by management.

9. **Unity of purpose.** Unity of purpose is just as important to safety as it is to quality. The guiding principles that accompany an organization's vision statement should clearly establish health and safety as organizational priorities. Organizationwide unity concerning health and safety will go a long way toward ensuring the effectiveness of a safety program.

10. **Empowerment.** In a QM organization, some of the best ideas for quality improvements come from employees who are empowered to think, suggest, and act. The same employees, equally empowered, could put their creative energy into making health and safety improvements.[6]

QM has excellent potential as an approach to health and safety management. In fact, other ties between quality and safety are so close that it can be argued that safety and quality must be improved simultaneously.

What Is Your Opinion?

"QM is a quality initiative. It has nothing to do with safety," said the CEO with a laugh.

"On the contrary," replied the Vice President for Health and Safety, "QM and safety management have a great deal in common. In fact, the two concepts are complementary."

Is there a relationship between QM and safety management? If so, what is it? If not, why not? What is your opinion?

What Is TSM?

TSM is to health and safety management what QM is to quality management. It is safety management according to the principles of QM. QM has revolutionized the way in which organizations do business and compete in the global marketplace.

Just as QM involves the total organization in continually improving quality, TSM involves the total organization in establishing and maintaining a work environment that is safe and conducive to quality and productivity. Both concepts are rooted firmly in the pressures of the global marketplace.

The origin of TSM can be traced back to the globalization of the marketplace that began after World War II, but really took hold in the 1970s. The need for TSM was created by the need for organizations to be competitive globally. Consequently, *TSM* is defined as follows:

> TSM is a performance- and process-oriented approach to health and safety management that gives organizations a sustainable competitive advantage in the global marketplace by establishing a safe and healthy work environment that is conducive to consistent peak performance and that is improved continually forever. It involves applying the principles of QM to the management of health and safety.

This definition contains several key elements that must be understood if one is to comprehend TSM fully. These elements are as follows:

1. **Sustainable competitive advantage.** Every organization that competes at any level, but especially those that compete at the global level, must have competitive advantages. These are capabilities or characteristics that allow them to outperform the competition. For example, if the organization in

question is a baseball team, it may have such competitive advantages as an excellent pitching staff, several speedy base runners, two or three power hitters, and outstanding fielders in key positions. These advantages, if exploited wisely, help make the baseball team a winner. If these advantages can be sustained over time, they help make the team a consistent winner. This same concept applies to organizations that compete in the global marketplace. To survive and prosper, companies need as many competitive advantages as possible. Traditionally, competitive advantages have been sought in the key areas of quality, productivity, service, and distribution. However, peak-performing organizations have learned that a safe and healthy work environment is essential to gaining competitive advantages in all of these critical areas. In fact, a safe and healthy work environment is itself a competitive advantage. In today's competitive marketplace, high-performance employers are adding one more critical area to the list of those in which competitive advantages are sought. This new addition is the work environment.

Peak-performance organizations are learning that a safe and healthy work environment gives them a doubly effective competitive advantage. First, it ensures that employees work in an environment that allows them to focus all of their attention, energy, and creativity on continually improving performance. Second, it prevents an organization's limited resources from being drained off by the non-value-added costs associated with accidents and injuries.

2. **Peak performance.** The primary driver behind TSM performance is organizational, team, and individual. An organization's ability to survive and prosper in the global marketplace is determined largely by the collective performance of individuals and teams. Consistent peak performance by all individuals and teams in an organization is essential to long term success in the global marketplace. The quality of the work environment is a major determinant of the performance levels that individuals, teams, and organizations are able to achieve. A better work environment promotes better performance.

3. **Continual improvement forever.** People work in an environment, and the quality of that environment affects the quality of their work. The work envi-

---

SAFETY FACT

A Radical Approach

As globalization of the workforce becomes ingrained in the minds of Canadians, it becomes easier to accept new concepts and ideas to manage safety in the workplace. This was not always the case. H. W. Heinrich was thinking "outside the box" in 1931 when he proposed looking at property damage accidents or "near misses" to predict disabling injuries. Known by many safety practitioners as the "father of safety", his ideas opened the door to a host of ideas that at one time may have seemed quite radical, but now form the basis of many safety management principles.

ronment is a major determinant of the quality of an organization's processes, products, and services. In the age of global competition, quality is an ever-changing phenomenon. Quality that is competitive today may not be tomorrow. Consequently, continual improvement is essential. If quality must be improved continually, it follows that the work environment must also be improved continually. Quality and safety are more than complementary; they are inseparable.

Fundamental Elements of TSM

TSM differs in several ways from traditional health and safety management. To appreciate these differences, one must understand the following fundamental elements of TSM:

- Strategically based.
- Performance and process oriented.
- Dependent on executive-level commitment.
- Teamwork oriented.
- Committed to employee empowerment and enlistment.
- Based on scientific decision making.
- Committed to continual improvement.
- Comprehensive, ongoing training.
- Unity of purpose.

Strategic Basis

The fact that TSM is strategically based means that an organization realizes that having a safe and healthy workplace gives it a competitive advantage in the marketplace. Consequently, the organization makes maintaining a safe and healthy workplace a part of its strategic plan. Traditional organizations, on the other hand, tend to view health and safety more from a compliance perspective. TSM is strategically based because it is considered part of an organization's overall strategy for competing globally.

To compete in the global marketplace, organizations must plan for and establish sustainable competitive advantages. This is known as *strategic planning*. Once the planned advantages have been established, they must be maintained over time and exploited to the fullest possible extent. Strategic planning is a matter of answering the following questions:

- **As an organization, what would we like to be? What is our dream?** This is the vision component of the strategic plan.
- **As an organization, what is our purpose?** This is the mission component of the strategic plan.
- **As an organization, what values are most important to us?** This is the guiding principles component of the strategic plan. A guiding principle is a high priority organizational value.
- **As an organization, what do we want to accomplish?** This is the broad objectives component of the strategic plan.

With TSM, a safe and healthy work environment shows up in the strategic plan as a competitive advantage that will be actively pursued and, having been established, will be maintained and continually improved over time. Health and safety concerns appear either in the guiding principles section of the strategic plan, the broad objectives section, or both. Employee health and safety may also appear in the strategic plan as a broad objective. For example, the following broad objective may appear in an organization's strategic plan:

> To maintain a safe and healthy work environment that is conducive to consistent peak performance on the part of all employees.

Performance Oriented

In any organization that is subject to federal and provincial regulations, compliance is an important issue. Failure to comply with applicable regulations can lead to fines and other non-value-added expenses. Companies in such sectors as manufacturing, processing, construction, transportation, and maritime services must comply with numerous government safety regulations.

In a *compliance-driven* setting, the safety department has a regulation orientation. Such an orientation can breed a big-brother-is-watching-you mentality among employees and managers that can cause them to resent the safety department's efforts. The resentment is magnified when employees and managers are pressed to meet deadlines and they see safety regulations as slowing them down.

With TSM, the safety department is **performance oriented**, and health and safety personnel are viewed as part of the equation for continually improving performance. Compliance is still important, of course, but compliance and productivity are no longer viewed as being mutually exclusive entities. Compliance is viewed as a natural extension of an organization's performance-improvement strategies and continues to be an important responsibility of the TSM facilitator.

PERFORMANCE ORIENTED
The goal of the safety department is to improve safety performance, not only to be in compliance with the regulations.

Executive Commitment

The TSM approach can be implemented successfully and fully only if an organization's executive management team is committed to providing a safe and healthy work environment as a performance-improvement strategy. For this reason, the health and safety professional must be able to articulate the TSM philosophy convincingly. If *executive commitment* does not exist, it will have to be generated. Naturally, responsibility for generating the necessary commitment falls to health and safety professionals.

Teamwork Oriented

In a traditional setting, workplace health and safety tend to be viewed as the responsibility of the safety department. In a *teamwork-oriented* TSM setting, although the safety department plays the key facilitating role, ensuring a safe and healthy workplace is everybody's responsibility. Improvement project teams (IPTs) are formed by the TSM steering committee and given charters to improve specific aspects of the work environment. When a team satisfies its charter, it is disbanded. As the need to improve the work environment continues, new teams are chartered, and the process continues forever.

Employee Empowerment and Enlistment

Empowerment means involving employees in ways that give them a real voice. With empowerment, employees are allowed to give input concerning workplace issues, problems, and challenges. If the issue is how to make the work environment safer, empowered employees are allowed and encouraged to make suggestions, and their suggestions are given serious consideration. *Enlistment* takes the concept of empowerment one step further. With enlistment, rather than allowing employees to give input, the organization expects them to do so.

In a TSM setting, employees are viewed as invaluable sources of information, knowledge, insight, and experience that should be tapped continually. Consequently, employee input is not just wanted, it is needed; it is not just sought, it is expected. Criteria that should be included on the performance-appraisal form of modern organizations reads as follows:

- To what extent does this employee provide input that is useful in making continual improvements in the workplace?

Frequently _____

Sometimes _____

Seldom   _____

Never   _____

Scientific Decision Making

It is no exaggeration to say that decisions about workplace health and safety can, on occasion, be life-or-death decisions. Whether they are or not, all such decisions are too important to be based on guesswork. With TSM, *scientific decision making* is the norm. This means that employees in organizations that adopt TSM must learn to use such decision-making tools as Pareto charts, statistical process control (SPC), charting, scatter diagrams, histograms, and fishbone diagrams. Such tools can take the guesswork out of decision making and problem solving and, as a result, lead to better decisions and better solutions.

Continual Improvement

With TSM, the status quo is never good enough, no matter how good it is. In a competitive marketplace, it must be assumed that the competition is improving continually. Consequently, today's competitive performance may not be tomorrow's. The state of the work environment can always be improved, and it should be. In an organization that adopts TSM, IPTs are always working to recommend accident prevention strategies that will make the workplace safer and more productive.

Comprehensive, Ongoing Training

In a TSM setting, training is an ongoing part of the job. If all employees are going to be involved in hazard identification and accident prevention, they must be trained in the basic techniques. If employees are going to be members of IPTs, they must be trained in the fundamentals of teamwork. If employees are going to use scientific tools in making recommendations for solving problems, they must be given instructions in the proper use of these tools.

**Figure 21–4
TSM-related training
opportunities.**

- TSM: What It Is and How to Do It
- Teamwork Fundamentals
- Scientific Decision Making/Problem Solving
- Stress and Safety
- Mechanical Hazards and Body Guarding
- Lifting Hazards
- Falling, Impact, and Acceleration Hazards
- Heat and Temperature Hazards
- Pressure Hazards
- Electrical Hazards
- Fire Hazards
- Toxic Substances
- Explosive Hazards
- Radiation Hazards
- Noise and Vibration Hazards
- Hazard Analysis
- Accident Prevention
- Emergency Preparation/Response
- Facility Assessment/Hazard Identification
- Accident Investigation and Reporting
- Industrial Hygiene
- Automation-Related Hazards
- Bloodborne Pathogens and Related Hazards
- Ergonomics in the Workplace

Training should be comprehensive and ongoing. Figure 21–4 contains a partial list of courses, seminars, and workshops to which employees in a TSM setting should have access. The specific training opportunities that should be provided are determined by the nature of the organization, its products, processes, and employees.

Unity of Purpose

In a TSM setting, all employees at all levels understand that health and safety are the responsibilities of everyone. The TSM facilitator and other health and safety professionals are responsible for planning, facilitating, coordinating, advising, and monitoring. In addition, employees are responsible for doing their part to make the workplace safe and healthy. Employees satisfy their responsibilities in this regard by

- Setting a positive example of working safely.
- Encouraging fellow employees to work safely.

- Practising hazard identification techniques constantly.
- Recommending accident prevention strategies.
- Serving effectively on IPTs.

Gaining unity of purpose begins with the commitment of executive management. An organization's executive management team must commit to health and safety, make it a priority issue in the organization's strategic plan, stress its importance through both words and example, and expect it to be a priority of all employees.

Rationale for TSM

The correlation between work environment and job performance is strong. It is this correlation that forms the basis of the rationale for TSM. Globalization has increased the level of competition in the marketplace exponentially. For many organizations, adjusting to globalization has been like jumping from high school athletic competition to the Olympics.

Organizations that find themselves in these circumstances need every competitive advantage that they can muster. They need to do everything possible to improve performance continually. What every organization can, and must, do is provide employees with a safe and healthy work environment that is conducive to consistent peak performance.

Implementing TSM: The Model

Figure 21–5 contains a three-phase, 15-step model that can be used for successfully implementing TSM in any organization. The three broad phases of activity are *planning and preparation*, *identification and assessment*, and *execution*. Phase One — planning and preparation — encompasses Steps 1 to 7. Each step is completed in order. Pursuing steps out of order can throw the implementation process into disarray. For example, Step 1 is a critical preparation activity. Failure to complete Step 1 successfully can jeopardize all subsequent steps. This is because the organization's attitude toward TSM is determined primarily by the attitudes of executive managers.

Step 2 is the activity in which the TSM steering committee is established. The ideal TSM steering committee is the organization's executive management team, possibly augmented as necessary to ensure that all functional departments are well represented. Steps 3 and 4 are preparation activities that involve training. In Step 3, the TSM steering committee undergoes teamwork training and team-building activities. In Step 4, the steering committee undergoes health and safety awareness training.

Steps 5 and 6 are planning activities in which the steering committee develops a mini-strategic plan for health and safety. This plan consists of a vision, guiding principles, mission, and broad objectives, all of which focus solely on health and safety in the workplace. This mini-strategic plan becomes a subset of the organization's overall strategic plan. In Step 7, the plan is communicated to all employees.

Phase Two of the implementation model — identification and assessment — encompasses Steps 8 to 12. The steps in this phase allow the steering committee to identify strengths that may work in favour of the implementation and

Figure 21–5
Model for
implementation
of TSM.

Planning and Preparation

1. Gain executive-level commitment.
2. Establish the TSM steering committee.
3. Mould the steering committee into a team.
4. Give the steering committee health and safety awareness training.
5. Develop the organization s health and safety vision and guiding principles.
6. Develop the organization's health and safety mission and objectives.
7. Communicate and inform.

Identification and Assessment

8. Identify the organization's health and safety strengths and weaknesses.
9. Identify health and safety advocates and resistors.
10. Benchmark initial employee perceptions concerning the work environment.
11. Tailor implementation to the organization.
12. Identify specific improvement projects.

Execution

13. Establish, train, and activate improvement project teams.
14. Activate the feedback loop.
15. Establish a TSM culture.

inhibitors that may work against it. Having identified strengths and inhibitors, the steering committee can tailor the implementation to exploit strengths while minimizing inhibitors.

Phase Three of the implementation model — execution — encompasses Steps 13 to 15. The steps in this phase involve actually assigning teams to specific improvement projects. As soon as a given improvement has been made, that IPT is disbanded, and a new team is formed to pursue other improvements. This process repeats itself continually forever. An outgrowth of the repetitive nature of the model is that TSM becomes ingrained in the organization's culture.

ENVIRONMENTAL MANAGEMENT

Like worker management, high standards of environmental management are critical if a company intends to compete globally. Health and safety professionals need to be prepared to confront potential hazards in all types of environments. Dealing with hazards of the environment involves protecting workers within a plant from dangerous environmental conditions and protecting the general public from unsafe conditions that may be created by the operations or products of the plant. This is a critical area for modern health and safety professionals and one in which their level of sophistication will have to increase continually.

Role of Safety and Health Professionals

Writing for *Occupational Hazards* magazine, Sandy Moretz uses the example of David Arthur of Smith's Tool Company. She shows three consecutive printings of Arthur's business card. On the first business card, his title is Safety Director. On the next card, his title is Health and Safety Manager. In the latest version of his business card, David Arthur's title is Director — Safety, Health, and Environment.[7]

In some companies, the health and safety professional will be asked to take on environmental responsibilities in addition to the traditional health and safety responsibilities. Other companies will employ one or more persons to be responsible for workplace health and safety and a separate person or persons to be responsible for environmental concerns, both positions reporting to an overall health, safety, and environmental issues manager. Such factors as the size of the company, the type of product produced, and the perceived impact of governmental regulations are also factors that determine how health, safety, and environmental departments will be structured.

A health and safety professional should be prepared to undertake the increased workload associated with environmental safety. Health and safety students should be prepared to study environmental courses or portions of courses in their college curricula. Practising health and safety professionals should be prepared to undertake continuing education in environmental issues.

Being aware of the various hazards in the environment and the negative impact that these hazards can have on humans is another requirement for health and safety professionals. This is true whether the environment is the natural environment or that of the workplace. Hammer lists some of the most common environmental hazards: "High humidity conditions, low relative humidity, sunlight, high temperature conditions, low temperature conditions, airborne salts, dust, sand, dirt . . . meteorological and micrometeorological conditions, lightning, high and low pressure, radiation, vibration and sound."[8]

Each of these potential hazards can have an effect on people, machines, systems, and other inhabitants of a given environment. For example, high-humidity conditions can cause condensation that, in turn, results in short circuits and inadvertent activations or disruptions of electrical systems.[9] For this reason, manufacturers of computers, consumer electric products, and other microelectronics-based products pay particular attention to humidity control in their plant. However, low relative humidity can also cause problems such as drying out and cracking of organic materials, an increased tendency for the creation of static electricity, and easier ignition of accidental fires and explosions.[10]

ENVIRONMENTAL MANAGEMENT SYSTEM (EMS)

A management system, regardless of its application, is the component of an organization responsible for leading, planning, organizing, and controlling. An

ENVIRONMENTAL MANAGEMENT SYSTEM (EMS)
That component of an organization with primary responsibility for leading, planning, organizing, and controlling as these functions relate specifically to an organization's processes, products, or services and the impact that they have on the environment.

environmental management system (EMS) is the component of an organization with primary responsibility for these functions as they relate specifically to the impact of an organization's processes, products, or services on the environment (Figure 21–6).

An organization's EMS may be a subset of its health and safety management system (Figure 21–7) or a separate component of the organization's overall management system. Regardless of where and how it fits into an organization, the EMS should do the following:

- Establish a comprehensive environmental protection policy (planning).
- Identify all government regulations and requirements that apply to the organization's processes, products, or services (controlling).
- Establish organizationwide commitment to environmental protection (leading).
- Establish responsibility and accountability relating to environmental protection (organizing).
- Incorporate environmental concerns in all levels of organizational planning including strategic, operational, and procedural (planning).
- Establish management processes for achieving performance benchmarks (controlling).
- Provide sufficient resources to ensure that performance benchmarks can be achieved on a continual basis (leading).
- Establish and maintain an effective emergency preparedness program (leading, planning, organizing, and controlling).
- Assess the organization's environmental performance against all applicable benchmarks and adjust as necessary (controlling).
- Establish a review process for auditing the EMS and identifying opportunities for improvement (organizing).
- Establish and maintain communications linkages with all stakeholders, internal and external (organizing).
- Promote the establishment of an EMS in contractors and suppliers (leading).[11]

Figure 21–6
An environmental management system's minimum components.

Principal Elements of an Environmental Management System

- Management commitment
- Conforming environmental policy
- Environmental planning
- Organizational structure and responsibility
- Awareness and competence training
- Internal and external communication
- Control of environmentally related operations and documentation
- Emergency response and preparedness capability
- Checking and auditing and corrective or preventive action
- Record keeping
- Management review
- Continual improvement mechanisms

Figure 21–7
Sample organizational structure.

Rationale for the EMS Movement

Different organizations have become interested in better environmental management for different reasons (Figure 21–8). Some organizations are responding to pressure brought by environmental advocacy groups and watchdog organizations. Such groups have become increasingly proficient in winning public support for their individual causes. This support, if effectively focused, can be translated into market pressure. When this happens, better environmental management becomes a market imperative.

Environmental groups have learned how to use the political process to gain support among elected officials and in key government agencies. Some elected officials and government employees are, themselves, environmental advocates. In most industrialized countries, a number of so-called "green parties" even run candidates for elective offices on environmental platforms. These factors, taken together, are giving environmental advocates steadily increasing influence. Business and industry are responding to this influence with increasing interest in environmental management.

Figure 21–8
Forces driving the interest in EMS.

One of the key drivers behind the EMS movement is the concept of competitive advantage. Some forward-looking organizations, particularly those that must compete in the global marketplace, have begun to view having an effective EMS as a competitive advantage. The advantage is the result of the following factors:

- Minimization of funds siphoned off into nonproductive activities such as litigation and crisis management.
- Ease of compliance with government regulations in the foreign countries that make up the global marketplace.
- Better public image in countries (especially European countries) where interest in environmental protection is high.

Improved public relations is an incentive to improve environmental management. The mood of the general public relating to the environment has become strongly pro-environment over the past several decades. Companies that are perceived as being harmful to the environment have begun to feel the public's displeasure in the marketplace, which is one reason why so many companies have begun recycling and voluntary clean-up programs.

An environmentally sensitive public often manifests itself in the form of environmentally sensitive customers. Such customers demand effective environmental management as a condition of their long term retention. Positive environmental impact is rapidly becoming an attribute that customers consider when deciding whether to select or stay with a given vendor or supplier. Direct pressure from the marketplace (customers) is one of the most potent motivators behind the EMS movement.

Another powerful motivator is the potential threat of legal liability and the economic threat that it represents. In today's litigious business environment, a company can see its financial solvency evaporate overnight as the result of class-action lawsuits. Increasingly, individuals and advocacy groups are using the courts as their first response in disagreements over environmental issues, and the economic stakes are high. Juries are showing an increasing tendency to award not only damages but also huge punitive fines against companies that are careless with the environment.

Reducing duplication promotes efficiency, which, in turn, promotes competitiveness. Companies that do business on a global basis are accustomed to dealing with regulations that can vary markedly from country to country. Differences in regulations often cause differences in production processes. Whenever a process must be modified to accommodate regulatory variations — or for any other reason — the price of the product is driven up. Consequently, globally competitive companies are interested in globally uniform standards — standards that help to level the playing field in such key areas as environmental management.

The potential emergence of a de facto requirement to adopt an international standard in order to do business in a given market has also created interest in EMS. The International Organization for Standardization has developed a voluntary standard (ISO 14000) to promote effective environmental management systems. Potential customers may decide unilaterally to do business only with companies that adopt the standard (discussed in the next section). In such cases, the marketplace makes adoption mandatory even though the government of the country in question has no such requirement.

The corollary to a de facto requirement is an actual government mandate to adopt an international EMS standard. The potential for a government mandate has gotten many companies interested in getting a head start in the adoption of an EMS.

Potential Benefits of an EMS

Regardless of why a company becomes interested, there are many benefits that can be realized from adopting an EMS. Joseph Cascio, chair of the Technical Advisory Group that represented the United States in developing ISO 14000, lists the following potential benefits:

1. **Ease of trade.** Uniform international standards knock down the barriers created by country-to-country variations.

2. **Improved compliance with regulations.** When all players must obey the same rules, regulatory compliance is improved by the resulting application of uniform accountability criteria.

3. **Credibility.** Third-party certification takes politics out of the process, thereby enhancing its credibility.

4. **Reduction in liability or risk.** Certification forces companies to focus on the issue of environmental impact. This focus on being environmentally friendly, in turn, reduces the likelihood of environmentally hazardous behaviour that may lead to expensive, nonproductive litigation.

5. **Regulatory incentives.** Companies that show initiative in establishing an effective EMS can take advantage of incentives that reward organizations for showing leadership in protecting the environment.

6. **Sentencing mitigation.** Adoption of a comprehensive EMS may serve as a mitigating factor when fines are assessed for failing to comply with regulations.

7. **Pollution prevention and waste reduction.** Better environmental management results in less waste and less pollution. These, in turn, result in attendant savings. This is the ounce-of-prevention, pound-of-cure concept.

8. **Profit.** Better management of any kind — quality, human resources, time, or environmental — translates into better profits.

9. **Improved internal management.** ISO 14000 certification requires the use of management methods that can improve all aspects of internal management. This, in turn, leads to a better overall profit ratio.

10. **Community goodwill.** Good environmental management makes companies good corporate citizens in their neighbourhoods, which, in turn, leads to community goodwill.

11. **Retention of a high-quality workforce.** Employees live in the communities where their companies are located. Companies that are good corporate citizens find it easier to retain their best and brightest employees than do companies whose environmental practices are embarrassing or irresponsible.

12. **Insurance.** Companies with established, effective environmental management systems may have fewer problems finding insurance policies that can be written at reasonable prices.

13. **Preference in lending.** One of the key factors that lending institutions consider before making a loan is the company's ability to pay. Because costly

environmental litigation can bankrupt even the most solvent of companies, lending institutions may begin to give preference to those with established environmental management systems.[12]

INTERNATIONAL ORGANIZATION FOR STANDARDIZATION (ISO)
A worldwide organization of national standards bodies.

INTERNATIONAL ORGANIZATION FOR STANDARDIZATION (ISO)

The **International Organization for Standardization (ISO)** is a worldwide organization of national standards bodies (Figure 21–9). The complete membership roster for ISO contains the standards bodies of 118 countries. The overall goal of ISO is to promote the development of standardization and related activities in the world with a view to facilitating the international exchange of

Figure 21–9
Addresses of selected ISO members.

Australia
Standards Australia
286 Sussex Street (corner of Bathurst Street)
Sydney, NSW 2000
GPO Box 5420
Sydney, NSW 2001
Australia
Tel: +61 2 8206 6000
Fax: +61 2 8206 6001
Email: intsect@standards.org.au
Web: http://www.standards.org.au/

Canada
Standards Council of Canada
270 Albert Street, Suite 200
Ottawa, Ontario K1P 6N7
Tel: 613 238 3222
Fax: 613 569 7808
Email: info@scc.ca
Web: http://www.scc.ca

France
Association française de normalisation
11, avenue Francis de Pressensé
93571 Saint-Denis La Plaine Cedex
France
Tel: +33 1 41 62 80 00
Fax: +33 1 49 17 90 00
Email: uari@afnor.org
Web: http://www.afnor.fr

Germany
Deutsches Institut für Normung (DIN)
Burggrafenstrasse 6
10772 Berlin
Germany
Tel: +49 30 2601-0
Fax: +49 30 2601 1231
Email: directorate.international@din.de
Web: http://www.din.de

United Kingdom
British Standards Institution
389 Chiswick High Road
London W4 4AL
United Kingdom
Tel: +44 208 996 7147
Fax: +44 208 996 7799
Email: standards.international@bsi-global.com
Web: http://www.bsi-global.com

United States
American National Standards Institute
1819 L Street, NW
Washington, DC 20036
and
25 West 43rd Street , Fourth Floor
New York, NY 10036
USA
Tel: +1 212 642 4900
Fax: +1 212 398 0023
Email: info@ansi.org
Web: http://www.ansi.org

goods and services and to developing cooperation in the sphere of intellectual, scientific, technological, and economic activity.[13]

Globalization of the marketplace has created a competitive environment that requires peak performance and continual improvement. The unrelenting demands of today's marketplace have given rise to new philosophies for doing business, most of which fall under the broad umbrella of quality management (QM). One of the initiatives under the QM umbrella is the ISO 9000 family of quality standards. These standards contain criteria for promoting effective quality management systems.

The International Organization for Standardization — the same organization that developed the ISO 9000 quality standards — has now developed the ISO 14000 family of standards to promote effective environmental management systems.

Just as the decision to adopt the QM philosophy or the ISO 9000 standards is voluntary, adoption of ISO 14000 is based on voluntary organizational commitment to environmental protection rather than government coercion. For health and safety managers accustomed to complying with government mandates, ISO 14000 certification is a novel approach.

Shifting attitudes and greater public awareness are making it essential that business firms be good neighbours in their communities. The marketplace demands that businesses produce high-quality products at competitive prices, without harming the environment. ISO 14000 provides the framework for making effective environmental management part of the organization's overall management system.

ISO 14000 Series of Standards

The term *ISO 14000 Series* refers to a family of environmental management standards that cover the five disciplines shown in Figure 21–10. All of the standards are in a constant state of evolution. The ISO 14000 Series contains two types of standards: specification standards and guidance standards.

A *specification standard* contains only the specific criteria that can be audited internally or externally by a third party. A *guidance standard* explains how to develop and implement environmental management systems and principles. Guidance standards are descriptive standards that also explain how to coordinate among various quality management systems.

Figure 21–11 illustrates the two broad classifications of standards in the ISO 14000 family and their respective subclassifications. The two broad

---

✓ Environmental management system

✓ Environmental auditor criteria (These criteria may be used by internal auditors and external third-party auditors.)

✓ Environmental performance evaluation criteria

✓ Environmental labelling criteria

✓ Life-cycle assessment methods

▶ **Figure 21–10 Environmental disciplines in the ISO 14000 series of standards.**

**Figure 21–11
Environmental man-
agement standards.**

classifications are (1) process- or organization-oriented standards, and (2) product-oriented standards. Process-oriented standards cover the following three
broad areas: environmental management system, environmental performance
evaluation, and environmental auditing. Product-oriented standards cover
three different broad areas of concern as follows: life-cycle assessment, environmental labelling, and environmental aspects in product standards.

DISCUSSION CASE

What Is Your Opinion?

The executive managers of Petroleum Processing, Inc. are debating the relative merits
of seeking ISO 14000 certification. The managers have polarized around two opinions.
The first opinion is that the company should proceed with preparations for certification immediately. In the words of one ISO proponent, "The sooner we get started, the
sooner we will realize the benefits of ISO 14000." The second opinion is that any certification that is not required should be ignored. In the words of one ISO opponent,
"Certification is time consuming and expensive. Why bother if we don't have to? We
already have to comply with provincial and federal legislation. Isn't that enough?"
Where do you stand on this issue? What is your opinion?

The six subclassifications shown in Figure 21–11 represent six distinct, but interrelated, areas of concern. There are actually 20 separate documents in the ISO 14000 series, all related to one of these six subclassifications. Of these 20 documents, only ISO 14000 is a standard against which a company is audited. The rest are guidance documents.

SUMMARY

1. Competitiveness is the ability to succeed and prosper in the local, regional, national, and global marketplace. The most competitive companies are those that consistently outperform their competitors in the key areas of quality, productivity, response time, service, cost, and image.

2. Productivity is a measure of output in goods and services compared to input of resources needed to produce or deliver them. Part of productivity is the concept of value added, which is measured as the difference between what it costs a company to produce a product and the competitive market price of that product.

3. Quality is a measure of the extent to which a product meets or exceeds customer expectations. It goes hand in hand with productivity. Quality without productivity results in costs that are too high to be competitive. Productivity without quality results in an unacceptable product.

4. Health and safety contribute to competitiveness in the following ways: (a) by helping companies attract and keep the best people; (b) by allowing employees to focus on peak performance without being distracted by concerns for their health and safety; (c) by freeing money that can be reinvested in technology updates; and (d) by protecting the corporate image.

5. Quality management (QM) is an approach to doing business that maximizes the competitiveness of an organization through continuous improvement of its products, services, people, processes, and environments.

6. QM can solve the same problems for safety managers that it solves for managers concerned about quality. QM makes quality everybody's responsibility, rather than limiting responsibility to quality personnel. It can do the same for safety managers. In addition, a quality product is a safe product, and the best environment in which to produce quality products is a safe and healthy environment.

7. The fundamental elements of TSM are its strategic basis, performance orientation, executive commitment, teamwork orientation, employee empowerment and enlistment, scientific decision making, continual improvement, comprehensive and ongoing training, and unity of purpose.

8. The rationale of TSM can be found in the connection between job performance and the work environment. To compete in the global marketplace, organizations need all employees performing at peak levels on a consistent basis. A safe and healthy workplace promotes peak performance.

9. Measures taken to clean up and protect the environment are ethically right. They may also be cost effective.

10. Health and safety professionals should be prepared to take responsibility for both workplace safety and environmental safety.

11. Some of the most common environmental hazards include high and low humidity, sunlight, high and low temperatures, airborne substances, meteorological and micrometeorological conditions, lightning, high and low air pressure, radiation, vibration, and sound.

12. ISO is the acronym for the International Organization for Standardization, a worldwide consortium of national standards bodies. ISO is the organization that developed the ISO 14000 family of standards.

13. A management system is that component of an organization that is responsible for leading, planning, organizing, and controlling. An environmental management system (EMS) is that component of an organization with primary responsibility for these functions as they relate specifically to an organization's impact on the environment.

14. The potential benefits of an EMS include the following: ease of international trade, improved compliance, credibility, reduction in liability/risk, regulatory incentives, sentencing mitigation, pollution prevention, waste reduction, profits, improved internal management, community goodwill, employee retention, and insurance and lending preferences.

KEY TERMS AND CONCEPTS

Competitiveness
Corporate image
Cost
Environmental management system (EMS)
Global marketplace
International Organization for Standardization (ISO)
Performance oriented
Productivity
Quality
Quality management (QM)
Response time
Total safety management (TSM)
Value added

REVIEW QUESTIONS

1. Explain how global competition can have a negative impact on health and safety in the workplace.

2. Define the terms *competitiveness*, *productivity*, and *value added quality*.

3. What are the common characteristics of the most competitive companies?

4. Explain the relationship between productivity and quality as it relates to competitiveness.

5. Define *QM*.

6. How does QM relate to safety?

7. Define the term *total safety management*.

8. What is the rationale for TSM?

9. What are the three broad phases that make up the model for implementing TSM?

10. How are environmental concerns changing the role of health and safety professionals?

11. What is an environmental management system?

12. What factors are behind the competitive advantage that can result from implementation of an EMS?

13. List five potential benefits of an EMS.

14. What is the purpose of ISO 14000 standards?

WEBLINKS

International Organization for Standardization (ISO)
www.iso.org

This is a link to information about ISO and the 9000 and 14000 standards they develop.

The David Suzuki Foundation
www.davidsuzuki.org

On this website, Canada's most popular advocate for environmental protection, David Suzuki, provides information on how we can help protect our planet from environmental degradation.

ENDNOTES

1. Institute for Corporate Competitiveness, *Manual of Services* (Niceville, FL: Institute for Corporate Competitiveness, 2003), 1.
2. T. Peters, *Thriving on Chaos* (New York: Harper & Row, 1987), 78.
3. D. L. Goetsch, *Effective Supervision* (Upper Saddle River, NJ: Prentice Hall, 2002), 210.
4. David L. Goetsch and Stanley Davis, *Quality Management* (Upper Saddle River, NJ: Prentice Hall, 2003), 6.
5. Eleanor J. White, "Saturn's Implementation of Deming's Fourteen Points," undated training document, 1.
6. Ibid., 3.
7. S. Moretz, "The Greening of Health and Safety," *Occupational Hazards* (April 1990): 61.
8. W. Hammer, *Occupational Safety Management and Engineering* (Upper Saddle River, NJ: Prentice Hall, 1989), 127–128.
9. Ibid., 127.
10. Ibid.
11. D. Philips, *Waste Reduction in Industrial Processes* (Pensacola: Pensacola Junior College/Florida Department of Environmental Regulation), 97–98.
12. Ibid., 98–99.
13. D. Goetsch and S. Davis, *ISO 14000 Environmental Management* (Upper Saddle River, NJ: Prentice Hall, 2001), 7.

22 CHAPTER

Stress and Safety

LEARNING OBJECTIVES

- Define workplace stress.
- Identify sources of workplace stress.
- Describe the human reactions to workplace stress.
- Explain how workplace stress can be measured.
- Explain how shift work affects stress levels and safety.
- Describe how reducing workplace stress can improve safety.
- List the causes of stress in safety managers.

WORKPLACE STRESS DEFINED

Stress is a pathological, and therefore generally undesirable, human reaction to psychological, social, occupational, or environmental stimuli.[1] Stress has been defined as the reaction of the human organism to a threatening situation.[2] The stressor is an external stimulus, and **stress** is the response of the human body to this stimulus.

This is a clinical definition of stress. Other definitions relate more directly to **workplace stress**. The National Institute for Occupational Safety and Health (NIOSH) defines job stress as "the harmful physical and emotional responses that occur when the requirements of the job do not match the capabilities, resources, or needs of the worker."[3]

Corporations tend to see stress as an individually based problem that is rooted in an employee's lifestyle, psychological makeup, and personality. Unions view stress as the result of excessive demands, poor supervision, or conflicting demands.[4] According to Singer, "The best definition probably includes both sets of factors."[5]

However it is defined, stress is a serious problem in the modern workplace. In fact, The Canadian Health Association estimates that workplace stress and related illnesses cost the economy approximately $5 billion a year.[6]

STRESS
A pathological, and therefore generally undesirable, human reaction to psychological, social, occupational, or environmental stimuli.

WORKPLACE STRESS
Human reaction to threatening situations at work or related to the workplace.

410

Workplace stress involves the emotional state resulting from a perceived difference between the level of occupational demand and a person's ability to cope with this demand. Because preparations and emotions are involved, workplace stress is considered a subjective state. An environment that a worker finds to be stressful may generate feelings of tension, anger, fatigue, confusion, and anxiety.

Workplace stress is primarily a matter of person–workload fit. The status of the person–workload fit can influence the acceptance of the work and the level of acceptable performance of that work. The perception of workload may be affected by the worker's needs and his or her level of job satisfaction. The relationship between job demands and the worker's ability to meet those demands further influences workplace stress. Because workplace stress may be felt differently by different people in similar situations, it must be concluded that there are many causes of workplace stress.

SOURCES OF WORKPLACE STRESS

The sources of on-the-job stress may involve physical working conditions, work overload, **role ambiguity**, lack of **feedback**, personality, personal and family problems, or role conflict. Other sources of workplace stress are discussed in the following paragraphs.

- **Task complexity** relates to the number of different demands made on the worker. A job perceived as being too complex may cause feelings of inadequacy resulting in emotional stress. Conversely, repetitive and monotonous work may lack complexity — so that the worker becomes bored and dissatisfied with the job and experiences stress associated with the boredom.
- **Control** over the job assignment can also be a source of workplace stress. Most workers experience less stress when they participate in determining the work routine, including schedule and selection of tasks. Several studies have indicated that workers prefer to take control of their job assignment and experience less workload stress if given this opportunity.[7] A related source of stress that has been introduced in the age of high technology is from electronic monitoring. According to a study conducted at the University of Wisconsin at Madison, "Video display terminal workers who are electronically monitored suffered greater health problems than those who are not."[8]
- A **feeling of responsibility** for the welfare or safety of family members may produce on-the-job stress. Being responsible for the welfare of his or her family may cause a worker to feel that options to take employment risks are limited. A worker may then perceive that he or she is "trapped in the job." Overly constrained employment options may lead to anxiety and stress. The feeling of being responsible for the safety of the general public has also been shown to be a stressor. Air traffic controllers are known to experience intense stress when their responsibility for public safety is tested by a near-accident event. A feeling of great responsibility associated with a job can transform a routine activity into a stress-inducing task.
- **Job security** involves the risk of unemployment. A worker who believes that his or her job is in jeopardy will experience anxiety and stress. The ready

ROLE AMBIGUITY
The condition that occurs when an employee is not clear concerning the parameters, reporting requirements, authority, or responsibilities of his or her job.

FEEDBACK
Employee's opinions of a project or an employer's opinion about an employee's job performance.

TASK COMPLEXITY
Relates to the number of different demands made on the worker.

CONTROL
When an employee participates in determining the work routine, including schedule and selection of tasks.

FEELING OF RESPONSIBILITY
Being responsible for the welfare of his or her family may cause a worker to feel that options to take employment risks are limited.

JOB SECURITY
A sense — real or imagined — of having the potential for longevity in a job and having a measure of control concerning that longevity.

availability of other rewarding employment and a feeling that one's professional skills are needed reduce the stress associated with job security issues.

- An *organizational culture* leaves the employee feeling left out, out of the loop, and ill-informed. Organizations in which managers fail to communicate frequently and effectively with employees are creating high-stress environments for workers.
- *Work schedules* that are unpredictable, never-changing, or ever-changing can induce stress in employees. Employees have lives outside of their jobs. Consequently, the ability to predict their work schedules is important. When work schedules are unpredictable, stress increases. Stress also increases when work schedules are inflexible — they cannot be changed no matter what other obligation the employee might have. On the other hand, ever-changing work schedules such as those associated with shift work can also increase the level of employee stress. The big-picture issue with regard to work schedules is the level of control employees have over their lives. The less control, the more stress.
- *Home and family problems* can create added stress for workers. There was a time when employees were expected to "leave their problems at the front door" when they came to work. This, of course, is a practical impossibility. The demands of raising children, working out home and job schedules, dealing with the conflicting agendas inherent in dual-career households, and otherwise handling the everyday work and home conflicts that inevitably arise can markedly increase an employee's stress level.
- *Work relationships* can lead to on-the-job stress. People are social beings by nature. They like to get along with the people they spend a lot of time with. However, office politics, turf battles, and internal competition for recognition and rewards can be hard on work relationships. When employees do not get along with their fellow workers, stress levels increase.
- *Human resource management (HRM) issues* can be a source of workplace stress. People who work have a vested interest in their wages, salaries, working conditions, and benefits. If even one of these factors is a negative, employee stress levels can increase significantly. In addition to these factors, other stress-inducing HRM issues include underemployment, failure to get promoted, and working in a position that is clearly not valued by management.
- *Workload demands* can stimulate stress when they are perceived as being overwhelming. These demands may involve time constraints and cognitive constraints such as speed of decision making and mandates for attention. Workload demands may also be physically overwhelming if the worker is poorly matched to the physical requirements of the job or is fatigued. Whenever the worker believes the workload to be too demanding, stress can result.
- *Psychological support* from managers and co-workers gives a feeling of acceptance and belonging and helps defuse stress. A lack of such support may increase the perception of a burdensome workload and result in greater levels of stress.
- The lack of *environmental safety* can also be a cause of stress. Feeling that one is in danger can be a stressor. Workers need to feel safe from environmental hazards such as extreme temperatures, pressure, electricity, fire, explosives, toxic materials, ionizing radiation, noises, and dangerous

machinery. To reduce the potential for stress due to environmental hazards, workers should feel that their managers are committed to safety and that their company has an effective safety program.

Common Causes of Stress in the Workplace

- The company was recently purchased by another company.
- Downsizing or layoffs have occurred in the past year.
- Employee benefits were significantly cut recently.
- Mandatory overtime is frequently required.
- Employees have little control over how they do their work.
- The consequences of making a mistake on the job are severe.
- Workloads vary greatly.
- Most work is machine-paced or fast-paced.
- Workers must react quickly and accurately to changing conditions.
- Personal conflicts on the job are common.
- Few opportunities for advancement are available.
- Workers cope with a great deal of bureaucracy in getting work done.
- Staffing, money, or technology is inadequate.
- Pay is below the going rate.
- Employees are rotated among shifts.[9]

Minter's work demonstrates that stress can lead to decreased productivity, higher absenteeism and job turnover, poor morale, and greater numbers of stress-related illnesses.

Technological developments have also introduced new sources of stress into the workplace. The proliferation of computers is increasing stress levels in ways that were not anticipated. According to Caroline Dow and Douglas Covert of the University of Evansville, "Workplaces using computers and video display terminals (VDTs) are unwittingly breeding stress, especially among women."[10]

Dow and Covert conducted an experiment in which they observed the effect of a 16-kilohertz pure tone sound on the stress levels of college-age women. They found that anxiety and irritation were the first responses to the sound. The loudness of the sound was not a major factor; even quiet tones caused noticeable stress.[11]

HUMAN REACTIONS TO WORKPLACE STRESS

Human reactions to workplace stress may be grouped into the following categories: subjective or emotional (anxiety, aggression, guilt); behavioural (being prone to accidents, trembling); cognitive (inability to concentrate or make decisions); physiological (increased heart rate and blood pressure); and organizational (absenteeism and poor productivity). Continual or persistent stress has been linked to many physiological problems.[12] Initially, the effects may be psychosomatic, but with continued stress, the symptoms show up as actual organic dysfunction. The most common forms of stress-related diseases are gastrointestinal, particularly gastric or duodenal ulcers. Research has also linked some autoimmune diseases with increased long-term workplace stress.[13]

The human response to workplace stress can be compared to a rubber band being stretched. As the stress continues to be applied, the rubber band stretches until a limit is reached when the rubber band breaks. For humans, various physical and psychological changes are observed with the repetitive stimuli of stress. Until the limit is reached, the harmful effects can be reversed. With an increase in intensity or duration of the stress beyond the individual's limit, the effects on the human become pathological.

Hans Selye identified three stages of the human stress response: (1) alarm, (2) resistance, and (3) exhaustion.[14] The alarm reaction occurs when the stress of a threat is sensed. The **stage of alarm** is characterized by pallor, sweating, and an increased heart rate. This stage is usually short. It prepares the body for whatever action is necessary.

When the stress is maintained, the **stage of resistance** initiates a greater physical response. The alarm symptoms dissipate, and the body develops an adaptation to the stress. The capacity for adaptation during this stage is, however, limited.

Eventually, with sustained stress, the **stage of exhaustion** is reached. This stage is demonstrated by the body's failure to adapt to the continued stress. Psychosomatic diseases such as gastric ulcers, colitis, rashes, and autoimmune disorders may begin during this stage. The tendency to develop a specific stress-related disease may be partially predetermined by heredity, personal habits such as smoking, and personality.

From an evolutionary viewpoint, the adverse effects of stress on health may be considered to be a maladaptation of humans to stress. What does this tell us? Either we (1) learn to do away with all stress (unlikely); (2) avoid all stressful situations (equally unlikely); (3) learn to adapt to being sick because of stress (undesirable); or (4) learn to adapt to workplace stress (the optimal choice). The first step in learning to adapt to stress is understanding the amount of stress to which we are subjected.

MEASUREMENT OF WORKPLACE STRESS

Workplace stress can be seen as an individual's psychological reaction to the work environment. Although psychological response cannot be directly measured in physical terms, one method commonly employed uses a measurement of mental workload. Mental workload can be measured in one of three ways:

1. With **subjective ratings**, the workers are asked to rate their perceived level of workload. The perceived workload is then viewed as a direct reflection of workplace stress. The workers may be asked to rate their mood in relation to the work situation. The data gathered by this method is obviously subjective and state dependent. State-dependent data are directly related to the circumstances or state under which they are collected and, therefore, have a built-in state bias.

2. **Behavioural time sharing** techniques require the simultaneous performance of two tasks. One of the tasks is considered the primary or most important; the other is of secondary importance. The decrease in performance efficiency of the secondary task is considered an index of workload for behavioural time sharing or human multi-tasking. Workplace stress is thought to increase as behavioural time sharing increases.

STAGE OF ALARM
Characterized by pallor, sweating, and an increased heart rate.

STAGE OF RESISTANCE
The alarm symptoms dissipate, and the body develops an adaptation to the stress.

STAGE OF EXHAUSTION
This stage is demonstrated by the body's failure to adapt to the continued stress.

SUBJECTIVE RATINGS
Ratings that are less than objective and can be affected by emotions, human biases, presumptions, and perceptions.

BEHAVIOURAL TIME SHARING
A technique requiring the simultaneous performance of two tasks.

3. **Psychophysiological techniques** require simultaneous measurement of heart rate and brain waves, which are then interpreted as indexes of mental workload and workplace stress.

Behavioural time sharing and psychophysiological techniques are related to theoretical models, making data easier to interpret. These two techniques, however, also require sophisticated equipment and data collection methods.

Subjective ratings may be collected using questionnaires or survey instruments. These instruments may ask about the physical working conditions, the individual's health and mental well-being, and their perceived overall satisfaction with the job. The data may then be compared to standardized scales developed by various researchers.[15]

Psychosocial questionnaires evaluate workers' emotions about their jobs. Workers may be asked about job satisfaction, workload, pace, opportunities for advancement, management style, and organizational climate. Psychosocial questionnaires are another form of subjective ratings and are also subject to state-dependent bias in the data. Regardless of the measurement method, because workplace stress is dependent on personal awareness, no direct, objective means of measuring workplace stress are currently available.

SHIFT WORK, STRESS, AND SAFETY

Shift work can require some employees to work when the majority of people are resting. In some cases, shift work requires rotating between two or three different starting times, which may vary by eight hours or more. Shift work has traditionally been required in health care, the transportation industry, utilities, security, and, increasingly, by retail sales.

Basic physiological functions are scheduled by the biological clock called the **circadian rhythm**. Many physical and psychological functions are affected by circadian rhythm. Blood pressure, heart rate, body temperature, and urine production are measurably slower at night. These same functions are normally faster during the day (active time). If a person takes a job starting at midnight, his or her body will still expect to be sleeping at night and active during the day.

Behavioural patterns also follow the circadian slower-at-night and more-active-during-the-day pattern. Sleep demand and sleep capacity for people age 14 or older is greatest at night and least during daylight hours. Alertness has been determined to be decreased at night.[16]

PSYCHOPHYSIOLOGI-CAL TECHNIQUES
Require simultaneous measurement of heart rate and brain waves, which are then interpreted as indexes of mental workload and industrial stress.

PSYCHOSOCIAL QUESTIONNAIRES
Evaluate workers' emotions about their jobs.

SHIFT WORK
Employees work at different times of the day instead of during the same hours.

CIRCADIAN RHYTHM
Biological clock.

SAFETY FACT

Workplace Stress and Health

The physical and mental health of working people is affected by their *psychological environment*. Autocratic, insensitive managers and supervisors can produce enough stress in employees to cause physical illness. When managers and supervisors show an interest in employees, empower them to participate, and provide positive reinforcement, fewer illnesses or cases of work-related depression are reported.

Workers surveyed have consistently reported lower job satisfaction with rotating shifts.[17] Day-shift workers with the same task definitions report higher job satisfaction and less stress than their second- or third-shift counterparts.[18] Rotating shifts over several weeks can result in desensitization to the circadian rhythms. With this desensitization comes a measurable loss in productivity, increased numbers of accidents, and reported subjective discomfort.[19] After returning to a predictable shift, workers regained their biological clock and circadian rhythm.

Not working the normal day-shift hours results in an increase in workplace stress, with rotating shifts being the most stressful. From a safety viewpoint, shift workers are subjected to more workplace stress in terms of weariness, irritability, depression, and a lack of interest in work. Shift work increases workplace stress and may lead to a less safe worker.

Reducing the Stress Associated with Shift Work

Shift work is and will probably always be a fact of life for employees in certain occupations. About three out of 10 workers in Canada work some type of shift work. To reduce the stress associated with shift work, health and safety professionals can apply the following strategies:

1. Encourage shift workers to exercise regularly. Regular exercise can have the double benefit of improving the quality of an individual's sleep and relieving pent-up stress.

2. Encourage shift workers to avoid caffeine, alcohol, or other drugs that can inhibit their ability to sleep.

3. If shift workers cannot sleep without some type of sleep aid, the food supplement, melatonin, or other natural sleep inducers should be recommended rather than sleeping pills that contain synthetic chemicals and can have side effects that might contribute to other stress-inducing effects.[20]

IMPROVING SAFETY BY REDUCING WORKPLACE STRESS

Not all sources of stress on the job can be eliminated, and employment screening is unlikely to identify all those who are sensitive to stress. People can learn to adapt to stress, however. Training can help people recognize and deal with stress effectively. Employees need to know what is expected of them at any given time and to receive recognition when it is deserved. Managers can reduce role ambiguity and stress caused by lack of feedback by providing frequent feedback.

JOB AUTONOMY
Control over one's job.

Stress can result from low participation or lack of **job autonomy**. A manager can help employees realize their full potential by helping them match their career goals with the company's goals and giving them more control over their jobs.

Managers can help design jobs in ways that lead to worker satisfaction, thereby lessening work stress. Physical stress can be reduced by improving the work environment and establishing a sound health and safety program. Managers can also assist in the effort to provide varied and independent work with good possibilities for contact and collaboration with fellow workers and for personal development.

Organizational approaches to coping with work stress include avoiding a monotonous, mechanically controlled pace, standardized motion patterns, and constant repetition of short-cycle operations. Other stress-inducing work design features to avoid include jobs that do not make use of a worker's knowledge and initiative, that lack human contact, and that have authoritarian-type supervision.

There are also several individual approaches to coping with stress. One of the most important factors in dealing with stress is learning to recognize its symptoms and taking them seriously. Handling stress effectively should be a lifelong activity that gets easier with practice. Keeping a positive mental attitude can help defuse some otherwise stressful situations.

People can analyze stress-producing situations and decide what is worth worrying about. Individuals can effectively respond to a stressful workload by delegating responsibility instead of carrying the entire load. Relaxation techniques can also help reduce the effects of stress. Some common relaxation methods include meditation, biofeedback, music, and exercise.

DISCUSSION CASE

What Is Your Opinion?

"We are beginning to see more and more stress-related problems. I'm afraid that if we don't deal with the issue, stress is going to cause even more serious injuries."

"Nonsense. We all have stress. There has always been stress on the job. It goes with the territory. A few employees go to a seminar on workplace stress and, all of a sudden, everyone is complaining about stress."

This discussion took place between the safety director and the CEO of Gulf Coast Electric Company. Is stress really a legitimate workplace hazard? What is your opinion?

The following strategies are recommended for reducing workplace stress.

- Management recognizes workplace stress and regularly takes steps to reduce this stress.
- Mental health benefits are provided in the employee's health insurance coverage.
- The employer has a formal employee communications program.
- Employees are given information on how to cope with stress.
- Workers have current, accurate, and clear **job descriptions**.
- Management and employees talk openly with one another.
- Employees are free to talk with each other during work.
- Employers offer exercise and other stress-reduction classes.
- Employees are recognized and rewarded for their contributions.

JOB DESCRIPTIONS
Written specifications that describe the tasks, duties, reporting requirements, and qualifications for a given job.

- Work rules are published and are the same for everyone.
- Child care programs are available.
- Employees can work flexible hours.
- Perks are granted fairly based on a person's level in the organization.
- Workers have the training and **technology access** that they need.
- Employers encourage work and personal support groups.
- Workers have a place and time to relax during the work day.
- Elder care programs are available.
- Employees' work spaces are not crowded.
- Workers can put up personal items in their work areas.
- Management appreciates humour in the workplace.[21]

TECHNOLOGY ACCESS
Access to time- and work-saving devices, processes, or equipment that are up to date.

Writing for *Occupational Hazards*, S. L. Smith recommends the following additional ways to reduce stress in the workplace:

- Match workload and pace to the training and abilities of employees.
- Make an effort to match work schedules with the personal lives of employees.
- Clearly define work roles.
- Before giving employees additional duties beyond their normal work roles, make sure they receive the necessary training.
- Promote teamwork among employees and encourage it throughout the organization.
- Involve employees in making decisions that affect them.
- Inform employees in a timely manner of organizational changes that might affect them.[22]

There is no one clear answer to workplace stress. The suggestions given here are a good starting place for management and employees to begin the process of being aware of and dealing effectively with workplace stress.

STRESS IN SAFETY MANAGERS

Health and safety management can be a stressful profession. Robert Scherer of Wright State University identified the following four conditions that frequently trigger stress among modern health and safety professionals:

- Role overload.
- Coping with regulatory breakdown.
- Communication breakdown.
- Competing loyalties.[23]

According to Scherer, health and safety professionals are sometimes overloaded when corporate *downsizing* results and they are delegated more and more responsibilities. Trying to keep up with the ever-changing multitude of regulations is a stress-inducing challenge. Communication relating to health and safety is always a challenge. However, when economic forces focus an organization's attention on other matters, it can be even more difficult than usual to get the health and safety message across. This increased difficulty can lead to increased stress. Line managers who are more concerned with meeting production quotas than with the safety of their employees sometimes try to influence

---

SAFETY MYTH

Managers Cannot Reduce Employee Stress

Of course, the workplace is stressful! This fact cannot be helped. Some people can handle stress, and some cannot. There is nothing managers can do. Right? Wrong. There is a lot that managers can do. Managers can provide training to help employees learn to recognize stress and deal with it. Managers can empower employees, giving them as much control as possible over their jobs. Managers can improve communication with employees. Managers can provide clear, understandable job descriptions that eliminate ambiguity. Managers can provide child care or child care assistance. Managers can provide exercise and stress reduction programs. There are many strategies that managers can employ to reduce stress on the job.

---

health and safety managers — their colleagues and sometimes their friends — to look the other way. This subjects health and safety managers to the pressures of competing loyalties.[24]

Scherer recommends that health and safety managers cope with these four common triggers of stress by applying the following strategies: (1) prioritize activities by focusing on those that present the most risk to the organization; (2) work closely with the organization's legal staff and subscribe to an online CD-ROM updating service; (3) formalize communication and hold regularly scheduled health and safety meetings for all operating employees; and (4) focus on the risks to the organization and refuse to take sides.[25]

SUMMARY

1. Stress is the harmful physical and emotional response that occurs when the requirements of the job do not match the capabilities, resources, or needs of the worker.

2. Workplace stress involves a worker's feelings resulting from perceived differences between the demands of the job and the person's capacity to cope with these demands.

3. Sources of workplace stress include environmental conditions, work overload, role ambiguity, lack of feedback, personality, personal and family problems, and role conflict. Other sources of workplace stress are task complexity, lack of control over the job, public safety responsibility, lack of job security, lack of psychological support, and environmental safety concerns.

4. A life insurance company poll of workers found that workplace stress may be caused by company reorganizations or buyout; layoffs; mandatory overtime; varying workloads; work pace; lack of opportunity for advancement; bureaucracy; shortages of staff, money, or technology; low pay; or rotating shifts.

5. Human reaction to workplace stress may be grouped into five categories: (a) subjective, (b) behavioural, (c) cognitive, (d) physiological, and (e) organizational.

6. Psychosomatic reaction to stress may eventually lead to autoimmune disease.

7. Until an individual's limit is reached, the effects of stress may be reversed. After that limit, with continuing stress, the effects can become pathological.

8. Research has shown three stages of human reaction to stress: (a) alarm, (b) resistance, and (c) exhaustion.

9. The best policy regarding stress is to learn to adapt to it. Efforts to rid the workplace of all sources of stress are unlikely to succeed.

10. Mental workload can be measured in three ways: (a) subjective ratings that are state dependent, (b) behavioural time sharing, and (c) psychophysiological techniques.

11. Psychosocial questionnaires study how workers feel about their jobs.

12. Shift work occurs when the majority of people are at leisure. The circadian rhythm, or biological clock within the body, determines when a person will be comfortable either working or sleeping. Workers surveyed have reported lower job satisfaction with rotating shifts. Shift work may result in loss of productivity and an increased number of accidents.

13. All sources of stress on the job cannot be eliminated.

14. Managers can reduce workplace stress by reducing role ambiguity and increasing feedback and job autonomy. Managers can also lessen workers' stress by reducing exposure to physical hazards, varying the work pace, and eliminating monotonous or short-cycle operations.

15. Workplace stress reduction, according to a life insurance study, can be accomplished by providing employee mental health insurance benefits, improving employee–management communications, providing workers with information about how to deal with stress, providing job descriptions, talking with employees regularly, recognizing and rewarding contributions, having published work rules, and offering child care and elder care programs. Other stress reducers include permitting flexible work hours, granting perks fairly, giving adequate training and technology access, providing a place and time to relax, having uncrowded workplaces with space to put up personal items, and having a management that keeps a sense of humour.

16. Individuals can effectively respond to a stressful workload by delegating responsibility and learning how to relax. Relaxation methods include meditation, biofeedback, music, and exercise.

17. One of the most important factors in dealing with stress is learning to recognize its symptoms and taking the symptoms seriously.

KEY TERMS AND CONCEPTS

Behavioural time sharing	Job autonomy
Circadian rhythm	Job descriptions
Control	Job security
Feedback	Psychophysiological techniques
Feeling of responsibility	Psychosocial questionnaires

Role ambiguity   Stress
Shift work   Subjective ratings
Stage of alarm   Task complexity
Stage of exhaustion   Technology access
Stage of resistance   Workplace stress

REVIEW QUESTIONS

1. Define *stress*.

2. How is workplace stress different from general stress?

3. List five sources of workplace stress and give an on-the-job example for each source.

4. Explain why lack of job autonomy may cause workplace stress.

5. Give five categories of human reaction to workplace stress.

6. How are psychosomatic reactions to stress and actual physiological illness related?

7. How are some autoimmune diseases and workplace stress related?

8. Explain three stages of human reaction to stress.

9. Explain three ways in which mental workload can be measured.

10. Discuss efforts to rid the workplace of all causes of workplace stress.

11. What type of data do psychosocial questionnaires provide? Discuss the bias in this type of data.

12. Discuss how shift work causes workplace stress. Give suggestions for minimizing workplace stress from shift work.

13. Give specific steps that can be taken by managers to help reduce workplace stress.

14. Discuss at least five methods to reduce workplace stress, according to the life insurance company research.

15. Explain how individuals can reduce workplace stress.

WEBLINKS

Canadian Centre for Occupational Health and Safety
www.ccohs.ca/oshanswers/psychosocial/stress.html

CCOHS provides information on identifying and dealing with workplace stress and offers advice on how to improve mental health.

Workplace Safety and Insurance Board of Ontario
**www.wsib.on.ca/wsib/wsibsite.nsf/LookupFiles/
    DownloadableFilePolicyReport15_2/$File/PR1502.pdf**

The trends seen in the WSIB Policy Report found at the link above are typical of Canadian workers' compensation boards, when dealing with traumatic mental stress.

ENDNOTES

1. S. Minter, "Too Much Stress?" *Occupational Hazards* 61, no. 5 (May 1999): 49.
2. Ibid.
3. Ibid.
4. Ibid.
5. Ibid.
6. Sandra Hokansson. (2002). "Canada's Knowledge Economy Shift: The Social and Financial Implications." [Online]. Available: http://www.adecco.com/Channels/ adecco/human+resources/adecco+viewpoint/workplace+stress+from+adecco+canada.asp. (Retrieved May 11, 2005).
7. E. Grandjean, *Fitting the Task to the Man* (New York: American Management Association, 1998), 176–77.
8. "Electronic Monitoring Causes Worker Stress," *Occupational Health & Safety Letter* 20, no. 21 (October 17, 1990): 168.
9. Minter, "Too Much Stress?" 51.
10. "Computer Sound in Workplace Linked to Stress," *Occupational Health & Safety Letter* 20, no. 17 (August 22, 1990): 141.
11. Ibid.
12. T. M. Fraser, *The Worker at Work* (New York: Wiley, 1997), 104, 110–11.
13. Ibid., 111.
14. Ibid., 111–15.
15. Grandjean, *Fitting the Task*, 177–78.
16. Fraser, *The Worker*, 116–17.
17. Ibid.
18. Ibid.
19. Ibid.
20. Diann Morshead, "Stress and Shiftwork," *Occupational Health & Safety* 71, no. 4 (April 2002): 36–37.
21. Minter, "Too Much Stress?" 51.
22. S. L. Smith, "Combating Stress," *Occupational Hazards* (March 1994): 57.
23. R. Scherer, "Stress Homes in on Our Safety's Ranks," *Occupational Hazards* (January 1994): 156–57.
24. Ibid., 157.
25. Ibid.

Preparing for Emergencies and Terrorism

CHAPTER 23

LEARNING OBJECTIVES

- Define emergency.
- List five types of emergencies that Canadians are likely to witness.
- Explain the jurisdictional responsibility for emergency preparedness legislation.
- Describe the four first aid requirements for emergency planning.
- Describe the primary and secondary function of an emergency response plan.
- List the essential components of an emergency action plan.
- Describe the four key considerations for evacuation planning.
- Explain the importance of dealing with emergency related trauma.
- Explain how the recovery process can help mitigate the effects of the emergency.
- Describe the role of the employer relating to terrorism in the workplace.

Despite the best efforts of all involved, emergencies do sometimes occur. In recent years, Canadians have witnessed naturally occurring emergencies, such as the Saguenay River flood in 1996, the Red River flood in 1997, the ice storm in 1998, and annual snow storms in the east and forest fires in the west. On a global scale, the tsunami that struck southwest Asia in December 2004 created an emergency of unprecedented proportion. There is also always the potential for human-caused emergencies such as acts of terrorism. It is very important to respond to such emergencies in a way that minimizes harm to people and damage to property. This chapter provides prospective and practising health and safety professionals with the information they need to prepare for emergencies in the workplace. This chapter pertains to all kinds of emergencies, including natural and human induced disasters. A special section relating specifically to terrorism is included at the end of the chapter.

RATIONALE FOR EMERGENCY PREPARATION

An **emergency** is a potentially life-threatening situation, usually occurring sud-denly and unexpectedly. Public Safety and Emergency Preparedness Canada (PSEPC) defines an emergency as an abnormal situation which, to limit damage to persons, property or the environment, requires prompt action beyond normal procedures.[1] Figure 23–1 lists some potential emergencies and their classifica-tion as used by PSEPC.

Have you ever witnessed the timely, organized, and precise response of a professional emergency medical crew at an automobile accident? While passers-by and spectators may wring their hands and wonder what to do, the emergency response professionals quickly organize, stabilize the situation, and administer assistance. Their ability to respond in this manner is the result of preparation. As shown in Figure 23–2, preparation involves a combination of *planning, practising, evaluating*, and *adjusting* to specific circumstances.

When an emergency occurs, immediate reaction is essential. Speed in responding can mean the difference between life and death or between minimal damage and major damage. Ideally, all those involved should be able to respond properly with a minimum of hesitation. This can happen only if all exigencies have been planned for and planned procedures have been practised, evaluated, and improved.

A quick and proper response — which results because of proper prepara-tion — can prevent panic, decrease the likelihood of injury and damage, and bring the situation under control in a timely manner. Because no workplace is immune to emergencies, preparing for them is critical. An important compo-nent of preparation is planning.

EMERGENCY PREPAREDNESS LEGISLATION IN CANADA

Which jurisdiction's legislation applies to a specific situation will often be decided by the magnitude of the emergency. In the event of an emergency, it is also likely that various agencies from different jurisdictions will be involved in the initial response, the mediation, and the recovery processes. In Canada, leg-islation enacted by federal, provincial/territorial, or municipal governments may apply. The two main pieces of federal legislation are the Emergency Act and the Emergency Preparedness Act.

The Emergency Act limits the authority of the government of Canada and holds it accountable to Parliament when an emergency is declared. National emer-gencies usually differ from provincial emergencies only in that the capacity to deal with the emergency exceeds that of the province or territory. The Emergency Act, which makes provisions to compensate disaster victims and protect Canadians' fundamental rights and freedoms, defines four types of national emergencies:

- **public welfare emergencies**: severe natural disasters or major accidents af-fecting public welfare, which are beyond the capacity or authority of a province or territory to handle.
- **public order emergencies**: which constitute threats to the security of Canada, and are so serious as to be national emergencies and are beyond the capacity or authority of a province or territory to handle.

Critical Infrastructure Systems

(Any system the disruption or loss of which would cause prejudice to lives and property.)

Cyber attack	Power failure
Failure of computer networks or other IT systems	Safety and security system loss
	Telecommunications failure
Financial institution linkage loss	Water/ wastewater loss

Naturally Occurring

Avalanches	Heat wave
Blizzards	High winds
Cold wave	Hurricanes
Crop disasters	Ice jams in shipping lanes and other
Droughts	critical areas
Earthquakes	Ice storms
Epidemics: Animal disease, Human disease, Plant disease	Landslides
	Magnetic storms
Fisheries emergencies	Sea and lake surges
Floods: Predictable, Flash, Dam burst	Severe thunderstorms
Fogs	Snow
Forest diseases and insect infestations	Tidal waves (tsunami)
Forest fires	Tornadoes
Frost and freeze-ups	Torrential rain
Hail	

Human Induced

Environmental: Endangering a species

Industrial: Explosions, Hazardous chemicals (in plant), Mining accidents, Nuclear reactor accidents, Power failures, Structural collapse, Urban fires

Pollution: Air, Land, Water

Political and social: Air piracy, Assassinations, Disturbances - Riots, Insurrections, Sabotage, Strikes, Civil disorders, Subversion, Terrorism

Transport: Hazardous materials in transit, Air, Rail, Road, Ship

International

War

Events occurring in or outside of Canadian territory that endanger Canadian interests or the interests of another country.

Offshore Emergency

Events occurring in the waters contiguous to Canada or on the continental shelf that endanger Canadian national interests.

Figure 23–1 Potential emergencies.
Source: PSEPC. (March 2, 2003). "Fact Sheets – List of Potential Emergencies for Developing Contingency Plans: Potential Emergencies" [Online]. Available: http://www.ocipep.gc.ca/info_pro/fact_sheets/general/EM_list_poten_e.asp. (Retrieved January 23, 2005).

**Figure 23–2
Elements of
emergency
preparation.**

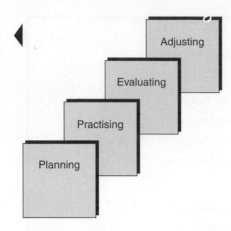

**INTERNATIONAL
EMERGENCIES**
Arise from international
acts of intimidation or
coercion or the use of
serious force or violence
that threaten the sover-
eignty, security, or territorial integrity of Canada
or its allies.

WAR EMERGENCIES
War or other armed con-
flict, real or imminent, involving Canada or any of
its allies.

**EMERGENCY
PREPAREDNESS ACT**
Legislation that estab-
lishes the role of the federal government in
preparing for civil emer-
gencies in Canada.

- **international emergencies**: which arise from acts of intimidation or coercion or the use of serious force or violence that threatens the sovereignty, security or territorial integrity of Canada or any of its allies.
- **war emergencies**: which means war or other armed conflict, real or imminent, involving Canada or any of its allies.[2]

The **Emergency Preparedness Act** establishes rules that enable the Government of Canada to be ready to deal with emergencies in cooperation with the provinces and territories. The Emergency Preparedness Act

> sets out the responsibilities and functions of the Minister Responsible for Emergency Preparedness with respect to the coordination and support of civil emergency plans, the enhancement of public awareness, and the conduct of training and education related to civil preparedness for emergencies;
>
> establishes the emergency preparedness responsibilities of all federal ministers in their respective areas of accountability;
>
> explicitly recognizes the interests of the provinces in relation to federal assistance provided during a provincial emergency;
>
> provides the legal basis for the Governor in Council to declare a provincial emergency to be of concern to the federal government, and to provide financial and other assistance requested by the affected province(s).[3]

Provincial or territorial legislation ensures that the province contributes to national emergencies as well as supporting the municipalities and individual response teams. The legislation varies, but the basic principles on which emergency management is based, apply to each jurisdiction. They include both that when the capabilities of the local community or municipality have been exhausted, progressively higher levels of government will provide resources and that the provinces/territories will support national emergency response efforts.

Most municipalities are required by the province or territory to have an emergency response plan, although in some provinces this may apply only to specific larger cities. An example of a municipality exercising its legal authority is when a *state of local emergency* is declared. During a state of local emergency, the municipality may assume additional powers while implementing its emergency plan, in order to protect the citizens from harm. During provincial or territorial emergencies, the province/territory may also exercise additional powers during a *state of emergency,* at which time it may or may not also seek federal assistance.

Provincial and Territorial Emergency Management Organizations

Alberta
Emergency Management Alberta
Phone: 780-422-9000
Toll-free (in Alberta): 310-0000-422-9000
Fax: 780-422-1549
Website: www.gov.ab.ca/ma/ema

British Columbia
Provincial Emergency Program (PEP)
Phone: 250-952-4913
Fax: 250-952-4888
Website: ww.pep.bc.ca

Manitoba
Emergency Measures Organization
Phone: 204-945-4772
Toll-free: 1-888-267-8298
Fax: 204-945-4620
Website: www.manitobaemo.ca

New Brunswick
Emergency Measures Organization
Phone: 506-453-2133
Toll-free: 1-800-561-4034
Fax: 506-453-5513
Website: www.gnb.ca/cnb/emo-omu/index-e.asp

Newfoundland & Labrador
Emergency Measures Division
Phone: 709-729-3703
Fax: 709-729-3857
Website: www.gov.nf.ca/mpa/emo.html

Northwest Territories
Emergency Measures Organization
Phone: 867-873-7785
Fax: 867-873-8193
Website: www.maca.gov.nt.ca/safety/
emergency_organization.html

Nova Scotia
Emergency Measures Organization
Phone: 902-424-5620
Fax: 902-424-5376
Website: www.gov.ns.ca/emo/

Nunavut
Nunavut Emergency Management
Phone: 867-975-5300
Fax: 867-979-4221

Ontario
Ontario Emergency Management
Ontario Ministry of Community Safety and
Correctional Services
77 Wellesley Street West, Box 222
Toronto, ON M7A 1N3
Phone: 416-314-3723
Fax: 416-314-3758
Website:www.mpss.jus.gov.on.ca/english/
pub_security/emo/about_emo.html

Prince Edward Island
Emergency Measures Organization
Phone: 902-368-4000
Fax: 902-368-5544
Website: www.gov.pe.ca/caag/emo-info/index.php3

Quebec
Direction générale de la sécurité civile et de la
sécurité incendie
Phone: 418-644-6826
Fax: 418-643-3194
Or one of the regional offices:
Gatineau : 819-772-3737
Montreal: 514-873-1300
Rimouski: 418-727-3589
Sillery (Quebec): 418-643-3244
Trois-Rivières: 819-371-6703 or your municipality
Website: www.msp.gouv.qc.ca/index_en.asp

Saskatchewan
Emergency Management Organization
Phone: 306-787-9563
Fax: 306-787-1694
Website:www.cps.gov.sk.ca/Safety/emergency/
default.shtml

Yukon Territory
Emergency Measures Organization
Phone: 867-667-5220
Toll-free (in Yukon): 1-800-661-0408
Fax: 867-393-6266
Website: www.gov.yk.ca/depts/community/emo/

Source: PSEPC. (February 24, 2005). "Provincial and Territorial Emergency Management Organizations." [Online]. Available: http://www.ocipep.gc.ca/ep/contact_e.asp. (Retrieved March 12, 2005).

FIRST AID IN EMERGENCIES

Workplace emergencies often require a medical response. The immediate response is usually first aid. First aid consists of life-saving measures taken to assist an injured person until medical help arrives. Because there is no way to predict when first aid may be needed, providing first-aid training to employees should be part of preparing for emergencies. In fact, most jurisdictions require that companies have at least one employee on site who has been trained in first aid. Figure 23–3 contains a list of the topics that may be covered in a first-aid class for industrial workers.

Figure 23–3
St. John Ambulance standard or emergency first-aid course lessons.

Both the Standard First Aid and Emergency First Aid courses include the same five compulsory lessons, which take about 4–5 hours to complete.

1. Emergency Scene Management
2. Shock, Unconsciousness, and Fainting
3. Artificial Respiration (Adult)
4. Choking (Adult)
5. Severe Bleeding

There are 19 elective lessons. The Emergency course includes approximately 1.5 hours of electives, while the Standard course includes about 7.5 hours.

6. Child Resuscitation
7. Infant Resuscitation
8. Cardiovascular Emergencies and One-Rescuer CPR (Adult casualty)
9. Two-Rescuer CPR (Adult)
10. Secondary Survey
11. Bone and Joint Injuries - Upper Limbs, Muscle Strains
12. Bone and Joint Injuries - Lower Limbs
13. Head/Spinal and Pelvic Injuries
14. Chest Injuries
15. Wound Care
16. Multiple Casualty Management
17. Rescue Carries
18. Eye Injuries
19. Burns
20. Poisons, Bites, and Stings
21. Medical Conditions (Diabetes, Convulsions, Asthma, Allergies)
22. Environmental Illness and Injuries
23. Emergency Childbirth and Miscarriage
24. Automated External Defibrillation

Source: St. John Ambulance. (2003). "Standard Level First Aid." [Online]. Available: http://www.sja.ca/english/in_the_workplace/courses/specialized_training.asp. (Retrieved March 11, 2005).

First-Aid Training Program

First-aid programs are usually available in most communities. The continuing education departments of community colleges and universities typically offer first-aid training. Classes can often be provided on site and customized to meet the specific needs of individual companies. The Canadian Red Cross and St. John Ambulance Canada are the two primary first aid training providers in Canada. They provide first aid training at various levels and for specific areas from babysitter safety to emergency response.

Beyond Training

Training employees in first-aid techniques is an important part of preparing for emergencies. However, training is only part of the preparation. In addition, it is important to do the following:

1. **Have well-stocked first-aid kits available.** First-aid kits should be placed throughout the workplace in clearly visible, easily accessible locations. They should be properly and fully stocked and periodically checked to ensure that they stay fully stocked.

2. **Have appropriate personal protective devices available.** With concerns about AIDS and hepatitis, administering first aid has become more complicated than in the past. The main concerns are with bleeding and other body fluids. Consequently, a properly stocked first-aid kit should contain rubber surgical gloves and facemasks or mouthpieces for CPR.

3. **Post emergency telephone numbers.** The advent of 911 service has simplified the process of calling for medical care, police, or firefighting assistance. If 911 services are not available, emergency numbers for ambulance, hospital, police, fire department, LEPC (local emergency planning committee), and appropriate internal personnel should be posted at clearly visible locations near all telephones in the workplace.

4. **Keep all employees informed.** Some companies require all employees to undergo first-aid training; others choose to train one or more employees in each department. Regardless of the approach used, it is important that all employees be informed and kept up to date concerning basic first-aid information.

HOW TO PLAN FOR EMERGENCIES

Responses to emergencies typically come from several people or groups of people, including medical, firefighting, security, and safety personnel as well as specialists from a variety of different fields. People in each of these areas have different but interrelated and often interdependent roles to play in responding to the emergency. Because of their disparate backgrounds and roles, organization and coordination are critical.

A company's **emergency response plan** should clearly identify the different personnel and groups that respond to various types of emergencies and, in each case, who is in charge. One person should be clearly identified and accepted by all emergency responders as the **emergency coordinator**. This person should be knowledgeable, at least in a general sense, about the responsibilities of each

EMERGENCY RESPONSE PLAN
A written document that identifies the different personnel or groups that respond to various types of emergencies and, in each case, who is in charge.

EMERGENCY COORDINATOR
A person who is clearly identified in a company emergency response plan as the responsible party for a specific type of emergency situation.

First Aid Kits

The Workplace Safety and Insurance Board of Ontario (WSIB) prescribes the following minimum items be contained in first aid kits where between 15 to 200 people are employed.

- A current edition of the St. John Ambulance Pocket Guide
- 1 card of safety pins
- 24 adhesive strips, individually wrapped
- 12 sterile gauze pads, 3" × 31' (7.5 cm × 9.5 m)
- 4 rolls gauze bandage, 2" × 5 yds (5 cm × 4.55 m)
- 4 rolls gauze bandage, 4" × 5 yds (10 cm × 4.55 m)
- 4 sterile surgical pads (pressure dressings)
- 6 triangular bandages
- 2 rolls of splint padding
- 1 roll-up splint

  PLUS

- 1 pair of scissors
- 1 roll adhesive tape
- 1 roll 2" (5 cm) gauze wrap

---

individual emergency responder and how each relates to those of all other responders. This knowledge must include the order of response for each type of emergency set forth in the plan.

A company's health and safety professional is the obvious person to organize and coordinate emergency responses. However, regardless of who is designated, it is important that (1) one person is in charge, (2) everyone involved knows who is in charge, and (3) everyone who has a role in responding to an emergency is given ample opportunities to practise in simulated conditions that come as close as possible to real conditions.

EMERGENCY ACTION PLAN (EAP)
A collection of small plans for every anticipated emergency (e.g., fire, hurricane, chemical spill, and so on).

Developing an **emergency action plan (EAP)** is a major step in preparing for emergencies. A preliminary step is to conduct a thorough analysis to determine the various types of emergencies that may occur. For example, depending on geography and the types of products and processes involved, a company may anticipate such emergencies as fires, chemical spills, explosions, toxic emissions, train derailments, hurricanes, tornadoes, lightning, floods, earthquakes, or volcanic eruptions.

A company's EAP should be a collection of small plans for each anticipated or potential emergency. The person developing the EAP has to consider the resources available locally and adjust the plan accordingly. For example, close proximity to a medical clinic or fire station would relieve the pressure from the areas of first aid and fire fighting. However, a propane storage facility or densely populated residential areas nearby would add to the potential seriousness of the emergency. These plans should have the following components:

1. **Procedures.** Specific, step-by-step emergency response procedures should be developed for each potential emergency.

2. **Coordination.** All cooperating agencies and organizations and emergency responders should be listed along with their telephone number and primary contact person.

3. **Assignments and responsibilities.** Every person who will be involved in responding to a given emergency should know his or her assignment. Each person's responsibilities should be clearly spelled out and understood. One person may be responsible for conducting an evacuation of the affected area, another for the immediate shutdown of all equipment, and another for telephoning for medical, fire, or other types of emergency assistance. When developing this part of the EAP, it is important to assign a backup person for each area of responsibility. Doing so ensures that the plan will not break down if a person assigned a certain responsibility is one of the victims.

4. **Accident prevention strategies.** The day-to-day strategies to be used for preventing a particular type of emergency should be summarized in this section of the EAP. In this way, the strategies can be reviewed, thereby promoting prevention.

5. **Schedules.** This section should contain the dates and times of regularly scheduled practice drills. It is best to vary the times and dates so that practice drills don't become predictable and boring. Figure 23–4 is a checklist that can be used for developing an EAP.

DISCUSSION CASE

What Is Your Opinion?

Peter, the safety manager for Dew-Line Manufacturing requested to the company president, Giovanni, that evacuation drills be conducted each quarter as opposed to semi-annually. Giovanni replied that the drills are a waste of time and are not required at all, because the chance of an evacuation being necessary is very remote and even if an alarm sounded, the workers know their way out of the building. Who is right in this case? What is your opinion?

EVACUATION PLANNING

In many situations, rapid egress from a facility can save lives or reduce injury. A written plan for the evacuation of the facility should be in place. Critical elements of the plan are marking of exit routes, communications, outside assembly, and training.

**Figure 23–4
Emergency planning
checklist.**

Type of Emergency

____Fire   ____Explosion
____Chemical spill   ____Toxic emission
____Train derailment   ____Hurricane
____Tornado   ____Lightning
____Flood   ____Earthquake
____Volcanic eruption

Procedures for Emergency Response
1. Controlling and isolating?
2. Communication?
3. Emergency assistance?
4. First aid?
5. Shutdown/evacuation/protection of workers?
6. Protection of equipment/property?
7. Egress, ingress, exits?
8. Emergency equipment (e.g., fire extinguishers)?
9. Alarms?
10. Restoration of normal operations?

Coordination
1. Medical care providers?
2. Fire service providers?
3. LEPC (local emergency planning committee) personnel?
4. Environmental protection personnel?
5. Civil defence personnel (in the case of public evacuations)?
6. Police protection providers?
7. Communication personnel?

Marking of Exit Routes

Clearly identified and marked routes of egress are critical during a time of crisis (fire, natural disaster, terrorist attack, etc.). To ensure that routes of egress and all related evacuation response items are clearly marked, safety professionals should answer the following questions about the facilities for which they are responsible:

1. Are all exit, emergency exit, and nonexit doors clearly identified and marked?

2. Are there up-to-date evacuation route maps mounted at strategic locations throughout the facility?

3. Are all egress route aisles, hallways, and stairs marked clearly and can the markings be seen in the event of darkness?

4. Are there low-level markings posted strategically throughout the facility that can be viewed in the event that smoke fills the facility?

5. Are all items of firefighting equipment clearly marked with directional signs so they can be easily located in the event of an emergency?

Assignments and Responsibilities
  1. Who cares for the injured?
  2. Who calls for emergency assistance?
  3. Who shuts down power and operations?
  4. Who coordinates communication?
  5. Who conducts the evacuation?
  6. Who meets emergency responders and guides them to the emergency site?
  7. Who contacts coordinating agencies and organizations?
  8. Who is responsible for ensuring the availability and upkeep of fire extinguishers?
  9. Who is responsible for ensuring that alarms are in proper working order?
 10. Who is responsible for organizing cleanup activities?

Accident Prevention Strategies
  1. Periodic safety inspections?
  2. Industrial hygiene strategies?
  3. Personal protective equipment?
  4. Ergonomic strategies?
  5. Machine safeguards?
  6. Hand and portable power tool safeguards?
  7. Material handling and storage strategies?
  8. Electrical safety strategies?
  9. Fire safety strategies?
 10. Chemical safety strategies?

Schedules
  1. Dates of practice drills:_____
  2. Times of practice drills:_____
  3. Duration of practice drills: _____

**Figure 23–4
(continued)**

6. Is all emergency first-aid equipment clearly marked with directional signs so that it can be easily located in the event of an emergency?

7. Are all electrical, chemical, and physical hazards identified and clearly marked?

8. Are all physical obstructions clearly outlined?

9. Are all critical shutdown procedures and equipment identified and clearly marked?

10. Are the handrails, treads, and risers on all stairs clearly marked?

11. In the case of multicultural workforce settings, are all signs and markings provided in a bilingual or pictogram format?[4]

Ensuring that all signs, pictograms, and other markings relating to facility evacuation are visible during power outages is critical. Battery backup systems are one approach that is widely used. However, there are environments in which even the smallest spark from a battery might set off an explosion. For this reason, some facilities find the use of photoluminescent signs a better alternative.

Photoluminescent signs and markings absorb normal light energy from their surroundings and then release this energy in the form of light during periods of darkness. Some of the better photoluminescent materials will give off light for as long as 24 hours and have a maintenance-free life expectancy of up to 25 years.

Communication and Alarm Procedures

People are so accustomed to false alarms in their lives that when the *real thing* occurs, it can be difficult to convince them that it's not just another drill. In addition, people tend to trust what they can see, smell, and hear. Consequently, if they cannot physically sense an emergency, they tend to ignore the warning. The communication component of a facility's evacuation plan should include procedures for early detection of a problem, procedures for reporting an emergency, procedures for initiating an evacuation, and procedures for providing the necessary information to employees who are being evacuated.[5]

Notifying employees of the emergency is the function of the facility's alarm system. However, just pulling the alarm switch is not sufficient communication. Once the alarm has been given, verbal instruction should be broadcast so that people know that the alarm is real (not just another drill) as well as specific actions they should take immediately. There must also be procedures for informing evacuated employees that the emergency is over and they can return to their work.

External communication procedures are also important. All employees should know how to notify outside authorities of the emergency. With the advent of 911 service, this problem has been simplified. However, do not assume that all employees will remember the number when under the stress of an emergency, or that they will remember to dial "9" or some other code to gain access to an outside line. This problem can be solved by placing clearly marked signs above or near telephones containing such messages as "In an emergency dial 911" or "In an emergency dial 9911" (if it is necessary to first access an outside line).

Outside Assembly

The company's evacuation plan should include an assembly area to which employees go once evacuated.[6] This area should be well known by all employees, and employees should understand that it is critical to assemble there so that a headcount can be taken. In addition, there should be a backup assembly area known to all employees so they know where to go if the primary assembly area has been rendered inaccessible or hazardous.

Part of the evacuation plan relating to assembly areas must be devoted to transient personnel — non employees such as vendors, visitors, contractors, and so on. How will they know where to assemble? Who will check to see that they have been notified of the emergency? These issues should be addressed in the evacuation plan.

Training

Training for evacuations is a critical element of the evacuation plan.[7] Developing a plan and then letting it just sit on the shelf gathering dust is a formula for disaster. Everything contained in the plan that requires action or knowledge on the part of employees should be part of the required evacuation training. Training should be provided when employees are first hired, and retraining should be provided periodically as various elements of the plan are updated.

Drills should be a major part of the training provided for employees. The old sports adage that says, "What you do in practice you will do in the game" applies here. When an emergency actually occurs should not be the first time employees have gone through the action required of them in an emergency.

DEALING WITH THE PSYCHOLOGICAL TRAUMA OF EMERGENCIES

In addition to the physical injuries and property damage that can occur in emergencies, modern health and safety professionals must also be prepared to deal with potential psychological damage. Psychological trauma among employees involved in workplace disasters is as common as it is among combat veterans. According to Johnson, "Traumatic incidents do not affect only immediate survivors and witnesses. Most incidents result in layers of victims that stretch far beyond those who were injured or killed."[8]

Trauma is psychological stress. It occurs as the result of an event, typically a disaster or some kind of emergency, so shocking that it impairs a person's sense of security or well-being. Johnson calls trauma response "the normal reactions of normal people to an abnormal event."[9] Traumatic events are typically unexpected and shocking, and they involve the reality or threat of death.

TRAUMA
Psychological stress.

Dealing with Emergency-Related Trauma

The typical approach to an emergency can be described as follows: Control it, take care of the injured, clean up the mess, and get back to work. Often, the psychological aspect is ignored. This leaves witnesses and other co-workers to deal on their own with the trauma they've experienced. "Left to their own inadequate resources, workers can become ill or unable to function. They may develop resentment toward the organization, which can lead to conflicts with bosses and co-workers, high employee turnover — even subconscious sabotage."[10]

It is important to respond to trauma quickly, within 24 hours if possible and within 72 hours in all cases. The purpose of the response is to help employees get back to normal by enabling them to handle what they have experienced. This is best accomplished by a team of people who have had special training. Such a team is typically called the trauma response team (TRT).

Trauma Response Team

A company's trauma response team may consist of health and safety personnel who have undergone special training or fully credentialled counselling personnel, depending on the size of the company. In any case, the TRT should be included in the assignments and responsibilities section of the EAP.

The job of the TRT is to intervene as early as possible, help employees acknowledge what they have experienced, and give them opportunities to express how they feel about it to people who are qualified to help. The *qualified to help* aspect is very important. TRT members who are not counsellors or mental health professionals should never attempt to provide care that they are not qualified to offer. Part of the trauma training that health and safety professionals receive involves recognizing the symptoms of employees who need professional care and referring them to qualified care providers.

In working with employees who need to deal with what they have experienced, but are not so traumatized as to require referral for outside professional care, a group approach is best. According to Johnson, the group approach offers several advantages:

- It facilitates public acknowledgment of what the employees have experienced.
- It keeps employees informed, thereby cutting down on the number of unfounded rumours and horror stories that will inevitably make the rounds.
- It encourages employees to express their feelings about the incident. This alone is often enough to get people back to normal and functioning properly.
- It allows employees to see that they are not alone in experiencing traumatic reactions (e.g., nightmares, flashbacks, shocking memories, and so on) and that these reactions are normal.[11]

Convincing Companies to Respond

Modern health and safety professionals may find themselves having to convince higher management of the need to have a TRT. Some corporate officials may not believe that trauma even exists. Others may acknowledge its presence but view trauma as a personal problem that employees should handle on their own.

POSTTRAUMATIC STRESS DISORDER
The ongoing symptoms of exposure to psychological stress.

In reality, psychological trauma that is left untreated can manifest itself as **posttraumatic stress disorder**, the same syndrome experienced by some war veterans. This disorder is characterized by "intrusive thoughts and flashbacks of the stressful event, the tendency to avoid stimulation, paranoia, concentration difficulties, and physiological symptoms such as rapid heartbeat and irritability."[12]

In today's competitive marketplace, companies need all of their employees operating at peak performance levels. Employees experiencing trauma-related disorders will not be at their best. Health and safety professionals should use this rationale when it is necessary to convince higher management of the need to provide a company-sponsored trauma response team.

EMERGENCY PLANNING
Developing procedures to reduce the negative effects of an emergency. An emergency plan will have provisions for reducing fatalities and injuries; limiting the damage to equipment, facilities, and product; and expediting the return to normal operation.

RECOVERING FROM DISASTERS

Many organizations put a great deal of effort into planning for disaster response including emergency evacuation. The primary function of **emergency planning** is to prevent injuries and protect life, but what about after the disaster? The secondary function of emergency planning should include provisions to expedite the return to normal operation.

Accordingly, a comprehensive disaster recovery plan should have at least the following components: recovery coordinator, recovery team, recovery analysis and planning, damage assessment and salvage operations, recovery communications, and employee support and assistance. The overall goal of a disaster recovery plan is to get an organization fully operational again as quickly as possible.

Recovery Coordinator

There must be one person who has ultimate responsibility and authority for disaster recovery. This person must have both the ability and the authority to take command of the situation, assess the recovery needs, delegate specific responsibilities, approve the necessary resources, interact with outside agencies, and activate the organization's overall response.

Recovery Team

The recovery team consists of key personnel to whom the disaster coordinator can delegate specific responsibilities. These responsibilities include facility management, security, human resources, environmental protection (if applicable), communications, and the various personnel needed to restart operations.

Recovery Analysis and Planning

This phase involves assessing the impact of the disaster on the organization and establishing both short- and long-term recovery goals. The more recovery analysis and planning that can be done, the better. One of the ways to do this is to consider various predictable scenarios and plan for them. This is the business equivalent of the war-gaming activities that take place in the military.

Damage Assessment and Salvage

This component of the plan has two elements: preparedness and recovery. The preparedness element should include the following information: (1) a comprehensive inventory of all property at the facility in question; (2) a checklist of the items on the inventory that are essential for maintaining the facility; (3) a list of all personnel who will aid in the recovery (make sure to have fully trained and qualified backup personnel in case a primary player is not available or is injured during the emergency); (4) a list of all vendors, contractors, and so on whose assistance will be needed during the damage assessment and salvage phase of recovery; (5) a worksheet that can be used to document all actions taken during recovery operations; and (6) procedures for quickly establishing a remote operational site.

The recovery element should include procedures for securing workspace for the recovery team and coordinator; identifying areas of the facility that must be accessible; maintaining security at the facility against looting and vandalism; analyzing and inspecting damage to the facility and reporting it to the recovery coordinator; assessing the extent of damage to goods, supplies, and equipment; photographing and videotaping damage to the facility; taking appropriate action to prevent additional damage to the facility; repairing, restoring and resetting fire detection and suppression equipment; and investigating accidents.

Recovery Communications

Communication is one of the most important considerations in disaster recovery. This component of the plan should deal with both who is to be notified and how that is to take place. The "how" aspects concern backup procedures for telephone service, email, and so forth. Will cell phones be used? Will radio stations be part of the mix? Will "walkie-talkie" type radios be used for communicating on site? The following list contains the people and organizations who might have to be contacted as part of the disaster recovery operation:

- Customers.
- Vendors and suppliers.
- Insurance representatives.
- Employees' families.
- Appropriate authorities.
- Media outlets (radio and television stations and newspapers).

TERRORISM IN THE WORKPLACE

Before September 11, 2001, terrorism was far from the forefront of most Canadians' minds. Of course, we have distant memories of the FLQ crisis in Quebec that resulted in the murder of Cabinet Minister Pierre Laporte. And another significant reminder of the presence of terrorism came with the 1985 Air India Bombing. (Although Canada was not directly attacked, the bombing of an Air India flight from Toronto, in 1985, resulted in the death of 329 people, most of whom were Canadian.) But the events of September 11 brought the threat of terrorism one step closer and have made the fear of terrorism more a part of our daily consciousness. The Canadian Security Intelligence Service (CSIS) warns, "Not only were there a number of Canadians among the approximately 3,000 victims of the World Trade Center attack but, because of Canada's solidarity with the United States in pursuing those responsible, our country — along with other western democracies — has now become a potential target for terrorist activity."[13]

As Chip Dawson observes, "The events of Sept. 11 and the ongoing threat of bioterrorism in American workplaces have many people living and working in fear. Unquestionably, the world has changed, and few of us are happy with the direction. It's important to put everything in perspective, however, and consider the proper role of the employer."[14] This section describes the roles that employers and their health and safety personnel can play in preparing for, preventing, and responding to terrorist attacks in the workplace.

Role of the Employer

Since 9/11, although the threat of terrorism has not actually increased, the public's awareness and level of anxiety has increased. Because of this, more and more workplaces are developing plans to prepare for the possibility of a terrorist attack, both by taking precautions to prevent such an attack and by developing a systematic plan of response to deal with an attack should it occur. Because terrorism threatens the health and safety of employees, it is more than just a security issue; it is also an occupational health and safety issue.

Chip Dawson summarizes the roles of employers and health and safety professionals relating to terrorism in the workplace:

Run a safe and caring operation. Employees watch the nightly news and read their morning newspapers. They know what is going on in their world. As a result, many are discomfited by the possibility that they or their workplace might become the target of a terrorist attack. Consequently, the first responsibility of the employer is to run a safe operation in which employees know their safety is a high priority. Many of the engineering, administrative, training, and enforcement actions taken to make the workplace safe from occupational hazards will also help mitigate the threat of terrorism.

Listen to employees. Employees are concerned about the threat of terrorism, and they have a right to be. Employers should take the concerns of employees seriously, and deal with them. Answer questions, communicate openly and frequently, and refer employees who need professional help to the employee assistance program.

Train employees. Security and safety procedures do little good unless employees know what they are and how to use them. In addition, personnel in certain positions need to have specialized knowledge relating to terrorism. For example, mailroom personnel need to be trained in how to screen incoming mail for biohazards and explosives.

Communicate. Talk with employees openly and frequently. Let them know what the company knows. It is better for employees to hear news from the company than to receive it in the form of third-party gossip and rumors. Before giving out information, however, it is a good idea to verify it. Check with local authorities or go online to one of the following Web sites: http://www.snopes.com or http://www. urbanlegends.com.

Know your personnel. Institute background checks as part of the hiring process. Make sure that supervisors get to know their direct reports well enough to sense when something is wrong with one of them. If inconsistencies in normal behavioral patterns occur, address them right away.

Empower personnel. Empower employees to back away from a situation that does not feel right or that makes them uncomfortable. Be flexible in allowing them to have time off for family activities. This can be especially important following particularly busy times for employees who have worked longer than normal hours.

Harden the site against external threats and restrict access. Insulate the workplace from negative outside influences, control who has access to the workplace, and take all necessary steps to reduce the exposure of employees to potential threats. Call in security experts if necessary to help develop and implement the necessary controls.

Remove any barriers to clear visibility around the facility. The better employees can see around them, the less likely it will be that a terrorist will be able to pull off a surprise attack. The trees, shrubs, and bushes that make the perimeter of the facility and parking lot so attractive can be used by unauthorized personnel to hide while attempting to gain access.

Have and enforce parking and delivery regulations. Arrange parking spaces so that no car is closer to a building than 100 feet. This will lessen the likelihood of damage from a car bomb. In addition, have strict delivery procedures so that terrorists posing as delivery personnel do not gain access through this means.

Make sure that visitors can be screened from a distance. Arrange the facility so that visitors are channeled into a specific area, an area in which they can be viewed by company personnel from a distance. This will lessen the likelihood of a terrorist gaining access by overpowering or killing access-control personnel.

Keep all unstaffed entrance doors locked and alarmed. Employees need to be able to get out of the building through any exit door, but access into the building should be channeled through doors staffed by access-control personnel.

Make air intakes and other utilities inaccessible to all but designated maintenance personnel. Releasing toxic material into the air intake is one way terrorists could harm the highest possible number of people. The likelihood of this happening can be decreased by locating air intakes in inaccessible locations.

Prevent access to roofs and upper stories. Terrorists who cannot gain access on the ground floor might simply gain entry through doors and other openings on the roof. Consequently, it is important to keep roof doors locked from the outside and alarmed. They should open from the inside, but doing so should trigger an alarm. It is also important to establish control procedures for emergency escape routes from the roof and upper stories so that these avenues are not used by terrorists trying to gain access into the building.

Secure trash containers. The grounds should be kept free of debris and clutter. Further, trash containers should be secured either by keeping them inside the building's wall or, if kept outside, at a distance from the building.

Ensure that employees, contractors, and visitors wear badges. Establish a system in which all employees, contractors, and visitors must wear badges in order to gain access to the facility. Require identification of all visitors and an internal sponsor before providing them with badges. Have visitors sign in and out on every visit.

Have an emergency response plan and practise it periodically. Plan for all predictable exigencies and practise the various components of the plan on a regular basis.

Be cautious of information placed on your company's website. Make sure that your company's website does not contain information that can be used by terrorists such as detailed maps, floor plans, or descriptions of hazardous materials stored on-site.

Keep up-to-date with the latest safety and security strategies. Crime Prevention Through Environmental Design (CPTED) should become part of the knowledge base of safety and health professionals. For the latest information concerning CPTED, visit the following website periodically: http://www.arch.vt.edu/crimeprev/pages/home.html.

Protect the integrity of your facility's key system. Terrorists can use any key from your facility to make their own master key if they know how, and many do. To make matters worse, they share information about how to make master keys via the Internet. The following procedures will help protect the integrity of your facility's key system: (a) restrict access to keys (including restroom keys); (b) consider not using master keys; and (c) switch from a key system to an electronic keycard or fingerprint recognition system.[15]

Securing Hazardous Materials

Clearly, one of the tactics of terrorists is to convert hazardous materials used in the workplace into weapons of mass destruction. Consequently, it is important for facilities that produce, use, or store any type of hazardous materials to develop, implement, and enforce a security program that denies terrorists access to these materials.[16] "The goal of the security plan should be to implement measures that deter, detect, delay, or defeat the threat. Deterrence can be improved by using highly visible measures and randomness. This is cost-efficient and complicates the threatening person or group's planning."[17]

A hazmat security plan should have two broad components: *personnel security* and *physical security*. The fundamental elements of the personnel component of the plan are to (1) determine who should be granted access to the materials; (2) conduct comprehensive background checks on all individuals who require access; (3) submit employees who require access to psychological screening to ensure stability; and (4) require identification badges with photographs or fingerprints of those authorized access.

The physical security component consists of measures taken to prevent or control access to the hazardous materials in question. Security practices in this component should be integrated and layered by using a combination of measures including fences, lights, electronic alarm systems, guards, reaction forces, and the *two-person rule* that requires two employees to be present in order to gain access to the hazardous materials.

SUMMARY

1. An emergency is a potentially life-threatening situation, usually occurring suddenly and unexpectedly. Emergencies may be the result of natural or human causes.
2. Preparing for emergencies involves planning, practising, evaluating, and adjusting. An immediate response is critical in emergencies.
3. The federal government, through Public Safety and Emergency Preparedness Canada, supports Canadians at all levels in preparing for and responding to emergencies.
4. For proper coordination of the internal emergency response, it is important that one person be in charge and that everyone involved knows who that person is.
5. Because there is no way to predict when first aid may be needed, part of preparing for emergencies should include training employees to administer first aid.
6. In addition to providing first-aid training, it is important to have well-stocked first-aid kits readily available, have personal protective devices available, post emergency telephone numbers, and keep all employees informed.
7. A company's emergency action plan should be a collection of small plans for each anticipated emergency. These plans should have the following components: procedures, coordination, assignments and responsibilities, accident prevention strategies, and schedules.
8. Critical elements of an evacuation plan are as follows: marking of exit routes, communications, outside assembly, and training.
9. EAPs should be customized to be location-specific by including a map, an organization chart, local coordination information, and local training schedules.
10. An emergency response team is a special team to handle general and localized emergencies, facilitate evacuation and shutdown, protect and salvage company property, and work with civil authorities.

11. Trauma is psychological stress. It typically results from exposure to a disaster or emergency so shocking that it impairs a person's sense of security or well-being. Trauma left untreated can manifest itself as posttraumatic stress disorder. This disorder is characterized by intrusive thoughts, flashbacks, paranoia, concentration difficulties, rapid heartbeat, and irritability.

12. A disaster recovery plan should have at least the following components: recovery coordinator, recovery team, recovery analysis and planning, damage assessment and salvage operations, recovery communications, and employee support and assistance.

13. Employers can help decrease the likelihood of a terrorist attack on their facilities by taking the following actions: Run a safe and caring operation; listen to employees; train employees; communicate; know your personnel; empower personnel; harden the site against external threats and restrict access; remove any barriers to clear visibility around the facility; have and enforce parking and delivery regulations; make sure that visitors can be screened from a distance; keep all unstaffed entrance doors locked from the outside and alarmed; make air intakes and other utilities inaccessible to all but designated personnel; prevent access to roofs and upper stories; secure trash containers; ensure that employees, contractors, and visitors wear badges; have an emergency response plan and practise it on a regular basis; be cautious about what information is placed on your company's website; keep up-to-date with the latest safety and security strategies; and protect the integrity of your facility's key system.

14. Secure hazardous materials so that terrorists cannot gain access to them for use in making bombs and other weapons of mass destruction. A hazmat security plan should have two components: personnel security and physical security.

KEY TERMS AND CONCEPTS

Emergency

Emergency action plan (EAP)

Emergency coordinator

Emergency planning

Emergency Preparedness Act

Emergency response plan

International emergencies

Posttraumatic stress disorder

Public order emergencies

Public welfare emergencies

Trauma

War emergencies

REVIEW QUESTIONS

1. Define the term *emergency*.

2. Explain the rationale for emergency preparation.

3. What types of natural or human induced emergencies are most likely to happen in your region of the country?

4. Explain how you would provide first-aid training if you were responsible for setting up a program at your company.

5. Besides training, what other first-aid preparation should a company take?

6. What is trauma?

7. Why should a company include trauma response in its EAP?

8. Describe how a company may respond to the trauma resulting from a workplace emergency.

9. What elements should a disaster recovery plan contain?

10. How can employers prepare for the threat of terrorism?

WEBLINKS

Public Safety and Emergency Preparedness Canada
www.ocipep.gc.ca/home/index_e.asp

The federal government's PSEPC website is a useful resource for individuals or businesses for dealing with major emergencies and terrorism. A list of addresses and websites for provincial and territorial emergency measures organizations is available in the Safety Fact box earlier in the chapter.

ENDNOTES

1. PSEPC. (December 30, 1999). "Fact Sheets – List of Potential Emergencies for Developing Contingency Plans." [Online]. Available: http://www.ocipep.gc.ca/info_pro/fact_sheets/general/EM_list_poten_e.asp. (Retrieved January 23, 2005).

2. PSEPC. (December 30, 1999). "Fact Sheets – List of Potential Emergencies for Developing Contingency Plans." [Online]. Available: http://www.ocipep.gc.ca/info_pro/fact_sheets/general/L_high_emer_e.asp. (Retrieved January 23, 2005).

3. PSEPC. (December 30, 1999). "Fact Sheets – List of Potential Emergencies for Developing Contingency Plans." [Online]. Available: http://www.ocipep.gc.ca/info_pro/fact_sheets/general/L_high_emer_prep_e.asp. (Retrieved January 23, 2005).

4. S. Larson, "Heading for the Exits," *Occupational Health & Safety* 72, no. 2 (February 2003): 60.

5. C. Schroll, "Evacuation Planning: A Matter of Life and Death," *Occupational Hazards* (June 2002): 50–54.

6. Ibid., 54.

7. Ibid., 54.

8. E. Johnson, "Where Disaster Strikes," *Safety & Health* 145, no. 2: 29.

9. Ibid., 28.

10. Ibid., 29.

11. Ibid., 30.

12. National Safety Council, "Trained for Trauma," *Safety & Health* 145, no. 2: 32.

13. Canadian Security Intelligence Service. (August 9, 2002). "Counter-Terrorism." [Online]. Available: http://www.csis-scrs.gc.ca/eng/operat/ct_e.html. (Retrieved January 23, 2005).

14. C. Dawson, "The Role of the Employer in Domestic Security," *Occupational Hazards* (January 2002): 31.

15. Ibid., 31–32.

16. D. M. Petroff, "Security of Hazardous Materials," *Occupational Health & Safety* 72, no. 4 (April 2003): 44–48.

17. Ibid., 48.

Computers, Automation, and Robots

CHAPTER 24

LEARNING OBJECTIVES

- Describe the impact of automation on workers.
- Describe the health and safety problems created by human–robot interaction.
- Define industrial medicine as it relates to automated machines.
- Explain the concept of technological alienation in the automated workplace.
- List the common problems of automation
- List safety measures for automated systems.

Automation of the workplace has changed, and continues to change, how work is done. The introduction of automated processes that involve computers and robots has changed the environment of the modern workplace and what is needed to succeed in it. According to Rinzo Ebukuro of NEC Corporation,

> Developments have changed the concepts of the factory and product, created knowledge-intensive jobs, and encouraged the development of management technology. Innovative technology calls for intelligent manpower and increases the severity of work.[1]

IMPACT OF AUTOMATION ON THE WORKPLACE

AUTOMATION
The state of being operated automatically.

The advent of **automation** in the workplace was the next logical step on a continuum of developments intended to enhance productivity, quality, and competitiveness. This continuum began when humans first developed simple tools to assist them in doing work. This was the age of hand tools and manual work. It was eventually superseded by the age of mechanization during the Industrial Revolution. During the age of mechanization, machines were developed to do work previously done by humans using hand tools. The 1960s saw the beginnings of broad-based efforts at automating mechanical processes and systems.

These early attempts at automation resulted in islands of automation— or individual automated systems lacking electronic communication with other related systems. Examples of islands of automation are a stand-alone computer numerical control milling machine or a personal computer-based word processing system, neither of which is connected to other related systems. Local area networks (LANs) for integrating personal computers are an example of integration in the office. Computer-integrated manufacturing is an example in the factory.

These developments are having an impact on the workplace. According to Ebukuro, automation and integration are having the following effects on workers:

- Reducing the amount of physical labour workers must perform.
- Increasing the amount of mental work required.
- Polarizing work into mental jobs and labour-intensive jobs.
- Increasing the stress levels of managers.
- Decreasing the need for traditional blue-collar workers.
- Decreasing the feelings of loyalty that workers feel toward employers.
- Increasing workers' feelings of powerlessness and helplessness.[2]

These various effects of automation are resulting in a marked increase in the amount of stress experienced by workers. Two factors in particular lead to increased levels of stress: rapid, continual change and an accompanying feeling of helplessness. With automation, the rate of change has increased. As a result, workers must continually learn and relearn their jobs with little or no relief. In addition, automated machines do more of the work that used to be done by humans. This can leave workers feeling as if they may be replaced by a machine and powerless to do anything about it. According to Ostberg,

> The development of a special curriculum known as robot medicine in Japan acknowledges the connection between emerging technology and stress. This course of study is offered to industrial doctors by the University of Occupational and Environmental Health, Japan. It is defined as the branch of medicine studying stress and other mental and physical problems of workers in automated and roboticized production.[3]

Workplace stress is a complex concept involving physiological, psychological, and social factors. People become stressed when there is an imbalance between the demands placed on them and their ability to respond.[4] Automation appears to be increasing the instances in which such an imbalance occurs. This chapter focuses on the health and safety concerns associated with computers, robots, and automation and appropriate measures for dealing with these concerns. Refer to Chapter 22 for detailed information on the cause and effect of workplace stress.

WORKPLACE STRESS
Human reaction to threatening situations at work or related to the workplace.

HUMAN–ROBOT INTERACTION

Every new tool developed to enhance the ability of humans to work efficiently and effectively has brought with it a new health and safety hazard. This is particularly the case with industrial robots. What makes robots more potentially dangerous than other machines can be summarized as follows: (1) their ability to acquire intelligence through programming; (2) their flexibility and range of motion; (3) their speed of movement; and (4) their power.

The often-discussed "peopleless" factory is still far in the future. However, robots are so widely used now that they are no longer the oddity they once were. Consequently, there is plenty of human–robot interaction in modern industry. The innovative hub for automation and the use of robots in Canada is in the manufacturing field, especially in the automotive manufacturing industry, where sophisticated robots perform tasks that require greater strength, endurance, and precision than can be provided by humans. Robots can also spare workers from exposure to hazardous environments created by welding, painting or cleaning processes. According to Yamashita, "At ordinary factories human workers and robots coexist, creating such problems as cooperation and competition between man and machines and safety."[5]

How does human–robot interaction differ from human interaction with other machines? This is an important question for health and safety professionals. According to Lena Martensson of the Royal Institute of Technology in Stockholm, Sweden, the modern factory has or is moving toward having the following characteristics:

- Workers will supervise machine systems rather than interact with individual pieces of production equipment.
- Workers will communicate with machines via video display terminals on which complex information processed by a computer will be displayed.
- Workers will be supported by expert systems for fault identification, diagnosis, and repair.[6]

Robots and other intelligent computer-controlled machines will play an increasingly important role in modern industry. As this happens, health and safety professionals must be concerned about the new workplace hazards that will be created.

HEALTH AND SAFETY PROBLEMS ASSOCIATED WITH ROBOTS

Robots are being used in industry for such applications as arc welding, spot welding, spray painting, material handling and assembly, and loading and unloading of machines. Figures 24–1 and 24–2 are examples of modern industrial robots being used in typical applications. According to the US National Safety Council the principal hazards associated with robots are as follows:

WORK ENVELOPE
The total area within which the moving parts of a robot actually move.

- Being struck by a moving robot while inside the work envelope. The **work envelope** of a robot is the total area within which the moving parts of the robot actually move. Figure 24–3 is an example of a robot's work envelope.
- Being trapped between a moving part of a robot and another machine, object, or surface.
- Being struck by a workpiece, tool, or other object dropped or ejected by a robot.[7]

Figure 24–1
Industrial robot in use.
Source: Courtesy of
Cincinnati Milicron.

Figure 24–2
Industrial robot in use.
Source: Courtesy of Unimation, Inc.

Until a worker enters the work envelope of a robot, there is little probability of an accident. However, whenever a worker enters a functioning robot's work envelope, the probability becomes very high. The only logical reason for a worker to enter the work envelope of an engaged robot is to teach it a new motion. According to the National Safety Council,

Model 762

320°

(Model 761–1500mm)

1250

11.75°

(Model 761–13.1°)

Inaccessible area
(can be reached
in lefty configuration)

514mm radius
Inaccessible to JT5
(Model 761–630mm radius)

1263mm radius swept by JT5
measured from centre
of JT1
(Model 761–1636mm radius)

Robot shown in
righty configuration

1388mm radius swept by
mounting flange
(Model 761–1636mm radius)

Cylindrical volume 112mm
diameter inaccessible to JT6
tool flange

220°

Many applications of robots use a mode of operation called the teach mode that makes them unique among industrial equipment as regards safeguarding them. In the teach mode, an operator may be required to place himself within the operating range of the robot in order to program its movements within very close tolerance parameters. The teaching of a robot is done at a greatly reduced speed of operation; however, a hazard may arise if the robot goes out of control and moves in an unpredictable fashion at a high rate of speed. It is in the teach mode where the highest degree of hazard exists. A Japanese survey showed that the greatest risk of accidents involving robots occurs during programming, teaching, and maintenance; all times when a person may be within the operating envelope of the robot.[8]

Minimizing the Health and Safety Problems of Robots

If human workers never had to enter a work envelope, the health and safety problems associated with robots would be minimal. However, workers must occasionally do so. Therefore health and safety professionals must be concerned with ensuring safe human–robot interaction.

The US National Safety Council recommends several strategies for minimizing the hazards associated with robots. The general strategies are summarized as follows:

- Ensure a glare-free, well-lit robot site. The recommended light intensity is 538.2–1076.4 Lux (lumen per m) (or 50–100 foot-candles [lumen per ft]).
- Keep the floors in and around the robot site carefully maintained, clean, and free of obstructions so that workers do not trip or slip into the work envelope.
- Keep the robot site free of associated hazards such as blinding light from welding machines or vapours from a paint booth.
- Equip electrical and pneumatic components of the robot with fixed covers and guards.
- Clear the work envelope of all nonessential objects and make sure all safeguards are in place before starting the robot.
- Apply lockout and proper test procedures before entering the work envelope.
- Remove and account for all tools and equipment used to maintain the robot before starting it.[9]

Because of the gradual evolution of robots and many other complex automated processes, they are not specifically mentioned in the safety legislation for most Canadian jurisdictions, but are usually considered to be the same as any other industrial machine. CSA, however, provides a comprehensive set of guidelines for the selection, installation, use, and maintenance of such equipment in their Z432-04, *Safeguarding of Machinery* standards. Safety personnel should be familiar with these standards along with the regulations covering their jurisdiction when robots are used in the workplace.

INDUSTRIAL MEDICINE AND ROBOTS

Industrial medicine is a specialized field that is concerned with work-related health and safety issues. Practitioners of **industrial medicine** are becoming increasingly concerned with the interaction of humans and automated machines, particularly robots and computers. They are concerned about maladaptation to an automated environment.

According to Masamitsu Oshima of Japan's Medical Information System Development Center, maladaptation can manifest itself as an urge to quit work; fatigue; problems with human relations; a drop in work performance; social pathological phenomena such as drug use or crime; mood swings; a loss of motivation; and accidents.[10] Practitioners of industrial medicine are concerned with improving the relationship between humans and automated machines by establishing methods whereby humans can work more adequately with the machines.[11]

Oshima makes the following recommendations for improving the interaction between humans and robots, computers, and other automated machines in the high-tech workplace:

- Match the human system and the computer system.
- Position machine systems as human-supportive systems.

INDUSTRIAL MEDICINE
A specialized field that is concerned with work-related health and safety issues.

- Adapt human–computer interaction to human use.
- Initiate job-changing opportunities.
- Allow suitable rest periods for users of automated equipment.
- Vitalize the workplace.
- Encourage recreation.
- Promote the effective use of nonworking hours.
- Increase the contact with nature.
- Free people from hazardous, dirty, and harmful jobs.
- Shorten working hours and promote work sharing.
- Expand human contact.
- Harmonize people, things, and the environment ergonomically.[12]

It should be obvious from reviewing this list that it was developed with the Japanese culture in mind. However, these recommendations can also be applied to the Canadian workplace. As human workers continually increase the amount of their interaction with automated machines, the potential for maladaptation also increases. One key to preventing maladaptation is to design automated systems around the needs of humans rather than designing them in a vacuum and then expecting humans to adapt. Another is to pay special attention to establishing and maintaining human contact for workers who interact primarily with automated machines and systems. These are areas in which attentive health and safety professionals can have a positive impact.

TECHNOLOGICAL ALIENATION IN THE AUTOMATED WORKPLACE

As technology has become more widely used in the workplace, particularly automated technology, some workers have come to resent its impact on their

---

SAFETY FACT

CTDs Are More Than Carpal Tunnel Syndrome

The personal computer has become an all-pervasive and universal tool. Jobs from the shop floor to the executive office now involve frequent, repetitive computer use. This means that people in the workplace are typing and clicking at an unprecedented pace. Frequent, and for some, constant computer use has led to an explosion of injuries heretofore seen mostly in the meat-packing industry. Collectively, these injuries are known as *cumulative trauma disorders (CTDs)*.

Cumulative trauma disorders are caused by forceful or awkward hand movements repeated frequently over time. Other aggravating factors include poor posture, an improperly designed workstation, and job stress. CTDs occur to the muscles, nerves, and tendons of the hands, arms, shoulders, and neck. For years, CTDs have been incorrectly referred to as carpal tunnel syndrome, which is actually just one type of CTD (like referring to all trees as oaks).

lives. This concept is known as **technological alienation**. According to Gary Benson of the University of Wyoming, this concept has several meanings, all of which encompass one or more of the following:

- **Powerlessness** is the feeling that workers have when they are not able to control the work environment. Powerless workers may feel that they are less important than the technology with which they work and that they are expendable.
- **Meaninglessness** is the feeling that workers get when their jobs become so specialized and so technology-dependent that they cannot see the meaning in their work as it relates to the finished product or service.
- **Normlessness** is the phenomenon in which people working in a highly automated environment can become estranged from society. Normless people lose sight of society's norms, rules, and mores.[13]

Benson investigated what he considers to be the most devastating form of technological alienation — **mindlessness**.[14] Mindlessness is the result of the process of "dumbing down" the workplace. This is a concept that accompanied automation. In the past, machines have been used to do physical work previously done by human workers. With the advent of computers, robots, and automation, machines began doing mental work. According to Benson,

> The net result is jobs and work environments where people do not have to use their minds or think to do their work — an environment where computers, robots, and other forms of high technology do the thinking.[15]

Mindlessness on the job should be of interest to health and safety professionals because of the other problems it can create. According to Benson, these problems can include an increase in alcoholism, drug abuse, employee theft, work-related accidents, absenteeism, sick leave abuse, turnover rates, and employee personal problems. Mindlessness can also lead to a decrease in job performance, productivity, and work quality.[16]

Each of these problems can, in turn, increase the potential for health and safety problems on the job. Employees who abuse alcohol and drugs represent a serious threat in the workplace. Absent employees force their co-workers to double up. High turnover results in a steady influx of inexperienced workers. Employees with personal problems may not be properly focused on accident prevention measures. Finally, when productivity and quality fall, supervisors can feel so much pressure to improve performance that they overlook or put aside safety precautions. These are the potentially negative health and safety effects of mindlessness in the automated workplace.

According to Benson,

> What is needed now are more employees who are aware of and willing to do something about the problem and more research into the phenomenon and causes of the solutions for mindlessness in technological alienation. This is surely a phenomenon of modern-day worklife that must be dealt with effectively — and immediately.[17]

MINIMIZING THE PROBLEMS OF AUTOMATION

The infusion of technology into the workplace has presented health and safety professionals with an entirely new set of challenges. Among the most pressing

TECHNOLOGICAL ALIENATION
The frame of mind that results when employees come to resent technology and the impact that it has on their lives.

POWERLESSNESS
The feeling that workers have when they are not able to control the work environment.

MEANINGLESSNESS
The feeling that workers get when their jobs become so specialized and so technology-dependent that they cannot see the meaning in their work as it relates to the finished product or service.

NORMLESSNESS
The phenomenon in which people working in a highly automated environment can become estranged from society.

MINDLESSNESS
The result of the process of dumbing down the workplace.

of these is the need to identify and minimize the new health and safety problems specifically associated with automation. Behavioural scientist A. B. Cherns developed a "sociotechnical system theory" for doing so that consists of the following components: variance control, boundary location, work group organization, management support, **design process**, and quality of work life.[18]

DESIGN PROCESS
A plan of action for reaching a goal.

Although the sociotechnical system theory was developed in 1977, it has even more relevance now than it did then. According to Yoshio Hayashi of Japan's Keio University,

> The safety and health of workers in this high technology age cannot be discussed within the conventional framework of one worker assigned to one machine. . . . The socio-technical system may be roughly understood if the *man* and *machine* in the man–machine system are replaced by *socio* and *technical* respectively. It refers to a system composed of a work group and high technology.[19]

The various components in the sociotechnical system theory explain what must happen if humans and technological systems are going to work together harmoniously and safely. Health and safety professionals can apply the theory as they work to minimize the potential problems associated with automation in the modern workplace. These components can be summarized as follows:

- *Variance control* involves controlling the unexpected events that can be introduced by new technologies. For example, a runaway, out-of-control industrial robot introduces unexpected safety hazards at variance with the expectations of workers and management. Variance control involves bringing the situation under control and establishing appropriate preventive measures for the future.
- The concept of *boundary location* involves the classification of work. What specific tasks are included in an employee's job description? Does a robot technician just operate the robot, or is she also required to teach and maintain the robot? The accident prevention measures learned by an employee should cover all tasks in his or her job description.
- The concept of *work group organization* involves identifying the tasks that a work group is to perform and how these tasks are to be performed. The key is to make sure that all work group members have the training needed to accomplish effectively and safely all tasks assigned to them.
- *Management support* is perhaps the most important of the components of the sociotechnical system theory. It states that, in the age of high technology, managers must be willing to accept occasional temporary declines in productivity without resorting to shortcuts or improvement efforts that may be unsafe or unhealthy. Management must be willing to emphasize safety in spite of temporary declines in productivity.
- The *design process* component refers to the ability of an organization to design itself in ways that promote productivity, quality, competitiveness, safety, and health. It also involves the ability to continually redesign as technological advances and other circumstances dictate.
- *Quality of work life* involves determining ways to promote the morale and best interests of workers. The key is to ensure that technology extends the abilities of humans and that technological systems are *human centred.* In other words, it is important to ensure that people control systems rather than vice versa.

- An *ergonomics management program* consists of activities undertaken to prevent ergonomics-related injuries and disorders. Such a program should have at least the following components: work-site analysis, hazard control, health surveillance, and training. Refer to Chapter 9 for a detailed explanation of this concept.[20]

If the sociotechnical system theory is fully applied, the health and safety hazards of the automated workplace can be minimized. Health and safety professionals can play a key role in making sure the theory is applied. To play such a role, these professionals must be technicians, diplomats, trainers, and lobbyists. They must work with the technical aspects of variance control, boundary location, work group organization, and the design process. They must be diplomats in working with supervisors and employees in promoting adherence to safe work practices. They must be trainers in order to ensure that all employees know how to apply safe work practices and appropriate accident prevention techniques. Finally, they must be lobbyists as they continually interact with management to establish and maintain management support for safety, health, and quality of life issues.

Safety Measures for Automated Systems

The sociotechnical system theory discussed in the previous section is broad and conceptual in nature. Modern health and safety professionals also need to know specific measures that can be taken to minimize the hazards associated with robots and other automated systems. Minoru Goto of the Nissan Motor Company's safety department developed specific safety measures in the categories of technological systems, auxiliary equipment, and training.[21]

Examples of safety measures that can be used at the technological systems level include

- Construction of a safety fence around the system that defines the work envelope of the system.
- Control of the speed of movement of system components when working inside the work fence.
- Installation of an emergency stop device coloured red and placed in an easily accessible location.
- Location of the control panel for the system outside of the safety fence.
- Establishment of automatic shutdown switches that activate any time a system component goes beyond its predetermined operational range.[22]

Safety measures relating to training include training system operators to work safely within the work envelope and to work together as a team when interacting with the system. Maintenance workers should be trained on the technical aspects of maintaining all machines and equipment that make up the system. This is important because the safety level of the system is the sum of the safety levels of its individual components. A system with four properly operating components and just one faulty component is an unsafe system.[23]

CHALLENGE FOR THE FUTURE

Much more effort has gone into developing automated systems to improve productivity than has gone into the appropriate matching of people and technology.

Now, with the speed of technical development being what it is, the health and safety problems associated with automation, particularly stress-related problems, are likely to increase. According to Kensaburo Tsuchiya of Japan's University of Occupational Health and Safety, the challenge for the future is "to create jobs which are free from stress and musculoskeletal overloads while at the same time being challenging and interesting for the individual."[24]

The future holds a number of problems that will have to be addressed to meet Tsuchiya's challenge. The most prominent of these are as follows:

- Increasingly intense international competition may magnify the tendency for companies to neglect health and safety precautions in favour of short-term productivity gains.
- The level of mental stress is likely to increase as the automated manipulation of information forces workers to try continually to handle too much information that is poorly understood.
- Automation and competition are likely to increase the level of anxiety as workers are required to make split-second decisions while knowing that their actions or inactions may have dire consequences.
- New **occupational diseases** relating to mental, visual, and musculoskeletal problems may arise whose remedies must be sought through a combination of ergonomics, psychology, occupational medicine, and design.
- There is likely to be increased introduction of robots into the workplace with even less foresight that will, in turn, introduce more unexpected health and safety risks.
- Ignorance may lead to the introduction of automation in an office or factory in forms that do not require workers to think, reason, or make judgments, giving rise to alienation and frustration.
- An aging workforce will continue to raise new issues concerning the special needs of older workers and their interaction with automated technologies.[25]

Because they are likely to face these inhibitors, the health and safety professionals of the future must be prepared to deal with them. They need to know what has to happen if the inhibitors are to be overcome. Tsuchiya suggests the following strategies for enhancing the health and safety of tomorrow's automated workplace:

- Technological systems and processes must be designed to take into account the physical, mental, and emotional needs of human workers.
- Workers will need training and continual retraining so that they can effectively and efficiently operate technological systems and interact with them from the perspective of mastery rather than inadequacy.
- Health and safety professionals, management, workers, psychologists, **ergonomists**, and practitioners of occupational medicine will have to work together as a team in all aspects of the health and safety program.
- The quality of work life and health and safety considerations will have to receive as much attention in the design and implementation of automated systems and processes as do economic and technological concerns.
- Additional research will have to be conducted to determine more clearly the psychological and physiological effects of human interaction with automated technologies.
- Much more comprehensive accident reporting will be needed. Implementation of the "critical incident" reporting system used in com-

OCCUPATIONAL DISEASES
Pathological conditions brought about by workplace conditions or factors.

ERGONOMISTS
Scientists who study the interaction of workers and their surroundings.

mercial aviation may be considered by companies for collecting health and safety data.

- Ergonomists should become involved in accident prevention. They should focus their accident prevention activities on accident and error analysis and simulation of accidents for training purposes. They should also be involved in systems design, human performance, cognitive performance, workload and methods design, the study of factors contributing to accidents and injuries related to equipment, tool, and workstation design, and issues relating to an aging and more diverse workforce.[26]

Tsuchiya sums up his thoughts regarding the future of the automated workplace as it relates to health and safety:

> A motivating, satisfying and good quality job should be consistent with a safe, healthy and efficient automated workplace. Intermediate stages of new technologies sometimes lead to repetitive and monotonous tasks and these must be replanned to minimize adverse reactions to them. Where technology reduces the number of operators, isolation should be avoided for safety and to increase social contacts to reduce stress. When people can work or act together in small groups, even for a short period of the working day, human and productivity advantages can arise (e.g., group discussion of production activities). Where technologies or products are changing rapidly a workforce with good intercommunications can be even more important in keeping productivity high.[27]

SUMMARY

1. The introduction of automation in the workplace has had several different effects on workers including reducing the amount of physical labour required, increasing the amount of mental work required (in some cases), increasing stress levels, and increasing feelings of powerlessness and helplessness.

2. What makes robots potentially dangerous to humans is their ability to acquire intelligence through programming, their flexibility and range of motion, their speed of movement, and their power.

3. Specific health and safety risks associated with robots include the following: being struck by a moving robot while inside the work envelope, entrapment between a moving robot and another machine, and being struck by a workpiece, tool, or other object dropped or ejected by a robot.

4. There are numerous strategies for minimizing the health and safety hazards of robots and other automated machines. They include ensuring a well-lit, glare-free robot site, maintaining good housekeeping around the robot site, keeping the robot site free of associated hazards (bright light from welding, paint vapours), having fixed covers over the electrical and pneumatic components of the robot, keeping the work envelope clear of all nonessential objects, using appropriate lockout and test procedures, and removing maintenance tools and supplies from the work envelope before starting the robot.

5. Maladaptation to automated technologies manifests itself as an urge to quit work, fatigue, problems with human relations, a drop in work performance, social pathological phenomena such as drug use and crime, mood swings, a loss of motivation, and accidents.

6. Technological alienation is the state of mind that exists when workers resent the impact of new technologies on their lives. It is characterized by feelings of powerlessness, meaninglessness, and normlessness.

7. Mindlessness is the result of the dumbing down of the workplace so that workers are not required to use their minds in their work.

8. Problems associated with mindlessness include an increase in alcoholism, drug abuse, employee theft, work-related accidents, absenteeism, sick leave abuse, turnover rates, and employee personal problems.

9. The sociotechnical system theory consists of the following components: variance control, boundary location, work group organization, management support, design process, and quality of work life.

10. Problems that are likely to be associated with automation in the future include the following: the tendency to overlook health and safety precautions for short-term productivity gains may be exacerbated by increasingly intense international competition; the level of mental stress to which workers are subjected is likely to increase; new occupational diseases are likely to be introduced; and the tendency to dumb down the workplace is likely to continue.

11. Strategies for overcoming anticipated future problems include better design of technological systems; training and continual retraining; teaming health and safety professionals with management, workers, psychologists, ergonomists, and practitioners of occupational medicine; more research; better accident reporting; and the involvement of ergonomists in accident prevention.

KEY TERMS AND CONCEPTS

Automation

Design process

Ergonomists

Industrial medicine

Meaninglessness

Mindlessness

Normlessness

Occupational diseases

Powerlessness

Technological alienation

Work envelope

Workplace stress

REVIEW QUESTIONS

1. Briefly summarize how automation has changed the workplace.

2. List five effects that automation of the workplace has had on workers.

3. Explain the four factors that make robots more potentially dangerous than other machines.

4. List and explain the specific hazards associated with human–robot interaction.

5. Explain four specific strategies for minimizing the hazards associated with interacting with a robot.

6. Explain three of the principles set forth by the Japanese Association of Industrial Health for developing health and safety measures for office automation.

7. List five strategies for minimizing the potential for occurrences of mal-adaptation.

8. Define the following automation-related terms: *technological alienation, powerlessness, meaninglessness, normlessness,* and *mindlessness.*

9. Mindlessness in the workplace can lead to a number of other problems. Name five of them.

10. What effect may increasingly intense international competition and the need to improve productivity have on workplace health and safety in the future?

WEBLINKS

Human Resources and Skills Development Canada

**www11.hrsdc.gc.ca/en/cs/sp/hrsdc/arb/publications/research/2002-000146/
page01.shtml**

On this HRSDC website, one can find a report called *The Effects of Computers on Workplace Stress, Job Security and Work Interest in Canada.*

ENDNOTES

1. R. Ebukuro, "Alleviation of the Impact of Microelectronics on Labour," in *Occupational Health and Safety in Automation and Robotics,* ed. K. Noro (Chicago: National Safety Council, 1987), 11.
2. Ibid., 5.
3. O. Ostberg, "Emerging Technology and Trends in Blue-Collar Stress," in *Occupational Health and Safety,* 15.
4. Ibid., 17.
5. T. Yamashita, "The Interaction Between Man and Robot in High Technology Industries," in *Occupational Health and Safety,* 140.
6. L. Martensson, "Interaction Between Man and Robots with Some Emphasis on 'Intelligent' Robots," in *Occupational Health and Safety,* 144.
7. National Safety Council, *Robots,* Data Sheet 1–717–85 (Chicago: National Safety Council, 1991), 1.
8. Ibid.
9. Ibid., 2–3.
10. M. Oshima, "The Role of Industrial Medicine at the Man–Robot Interface," in *Occupational Health and Safety,* 284–285.
11. Ibid., 284.
12. Ibid., 285.
13. G. Benson, "Mindlessness: A New Dimension of Technological Alienation — Implications for the Man–Machine Interface in High Technology Work Environments," in *Occupational Health and Safety,* 326–327.

14. Ibid., 328.

15. Ibid.

16. Ibid., 332.

17. Ibid., 336.

18. A. B. Cherns, "Can Behavioral Science Help Design Organizations?" *Organizational Dynamics,* 44–64.

19. Y. Hayashi, "Measures for Improving the Occupational Health and Safety of People Working with VDTs or Robots — Small-Group Activities and Safety and Health Education," in *Occupational Health and Safety,* 383.

20. Ibid., 384.

21. M. Goto, "Occupational Safety and Health Measures Taken for the Introduction of Robots in the Automobile Industry," in *Occupational Health and Safety,* 399–417.

22. Ibid., 404–408.

23. Ibid., 411–413.

24. K. Tsuchiya, "Summary Report on the Fifth University of Occupational and Environmental Health International Symposium," in *Occupational Health and Safety,* 422.

25. Ibid., 422–426.

26. Ibid.

27. Ibid., 425–426.

Ethics and Safety

25
CHAPTER

LEARNING OBJECTIVES

- Define ethics.
- List five guidelines that may be used to guide ethical choices.
- Describe the health and safety professional's role in ethics.
- Describe the company's role in ethics.
- Explain why whistle-blowing may be difficult for some employees.

Practically everyone agrees that the business practices of industrial firms should be above reproach with regard to ethical standards. Few people are willing to defend unethical behaviour. And for the most part, industry in Canada operates within the scope of accepted legal and ethical standards. According to Peter Drucker,

> Business ethics is rapidly becoming the 'in' subject . . . there are countless seminars on it, speeches, articles, conferences and books, not to mention the many earnest attempts to write "business ethics" into the law.[1]

However, unethical behaviour does occur frequently enough that modern health and safety professionals should be aware of the types of ethical dilemmas that they may occasionally face and should know how to deal with such issues. How to deal successfully and effectively with ethics on the job is the subject of this chapter.

AN ETHICAL DILEMMA

According to Stead, Worrell, and Stead,

Managing ethical behavior is one of the most pervasive and complex problems facing business organizations today. Employees' decisions to behave ethically or unethically are influenced by a myriad of individual and situational factors. Background, personality, decision history, managerial philosophy, and reinforcement are but a few of the factors which have been identified by researchers as determinants of employees' behavior when faced with ethical dilemmas.[2]

Consider the following example of an ethical dilemma:

Mil-Tech Manufacturing Company is a Department of National Defence contractor that produces air- and watertight aluminum containers for shipping non-nuclear munitions such as missiles, bombs, and torpedoes. Business has been good and Mil-Tech is prospering. However, the company's management team has a problem.

Mil-Tech has been awarded a contract to produce 10 000 boxes in six months. The company's maximum capacity is currently 1000 boxes per month. Unless Mil-Tech can find a way to increase its capacity, the company will be forced to add new facilities, equipment, and personnel — an expensive undertaking that will quickly eat up the projected profits of the new contract.

The most time-consuming bottleneck in the production of the boxes is the painting process, the last step. The problem is with the paint that Mil-Tech uses. It poses no health, safety, or environmental hazards, but it is difficult to apply and requires at least two hours to dry. Clearly, the most expeditious way to increase productivity is to find a paint that is easier to apply and takes less time to dry.

The production manager has been searching frantically for a substitute paint for two weeks and has finally found one. The new paint is easy to apply, and it dries almost on contact. However, it is extremely toxic and can be dangerous to anyone exposed to it at any time before it dries. Personal protective equipment and other hazard-prevention techniques can minimize the health problems, but they must be used properly with absolutely no shortcuts. In addition, it is recommended that every employee who will work with the paint complete three full days of training.

Mil-Tech's management team is convinced that the union will not consent to the use of this paint even if the personal protective equipment is purchased and the training is provided. To complicate matters, the supplier of the paint cannot provide the training within a timeframe that meets Mil-Tech's needs. In a secret meeting, top management officials decide to purchase personal protective equipment, use the new paint, and forego the training. More importantly, the management team decides to withhold all information about the hazards associated with the new paint.

Camillo Garcia, Mil-Tech's health and safety manager, was not invited to the secret meeting. However, the decisions made during the meeting were slipped to him anonymously. Garcia now faces an ethical dilemma. What should he do?

If he chooses to do nothing, Mil-Tech employees may be inappropriately exposed to an extremely hazardous substance. If he confronts the management team with what he knows, he could fall into disfavour or even lose his job. If he shares what he knows with union leaders, he may be called on to testify about what he knows. This is an example of the type of ethical dilemma that health and safety professionals might face on the job.

ETHICS DEFINED

There are many definitions of the term *ethics.* However, no one definition has emerged as universally accepted. According to Paul Taylor, the concept can be defined as "inquiry into the nature and grounds of morality where morality is taken to mean moral judgments, standards, and rules of conduct."[3] According to Arlow and Ulrich, ethical dilemmas in the workplace are more complex than ethical situations in general.[4] They involve societal expectations, competition, and social responsibility — as well as the potential consequences of an employee's behaviour on customers, co-workers, competitors, and the public at large. The result of the often-conflicting and contradictory interests of workers, customers, competitors, and the general public is a natural tendency for ethical dilemmas to occur frequently in the workplace.

Whenever ethics is the topic of discussion, such terms as *conscience, morality,* and *legality* are frequently heard. Although these terms are closely associated with ethics, they do not, by themselves, define it. For the purpose of this book, **ethics** is defined as follows:

> Ethics is the study of morality within a context established by cultural and professional values, social norms, and accepted standards of behaviour.

Morality refers to the values that are subscribed to and fostered by society in general and individuals within society. Ethics attempts to apply reason in determining rules of human conduct that translate morality into everyday behaviour. **Ethical behaviour** is that which falls within the limits prescribed by morality.

How, then, does a health and safety professional know if someone's behaviour is ethical? Ethical questions are rarely black and white. They typically fall into a grey area between the two extremes of right and wrong. Personal experience, self-interest, point of view, and external pressure often cloud this grey area further.

Guidelines for Determining Ethical Behaviour

Guidelines are needed for health and safety professionals to use when trying to sort out matters that are not clearly right or wrong. First, however, it is necessary to distinguish between the concepts of *legal* and *ethical.* They are not the same thing. Just because an option is legal does not necessarily mean it is ethical.

In fact, it is not uncommon for people caught in the practice of questionable behaviour to use the "I didn't do anything illegal" defence. A person's behaviour can be well within the scope of the law and still be unethical. The following guidelines for determining ethical behaviour assume that the behaviour in question is legal (Figure 25–1):

- Apply the **morning-after test**. This test asks, "If you make this choice, how will you feel about it tomorrow morning?"
- Apply the **front-page test**. This test encourages you to make a decision that would not embarrass you if printed as a story on the front page of your hometown newspaper.
- Apply the **mirror test**. This test asks, "If you make this decision, how will you feel about yourself when you look in the mirror?"

ETHICS
The study of morality.

ETHICAL BEHAVIOUR
That which falls within the limits prescribed by morality.

MORNING-AFTER TEST
Encourages people to make choices based on how they will feel about their decision the next day.

FRONT-PAGE TEST
Encourages persons to make a decision that would not embarrass them if it were printed as a story on the front page of their hometown newspaper.

MIRROR TEST
Encourages people to make choices based on how they will feel about their decision when they look in the mirror.

ROLE-REVERSAL TEST
Requires a person to trade places with the people affected by the decision that he or she made and to view the decision through their eyes.

COMMON-SENSE TEST
Requires person to listen to what instincts and common sense are telling him or her.

- Apply the **role-reversal test**. This test requires you to trade places with the people affected by your decision and view the decision through their eyes.
- Apply the **common-sense test**. This test requires you to listen to what your instincts and common sense are telling you. If it feels wrong, it probably is.

Blanchard and Peale suggest their own test for deciding what the ethical choice is in a given situation.[5] Their test consists of the following three questions:

- Is it legal?
- Is it balanced?
- How will it make me feel about myself?

If a potential course of action is not legal, no further consideration is in order. If an action is not legal, it is also not ethical. If an action is balanced, it is fair to all involved. This means that health and safety professionals and their team members have responsibilities that extend well beyond the walls of their unit, organization, and company. If a course of action is in keeping with your own moral structure, it will make you feel good about yourself. Blanchard and Peale also list the following "Five P's of Ethical Power":

- **Purpose.** Individuals see themselves as ethical people who let their conscience be their guide and in all cases want to feel good about themselves.
- **Pride.** Individuals apply internal guidelines and have sufficient self-esteem to make decisions that may not be popular with others.
- **Patience.** Individuals believe right will prevail in the long run, and they are willing to wait when necessary.
- **Persistence.** Individuals are willing to stay with an ethical course of action once it has been chosen and see it through to a positive conclusion.
- **Perspective.** Individuals take the time to reflect and are guided by their own internal barometer when making ethical decisions.[6]

These tests and guidelines will help health and safety professionals make ethical choices in the workplace. In addition to internalizing the guidelines themselves, health and safety professionals may want to share these values with all employees with whom they interact.

ETHICAL BEHAVIOUR IN ORGANIZATIONS

Research by Trevino suggests that ethical behaviour in organizations is influenced by both individual and social factors.[7] Trevino identified three personality measures that can influence an employee's ethical behaviour: (1) ego strength, (2) Machiavellianism, and (3) locus of control.

**Figure 25–1
Guidelines for determining what is ethical.**

Guidelines for Ethical Choices

1. Apply the morning-after test.
2. Apply the front-page test.
3. Apply the mirror test.
4. Apply the role-reversal test.
5. Apply the common-sense test.

An employee's **ego strength** is his or her ability to undertake self-directed tasks and to cope with tense situations. A measure of a worker's **Machiavellianism** is the extent to which he or she will attempt to deceive and confuse others. **Locus of control** is the perspective of workers concerning who or what controls their behaviour. Employees with an internal locus of control feel that they control their own behaviour. Employees with an external locus of control feel that their behaviour is controlled by external factors (e.g., rules, regulations, their health and safety professional, and so on).

Preble and Miesing suggest that social factors also influence ethical behaviour in organizations.[8] These factors include gender, role differences, religion, age, work experience, nationality, and the influence of other people who are significant in an individual's life. Luthans and Kreitner state that people learn appropriate behaviour by observing the behaviour of significant role models (parents, teachers, public officials, and so on).[9] Because health and safety professionals represent a significant role model for their team members, it is critical that they exhibit ethical behaviour that is beyond reproach in all situations.

EGO STRENGTH
An employee's ability to undertake self-directed tasks and to cope with tense situations.

MACHIAVELLIANISM
The extent to which an employee will attempt to deceive and confuse others.

LOCUS OF CONTROL
The perspective of workers concerning who or what controls their behaviour.

SAFETY FACT

Models for Determining Ethical Behaviour

In addition to the various tests that can be used for determining ethical behaviour, there are also numerous models:

- Categorical imperative (black and white)
- Conventionalistic ethic (anything legal is ethical)
- Disclosure rule (explain actions to a wide audience)
- Doctrine of the mean (virtue through moderation)
- Golden Rule (do unto others . . .)
- Intuition rule (you will know what is right)
- Market ethic (whatever makes a profit is right)
- Means-end ethic (end justifies the means)
- Might-equals-right ethic (self-explanatory)
- Organizational ethic (loyalty to the organization)
- Practical imperative (treat people as ends, not means)
- Equal freedom (full freedom unless it deprives another)
- Proportionality ethic (good outweighs the bad)
- Professional ethic (do only what can be explained to your peers)
- Revelation ethic (answers revealed by prayer)
- Rights ethic (protect rights of others)
- Theory of justice (impartial, even-handed)

HEALTH AND SAFETY PROFESSIONALS' ROLE IN ETHICS

Using the guidelines set forth in the previous section, health and safety professionals should be able to make responsible decisions concerning ethical choices. Unfortunately, deciding what is ethical is much easier than actually doing what is ethical. In this regard, trying to practise ethics is like trying to diet. It is not so much a matter of knowing you should cut down eating; it is a matter of following through and actually doing it.

It is this fact that defines the role of health and safety professionals with regard to ethics. Their role has three parts. First, they are responsible for setting an example of ethical behaviour. Second, they are responsible for helping fellow employees make the right decision when facing ethical questions. Finally, health and safety professionals are responsible for helping employees follow through and actually undertake the ethical option once the appropriate choice has been identified. In carrying out their roles, health and safety professionals can adopt one of the following approaches (Figure 25–2): the best-ratio approach, the black-and-white approach, or the full-potential approach.

Best-Ratio Approach

BEST-RATIO APPROACH
People are basically good and under the right circumstances behave ethically.

The **best-ratio approach** is the pragmatic approach. Its philosophy is that people are basically good and under the right circumstances behave ethically. However, under certain conditions, they can be driven to unethical behaviour. Therefore, the health and safety professional should do everything possible to create conditions that promote ethical behaviour and try to maintain the best possible ratio of good choices to bad. When hard decisions must be made, the appropriate choice is the one that does the most good for the most people. This is sometimes referred to as *situational ethics*.

Black-and-White Approach

BLACK-AND-WHITE APPROACH
Right is right, wrong is wrong, and circumstances are irrelevant.

Using the **black-and-white approach**, right is right, wrong is wrong, and circumstances are irrelevant. The health and safety professional's job is to make ethical decisions and carry them out. It is also to help employees choose the eth-

Figure 25–2
Three basic approaches to handling ethical problems.

ical route. When difficult decisions must be made, health and safety professionals should make fair and impartial choices regardless of the outcome.

Full-Potential Approach

Health and safety professionals who use the **full-potential approach** make decisions based on how the outcomes affect the ability of those involved to achieve their full potential. The underlying philosophy is that people are responsible for realizing their full potential within the confines of morality. Choices that can achieve this goal without infringing on the rights of others are considered ethical.

Decisions made may differ, depending on the approach selected. For example, consider the ethical dilemma presented at the beginning of this chapter. If the health and safety manager, Camillo Garcia, applies the best-ratio approach, he may decide to keep quiet, encourage the proper use of personal protective equipment, and hope for the best. On the other hand, if he takes the black-and-white approach, he will be compelled to confront the Mil-Tech management team with what he knows.

FULL-POTENTIAL APPROACH
People are responsible for realizing their full potential within the confines of morality.

COMPANY'S ROLE IN ETHICS

Industrial firms have a critical role to play in promoting ethical behaviour among their employees. Health and safety professionals cannot set ethical examples alone or expect employees to behave ethically in a vacuum. A company's role in ethics can be summarized as (1) creating an internal environment that promotes, expects, and rewards ethical behaviour; and (2) setting an example of ethical behaviour in all external dealings (Figure 25–3).

DISCUSSION CASE

What Is Your Opinion?

The city council members are in a real quandary about the request from International Plastics Corporation (IPC) to open a new plant on a 100-acre plot owned by the city. On the one hand, the city needs the new jobs that the IPC plant would bring — badly. High unemployment is the city's most serious problem, and every member of the city council ran on a job-creation platform in the last election. On the other hand, the council members have learned that IPC is not always a good corporate citizen in spite of its claims to the contrary.

Several cities with IPC plants have had problems enforcing their health and safety regulations. The consensus among other cities is that IPC officials say all of the right things until contracts are signed. Then, all of a sudden, they begin to procrastinate, stonewall, and break promises. Should the city council allow IPC to build the new plant? What is your opinion?

**Figure 25–3
Ethics cannot be
practised in a vacuum.
The company has a
critical role to play.**

Creating an Ethical Environment

A company creates an ethical environment by establishing policies and practices that ensure all employees are treated ethically and then enforcing these
policies. Do employees have the right of due process? Do employees have access
to an objective grievance procedure? Are there appropriate health and safety
measures to protect employees? Are hiring practices fair and impartial? Are promotion practices fair and objective? Are employees protected from harassment
based on race, gender, or other reasons? A company that establishes an environment that promotes, expects, and rewards ethical behaviour can answer yes
to all of these questions.

One effective way to create an ethical environment is to develop an ethics
philosophy and specific, written guidelines for implementing that philosophy
that are shared with all employees. Stelco Inc., Canada's largest steel producer,
has a Code of Ethics and Business Conduct that it shares with all employees.
The code begins with the following statement of philosophy:

> Stelco is committed to conducting its business affairs in compliance with all appli-
> cable laws, statutes and regulations and expects its employees acting on its behalf
> to do likewise. In addition business dealings among employees and by employees,
> with customers, shareholders and suppliers, community organizations and govern-
> mental and regulatory authorities must be based on principles of honesty, integrity
> and the ethical standards outlined below. [10]

This statement sets the tone for all employees at Stelco. It lets them know
that higher management not only supports ethical behaviour but also expects it.
This approach makes it less difficult for health and safety professionals when
they find themselves caught in the middle between the pressures of productivity and the maintenance of safe work practices.

An ethics credo shows employees that they have obligations extending well
beyond their work units and that how they perform their work can have an
impact, negative or positive, on fellow employees, the company, customers, and
the country. Although the emphasis on ethics in the workplace is relatively
new, the concept is not. According to Shanks, Robert Wood Johnson, the leader
who built Johnson & Johnson into a major international corporation, developed
an ethics credo for his company as early as the mid-1940s.[11]

Johnson's credo read as follows:

- To customers and users: quality and service at reasonable prices
- To suppliers: a fair opportunity
- To employees: respect, equal opportunity, and a sense of job security
- To communities: a civic responsibility
- To the environment: protection
- To shareholders: a fair return[12]

Written philosophies and guidelines such as those developed by Stelco and Johnson & Johnson are the first step in creating an ethical environment in the workplace. Health and safety professionals can play a key role in promoting ethical behaviour on the job by encouraging higher management to develop written ethics philosophies, credos, and guidelines and then by modelling the behaviour that they encourage.

Setting an Ethical Example

Companies that take the "Do as I say, not as I do" approach to ethics will not succeed. Employees must be able to trust their company to conduct all external and internal dealings in an ethical manner. Companies that do not pay their bills on time; companies that pollute; companies that place short-term profits ahead of employee health and safety; companies that do not live up to advertised quality standards; companies that do not stand behind their guarantees; and companies that are not good neighbours in their communities are not setting a good ethical example. Such companies can expect employees to mimic their unethical behaviour.

In addition to creating an ethical internal environment and handling external dealings in an ethical manner, companies must support health and safety professionals who make ethically correct decisions. This support must be given not just when such decisions are profitable, but in all cases. For example, in the ethical dilemma presented earlier in this chapter, say Camillo Garcia decided that his ethical choice was to confront the management team with his knowledge of the hazards associated with the new paint. Management gave the order to withhold critical information. This is obviously the profitable choice in the short run. But is it the ethical choice? If Camillo Garcia does not think so, will Mil-Tech stand behind him? If not, everything else that the company does to promote ethics will fail.

HANDLING ETHICAL DILEMMAS

No person will serve long as a health and safety professional without confronting an ethical dilemma. How, then, should one proceed when confronting an ethical dilemma? There are three steps (Figure 25–4):

1. Apply the various guidelines for determining what is ethical presented earlier in this chapter.
2. Select one of the three basic approaches to handling ethical questions.
3. Proceed in accordance with the approach selected, and proceed with consistency.

Apply the Guidelines

In this step, as a health and safety professional, you should apply as many of the tests set forth in Figure 25–1 as necessary to determine the ethically correct decision. In applying these guidelines, attempt to block out all mitigating circumstances and other factors that tend to cloud the issue. At this point, the goal

**Figure 25–4
Handling ethical
dilemmas.**

> **Steps for Handling Ethical Dilemmas**
>
> 1. Apply the guidelines.
> 2. Select the approach.
> 3. Proceed accordingly and consistently.

is only to identify the ethical choice. Deciding whether to implement the ethical choice comes in the next step.

Select the Approach

When deciding how to proceed after Step 1, you have three basic approaches. These approaches, as set forth in Figure 25–2, are the best-ratio, black-and-white, and full-potential approaches. These approaches and their ramifications can be debated ad infinitum; however, selecting an approach to ethical questions is a matter of personal choice. Factors that will affect the ultimate decision include your personal makeup, the expectations of the company, and the degree of company support.

Proceed with the Decision

The approach selected in Step 2 will dictate how you should proceed as a health and safety professional. Two things are important in this final step. The first is to proceed in strict accordance with the approach selected. The second is to proceed consistently. **Consistency** is critical when handling ethical dilemmas. Fairness is a large part of ethics, and consistency is a large part of fairness. The grapevine will ensure that all employees know how a health and safety professional handles an ethical dilemma. Some will agree, and some will disagree, regardless of the decision. Such is the nature of human interaction. However, regardless of the differing perceptions of the problem, employees respect consistency. Conversely, even if the decision is universally popular, you may lose respect if the decision is not consistent with past decisions.

CONSISTENCY
The rules are enforced in the same manner every time with no regard to any outside factors.

QUESTIONS TO ASK WHEN MAKING DECISIONS

Health and safety professionals often must make decisions that have ethical dimensions. A constant state of tension often exists between meeting production schedules and maintaining employee safety. Health and safety professionals usually are right in the middle of these issues. Following are some questions that can and should be asked by managers when making decisions about issues that have ethical dimensions. Health and safety professionals should ask these questions themselves, and they should encourage other decision makers within their organizations to do the same.

- Has the issue or problem been thoroughly and accurately defined?

- Have all dimensions of the problem (productivity, quality, cost, safety, health, and so on) been identified?
- Would other stakeholders (employees, customers) agree with your definition of the problem?
- What is your real motivation in making this decision? Meeting a deadline? Outperforming another organizational unit or a competitor? Self-promoting? Getting the job done right? Protecting the health and safety of employees? Some combination of these?
- What is the probable short term result of your decision? What is the probable long term result?
- Who will be affected by your decision and in what way? In the short term? In the long term?
- Did you discuss the decision with all stakeholders (or all possible stakeholders) before making it?
- Would your decision withstand the scrutiny of employees, customers, colleagues, and the general public?

Safety professionals should ask themselves these questions, but equally important, they should insist that other managers do so. The manager responsible for meeting this month's production quota may be so focused on the numbers that he or she overlooks safety. The manager who is feeling the pressure to cut production costs may make decisions that work in the short term but have disastrous consequences in the long term. Questions such as those posed above can help managers broaden their focus and consider the long-range impact when making decisions.

ETHICS AND WHISTLE-BLOWING

What can health and safety professionals do when their employer is violating legal or ethical standards? The first option, of course, should be to bring violations to the attention of appropriate management executives through established channels. In most cases, this will be sufficient to stop the illegal or unethical behaviour. But what about those occasions when the health and safety professional is ignored or, worse yet, told to "mind your own business"? These are the types of situations that have led to the concept of **whistle-blowing**, which can be defined as follows:

WHISTLE-BLOWING Act of informing an outside authority or media organ of alleged illegal or unethical acts on the part of an organization or individual.

> Whistle-blowing is the act of informing an outside authority or media organ of alleged illegal or unethical acts on the part of an organization or individual.

Problems with Whistle-Blowing

Even when the illegal or unethical practice in question threatens the health and safety of employees, some people still don't like whistle-blowers. There is often a "don't tell" mentality that causes whistle-blowers to be shunned and viewed as outcasts. As children we learned not to be "tattle-tales." Many adults still seem to hold to this philosophy.

What Is Your Opinion?

Following are two ethical dilemmas that a health and safety professional may face. What is the right thing to do in each case? What is your opinion?

- You are the safety director for West Coast Power Company. Your son is a line worker for a branch of the company that is located in another city. He is visiting you while recuperating from a back injury for which he is collecting workers' compensation. While visiting, he jogs, lifts weights, and plays softball with friends. You finally realize that he is not really injured. What should you do?

- The manufacturing director and the union representative have just had a chin-to-chin argument about removing the new machine guards from the milling machines. They have asked you — the company's safety director — to mediate the dispute. According to the manufacturing director, "We ran these machines for five years without an accident. The only reason we put them on was because some government inspector suggested it. They're fine when we are not in a hurry, but they slow us down when the rush is on. Unless we remove the guards, this job will not be shipped on time." The union representative counters by saying, "These machines are dangerous." What is the right thing to do here? What is your opinion?

The "don't be a tattle-tale" attitude is only one of the problems that works against whistle-blowing. Others are as follows:

- **Retribution.** People who blow the whistle on their employer may be subjected to retribution. They may be fired, transferred to an undesirable location, or reassigned to an undesirable job. They may also be shunned. There are numerous ways — legal ways — for an employer to take retribution against a whistle-blower.

- **Damaged relationships and hostility.** Blowing the whistle about an illegal or unethical practice can often damage relationships. Somebody in the company — by acts of commission or omission — is responsible. That person or those persons may be disciplined as a result. When this happens, people tend to choose a side, which, in turn, leads to damaged relationships. Damaged relationships are often manifested as hostility directed toward the whistle-blower.

- **Loss of focus.** Whistle-blowers often find that their time, energy, and attention are overtaken by the events surrounding the claim of illegal or unethical behaviour. Rather than focusing on doing their jobs, they find themselves dealing with retribution, damaged relationships, and hostility.

- **Scapegoating.** Negative consequences certainly can occur as a result of whistle-blowing. Because of this, some health and safety professionals may decide to ignore the issue or to raise it to the next level of management and let it drop there. The problem with this approach is the issue of *accountability*. When an employee is injured or the environment is damaged, the actions of health and safety professionals are certain to be closely scrutinized. "Did you know about the hazardous condition?" "Did you do everything in your power to prevent the accident or incident?" These types of questions are always asked when litigation is brought, as is often the case. An irresponsible organization facing charges of negligence may begin looking for a convenient scapegoat. One obvious candidate in such situations is the organization's chief health and safety professional.

Most statutes that protect the whistle-blower were developed with environmental protection or employment standards in mind, however, some legislation, such as the Ontario Occupational Health and Safety Act prohibits the employer from taking reprisals against a worker who is acting in compliance with the Act.

DISCUSSION CASE

What Is Your Opinion?

Jack Wilson, safety director for Leader, Inc., is facing a dilemma. His employer is seeking registration as an ISO 14000 company. Internal assessments and trial audits show that the company is ready and will probably pass the registration audit with flying colours. If so, Leader will be able to double its business in just two years. A European company is looking for a partner in Canada. Leader wants to be that partner, but ISO 14000 registration is a prerequisite.

Leader looks good on paper, but Jack Wilson knows of a least two serious environmental problems that the company is covering up rather than correcting. Leader's Environmental Management Plan, required by ISO 14000, shows that the environmental problems have been corrected. They haven't. Worse yet, Jack Wilson has been warned to say or do nothing that may jeopardize Leader's ISO 14000 registration. On the other hand, if the environmental problems in question are not corrected soon, the community's water supply could be contaminated in the future. What should Jack Wilson do?

SUMMARY

1. Ethics is the study of morality. Morality refers to the values that are subscribed to and fostered by society. Ethics attempts to apply reason in determining rules of human conduct that translate morality into everyday behaviour.

2. Ethical behaviour is that which falls within the limits prescribed by morality.

3. *Legal* and *ethical* are not the same. If something is illegal, it is also unethical. However, just because something is legal does not mean that it is ethical. An act can be legal but unethical.

4. To determine if a choice is ethical, you can apply the following tests: morning-after, front-page, mirror, role-reversal, and common-sense.

5. Health and safety professionals have a three-pronged role with regard to ethics. They are responsible for setting an ethical example, helping employees to identify the ethical choices when facing ethical questions, and helping employees to follow through and actually undertake the ethical option.

6. Health and safety professionals have three approaches available in handling ethical dilemmas: best-ratio, black-and-white, and full-potential.

7. The company's role in ethics is to create an ethical environment and to set an ethical example. An effective way to do this is to develop a written ethics philosophy and share it with all employees.

8. Three personality characteristics that can influence an employee's ethical behaviour are ego strength, Machiavellianism, and locus of control.

9. People facing ethical dilemmas should apply the tests for determining what is ethical, select one of the three basic approaches, and proceed consistently.

10. Whistle-blowing is the act of informing an outside authority or the media of alleged illegal or unethical acts on the part of an organization or individual.

KEY TERMS AND CONCEPTS

Best-ratio approach

Black-and-white approach

Common-sense test

Consistency

Ego strength

Ethical behaviour

Ethics

Front-page test

Full-potential approach

Locus of control

Machiavellianism

Mirror test

Morning-after test

Role-reversal test

Whistle-blowing

REVIEW QUESTIONS

1. Define the term *morality*.

2. Define the term *ethics*.

3. Briefly explain each of the following ethics tests: morning-after, front-page, mirror, role-reversal, and common sense.

4. What is the health and safety professional's role with regard to ethics?

5. Briefly explain the following approaches to handling ethical behaviour: best-ratio, black-and-white, and full-potential.

6. Briefly explain a company's role with regard to ethics.

7. Explain how one should proceed when facing an ethical dilemma.

8. Write a brief ethics philosophy for a chemical company.

9. List the individual and social factors that may influence an employee's ethical behaviour.

10. List and briefly describe the Five P's of Ethical Power as set forth by Blanchard and Peale.

11. What questions should health and safety professionals ask when making decisions that have an ethical component?

12. Explain the most common problems associated with whistle-blowing.

WEBLINKS

EthicsWeb.ca
www.ethicsweb.ca

The EthicsWeb.ca website provides useful tools for developing your own code of ethics and also has links to several organizations and associations of an ethical nature.

Public Service Values and Ethics
www.hrma-agrh.gc.ca/veo-bve/res_e.asp

On this website, the federal government reveals the initiatives on values and ethics in the public service.

ENDNOTES

1. P. F. Drucker, "What Is Business Ethics?" *Across the Board* (October 1981): 22–32.

2. E. W. Stead, D. L. Worrell, and J. G. Stead, "An Integrative Model for Understanding and Managing Ethical Behavior in Business Organizations," *Journal of Business Ethics* 5, no. 9: 233.

3. P. Taylor, *Principles of Ethics: An Introduction* (Encino, CA: Dickson, 1975), 96.

4. P. Arlow and T. A. Ulrich, "Business Ethics, Social Responsibility, and Business Students: An Empirical Comparison of Clark's Study," *Akron Business and Economic Review* 4, no. 3: 17–23.

5. K. Blanchard and N. V. Peale, *The Power of Ethical Management* (New York: Ballantine Books), 10–17.

6. Ibid., 79.

7. L. K. Trevino, "Ethical Decision Making in Organizations: A Person-Situation Interactionist Model," *Academy of Management Review* 11, no. 3: 601–617.

8. J. F. Preble and P. Miesing, "Do Adult MBA and Undergraduate Business Students Have Different Business Philosophies?" *Proceedings of the National Meeting of the American Institute for the Decision Sciences,* November 1984, 346–348.

9. F. Luthans and R. Kreitner, *Organizational Behavior Modification and Beyond: An Operant and Social Learning Approach* (Glenview, IL: Scott Foresman).

10. Stelco Inc. (March 2003). "Code of Ethics and Business Conduct." [Online]. Available: http://www.stelco.com/code/CodeofEthics-ENG-Mar03.pdf. (Retrieved March 12, 2005).

11. D. C. Shanks, "The Role of Leadership in Strategy Development," *Journal of Business Strategy* (January/February 1989): 32.

12. Ibid., 33.

Violence in the Workplace

CHAPTER

26

LEARNING OBJECTIVES

- Define key terms used when discussing workplace violence.
- Describe five strategies used to reduce the risk of workplace violence.
- Describe the social and cultural factors that contribute to workplace violence.
- Explain how administrative controls work to reduce workplace violence.
- List the steps that may be taken to mitigate the effect of workplace violence.
- Describe conflict resolution guidelines that may reduce workplace violence.

> Long before Pierre Lebrun tragically shot 4 of his co-workers at the Ottawa Transit terminal in 1999, much had been written about the deceptively slow increase in workplace violence. Content to brand such renegade behaviour as either mental illness, or a blatantly US phenomena [sic], Canadians have all but sheltered themselves from workplace violence. It takes only one or two conspicuous incidents to jar us into a heightened state of reality, one in which we quickly realize that Canada is not immune to acts of violence. In fact, if one was to scratch the surface of Canadian workplaces, it doesn't take long to realize that workplace violence, in a variety of forms, has germinated in Canada and is quietly growing.[1]

The prevention of workplace violence is a natural extension of the responsibilities of health and safety professionals. Hazard analysis, records analysis and tracking, trend monitoring, incident analysis, and prevention strategies based on administrative and engineering controls are all fundamental to both concepts. In addition, emergency response and employee training are key elements of both. Consequently, occupational health and safety professionals are well suited to add the prevention of workplace violence to their normal duties.

WORKPLACE VIOLENCE: DEFINITIONS

Health and safety professionals should be familiar with the language that has developed around the issue of workplace violence. This section contains the definitions of several concepts as they relate specifically to workplace violence.

474

Workplace Violence — Not a Problem in Canada?

Most Canadians feel safe at their jobs, and when asked say that, in terms of workplace violence, we are much better off than the United States. A study conducted in 1996 by the International Labour Organization (ILO) concludes that we rank fourth in developed countries, far worse than the US in seventh place. The ILO survey interviewed more than 2000 Canadian employees. The findings indicate that 9.7% of women surveyed said they had been victims of "sexual incidents" while on the job. As well, 5% of women and 3.9% of men reported being assaulted at work.

Source: Glen French and Paul Morgan. (2005). "Addressing Workplace Violence." *Legal Focus,* Longwoods Publishing. [Online]. Available: http://www.longwoods.com/legalfocus/62-02/feature.html. (Retrieved January 30, 2005).

- **Workplace violence.** Violent acts, behaviour, or threats that occur in the workplace or are related to it. Such acts are harmful or potentially harmful to people, property, or organizational capabilities.
- **Occupational violent crime (OVC).** Intentional battery, rape, or homicide during the course of employment.[2]
- **Employee.** An individual with an employment-related relationship (present or past) with the victim of a workplace-violence incident.
- **Outsider.** An individual with no relationship of any kind with the victim of a workplace-violence incident or with the victim's employer.
- **Employee-related outsider.** An individual with some type of personal relationship (past or present) with an employee, but who has no work-related relationship with the employee.
- **Customer.** An individual who receives products or services from the victim of a workplace-violence incident or from the victim's employer.

Each of these terms has other definitions, which are used in other contexts. Those presented above reflect how the terms are used in the language that has evolved around workplace violence.

WORKPLACE VIOLENCE
Violent acts, behaviour, or threats that occur in the workplace or are related to it.

High-Risk Occupations and People

High-risk occupations in terms of workplace violence are taxicab drivers; retail workers; police and security officers; and finance, insurance, real estate, health care, and community service employees. Employees 65 years and older are more likely to be victims than are younger employees.

**Figure 26–1
Checklist for work-
place violence risk
reduction.**

✓   Identify high-risk areas and make them visible. Secluded areas invite violence.

✓   Install good lighting in parking lots and inside all buildings.

✓   Minimize the handling of cash by employees and the amount of cash available on the premises.

✓   Install silent alarms and surveillance cameras where appropriate.

✓   Control access to all buildings (employee badges, visitor check-in and check-out procedure, visitor passes, and so on).

✓   Discourage working alone, particularly late at night.

✓   Provide training in conflict resolution as part of a mandatory employee orientation.

✓   Conduct background checks before hiring new employees.

✓   Train employees how to handle themselves and respond when a violent act occurs on the job.

✓   Develop policies that establish ground rules for employee behaviour and responses in threatening or violent situations.

✓   Nurture a positive, harmonious work environment.

✓   Encourage employees to report suspicious individuals and activities or potentially threatening situations.

✓   Deal with allegations of harassment or threatened violence promptly before the situation escalates.

✓   Take threats seriously and act appropriately.

✓   Adopt a *zero-tolerance* policy toward threatening or violent behaviour.

✓   Establish a *violence hot line* so that employees can report potential problems anonymously.

✓   Establish a *threat-management team* with responsibility for preventing and responding to violence.

✓   Establish an *emergency response team* to deal with the immediate trauma of workplace violence.

RISK-REDUCTION STRATEGIES

Figure 26–1 is a checklist that can be used by employers to reduce the risk of workplace violence in their facilities. Most of these risk-reduction strategies grow out of the philosophy of *crime reduction through environmental design (CRTED)*.[3] CRTED has the following four major elements, to which the author has added a fifth (administrative controls).

• Natural surveillance
• Control of access
• Establishment of territoriality
• Activity support
• Administrative controls

The following explains how these elements can help avoid workplace violence:

1. **Natural surveillance.** This strategy involves designing, arranging, and operating the workplace in a way that minimizes secluded areas. Making all areas inside and outside of the facility easily observable allows for natural surveillance.

2. **Control of access.** One of the most common occurrences of workplace violence involves an outsider entering the workplace and harming employees. The most effective way of stopping this type of incident is to control access to the workplace. Channelling the flow of outsiders to an access-control station, requiring visitor's passes, issuing access badges to employees, and isolating pickup and delivery points can minimize the risk of violence perpetrated by outsiders.

3. **Establishment of territoriality.** This strategy involves giving employees control over the workplace. With this approach, employees move freely within their established territory but are restricted in other areas. Employees come to know everyone who works in their territory and can, as a result, immediately recognize anyone who shouldn't be there.

4. **Activity support.** Activity support involves organizing work flow and natural traffic patterns in ways that maximize the number of employees conducting natural surveillance. The more employees observing the activity in the workplace, the better.

5. **Administrative controls.** Administrative controls consist of management practices that can reduce the risk of workplace violence. These practices include establishing policies, conducting background checks, and providing training for employees.

NATURAL SURVEILLANCE
A strategy involving designing, arranging, and operating the workplace in a way that minimizes secluded areas, making all areas inside and outside of the facility easily observable.

CONTROL OF ACCESS
Controlling access to the workplace by various means in order to maintain safety and security.

ACTIVITY SUPPORT
Organizing work flow and natural traffic patterns in ways that maximize the number of employees conducting natural surveillance, thus improving workplace safety and security.

DISCUSSION CASE

What Is Your Opinion?

A man walks into an office building and asks to see his wife. The man is well known to the other employees, one of whom escorts him to his wife's workstation. Suddenly, the man pulls a gun and shoots his wife and another employee who tries to intervene. Is this an on-the-job event? Is the employer at fault? What is your opinion about this incident involving an employee-related outsider?

CONTRIBUTING SOCIAL AND CULTURAL FACTORS

Another way to reduce the risk of workplace violence is to ensure that managers understand the social and cultural factors that can lead to it. These factors fall into two broad categories: individual and environmental factors.

Individual Factors Associated with Violence

The factors explained in this section can be predictors of the potential for violence. Employees and individuals with one or more of the following factors may respond to anger, stress, or anxiety in a violent way.

1. **Record of violence.** Past violent behaviour is typically an accurate predictor of future violent behaviour. Consequently, thorough background checks should be a normal part of the employment process.

2. **Membership in a hate group.** Hate groups often promote violence against the subjects of their prejudice. Hate-group membership on the part of an employee should raise a red flag in the eyes of management.

3. **Psychotic behaviour.** Individuals who incessantly talk to themselves, express fears concerning conspiracies against them, say that they hear voices, or become increasingly dishevelled over time may be violence-prone.

4. **Romantic obsessions.** Workplace violence is often the result of romantic entanglements or love interests gone awry. Employees who persist in making unwelcome advances may eventually respond to rejection with violence.

5. **Depression.** People who suffer from depression are prone to hurt either themselves or someone else. An employee who becomes increasingly withdrawn or overly stressed may be suffering from depression.

6. **Finger pointers.** Refusal to accept responsibility is a factor often exhibited by perpetrators of workplace violence. An employee's tendency to blame others for his or her own shortcomings should raise the caution flag.

7. **Unusual frustration levels.** The workplace has become a competitive, stressful, and sometimes frustrating place. When frustration reaches the boiling point, the emotional explosion that results can manifest itself in violence.

8. **Obsession with weapons.** Violence in the workplace often involves a weapon (gun, knife, or explosive device). A normal interest in guns used for hunting or target practice need not raise concerns. However, an employee whose interest in weapons is unusually intense and focused is cause for concern.

9. **Drug dependence.** It is common for perpetrators of workplace violence to be drug abusers. Consequently, drug dependence should cause concern not only for all of the usual reasons but also for its association with violence on the job.

Environmental Factors Associated with Violence

The environment in which employees work can contribute to workplace violence. An environment that produces stress, anger, frustration, feelings of powerlessness, resentment, and feelings of inadequacy can increase the potential for violent behaviour. The following factors can result in such an environment:

1. **Dictatorial management.** Dictatorial, overly authoritative management that shuts employees out of the decision-making process can cause them to feel powerless, as if they have little or no control over their jobs. Some people respond to powerlessness by striking out violently — a response that gives them power, if only momentarily.

2. **Role ambiguity.** One of the principal causes of stress and frustration on the job is role ambiguity. Employees need to know for what they are responsible, how they will be held accountable, and how much authority they have. When these questions are not clear, employees become stressed and frustrated, factors often associated with workplace violence.

Eight Steps for Preventing Workplace Violence

- Complete a risk-assessment survey of the entire workplace.
- Review existing security procedures.
- Develop and publish a policy statement that explains expectations, rules for behaviour, roles, duties, and responsibilities.
- Develop work-site-specific prevention procedures.
- Train all managers, supervisors, and employees.
- Establish incident reporting and investigation procedures.
- Establish incident follow-up procedures (trauma plan, counselling services, and disciplinary guidelines).
- Monitor, evaluate, and adjust.

---

3. **Partial, inconsistent supervision.** Supervisors who play favourites engender resentment in employees who aren't the favourite. Supervisors who treat one employee differently than another or one group of employees differently from another group also cause resentment. Employees who feel that they are being treated unfairly or unequally may show their resentment in violent ways.

4. **Unattended hostility.** Supervisors who ignore hostile situations or threatening behaviour are unwittingly giving them their tacit approval. An environment that accepts hostile behaviour will have hostile behaviour.

5. **No respect for privacy.** Supervisors and managers who go through the desks, files, tool boxes, and work areas of employees without first getting their permission can make them feel invaded or even violated. Violent behaviour is a possible response to these feelings.

6. **Insufficient training.** Holding employees accountable for performance on the job without providing the training that they need to perform well can cause them to feel inadequate. People who feel inadequate can turn their frustration inward and become depressed or turn it outward and become violent.

The overriding message in this section is twofold: First, managers should endeavour to establish and maintain a positive work environment that builds employees up rather than tearing them down. Second, managers should be aware of the individual factors that can contribute to violent behaviour and respond promptly if employees show evidence of responding negatively to these factors.

Workplace Analysis

Workplace analysis is the same process used by health and safety professionals to identify potentially hazardous conditions unrelated to workplace violence. Work-site analysis should be ongoing and have at least four components

WORKPLACE ANALYSIS
An in-depth study of the workplace used to identify hazards.

(Figure 26–2). An effective way to conduct an ongoing program of workplace analysis is to establish a threat-assessment team with representatives from all departments and led by the organization's chief health and safety professional.

RECORDS MONITORING AND TRACKING The purpose of *records monitoring and tracking* is to identify and chart all incidents of violence and threatening behaviour that have occurred within a given time frame. Records to analyze include the following: incident reports, police reports, employee evaluations, and letters of reprimand. Of course, individual employees' records should be analyzed in confidence by the human resources member of the team. The type of information that is pertinent includes the following:

- Where specifically did the incident occur?
- What time of day or night did the incident occur?
- Was the victim an employee? Customer? Outsider?
- Was the incident the result of a work-related grievance? Personal?

TREND MONITORING AND INCIDENT ANALYSIS *Trend monitoring* and *incident analysis* may prove helpful in determining patterns of violence. If there have been enough incidents to create one or more graphs, the team will want to determine if the graphs suggest a trend or trends. If the organization has experienced only isolated incidents, the team may want to monitor national trends. By analyzing both local and national incidents, the team can generate information that will be helpful in predicting and, thereby, preventing workplace violence. The team should look for trends in severity, frequency, and type of incidents.

EMPLOYEE SURVEYS AND FOCUS GROUPS Employees are one of the best sources of information concerning workplace hazards. This is also true when it comes to identifying vulnerabilities to workplace violence. Employee input

Figure 26–2
Four components of workplace analysis.

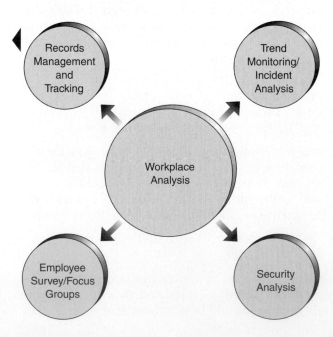

should be solicited periodically through either written employee *surveys or focus groups* or both. Where are we vulnerable? What practices put our employees at risk? These are the types of questions that should be asked of employees. An effective strategy for use with focus groups is to give participants case studies of incidents that occurred in other organizations. Then ask such questions as, "Could this happen here? Why? Or why not? How can we prevent such incidents from occurring here?"

SECURITY ANALYSIS Is the workplace secure or could a disgruntled individual simply walk in and harm employees? It is important to ask this question. The team should periodically perform a *security analysis* of the workplace to identify conditions, situations, procedures, and practices that make employees vulnerable. The types of questions to ask include the following:

- Are there physical factors about the facility that make employees vulnerable (e.g., areas that are isolated, poorly lit, infrequently travelled, or unobservable)?
- Is there a process for handling disgruntled customers? Does it put employees at risk?
- Are the prevention strategies already implemented working?
- Is the training provided to employees having a positive effect? Is more training needed? Who needs the training? What kind of training is needed?
- Are there situations in which employees have substantial amounts of money in their possession, on- or off-site?
- Are there situations in which employees are responsible for highly valuable equipment or materials late at night or at isolated locations?

Hazard Prevention and Control

Once hazardous conditions have been identified, the strategies and procedures necessary to eliminate them must be put in place. The two broad categories of prevention strategies are engineering controls and administrative controls, just as they are with other health and safety hazards. In addition to these, organizations should adopt post-incident response strategies as a way to prevent future incidents.

ENGINEERING CONTROLS **Engineering controls** relating to the prevention of workplace violence serve the same purpose as engineering controls relating to other hazards. They either remove the hazard, or they create a barrier between it and employees. Engineering controls typically involve changes to the workplace. Examples of engineering controls include the following:

ENGINEERING CONTROLS
Strategies such as the design of tools and equipment or processes that eliminates the hazard at the source.

- Installing devices and mechanisms that give employees a complete view of their surroundings (e.g., mirrors, glass or clear plastic partitions, interior windows, and so on).
- Installing surveillance cameras and television screens that allow for monitoring of the workplace.
- Installing adequate lighting, particularly in parking lots.
- Pruning shrubbery and undergrowth outside and around the facility.
- Installing fencing so that routes of egress and ingress to company property can be channelled and, as a result, better controlled.
- Arranging outdoor sheds, storage facilities, recycling bins, and other outside facilities for maximum visibility.

ADMINISTRATIVE CONTROLS Whereas engineering controls involve making changes to the workplace, **administrative controls** involve making changes to how work is done. This amounts to changing work procedures and practices. Administrative controls fall into four categories (Figure 26–3).

- Proper work practices are those that minimize the vulnerability of employees. For example, if a driver has to make deliveries in a high-crime area, the company may employ a security guard to go along, change delivery schedules to daylight hours only, or both.
- Monitoring and feedback ensures that proper work practices are being used and that they are having the desired effect. For example, say a company established a controlled access system in which visitors must check in at a central location and receive a visitor's pass. Is the system being used? Are all employees sticking to specified procedures? Has unauthorized access to the workplace been eliminated?
- Adjustments and modifications are made to violence prevention practices if it becomes clear from monitoring and feedback that they are not working or that improvements are needed.
- Enforcement involves applying meaningful sanctions when employees fail to follow the established and proper work practices. An employee who has been fully informed concerning a given administrative control, has received the training needed to practice it properly, but consciously decides not to follow the procedure should be disciplined appropriately.

POST-INCIDENT RESPONSE Post-incident response relating to workplace violence is the same as post-incident response relating to traumatic accidents. The first step is to provide immediate medical treatment for injured employees. The second step involves providing psychological treatment for traumatized employees. This step is even more important in cases of workplace violence than with accidents. Employees who are present when a violent incident occurs in the workplace, even if they don't witness it, can experience the symptoms of psychological trauma shown in Figure 26–4. Employees experiencing such symptoms or any others growing out of psychological trauma should be treated by professionals such as psychologists, psychiatrists, clinical nurse specialists,

**Figure 26–3
Categories of
administrative
controls.**

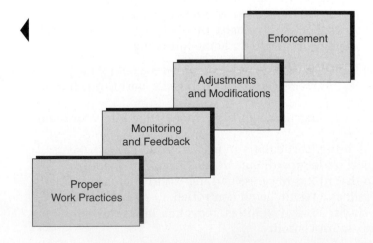

✓ Fear of returning to work
✓ Problems in relationships with fellow employees and/or family members
✓ Feelings of incompetence
✓ Guilt feelings
✓ Feelings of powerlessness
✓ Fear of criticism by fellow employees, supervisors, and managers

▶ **Figure 26–4
Symptoms of psychological trauma in cases of workplace violence.**

or certified social workers. In addition to one-on-one counselling, employees may also be enrolled in support groups. The final aspect of post-incident response is the investigation, analysis, and report. In this step, safety professionals determine how the violent incident occurred and how future incidents may be prevented, just as post-accident investigations are handled.

Training and Education

Training and education are as fundamental to the prevention of workplace violence as they are to the prevention of workplace accidents and health-threatening incidents. A complete health and safety training program should include a comprehensive component covering all aspects of workplace violence (e.g., workplace analysis, hazard prevention, proper work practices, and emergency response). Such training should be provided on a mandatory basis for supervisors, managers, and employees.

CONFLICT RESOLUTION AND WORKPLACE VIOLENCE

When developing a violence prevention program for an organization, the natural tendency is to focus on protecting employees from outsiders. This is important. However, increasingly with workplace violence, the problem is internal. All too often in the modern workplace, conflict between employees is turning violent. Consequently, a violence prevention program is not complete without the following elements: *conflict management* and **anger management.**[4]

Conflict Management Component

Disagreements on the job can generate counterproductive conflict. This is one of the reasons why managers in organizations should do what is necessary to manage conflict properly. However, it is important to distinguish between just conflict and counterproductive conflict. Not all conflict is bad. Properly managed conflict that has the improvement of products, processes, people, and the work environment as its goal is positive conflict.

ANGER MANAGEMENT
A formal system for teaching employees techniques for handling their anger, in order to facilitate good communication and create a safe and secure workplace.

CONFLICT MANAGEMENT
A formal system for managing conflict in the workplace involving establishing conflict guidelines, helping employees develop conflict prevention and resolution skills, and helping employees develop anger management skills.

CONFLICT GUIDELINES
Ground rules for discussing and debating differing points of view, differing ideas, and differing opinions concerning how best to accomplish the organization's vision, mission, and broad objectives.

Counterproductive conflict — the type associated with workplace violence — occurs when employees behave in ways that work against the interests of the overall organization and its employees. This type of conflict is often characterized by deceitfulness, vindictiveness, personal rancour, and anger. *Productive conflict* occurs when right-minded, well-meaning people disagree, without being disagreeable, concerning the best way to support the organization's mission. **Conflict management** has the following components:

- Establishing conflict guidelines.
- Helping all employees develop conflict prevention and resolution skills.
- Helping all employees develop anger management skills.

Establishing Conflict Guidelines

Conflict guidelines establish ground rules for discussing and debating differing points of view, differing ideas, and differing opinions concerning how best to accomplish the organization's vision, mission, and broad objectives. Figure 26–5 is an example of an organization's conflict guidelines. Guidelines such as these should be developed with a broad base of employee involvement from all levels in the organization.

Figure 26–5
Sample conflict guidelines.

Conflict Guidelines
Micro Electronics Manufacturing (MEM)

Micro Electronics Manufacturing encourages discussion and debate among employees at all levels concerning better ways to improve continually the quality of our products, processes, people, and work environment. This type of interaction, if properly handled, will result in better ideas, policies, procedures, practices, and decisions. However, human nature is such that conflict can easily get out of hand, take on personal connotations, and become counterproductive. Consequently, in order to promote productive conflict, MEM has adopted the following guidelines. These guidelines are to be followed by all employees at all levels:

- The criteria to be applied when discussing/debating any point of contention are as follows: Which recommendation is most likely to move our company closer to accomplishing its mission?
- Disagree, but don't be disagreeable. If the debate becomes too hot, stop and give all parties an opportunity to cool down before continuing. Apply your conflict resolution skills and anger management skills. Remember, even when we disagree about how to get there, we are all trying to reach the same destination.
- Justify your point of view by tying it to our mission and require others to do the same.
- In any discussion of differing points of view, ask yourself the following question: "Am I just trying to win the debate for the sake of winning (ego), or is my point of view really the most valid?"

SAFETY FACT

Aggressive Employees Threaten Productivity

No one wants to work with or around an aggressive person. As a result, aggressive employees cause tardiness, absenteeism, and turnover. All three of these factors are known to harm productivity. Consequently, it is important to deal with aggressive employees through counselling, aggression-management training, or even termination.

Develop Conflict Prevention and Resolution Skills

If managers are going to expect employees to disagree without being disagreeable, they are going to have to ensure that all employees are skilled in the art and science of conflict resolution. The first guideline in Figure 26–5 is an acknowledgment of human nature. It takes advanced human relations skills and constant effort to disagree without being disagreeable. Few people are born with this ability. Fortunately, it can be learned. The following strategies are based on a three-phase model developed by Tom Rusk and described in his book, *The Power of Ethical Persuasion.*[5]

EXPLORE THE OTHER PERSON'S VIEWPOINT Allow the other person to present his or her point of view. The following strategies will help make this phase of the discussion more positive and productive.

1. Establish that your goal at this point is mutual understanding.
2. Elicit the other person's complete point of view.
3. Listen nonjudgmentally and do not interrupt.
4. Ask for clarification if necessary.
5. Paraphrase the other person's point of view and restate it to show that you understand.
6. Ask the other person to correct your understanding if it appears to be incomplete.

EXPLAIN YOUR VIEWPOINT After you accurately and fully understand the other person's point of view, present your own. The following strategies will help make this phase of the discussion more positive and productive:

1. Ask for the same type of fair hearing for your point of view that you gave the other party.
2. Describe how the person's point of view affects you. Don't point the finger of blame or be defensive. Explain your reactions objectively, keeping the discussion on a professional level.
3. Explain your point of view accurately and completely.
4. Ask the other party to paraphrase and restate what you have said.
5. Correct the other party's understanding if necessary.

6. Review and compare the two positions (yours and that of the other party). Describe the fundamental differences between the two points of view and ask the other party to do the same.

AGREE ON A RESOLUTION Once both viewpoints have been explained and are understood, it is time to move to the resolution phase. This is the phase in which both parties attempt to come to an agreement. Agreeing to disagree — in an agreeable manner — is an acceptable solution. The following strategies will help make this phase of the discussion more positive and productive:

1. Reaffirm the mutual understanding of the situation.
2. Confirm that both parties are ready and willing to consider options for coming to an acceptable solution.
3. If it appears that differences cannot be resolved to the satisfaction of both parties, try one or more of the following strategies:

>Take time out to reflect and try again.
>
>Agree to third-party arbitration or neutral mediation.
>
>Agree to a compromise solution.
>
>Take turns suggesting alternative solutions.
>
>Yield (this time), once your position has been thoroughly stated and is understood. The eventual result may vindicate your position.
>
>Agree to disagree while still respecting each other.

Develop Anger Management Skills

It is difficult, if not impossible, to keep conflict positive when anger enters the picture. If individuals in an organization are going to be encouraged to question, discuss, debate, and even disagree, they must know how to manage their anger. Anger is an intense, emotional reaction to conflict in which self-control may be lost. Anger is a major cause of workplace violence. Anger occurs when people feel that one or more of their fundamental needs are being threatened. These needs include the following:

- Need for approval.
- Need to be valued.
- Need to be appreciated.
- Need to be in control.
- Need for self-esteem.

When one or more of these needs is threatened, a normal human response is to become angry. An angry person can respond in one of four ways:

1. **Attacking.** With this response, the source of the threat is attacked. This response often leads to violence, or at least verbal abuse.
2. **Retaliating.** With this response, you fight fire with fire, so to speak. Whatever is given, you give back. For example, if someone calls your suggestion ridiculous (threatens your need to be valued), you may retaliate by calling his or her suggestion dumb. Retaliation can escalate into violence.
3. **Isolating.** This response is the opposite of venting. With the isolation response, you internalize your anger, find a place where you can be alone,

and simmer. The childhood version of this response was to go to your room and pout. For example, when someone fails to even acknowledge your suggestion (threatens your need to be appreciated), you may swallow your anger, return to your office, and boil over in private.

4. **Coping.** This is the only positive response to anger. Coping does not mean that you don't become angry. Rather, it means that, even when you do, you control your emotions instead of letting them control you. A person who copes well with anger is a person who, in spite of his or her anger, stays in control. The following strategies will help employees manage their anger by becoming better at coping:

> Avoid the use of anger-inducing words and phrases including the following: *but, you should, you made me, always, never, I can't, you can't*, and so on.
>
> Admit that others don't make you angry; you allow yourself to become angry. You are responsible for your emotions and your responses to them.
>
> Don't let pride get in the way of progress. You don't have to be right every time.
>
> Drop your defences when dealing with people. Be open and honest.
>
> Relate to other people as equals. Regardless of position or rank, you are no better than they, and they are no better than you.
>
> Avoid the human tendency to rationalize your angry responses. You are responsible and accountable for your behaviour.

If employees in an organization can learn to manage conflict properly and to deal with anger positively, the potential for workplace violence will be diminished substantially. Conflict and anger management will not prevent violent acts from outsiders. There are other methods for dealing with outsiders. However, properly managing conflict and anger can protect employees from each other.

DOS AND DON'TS FOR SUPERVISORS

Supervisors can play a pivotal role in the prevention of workplace violence. Following are some rules of thumb that will enhance the effectiveness of supervisors in this regard:

- *Don't* try to diagnose the personal, emotional, or psychological problems of employees.
- *Don't* discuss an employee's drinking unless it occurs on the job. Restrict comments to performance.
- *Don't* preach to employees. Counsel employees about attendance, tardiness, and job performance, not about how they should live their lives.
- *Don't* cover up for employees or make excuses for inappropriate behaviour. Misguided kindness may allow problems to escalate and get out of hand.
- *Don't* create jobs to get problem employees out of the way. Stockpiling an employee simply gives him or her more time to brood and to allow resentment to build.
- *Don't* ignore the warning signs explained earlier in this chapter. The problems that they represent will not simply go away. Sooner or later, they will have to be handled. Sooner is better.

- *Do* remember that chemical dependence and emotional problems tend to be progressive. Left untreated, they get worse, not better.
- *Do* refer problem employees to the employee assistance program or to other mental health service providers.
- *Do* make it clear to employees that job performance is the key issue. They are expected to do what is necessary to maintain and improve their performance.
- *Do* make it clear that inappropriate behaviour will not be tolerated.[6]

EMERGENCY PREPAREDNESS PLAN

To be prepared for properly handling a violent incident in the workplace, employers should form a crisis management team.[7] The team should have only one mission — immediate response to violent acts on the job — and be chaired by a health and safety professional. Team members should receive special training and be updated regularly. The team's responsibilities should be as follows:

- Undergo trauma response training.
- Handle media interaction.
- Operate telephone and communication teams.
- Develop and implement, as necessary, an emergency evacuation plan.
- Establish a backup communication system.
- Calm personnel after an incident.
- Debrief witnesses after an incident.
- Ensure that proper security procedures are established, kept up-to-date, and enforced.
- Help employees deal with posttraumatic stress.
- Keep employees informed about workplace violence as an issue, how to respond when it occurs, and how to help prevent it.

SUMMARY

1. Preventing workplace violence is a natural extension of the responsibilities of health and safety professionals. Like the traditional responsibilities of such professionals, dealing with workplace violence involves such activities as hazard analysis, records analysis and tracking, trend monitoring, and incident analysis.
2. Key concepts relating to workplace violence include the following: occupational violent crime (OVC), employee, outsider, employee-related outsider, and customer. These terms have special definitions that relate specifically to workplace violence.
3. Canadian workplaces are not free from violence, especially for women.
4. Employees 65 years and older are more likely to be victims than are younger employees.
5. A violent act can be considered an on-the-job incident, even if it is committed away from the workplace.
6. The concept of crime reduction through environmental design (CRTED) has four major elements: natural surveillance, control of access, establishment

of territoriality, and activity support. The author has added another: administrative controls.

7. Violence is not a completely unpredictable event and certain factors can be predictors of the potential for violence. Employees and individuals with one or more of the following factors may be more likely than others to become violent: past record of violence, membership in a hate group, psychotic behaviour, romantic obsessions, depression, refusal to accept responsibility, unusual frustration levels, obsession with weapons, drug dependence. Managers should be aware of the individual factors that can contribute to violent behaviour and respond promptly if employees show evidence of responding negatively to these factors.

8. An environment that produces stress, anger, frustration, feelings of powerlessness, resentment, and feelings of inadequacy can also increase the potential for violence. The following factors in the work environment can increase the likelihood of violent behaviour: dictatorial management; role ambiguity; partial, inconsistent supervision; unattended hostility; no respect for privacy; insufficient training. Managers should make their expectations of employees clear and should provide consistent supervision; they should endeavour to establish and maintain a positive work environment that builds employees up rather than tearing them down.

9. Managers should ensure that all conflict in their workplaces is positive conflict by establishing conflict guidelines, helping all employees develop conflict prevention and resolution skills, and helping all employees develop anger management skills.

KEY TERMS AND CONCEPTS

Activity support

Administrative controls

Anger management

Conflict guidelines

Conflict management

Control of access

Engineering controls

Natural surveillance

Workplace analysis

Workplace violence

REVIEW QUESTIONS

1. Define the following terms as they relate to violence in the workplace: *occupational violent crime*, *employee*, and *outsider*.

2. Defend or refute the following statement: A violent act that occurs away from the employer's premises cannot be considered work related.

3. Explain the concept of crime reduction through environmental design (CRTED).

4. What measures can be taken to reduce the risk of violence on the job?

5. What are the primary causes of conflict on the job?

6. Explain the four ways in which an angry person might respond in a work setting.

7. What are some conflict resolution techniques that can be used to resolve tense situations at work?

WEBLINKS

The Canadian Initiative on Workplace Violence
www.workplaceviolence.ca/home.html

The CIWV website offers insight into the cause of workplace violence and various means of curbing workplace aggression.

Canadian Centre for Occupational Health and Safety
www.ccohs.ca/oshanswers/psychosocial/violence.html

This CCOHS website provides workers and employers with information to identify signs of pending workplace violence and answers other questions on the topic.

ENDNOTES

1. Glen French and Paul Morgan. (2005). "Addressing Workplace Violence." *Legal Focus,* Longwoods Publishing. [Online]. Available: http://www.longwoods.com/legalfocus/ 62-02/feature.html. (Retrieved January 30, 2005).

2. Lloyd G. Nigro, "Violence in the American Workplace: Challenges to the Public Employees," *Public Administration Review* 56, no. 4: 326.

3. Janice L. Thomas, "A Response to Occupational Violent Crime," *Professional Safety* 37(b) (June 1992): 27–31.

4. US Department of Labor, Occupational Health and Safety Administration, *Guidelines for Workplace Violence Prevention Programs for Night Retail Establishments.*

5. Tom Rusk, *The Power of Ethical Persuasion* (New York: Penguin Books, 1993), xv–xvii.

6. Illinois State Police, *Do's and Don'ts for the Supervisor,* [Online]. Available: http://www.state.il.us/isp/viowkplc/vwpp6c.htm.

7. Illinois State Police, *Do's and Don'ts for the Supervisor,* [Online]. Available: http://www.state.il.us/isp/viowkplc/vwpp8.htm.

GLOSSARY

ABSORPTION Passage through the skin and into the bloodstream.

ACCELERATION Increase in the speed of a falling object before impact.

ACCIDENT-ANALYSIS REPORT Report identifying the root cause of an accident.

ACCIDENT INVESTIGATION The process of collecting facts to determine the cause of an accident.

ACCIDENT PREVENTION The act of preventing a happening that may cause loss or injury to a person.

ACCIDENT REPORT Records the findings of an accident investigation, the cause or causes of an accident, and recommendations for corrective action.

ACCIDENT SCENE The area where an accident occurred.

ACCIDENT/INCIDENT THEORY Theory of accident causation in which overload, ergonomic traps, or a decision to err lead to human error.

ACCIDENT An unplanned or unexpected event that results in injuries to people or loss of product or process.

ACCLIMATIZATION Process by which the body becomes gradually accustomed to heat or cold in a work setting.

ACGIH American Conference of Governmental Industrial Hygienists. A professional association that develops and publishes recommended exposure limits for chemical and physical agents.

ACT Document containing laws made by provincial legislature or federal parliament.

ACTIVITY SUPPORT Organizing work flow and natural traffic patterns in ways that maximize the number of employees conducting natural surveillance, thus improving workplace safety and security.

ACUTE Describes the effect of short term exposure.

ADJUSTABLE GUARDS Devices that provide a barrier against a variety of different hazards associated with different production operations.

ADMINISTRATIVE CONTROLS Procedures that are adopted to limit employee exposure to hazardous conditions.

AIDS Acquired immunodeficiency syndrome, describes the condition caused by the human immunodeficiency virus (HIV).

AIR DOSE Dose measured by an instrument in the air at or near the surface of the body in the area that has received the highest dosage of a toxic substance.

ALTERNATING CURRENT (AC) Electrical current in which the direction of flow alternates from one direction to the other.

ALTITUDE SICKNESS A form of hypoxia associated with high altitudes.

AMPERE The unit of measurement for electrical current.

ANCESTRY A person's line of descent.

ANESTHETICS In carefully controlled dosages, anesthetics can inhibit the normal operation of the central nervous system without causing serious or irreversible effects.

ANGER MANAGEMENT A formal system for teaching employees techniques for handling their anger, in order to facilitate good communication and create a safe and secure workplace.

ANTI-LABOUR LAWS Nineteenth century laws that strongly favoured employers.

ASEPTIC NECROSIS A delayed effect of decompression sickness involving damage to marrow generation as well as to healthy bone cells.

ASPHYXIANTS Substances that can disrupt breathing so severely as to cause suffocation.

ASSUMPTION OF RISK Based on the theory that people who accept a job assume the risks that go with it. It says employees who work voluntarily should accept the consequences of their actions on the job rather than blaming the employer.

AUDIOGRAM The results of an audiometric test to determine the noise threshold at which a subject responds to different test frequencies.

AUDIOMETRIC TESTING Measures the hearing threshold of employees.

AUTO-IGNITION TEMPERATURE The lowest temperature at which a vapour-producing substance or a flammable gas will ignite even without the presence of a spark or a flame.

AUTOMATIC EJECTION A system that ejects work pneumatically and mechanically.

AUTOMATIC FEED A system that feeds stock to the machine from rolls.

AUTOMATION The state of being operated automatically.

AVIAN INFLUENZA An infectious disease of birds caused by type A strains of the influenza virus.

BACTERIA Microscopic single cell organisms found in food, water, and air.

BAROMETER Scientific device for measuring atmospheric pressure.

BEHAVIOURAL TIME SHARING A technique requiring the simultaneous performance of two tasks.

BENDS Common name for decompression sickness.

BEST-RATIO APPROACH People are basically good and under the right circumstances behave ethically.

BILL Law in draft form.

BIOLOGICAL AGENTS Living things or substances produced by living things that may cause harm to humans.

BIOLOGICAL EXPOSURE INDICES (BEIS) Procedures used to determine the amount of material absorbed into the human body.

BLACK-AND-WHITE APPROACH Right is right, wrong is wrong, and circumstances are irrelevant.

BLACKBALL To ostracize an employee.

BLOODBORNE PATHOGEN A disease-producing agent found in the blood.

BODY SURFACE AREA (BSA) When assessing the severity of burns, the amount of body surface area that is covered with burns is an important factor.

BONDING Used to connect two pieces of equipment by a conductor. Also, involves eliminating the difference in static charge potential between materials.

BOYLE'S LAW States that the product of a given pressure and volume is constant with a constant temperature.

BRITISH NORTH AMERICA ACT (BNA ACT, 1876) Established the constitutional layout of the new country, Canada, including the powers of the provincial and federal governments.

BULK SHIPMENT A shipment of controlled product that is contained without intermediate packaging.

CANADA LABOUR CODE Legislation that sets out the rights and duties of federal employees who work under federal jurisdiction. About 10% of the Canadian workforce is covered by the Canada Labour Code.

CANADIAN CENTRE FOR OCCUPATIONAL HEALTH AND SAFETY (CCOHS) A federal government agency established to research and provide safety information resources to all Canadian workers.

CANADIAN STANDARDS ASSOCIATION (CSA) Independent agency that develops national standards for the performance of many products inside and outside of the workplace.

CARCINOGEN Any substance that can cause a malignant tumour or a neoplastic growth.

CARPAL TUNNEL SYNDROME (CTS) An injury to the median nerve inside the wrist.

CAUSAL RELATIONSHIP A situation in which an action leads to a certain result.

CEILING The level of exposure that should not be exceeded at any time for any reason.

CENTRAL FACTOR The main issue or factor in a problem or act.

CERVICAL RADICULOPATHY Compression of the cervical vertebrae in the neck.

CHEMICAL AGENTS Single elements or compounds that may be toxic to humans.

CHEMICAL BURNS Burn damage to the skin caused by chemicals such as acids and alkalies.

CHOKES Coughing and choking, resulting from bubbles in the respiratory system.

CHRONIC Effect of exposure over time.

CIRCADIAN RHYTHM Biological clock.

CIRCUIT TESTER An inexpensive piece of test equipment with two wire leads capped by probes and connected to a small bulb.

CODE OF HAMMURABI Developed around 2000 B.C. during the time of the Babylonians by the ruler Hammurabi, this code encompassed all of the laws of the land at that time. The significant aspect for our purposes is that it contained clauses dealing with injuries, allowable fees for physicians, and monetary damages assessed against those who injured others.

CODE A set of standards, rules, or regulations relating to a specific area.

COEFFICIENT OF FRICTION A numerical correlation of the resistance of one surface against another surface.

COLD STRESS Physical or mental stress that results from working in cold conditions.

COMBINATION THEORY The actual cause of an accident may be explained by combining many models.

COMBUSTIBLE SUBSTANCE Any substance with a flash point of 37.8°C (100°F) or higher.

COMBUSTION POINT The temperature at which a given fuel can burst into flame.

COMBUSTION A chemical reaction between oxygen and a combustible fuel.

COMMON-SENSE TEST Requires person to listen to what instincts and common sense are telling him or her.

COMPETITIVENESS The ability to succeed and prosper consistently in the marketplace whether it is local, regional, national, or global.

CONDUCTION The transfer of heat between two bodies that are touching or from one location to another within a body.

CONDUCTORS Substances that have many free electrons at room temperature and can conduct electricity.

CONFINED SPACE An area with limited means of egress that is large enough for a person to fit into, but is not designed for occupancy.

CONFLICT GUIDELINES Ground rules for discussing and debating differing points of view, differing ideas, and differing opinions concerning how best to accomplish the organization's vision, mission, and broad objectives.

CONFLICT MANAGEMENT A formal system for managing conflict in the workplace involving establishing conflict guidelines, helping employees develop conflict prevention and resolution skills, and helping employees develop anger management skills.

CONSISTENCY The rules are enforced in the same manner every time with no regard to any outside factors.

CONTINUITY TESTER May be used to determine whether a conductor is properly grounded or has a break in the circuit.

CONTRIBUTORY NEGLIGENCE An injured worker's own negligence contributed to the accident. If the actions of employees contributed to their own injuries, the employer is absolved of any liability.

CONTROL OF ACCESS Controlling access to the workplace by various means in order to maintain safety and security.

CONTROL When an employee participates in determining the work routine, including schedule and selection of tasks.

CONTROLLED PRODUCTS Products identified under the federal Hazardous Products Act, whose use and handling are controlled under WHMIS legislation.

CONTUSION A bruise resulting from a blow.

CONVECTION The transfer of heat from one location to another by way of a moving medium.

CORIUM The inner layer of human skin.

CORPORATE IMAGE How a company is perceived to interact with its workers, customers, and community.

COST ALLOCATION Spreading the cost of workers' compensation appropriately and proportionately among industries, ranging from the most to the least hazardous.

COST–BENEFIT The relationship between the cost of a remedy and the benefit it produces.

COST The amount of money needed to produce a product, not to be confused with "price," which is the amount of money needed to purchase a product after the cost has been marked up.

CREEPS Caused by bubble formation in the skin, which causes an itchy, crawling, rashy feeling in the skin.

CRITICAL BURNS Second-degree burns covering more than 30% of the body and third-degree burns covering over 10% are considered critical.

CRITICAL INJURY Injuries where a specified degree of seriousness has been reached. The specific requirements for classifying an injury as "critical" are provided in the statutes of some jurisdictions.

CRUSHING Occurs when a part of the body is caught between two hard surfaces that progressively move together, thereby crushing anything between them.

CUMULATIVE TRAUMA DISORDERS (CTDS) A term that covers a number of injuries caused by forceful or awkward movements repeated frequently over time.

CUTIS The inner layer of human skin.

CUTTING Occurs when a body part comes in contact with a sharp edge.

DALTON'S LAW OF PARTIAL PRESSURES States that in a mixture of theoretically ideal gases, the pressure exerted by the mixture is the sum of the pressures exerted by each component gas of the mixture.

DECIBEL The unit applied when measuring sound. One-tenth of a bel. One decibel is the smallest difference in the level of sound that can be perceived by the human ear.

DECOMPRESSION SICKNESS Can result from the decompression that accompanies a rapid rise from sea level to at least 5500 metres (18 000 feet) or a rapid ascent from around 40 to 20 metres (132 to 66 feet) under water.

DERMIS The inner layer of human skin.

DESIGN FLAW A defect in equipment or in the work space that can lead to an accident or injury.

DESIGN PROCESS A plan of action for reaching a goal.

DESTRUCTIVE TESTING Testing by these methods destroys the material being checked.

DIRECT COST Identifiable uninsured cost incurred as a result of an accident.

DOMINO THEORY Injuries are caused by the action of preceding factors. Removal of the central factor negates the action of the preceding factors and, in so doing, prevents accidents and injuries.

DOSE THRESHOLD The minimum dose required to produce a measurable effect.

DOSE The amount of ionizing radiation absorbed per unit of mass by part of the body or the whole body.

DOSIMETER Measures the external dose from nearby sources of radiation.

DOSIMETER Provides a time-weighted average over a period such as one complete work shift.

DOUBLE INSULATION A means of increasing electrical equipment safety.

DUE DILIGENCE Application of adequate effort under the circumstances.

DYSBARISM The formation of gas bubbles due to rapid ambient pressure reduction.

EGO STRENGTH An employee's ability to undertake self-directed tasks and to cope with tense situations.

ELECTRICAL HAZARDS Potentially dangerous situations related to electricity (e.g., a bare wire).

ELECTRICAL SYSTEM GROUNDING Achieved when one conductor of the circuit is connected to the earth.

ELECTRICITY The flow of negatively charged particles called electrons through an electrically conductive material.

ELECTROLYTES Minerals that are needed for the body to maintain the proper metabolism and for cells to produce energy.

ELECTROMAGNETIC FIELD (EMF) Form of nonionizing radiation produced as electrical current flows.

ELECTROMECHANICAL DEVICES Contact bars that allow only a specified amount of movement between the worker and the hazard.

ELECTRONS Negatively charged particles.

ELECTROSTATIC HAZARDS Shocks from static electricity discharge.

EMERGENCY ACTION PLAN (EAP) A collection of small plans for every anticipated emergency (e.g., fire, hurricane, chemical spill, and so on).

EMERGENCY COORDINATOR A person who is clearly identified in a company emergency response plan as the responsible party for a specific type of emergency situation.

EMERGENCY PLANNING Developing procedures to reduce the negative effects of an emergency. An emergency plan will have provisions for reducing fatalities and injuries; limiting the damage to equipment, facilities, and product; and expediting the return to normal operation.

EMERGENCY PREPAREDNESS ACT Legislation that establishes the role of the federal government in preparing for civil emergencies in Canada.

EMERGENCY RESPONSE PLAN A written document that identifies the different personnel or groups that respond to various types of emergencies and, in each case, who is in charge.

EMERGENCY An undesirable, unplanned event that, in order to limit damage to people and property, would require resources beyond those that are normally available.

EMPLOYEE NEGLIGENCE Condition that exists when an employee fails to take necessary and prudent precautions.

EMPLOYER-BIASED LAWS A collection of laws that favoured employers over employees in establishing a responsibility for workplace safety.

EMPLOYER LIABILITY In 1877, the Employer's Liability Law was passed and established the potential for employers to be liable for accidents that occurred in the workplace.

ENDOTHERMIC Reactions that consume more heat than they generate.

ENGINEERING CONTROLS Strategies such as the design of tools and equipment or processes that eliminates the hazard at the source.

ENVIRONMENT The aggregate of social and cultural conditions that influence the life of an individual.

ENVIRONMENTAL FACTORS Characteristics of the environment in which an employee works that can affect his or her state of mind or physical conditions, such as noise or distractions.

ENVIRONMENTAL HEAT Heat that is produced by sources outside the body.

ENVIRONMENTAL MANAGEMENT SYSTEM (EMS) That component of an organization with primary responsibility for leading, planning, organizing, and controlling as these functions relate specifically to an organization's processes, products, or services and the impact that they have on the environment.

EPIDEMIOLOGICAL THEORY Holds that the models used for studying and determining epidemiological relationships can also be used to study causal relationships between environmental factors and accidents or diseases.

EPIDERMIS The outer layer of human skin.

ERGONOMIC TRAP An unsafe condition unintentionally designed into a workstation.

ERGONOMICS The science of conforming the workplace and all of its elements to the worker.

ERGONOMISTS Scientists who study the interaction of workers and their surroundings.

ETHICAL BEHAVIOUR That which falls within the limits prescribed by morality.

ETHICS The study of morality.

EVOLVED GAS EFFECTS Happens when gas is being absorbed faster than it is being exhaled. These bubbles of gas, which are often nitrogen, may form in the blood and other tissues.

EXCHANGE RATE Indicates the increase in sound level that is permitted as the time of exposure is halved.

EXOTHERMIC Chemical reactions that create heat.

EXPERIENCE RATING The recent safety performance of the company is reflected in the premiums charged.

EXPIRATION When pressure within the lungs is greater than atmospheric pressure, air moves down a pressure gradient from the lungs to the outside.

EXPLOSION A very rapid, contained fire.

EXPLOSIVE RANGE Defines the concentrations of a vapour or gas in air that can ignite from a source.

FEEDBACK Employee's opinions of a project or an employer's opinion about an employee's job performance.

FEELING OF RESPONSIBILITY Being responsible for the welfare of his or her family may cause a worker to feel that options to take employment risks are limited.

FELLOW SERVANT RULE Employers are not liable for workplace injuries that result from negligence of other employees.

FIRE HAZARD Conditions that favour the ignition and spread of fire

FIRE POINT The minimum temperature at which the vapours or gas in air can ignite from a source of ignition.

FIRE A chemical reaction between oxygen and a combustible fuel.

FIRST-DEGREE BURN Results in a mild inflammation of the skin known as erythema.

FIXED GUARDS Provide a permanent barrier between workers and the point of operation.

FLAMMABLE SUBSTANCE Any substance with a flash point below 37.8°C (100°F).

FLASH POINT The lowest temperature for a given fuel at which vapours are produced in sufficient concentrations to flash in the presence of a source of ignition.

FLUID LOSS Depletion of necessary body fluids, primarily through perspiration.

FOREIGN OBJECT Any object that is out of place or in a position to trip someone or to cause a slip.

FOUR-TO-ONE RATIO Base one foot away from the wall for every four feet between the ground and the top support point of a ladder.

FREEZE The inability to release one's grip voluntarily from a conductor of electricity.

FREQUENCY The number of cycles per second in hertz (Hz).

FREQUENCY The number of events in a given time.

FRIABLE ASBESTOS Asbestos that is in a state of crumbling deterioration. When asbestos is in this state, it is most dangerous.

FRONT-PAGE TEST Encourages persons to make a decision that would not embarrass them if it were printed as a story on the front page of their hometown newspaper.

FULL-POTENTIAL APPROACH People are responsible for realizing their full potential within the confines of morality.

FUNGI Simple plants that feed on dead or living tissue of other organisms.

FUSES Consist of a metal strip or wire that will melt if a current above a specific value is conducted through the metal.

GATES Provide a barrier between the danger zone and workers.

GLOBAL MARKETPLACE The worldwide economic market in which many companies must compete for business.

GOOD HOUSEKEEPING Proper cleaning and maintenance of a work area.

GROUND FAULT CIRCUIT INTERRUPTER (GFCI) Can detect the flow of current to the ground and open the circuit, thereby interrupting the flow of current.

GROUND FAULT When the current flow in the hot wire is greater than the current in the neutral wire.

HAM COMMISSION Royal commission headed by Dr. James Ham in 1975, dealing with miners illnesses, laid the foundation for Ontario's first Occupational Health and Safety Act.

HAND-ARM VIBRATION (HAV) SYNDROME A form of Raynaud's syndrome that afflicts workers who use vibrating power tools frequently over time.

HARMFUL ENVIRONMENT A work environment in which physical or psychological factors exist that are potentially hazardous.

HAZARD ANALYSIS A systematic process for identifying hazards and recommending corrective action.

HAZARD CLASS One of six categories into which controlled products are placed.

HAZARD A condition with the potential of causing injury to personnel, damage to equipment or structures, loss of material, or lessening of the ability to perform a prescribed function.

HAZARDOUS CONDITION A condition that exposes a person to risks.

HAZARDOUS NOISE Any sound for which any combination of frequency, intensity, or duration is capable of causing permanent hearing loss in a specified population.

HEALTH AND SAFETY PROFESSIONAL An individual whose profession (job) is to be concerned with health and safety measures in the workforce.

HEAT STRAIN The overall physiological response resulting from heat stress.

HEAT STRESS The net heat load to which a worker is exposed.

HEPATITIS An infection or inflammation of the liver.

HIGH-RADIATION AREA Any accessible area in which radiation hazards exist that could deliver a dose in excess of 100 millirem within one hour.

HORIZONTAL WORK AREA Refers to the limits of the horizontal plane in which the worker is required to perform a task. A good horizontal work area is designed and positioned so that it does not require the worker to bend forward or to twist the body from side to side.

HUMAN ERROR A mistake that is made by a human, not a machine.

HUMAN FACTORS THEORY Attributes accidents to a chain of events ultimately caused by human error.

HUMAN IMMUNO- DEFICIENCY VIRUS (HIV) The virus that causes acquired immunodeficiency syndrome (AIDS).

HUMIDIFICATION Adding moisture to the air to reduce electrical static.

HYPERGOLIC Fuels that ignite spontaneously on contact with an oxidizer.

HYPEROXIA Too much oxygen or oxygen breathed under too high a pressure.

HYPOTHERMIA The condition that results when the body's core temperature drops to dangerously low levels (35°C or 95°F).

HYPOXIA Too little oxygen getting to body tissues.

IAPA Industrial Accident Prevention Association, the largest health and safety consulting association in Canada.

IGNITION TEMPERATURE The temperature at which a given fuel can burst into flame.

IMPACT ACCIDENTS Involve a worker being struck by or against an object.

IMPACT The consequences of an action or event.

IMPULSE NOISE Consists of transient pulses that can occur repetitively or nonrepetitively.

INANIMATE POWER Power that is lacking life or spirit. During the Industrial Revolution, humans and animals were replaced with inanimate power (e.g., steam power).

INAPPROPRIATE ACTIVITIES Activities undertaken with disregard for established safety procedures.

INAPPROPRIATE RESPONSE A response in which a person disregards an established safety procedure.

INCENTIVES Rewards for desirable performance.

INCIDENT RATE The number of accidents per given number of workers.

INCOME REPLACEMENT Replacement of current and future income, based on 90% of net pay for most jurisdictions.

INDIRECT COSTS Costs that are not directly identifiable with workplace accidents.

INDUSTRIAL HYGIENE An area of specialization in the field of industrial health and safety that is concerned with predicting, recognizing, assessing, controlling, and preventing environmental stressors in the workplace that can cause sickness or serious discomfort.

INDUSTRIAL MEDICINE A specialized field that is concerned with work-related health and safety issues.

INFECTION The body's response to contamination by a disease-producing microorganism.

INFRARED RADIATION Electromagnetic radiation with a frequency less than that of visible light and greater than that of most radio waves.

INGESTION Entry through the mouth.

INHALATION Taking gases, vapours, dust, smoke, fumes, aerosols, or mists into the body by breathing in.

INJECTION A means of entry of toxic substances into the body through punctured skin.

INSPIRATION When atmospheric pressure is greater than pressure within the lungs, air flows down this pressure gradient from the outside into the lungs.

INTERLOCKED GUARDS Shut down the machine when the guard is not securely in place or is disengaged.

INTERLOCKS Automatically break the circuit when an unsafe situation is detected.

INTERNAL FACTORS Factors that can add a burden on a person and interfere with his or her work, such as personal problems.

INTERNAL RESPONSIBILITY SYSTEM A mechanism to allow employers, supervisors, and workers to monitor each other's actions and ensure compliance with the act.

INTERNATIONAL EMERGENCIES Arise from international acts of intimidation or coercion or the use of serious force or violence that threaten the sovereignty, security, or territorial integrity of Canada or its allies.

INTERNATIONAL ORGANIZATION FOR STANDARDIZATION (ISO) A worldwide organization of national standards bodies.

INTRAVENOUS DRUG USER One who is administered drugs by means of injecting them directly into their veins.

IONIZER Ionizes the air surrounding a charged surface to provide a conductive path for the flow of charges.

IONIZING RADIATION Radiation that becomes electrically charged or changed into ions.

IRRITANTS Substances that cause irritation to the skin, eyes, and the inner lining of the nose, mouth, throat, and upper respiratory tract.

JOB AUTONOMY Control over one's job.

JOB DESCRIPTIONS Written specifications that describe the tasks, duties, reporting requirements, and qualifications for a given job.

JOB SECURITY A sense — real or imagined — of having the potential for longevity in a job and having a measure of control concerning that longevity.

KINETIC ENERGY The energy resulting from a moving object.

LABORATORY LABEL Label required on controlled products that are intended solely to be used or tested in a lab. There are two types of laboratory labels: supply house labels and sample labels.

LANYARD A flexible line for connecting the body belt or body harness to a deceleration device, lifeline, or anchorage.

LASER Light amplification by stimulated emission of radiation.

LATENCY PERIOD Time after exposure to a hazardous product before symptoms appear.

LAWS Rules that limit behaviour.

LEGISLATION Laws brought into force by a legislative body.

LET-GO CURRENT The highest current level at which a person in contact with a conductor of electricity can release the grasp of the conductor.

LETHAL CONCENTRATION The concentration in air that is lethal to the test subject.

LETHAL DOSE The dose that is lethal to the test subject by exposure through any means other than inhalation.

LIFTING HAZARD Any factor that if not properly dealt with may lead to an injury from lifting.

LIGHTNING Static charges from clouds following the path of least resistance to the earth, involving very high voltage and current.

LOAD A device that uses currents.

LOCKOUT/TAGOUT SYSTEM A system for incapacitating a machine until it can be made safe to operate. "Lockout" means physically locking up the machine so that it cannot be used without removing the lock. "Tagout" means applying a tag that warns employees not to operate the machine in question.

LOCUS OF CONTROL The perspective of workers concerning who or what controls their behaviour.

LOST TIME INJURY An injury or illness due to a work-related accident or exposure to a noxious substance that results in an employee missing work and for which the employee receives compensation for lost income.

LOST TIME The amount of time that an employee was unable to work due to an injury.

MACHIAVELLIANISM The extent to which an employee will attempt to deceive and confuse others.

MAGNA CARTA Charter enacted in 1215 that limited the power of King John of England.

MANUAL MATERIAL HANDLING Moving goods or equipment without the aid of machinery.

MANUAL MATERIALS HANDLING Moving goods or equipment without the aid of machinery.

MATERIAL SAFETY DATA SHEETS (MSDSS) These sheets contain all of the relevant information needed by safety personnel concerning specific hazardous materials.

MEANINGLESSNESS The feeling that workers get when their jobs become so specialized and so technology-dependent that they cannot see the meaning in their work as it relates to the finished product or service.

MEANS OF EGRESS A route for exiting a building or other structure.

MECHANICAL HAZARDS Those associated with power-driven machines, whether automated or manually operated.

MECHANICAL INJURIES Injuries that have occurred due to misuse of a power-driven machine.

MEDICAL REHABILITATION Designed to provide the needed medical care at no cost to the injured employee until he or she is pronounced fit to return to work.

METABOLIC HEAT Produced within a body as a result of activity that burns energy.

MINDLESSNESS The result of the process of dumbing down the workplace.

MINOR BURNS All first-degree burns are considered minor as well as second-degree burns covering less than 15% of the body.

MIRROR TEST Encourages people to make choices based on how they will feel about their decision when they look in the mirror.

MODERATE BURNS Second-degree burns covering less than 30% of the body and third- degree burns covering less than 10% are considered moderate.

MORNING-AFTER TEST Encourages people to make choices based on how they will feel about their decision the next day.

NARCOTIC A substance that produces numbness or stupor.

NARROW BAND NOISE Noise that is confined to a narrow range of frequencies.

NATURAL SURVEILLANCE A strategy involving designing, arranging, and operating the workplace in a way that minimizes secluded areas, making all areas inside and outside of the facility easily observable.

NEEDLESTICK INJURIES Injuries obtained through inadvertent puncture of the skin with hypodermic needles.

NEGATIVE PRESSURES Pressures below atmospheric level.

NEOPLASTIC GROWTH Cancerous tissue or tissue that might become cancerous.

NEUTRONS Particles that neutralize the negative charge of electrons. They act as temporary energy repositories between positively charged particles called protons and electrons.

NOISE Unwanted sound.

NONDESTRUCTIVE TESTING Testing by these methods does not harm the material being tested.

NONIONIZING RADIATION Radiation on the electromagnetic spectrum that has a frequency of 10 or less and a wavelength in metres of 3 ¥ 10 or less.

NONSKID FOOTWEAR Shoes that have special nonskid soles.

NORMLESSNESS The phenomenon in which people working in a highly automated environment can become estranged from society.

OBJECTIVITY Rules are enforced equally regardless of who commits an infraction, from the newest employee to the chief executive officer.

OCCUPATIONAL ACCIDENT Unplanned event that causes injury to a worker.

OCCUPATIONAL DISEASES Pathological conditions brought about by workplace conditions or factors.

OCCUPATIONAL HEALTH AND SAFETY ACT Legislation that sets out the rights and duties of all parties in the workplace for the protection of workers against hazards on the job.

OHM'S LAW describes the relationship among volts, ohms, and amps. One ohm is the resistance of a con-

ductor that has a current of one amp under the potential of one volt.

OHMS Measure of resistance.

OPEN-ENDED Questions that do not lead the witness to give certain answers or suggest any prejudgment of the answers.

OPEN GROUND Electrical wiring condition in which current has no path to ground.

ORGANIZED LABOUR A group of employees who joined together to fight for the rights of all employees (i.e., unions).

OVEREXERTION The result of employees working beyond their physical limits.

OVERLOAD Amounts to an imbalance between a person's capacity at any given time and the load that person is carrying in a given state.

PARASITE An animal or plant that lives in or on a host.

PERFORMANCE ORIENTED The goal of the safety department is to improve safety performance, not only to be in compliance with the regulations.

PERSONAL MONITORING DEVICES Devices worn or carried by an individual to measure radiation doses received.

PERSONAL PROTECTIVE EQUIPMENT (PPE) Any type of clothing or device that puts a barrier between the worker and the hazard (e.g., safety goggles, gloves, hard hats, and so on).

PHOTOELECTRIC DEVICES Optional devices that shut down the machine any time the light field is broken.

PHYSICAL HAZARDS Include noise, vibration, extremes of temperature, and excessive radiation.

PLACARDS Alternative to a temporary label or when workplace labels are not practical.

POINT-OF-OPERATION GUARDS Machine guards that provide protection right at the point where the user operates the machine.

POSTTRAUMATIC STRESS DISORDER The ongoing symptoms of exposure to psychological stress.

POWERLESSNESS The feeling that workers have when they are not able to control the work environment.

PRECEDING FACTORS Factors that led up to an accident.

PREDISPOSITIONAL CHARACTERISTICS Human personality characteristics that can have a catalytic effect in causing an accident.

PRELIMINARY HAZARD ANALYSIS (PHA) Conducted to identify potential hazards and prioritize them according to (1) the likelihood of an accident or injury being caused by the hazard; and (2) the severity of injury, illness, or property damage that could result if the hazard caused an accident.

PRESSURE HAZARD A hazard caused by a dangerous condition involving pressure.

PRESSURE The force exerted against an opposing fluid or thrust distributed over a surface.

PRIMARY WITNESS An eyewitness to an accident.

PRINCIPAL'S OFFICE SYNDROME When an accident witness is unable to communicate freely about what they saw because he or she is intimidated or uncomfortable in the interview situation.

PROBABILITY The statistical likelihood of an action or event taking place.

PRODUCTIVITY The concept of comparing output of goods or services to the input of resources needed to produce or deliver them.

PROOF PRESSURE TESTS Tests in which containers are "proofed" by subjecting them to specified pressures for specified periods.

PROTONS Positively charged particles.

PSYCHOPHYSIOLOGI-CAL TECHNIQUES Require simultaneous measurement of heart rate and brain waves, which are then interpreted as indexes of mental workload and industrial stress.

PSYCHOSOCIAL QUESTIONNAIRES Evaluate workers' emotions about their jobs.

PUBLIC ORDER EMERGENCIES Constitute threats to the security of Canada and are so serious as to be national emergencies and, as such, are beyond the capacity or authority of a province or territory to handle.

PUBLIC WELFARE EMERGENCIES Severe natural disasters or major accidents, affecting public welfare, which are beyond the capacity or authority of a province or territory to handle.

PULLBACK DEVICES Pull the operator's hands out of the danger zone when the machine starts to cycle.

PUNCTURING Results when an object penetrates straight into the body and pulls straight out, creating a wound in the shape of the penetrating object.

QUALITY MANAGEMENT (QM) A way of managing a company that revolves around a total and willing commitment of all personnel at all levels to quality.

QUALITY A measure of the extent to which a product or service meets or exceeds customer expectations.

RAD A measure of the dose of ionizing radiation absorbed by body tissue stated in terms of the amount of energy absorbed per unit of mass of tissue.

RADIANT HEAT The result of electromagnetic nonionizing energy that is transmitted through space without the movement of matter within that space.

RADIATION AREA Any accessible area in which radiation hazards exist that could deliver doses such that (1) within one hour, a major portion of the body could receive more than 5 millirem; or (2) within five consecutive days, a major portion of the body could receive more than 100 millirem.

RADIATION Consists of energetic nuclear particles and includes alpha rays, beta rays, gamma rays, X-rays, neutrons, high-speed electrons, and high-speed protons.

RADIO-FREQUENCY DEVICES Capacitance devices that brake the machine if the capacitance field is interrupted by a worker's body or another object.

RADIOACTIVE MATERIAL Material that emits corpuscular or electromagnetic emanations as the result of spontaneous nuclear disintegration.

RECEPTACLE WIRING TESTER A device with two standard plug probes for insertion into an ordinary 110-volt outlet and a probe for the ground.

REENACTMENT A technique in which a witness to an accident goes through the same set of actions as the accident victim in order to demonstrate what happened to the investigator. The witness should simulate the actions rather than actually performing them or there may be another accident.

REGULATIONS Specific rules that often support other legislation.

REM A measure of the dose of ionizing radiation to body tissue stated in terms of its estimated biological effect relative to a dose of one roentgen of X-rays.

REPETITIVE MOTION Short-cycle motion that is repeated continually.

REPETITIVE STRAIN INJURY (RSI) A broad and generic term that encompasses a variety of injuries resulting from cumulative trauma to the soft tissues of the body.

RESISTANCE A tendency to block flow of electric current.

RESPONSE TIME The amount of time between when an order is placed and when the product is delivered.

RESTRAINT DEVICES Hold back the operator from the danger zone.

RESTRICTED AREA Any area to which access is restricted in an attempt to protect employees from exposure to radiation or radioactive materials.

RETROFIT Renovating rather than replacing.

RIGHT TO KNOW Workers' basic right to be informed of any hazards that exist in the workplace.

RIGHT TO PARTICIPATE Workers' basic right to participate in their own safety (i.e., committees).

RIGHT TO REFUSE Workers' basic right to refuse work that they feel is unsafe.

RISK ANALYSIS An analytical methodology normally associated with insurance and investments.

RISK ASSESSMENT The process of quantifying the level of risk.

ROLE-REVERSAL TEST Requires a person to trade places with the people affected by the decision that he or she made and to view the decision through their eyes.

ROLE AMBIGUITY The condition that occurs when an employee is not clear concerning the parameters, reporting requirements, authority, or responsibilities of his or her job.

SAFETY MOVEMENT Began during World War II when all of the various practitioners of occupational health and safety began to see the need for cooperative efforts. This movement is very strong today.

SAFETY POLICY A written description of an organization's commitment to maintaining a safe and healthy workplace.

SAFETY TRIP DEVICES Include trip wires, trip rods, and body bars that stop the machine when tripped.

SECOND-DEGREE BURN Results in blisters forming on the skin.

SECONDARY WITNESS Someone who was present at the scene of an accident but did not actually see the accident.

SEMIAUTOMATIC EJECTION A system that ejects the work using mechanisms that are activated by the operator.

SEMIAUTOMATIC FEED A system that uses a variety of approaches for feeding stock to the machine.

SEMICONDUCTORS Substances that are neither conductors nor insulators.

SEVERE ACUTE RESPIRATORY SYNDROME (SARS) A respiratory infection similar to pneumonia.

SEVERITY The magnitude of the results of an event of action.

SHEARING Results from forces being applied to a body by two contacting parts moving parallel to the plane of contact.

SHIFT WORK Employees work at different times of the day instead of during the same hours.

SHOCK A depression of the nervous system.

SHORT CIRCUIT A circuit in which the load has been removed or bypassed.

SHORT TERM EXPOSURE LIMIT The maximum concentration of a given substance to which employees may be safely exposed for up to 15 minutes without suffering irritation, chronic or irreversible tissue change, or narcosis to a degree sufficient to increase the potential for accidental injury, impair the likelihood of self-rescue, or reduce work efficiency.

SIEVERT A single unit used to indicate the effective dose absorbed by various organs or tissue. The effective dose or Sv is used to assess the risk to humans and not plants and other animals.

SITUATIONAL CHARACTERISTICS Factors that can change from setting to setting and can have a catalytic effect in causing an accident.

SITUATIONAL FACTORS Environmental factors that can affect an employee's safety and that can differ from situation to situation.

SLIP AND FALL Accidents that occur when the worker's centre of gravity is suddenly thrown out of balance.

SOCIAL ENVIRONMENT The general value system of the society in which an individual lives, works, grows up, and so on.

SOUND LEVEL METER Produces an immediate reading that represents the noise level at a specific instant in time.

SOUND Any change in pressure that can be detected by the ear.

SPONTANEOUS COMBUSTION Result of sufficient fuel and heat from decomposing organic material for ignition.

SPRAIN The result of torn ligaments.

STAGE OF ALARM Characterized by pallor, sweating, and an increased heart rate.

STAGE OF EXHAUSTION This stage is demonstrated by the body's failure to adapt to the continued stress.

STAGE OF RESISTANCE The alarm symptoms dissipate, and the body develops an adaptation to the stress.

STANDARD An operational principle, criterion, or requirement pertaining to working conditions, methods, equipment, or materials in the workplace.

STANDPIPE AND HOSE SYSTEMS Provide the hose and pressurized water for firefighting.

STATIC ELECTRICITY A surplus or deficiency of electrons on the surface of a material.

STATUTE Law made by provincial legislature or federal parliament.

STEP AND FALL An accident that occurs when a person's foot encounters an unexpected step down.

STRAIN The result of over-stretched or torn muscles.

STRAIN The result of overstretched or torn muscles.

STRESS A pathological, and therefore generally undesirable, human reaction to psychological, social, occupational, or environmental stimuli.

STRESSORS Stimuli that cause stress.

STUMP AND FALL An accident that occurs when a worker's foot suddenly meets a sticky surface or a defect in the walking surface.

SUBJECTIVE RATINGS Ratings that are less than objective and can be affected by emotions, human biases, presumptions, and perceptions.

SUPPLIER LABEL Identified by the WHMIS broken border, the supplier label is required as a condition of sale of controlled products.

SYSTEMS THEORY Views a situation in which an accident may occur as a system comprising the following components: person (host), machine (agency), and environment.

TASK COMPLEXITY Relates to the number of different demands made on the worker.

TDG ACT, 1992 Federal legislation governing the transportation of dangerous goods.

TECHNOLOGICAL ALIENATION The frame of mind that results when employees come to resent technology and the impact that it has on their lives.

TECHNOLOGY ACCESS Access to time- and work-saving devices, processes, or equipment that are up to date.

TENDINITIS Painful result of small tears in the tendon from overwork.

TENOSYNOVITIS A condition resulting from an excess buildup of fluid that causes pressure on the surrounding nerve.

TERMS OF REFERENCE A set of rules under which the health and safety committee are to operate.

TERTIARY WITNESS Someone who may have information that is relevant to an accident investigation although they were not present when the accident happened.

THE CONSTITUTION ACT, 1982 Provided Canada with a new constitution that included the charter of rights and freedoms.

THIRD-DEGREE BURN Penetrates through both the epidermis and the dermis. It may be fatal.

THREE E'S OF SAFETY Engineering, education, and enforcement.

THRESHOLD LIMIT VALUES (TLVS) The levels of exposure at which all employees may be repeatedly exposed to specified concentrations of airborne substances without fear of adverse effects. Exposure beyond TLVs is considered hazardous.

THRESHOLD OF HEARING The weakest sound that can be heard by a healthy human ear in a quiet setting.

THRESHOLD OF PAIN The maximum level of sound that can be perceived without experiencing pain.

TIME-WEIGHTED AVERAGE The level of exposure to a toxic substance to which a worker can be repeatedly exposed on a daily basis without suffering harmful effects.

TOTAL SAFETY MANAGEMENT (TSM) The principles of total quality management (TQM) applied to safety management.

TOXIC SUBSTANCE A substance that has a negative effect on the health of a person or animal or interferes with the normal biological function of the person.

TRAPPED GAS EFFECTS With a decrease in pressure, gases in the body increase in volume. These occurrences often cause pain or discomfort and may result in injuries if the pressure change is rapid.

TRAUMA Psychological stress.

TRIP AND FALL An accident that occurs when a worker encounters an unseen foreign object in his or her path.

TUNNEL SYNDROMES Injuries caused by compression of the nerves passing through a tunnel (a conduit formed by ligaments and other soft tissues)

TWO-HAND CONTROLS Require the operator to use both hands concurrently to activate the machine.

ULTRASONIC TESTING Use of acoustic waves for detecting foreign objects.

ULTRAVIOLET RADIATION Electromagnetic radiation with a frequency between visible violet light and X rays.

UNRESTRICTED AREA Any area to which access is not controlled because no radioactivity hazard is present.

UNSAFE ACT An act that is not safe for an employee.

UNSAFE BEHAVIOUR The manner in which people conduct themselves that is unsafe to them or to another.

USEFUL CONSCIOUSNESS A state of consciousness in which a person is clear-headed and alert enough to make responsible decisions.

VACUUMS Areas where there is little or no matter, creating an area of negative pressure (pressure below atmospheric level).

VALUE ADDED The difference between what it costs to produce a product and the value the marketplace puts on it.

VERTICAL WORK AREA Refers to the limits of the vertical plane in which the worker is required to perform a task. A good vertical work area is designed and positioned so that workers are not required to lift their hands above their shoulders or bend down in order to perform any task.

VIBRATION Oscillations of solid or semi-solid objects that can be perceived by the sense of touch.

VIDEO DISPLAY TERMINAL (VDT) A device on which computer data or graphics can be displayed.

VIRUS A microscopic organism that invades a host to reproduce.

VISIBLE RADIATION Radiation that distorts light, making it visible.

VOCATIONAL REHABILITATION Involves providing the education and training needed to prepare the worker for a new occupation.

VOLTAGE Measures the potential difference between two points in a circuit.

WAR EMERGENCIES War or other armed conflict, real or imminent, involving Canada or any of its allies.

WATER HAMMER A series of loud noises caused by liquid flow suddenly stopping.

WATT Measure of electrical power.

WELLNESS PROGRAM Any program designed to help and encourage employees to adopt a healthier lifestyle.

WHISTLE-BLOWING Act of informing an outside authority or media organ of alleged illegal or unethical acts on the part of an organization or individual.

WHMIS Workplace Hazardous Material Information System. A national communication system, implemented on October 31, 1988, that provides the worker with information on the production, use, storage, and safe handling of hazardous materials in the workplace.

WHMIS Workplace Hazardous Materials Information System. A national communication system, implemented on October 31, 1988, that provides the worker with information on the production, use, storage, and safe handling of hazardous materials in the workplace.

WIDE BAND NOISE Noise that is distributed over a wide range of frequencies.

WORK ENVELOPE The total area within which the moving parts of a robot actually move.

WORKERS' COMPENSATION Developed to allow injured employees to be compensated appropriately without having to take their employer to court.

WORKPLACE ACCIDENTS Accidents that occur at an employee's place of work.

WORKPLACE ANALYSIS An in-depth study of the workplace used to identify hazards.

WORKPLACE INJURIES Injuries that occur while an employee is at work.

WORKPLACE LABEL Required on controlled products in the workplace. Workplace labels require less content than supplier labels.

WORKPLACE STRESS Human reaction to threatening situations at work or related to the workplace.

WORKPLACE VIOLENCE Violent acts, behaviour, or threats that occur in the workplace or are related to it.

ZERO POTENTIAL State of a neutral electrical charge.

Index